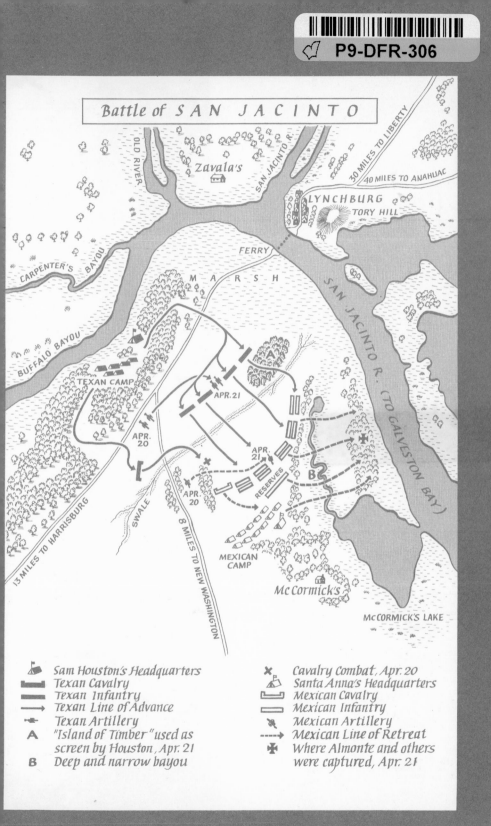

Battle of SAN JACINTO

OLD RIVER

Zavala's

SAN JACINTO R.

30 MILES TO LIBERTY

40 MILES TO ANAHUAC

LYNCHBURG

TORY HILL

FERRY

CARPENTER'S BAYOU

MARSH

SAN JACINTO R. (TO GALVESTON BAY)

BUFFALO BAYOU

TEXAN CAMP

A

APR. 21

APR. 20

APR. 21

B

13 MILES TO HARRISBURG

SWALE

8 MILES TO NEW WASHINGTON

APR. 20

RESERVES

MEXICAN CAMP

McCormick's

McCORMICK'S LAKE

Sam Houston's Headquarters
Texan Cavalry
Texan Infantry
Texan Line of Advance
Texan Artillery
A "Island of Timber" used as screen by Houston, Apr. 21
B Deep and narrow bayou

Cavalry Combat, Apr. 20
Santa Anna's Headquarters
Mexican Cavalry
Mexican Infantry
Mexican Artillery
Mexican Line of Retreat
Where Almonte and others were captured, Apr. 21

Magnificent Destiny

Books by Paul I. Wellman

NOVELS

Broncho Apache
Jubal Troop
Angel with Spurs
The Bowl of Brass
The Walls of Jericho
The Chain
The Iron Mistress
The Comancheros
The Female
Jericho's Daughters
Ride the Red Earth
The Fiery Flower
Magnificent Destiny

HISTORY

Death on the Prairie
Death in the Desert
    (Republished together as
    The Indian Wars of the West.)
The Trampling Herd
Glory, God and Gold
A Dynasty of Western Outlaws

BIOGRAPHY

Stuart Symington

REMINISCENCE

Portage Bay

FOR YOUNGER READERS

Gold in California
Indian Wars and Warriors: East
Indian Wars and Warriors: West
Race to the Golden Spike

Magnificent Destiny

A NOVEL ABOUT THE GREAT SECRET ADVENTURE OF
Andrew Jackson and Sam Houston

PAUL I. WELLMAN

Doubleday & Company, Inc.
Garden City, New York
1962

Material from *War through the Ages*, by Lynn Montross,
published by Harper & Brothers and used with their permission.

To

KEN McCORMICK

both editor and friend to me these many
years, who first suggested the theme of this
book

Library of Congress Catalog Card Number 62–14180

At about the time of Andrew Jackson's death, John L. O'Sullivan, editor of the *Democratic Review*, wrote for the July–August issue of his journal an article which contained a reference to:

> . . . *our Manifest Destiny*
> *to overspread the continent al-*
> *lotted by Providence for the free*
> *development of our yearly expand-*
> *ing millions.*

Called by Bernard De Voto "one of the most dynamic phrases ever minted," Manifest Destiny expressed both the dream of Andrew Jackson, and the emotion that created the great westward surge of the American people toward a Destiny that was to be Magnificent.

Foreword

In approaching a character so strange and powerful as that of Andrew Jackson, the novelist must perforce view persons and affairs through the eyes, or at least according to the attitudes, of his protagonist.

The few really great men who have been willing to assume and able to carry out mighty responsibilities loom up like mountain peaks in American history. In this company Andrew Jackson stands as tall as the tallest.

He was single-minded in his devotion to his country, and his will conquered every passion of his mind and body, except his loyalties and his detestations. To him all things were good or bad, black or white: there were no grays or intermediate shadings.

With this understanding, his enmity against the British, today our greatest friends and allies, must be judged by his time and generation, conditioned by two devastating wars with England. Similarly, his prejudice against the Indians, who assuredly had their side to the argument, was predicated on the fact that they still were a menace on every frontier, and the record of their atrocities in warfare was too recent to be viewed dispassionately.

In like manner his feuds with men like Henry Clay and John Calhoun are in this novel chronicled as Jackson saw them, for he could discern in them none of the virtues which history has since accorded them.

I have taken a novelist's liberty in transposing a few minor events for smoothness and pace of the story, but all important occurrences are as accurate as a good deal of research and study can make them, within the framework I have outlined above.

Paul I. Wellman
Los Angeles, California

The Horseshoe Bend,
*** 1814

In the year 1812 a young and awkward nation, ill-equipped and still stumbling in its experiment of democratic government, declared war on the greatest and best-organized power on earth, Great Britain.

The War of 1812 was a mistake on both sides. It had its seeds in animosities still lingering from the Revolution, and was engendered on the one side by Britain's arrogant maritime policy and the over-friendly relations of her agents with Indian tribes hostile to the American frontiersmen, and on the other side by the ambitions of some political leaders, chiefly from the South and West—the so-called "War Hawks"—who hoped to gain territory at Britain's expense in the West and North.

From the first, British public opinion and political leadership were divided on this war, and the full power of British arms was never brought to bear on America. For their part, the so-called United States were anything but united. New England's counting houses were bitter over their profit-and-loss columns, which showed more loss than profit due to what they called "Mr. Madison's War." The broken ranks of the old Federalist Party, in a last bid for power, fostered antiwar sentiments throughout the East, even to the verge of threatened secession.

But in what then was called the West—the states of Tennessee, Kentucky, and Ohio, with the Northwest Territory—men believed that since war had been declared, even though its early stages were shamefully disastrous, it must be fought out to the finish, whatever the cost. In this sentiment frontier Tennessee was pre-eminent, and largely because of the personality of a single man.

*Raw and crude, still hewing its clearings out of the forest, and peo-
pled strongly by men who had fought either in the Revolution or in the
recurring Indian wars, Tennessee was filled with military tradition; so
much so that almost every man of consequence bore some military title,
if only by courtesy. There was even said to be a way of telling a man's
rank by the number of chimneys on his house. If the house had two
chimneys, he was spoken of as major; if three, he was promoted to
colonel; but if there were four chimneys, he was by common consent
styled general.*

*Yet in this plethora of generals, there was only one man whom the
frontier spoke of as The General, as if he were the only real general
and entitled to have his rank capitalized. That man was Andrew
Jackson.*

*A man's excellences win him respect; but it is his human failings that
win him affection after the respect is established. Andrew Jackson had
a sufficiency of both.*

*Though he had his enemies, and bitter ones, most of the frontier
regarded him with affection and pride. For in his stormy life he had
seemed to combine in himself, as if he were the very genius of the
frontier, all its strengths and wildness; its reckless courage and high-
toned notions of honor; its unreckoning loyalty to a friend or a cause.
And also he possessed many of its weaknesses; such as a fever for gambling, horse-racing, and cock-fighting; a hot-headed inclination to plunge
into trouble; a deadly and unforgiving hatred of a foe; and a tendency
toward strong drink and spectacular profanity when he was in the mood.*

Such was the West—and such was Andrew Jackson.

Chapter One

*I'll thank you to remember, that when I
require your advice, I'll ask for it!*

1

Riding south from Knoxville, along the frozen ruts of the narrow
trace through the gray Tennessee woods which had as yet put forth no
leaves, and with enough frost in the air that a man could see the white
steam of his breath before his face, young Captain Reid noticed with
concern that in spite of the greatcoat he was wearing and the woolen
muffler about his lean neck, the General looked pinched and cold, and
somehow older.

It was early in March of the year 1813, and on this morning Andrew
Jackson was suffering a recurrence of his chronic ailment, the dysentery
he had acquired in the abortive Natchez campaign, coupled with a return of his recurrent fever and cough. Only he knew how much these
illnesses weakened him and sometimes caught him up in a web of
anguish.

But John Reid had at least some conception of it, and he was aware
that Jackson had slept little the previous night at the Knoxville Inn.
That very morning, when they arose long before dawn, for they were
due at Maryville by noon, the captain had ventured a protest against
the twenty-mile ride.

"Let me entreat you, General, sir, to take it easy," he said. "You were
up most of the night, sir, and if I may be so bold, you're in no condition
to be riding."

But it was temerity to argue with Andrew Jackson. He turned on
the captain a chilling stare.

"Hell and damnation, sir!" he said, in his high, harsh voice. "I'll thank
you to remember, Captain Reid, that when I require your advice, I'll
ask for it!"

Reid straightened and flushed. It was clear that the General was too touchy to reason with. When he was in good humor he always called his aide by his first name, with a sort of fatherly affection.

So now they were riding in the cold and silence on the frozen road. To the captain it was a marvel how a man would sacrifice himself just to keep a casual promise. Then he remembered that any promise—even one as unimportant as the acceptance of an invitation to speak at a hamlet like Maryville—was sacred to his chief.

The General was not in uniform this day. He rode half-slumped on his high bay horse, his greatcoat seeming too voluminous for his lean body, his tall beaver hat tipped forward over his long nose: an attitude which clearly indicated his physical debility.

Anyone who viewed for the first time the man's strange, almost whimsical figure, would have found it hard to believe that here was the most famous personage on the frontier. Andrew Jackson possessed few of the commonly accepted physical aspects of a popular hero.

He was painfully gaunt, his thighs meager, his boots seeming loose on his thin shanks, his shoulders high and narrow. His voice, far from being a trumpet blast to inspire troops in the rage of battle, was thin, high, almost shrill.

Once red as a rusted gun barrel, his hair now was heavily shot with gray. His visage, seldom smiling, hollow-cheeked, deeply lined, and disfigured by smallpox pits and the long white weal of a scar across one cheek, was of the type sometimes called "horse-faced."

Voice and figure might almost have seemed ludicrous in a lesser being; but nobody laughed at Andrew Jackson. Those intense blue eyes of his could turn to icy fire in his wrath; and it was known that even to use this man's name lightly was dangerous.

In contrast, Reid was quite dashing in his long blue army surtout, cocked hat, and polished boots. The captain prided himself on his appearance. He was a fine, handsome young man, with a full colored face and brown hair roached back from his forehead; and he had literary ambitions, but no great military qualities save his unquestioning loyalty to his chief, and the ability to wear a uniform in such a manner as to attract every feminine eye.

John Reid was proud to be riding with the General, proud of his close association with this man. He had seen Jackson's disappointments, and his stubborn achievements, and he knew something of the problems and ambitions that occupied that strange, furious genius. On this cold March morning he was content to keep silence and not break in on the thoughts of the man he worshiped.

Jackson's thoughts were weary ones. His debts oppressed him. There was the sum of sixteen hundred and fifty dollars he had borrowed to cover his extraordinary personal expenses in raising and helping equip the Tennessee Legion, which he marched to Natchez, hoping to face the British on the lower Mississippi. And there was the additional one thousand dollars he had borrowed when he marched them home again, refusing to disband them and leave them to their fate after the double-dealing General James Wilkinson induced the War Department to dismiss him and them.

On that bitter occasion he hired wagons out of his own pocket to transport the sick, and led his men home on foot. Out of it came something, insignificant perhaps, but in which he took a secret pride: a nickname, no more.

Seeing him on that hungry march from Natchez, going up and down the column, always striding along in the mud because he had lent his horse to a sick man, the backwoods soldiers whispered to one another.

"He's tough," one said.

"Tougher'n a boot," said another.

"Tough as hickory," a third added, naming the toughest thing he knew.

Before he got them back home, Jackson became aware that his men were calling him, behind his back, "Old Hickory"—no bad compliment.

That pleased him, but the nearly three thousand dollars—including interest—which he owed, pleased him not at all. He wondered how Colonel Tom Benton was getting along with his affairs in Washington. Tom Benton—Thomas Hart Benton he liked to call himself, being somewhat magniloquent—a lawyer by profession and an orator by vocation, was one of the most ridiculously vain men Jackson had ever known, but he had served in the Natchez campaign, and he was in Washington now with letters of introduction from Jackson, partly on his own business, and partly to seek to stir the slow-moving government to allow repayment to the General of the money he had laid out of his own pocket for the army, and thus restore his credit. Gloomily, Jackson doubted that Benton could accomplish much along this line.

He was brought out of this abstraction when his horse suddenly slipped in an icy rut. The animal was spirited—Jackson had a nice taste in horseflesh—and he snorted and sidled as he recovered his footing.

Roused from his preoccupation, the General straightened up his mount, and Reid took the opportunity to speak.

"Pardon, sir," he said, "but there appears to be the beginnings of some sort of a clearing yonder."

Jackson nodded. "That ought to be Maryville."

"Likely there'll be some sort of a welcoming committee, sir."

The General understood that this was a mild hint that he should prepare himself for the reception. Always it was something of an effort for him to make a proper entrance when much was expected of him. He must be alert, on his guard, keep a face carefully impassive even when smiling, carry himself well, and speak with due regard for the fact that where many heard his words, their meaning might be twisted if they were not clear. In his ailing condition all this was a strain on both mind and body.

Nevertheless, he straightened his hat, smoothed down the skirts of his greatcoat, squared his shoulders, and turned out the toes of his boots in the stirrups. The bay gelding, sensing his rider's new attitude, arched his neck and pranced briskly.

They reached the edge of the clearing, a wide opening where the forest had been hewed away from an area roughly a square mile in extent. In the center of this stood the log buildings of the town, with people thronging among them. Distant shouts rang in the frosty air.

"I'm sorry, sir—there seems to be no welcoming committee after all." Reid was angry and disappointed at what he considered an affront to his chief.

But Jackson, for the first time that day, gave a bare indication of a grin, showing the edges of his teeth only.

"Likely there's a fight or a foot race going on," he said, out of his knowledge of frontier ways. "Come on. Let's see." He spurred his horse and led the way at a canter.

2

The few log houses and stores of Maryville huddled in the center of the extensive, stump-dotted clearing, from which the trees had been so ruthlessly cut that not one was left to offer shade in summer: a reminder that here was a beginning civilization, still in its youth, unkempt, crassly utilitarian, with as yet small appreciation for beauty.

Customarily, in Maryville, the day started slowly, with the morning clamor of hound dogs, and the grunting and squealing of swine which made their abodes under the log houses and now went forth to perform their scavenger duty in the street and yards. Undisturbed by any fear of traffic, matronly old hens led forth their broods to scratch among the dried weeds and rubbish. Cows, newly milked, wandered out into the clearing or beyond it into the woods to browse. Upon the steps of the courthouse—a two-story log building, distinguished by a porch in front and a jail and pair of stocks in the rear—a band of vagabond goats performed feats of agility.

At easy tempo the human populace did its morning chores and ate breakfast. Gradually the few stores opened; the town loafers gathered to whittle and spit tobacco juice; "eye-openers" were drunk at the tavern bar; and gossip and goods were purveyed in a manner comfortably sleepy and slow.

On this day, however, the seemly decorum had been all upset. At earliest dawn vehicles began to rumble and rattle in from the country about, crowded with families; and many came on horseback, the men astride bareback nags, and often women sitting behind holding to them.

Hens and their broods, with scandalized squawks, were scattered. Hogs squealed as they were routed from their accustomed wallows in the middle of the main street. Even the goats were evicted from the courthouse steps.

Long before noon all the hitch racks were crowded with tethered horses. Oxen lay chewing their cuds beside the wagons they had drawn. Buggies, carriages, and one coach—belonging to Squire William Toole —mingled with the more bucolic carts and wains.

In some of the elegant equipages sat the high-toned ladies of the community, bundled against the brisk day, each wearing one of the new "coal-scuttle" bonnets, just become the rage. Their gentlemen, in tall hats and claw-hammer coats of bottle green or blue, mingled afoot with the commonality—buckskin-clad men from the backwoods clearings, their shawled women in homespun or linsey, and their tousle-headed children. For politics was in the air, and it was well for a man of standing to make himself affably pleasant to the poor folks.

Across from the courthouse stood Russell's Tavern, a dingy structure of hewn logs, with a narrow-roofed porch and a large woodpile in the rear. The door to the barroom was open, even though the day was chill, as an invitation to all who wished refreshment; for in Tennessee liquor was the one everlasting essential for every notable occasion, and a tavern keeper who failed to offer hospitality would be guilty of neglecting his clearly indicated public duty.

The present occasion was sufficiently notable to warrant the inpourings of the country people. There was to be a military recruiting rally, with a demonstration of close-order drill. Of far greater moment, General Andrew Jackson was to be present, to be seen and heard by all.

As Captain Reid surmised, a committee of honor had been appointed, consisting of the town's most notable personages: Squire Toole, portly and florid, with gray side whiskers, gazing about him with a proprietary eye since he held mortgages on half the village property; Captain John Cusack of the (very irregular) Maryville Mounted Rifles, an occasional practitioner of law who was attired this day in an old uniform of buff and blue, complete with tarnished epaulets; and the Reverend Mark Moore, principal of Porter Academy, the town's institution of learning, who sought to make up for his cadaverousness of figure by wearing a pair of square-lensed, steel-rimmed glasses for dignity.

3

As noon approached, the crowd waited expectantly for the arrival of the distinguished guest. Meantime it diverted itself as it could.

In front of the courthouse backwoods youths and not a few plump lasses in linsey gawked at the soldiers, who lounged on the steps, their muskets stacked, ostentatiously indifferent to the stares, except when now and then one of them favored a wide-eyed country girl with a grin intended to be meaningful, as a promise of gallant attention when duty was finished and the son of Mars free to pursue his personal bents.

Of the soldiers there were only eleven: an infantry squad of eight, with a sergeant, a fifer, and a drummer. But these were no lackluster militia. Tall visored shakos, handsome blue coats with brass buttons and white crossbelts, and white pantaloons proclaimed them as regulars—an eye-filling spectacle to Maryville.

Behind the courthouse, between the jail and the stocks (both for the moment empty), half a dozen horseshoe-pitching contests went forward with the usual wrangling and closely scrutinized measurements. Elsewhere an impromptu dogfight drew a yelling, betting crowd.

Near the tavern two young men, in a friendly wrestling match—slugging, gouging, biting, and kicking barred—warily grappled for holds, while a circle of onlookers offered advice, encouragement, or derision.

Presently from the tavern bar appeared a brawny fellow in a bright-red flannel shirt and coarse brown homespun trousers. On his head, at a truculent angle, was a flop-brimmed wool hat, with a scarlet-dyed turkey feather stuck in the band.

The red feather had significance. Every frontier community had its champion—usually called the town "boss" or "bully"—who could whip any other fighter in the settlement. But possession of the scarlet plume meant more. It advertised the wearer as one who had gone downriver in a keelboat, all the way to Natchez or even New Orleans; and that he had been cock-of-the-walk on his boat; and perhaps had challenged and defeated champions of other boats in the ugly rough-and-tumble fights of the period, until he gained more than local reputation.

This man's name was Mike Hooten, his age around thirty, his occupation uncertain, his disposition dangerous and quarrelsome, especially when he was drinking. In Maryville other men viewed him uneasily and were careful to avoid affronting him, since none felt inclined to suffer a broken arm or back, kicks in the belly or crotch, loss of an ear or nose by biting, or an eye gouged out—these being forms of punishment dealt out by the boss fighter in his ruthless combats.

Just drunk enough to be ugly, and looking for trouble, Mike Hooten stood on the tavern porch and glowered at the two wrestlers and the good-natured, noisy crowd about them. It offended him that anyone save himself should be the center of this kind of attention.

Suddenly he leaped down from the porch, burst through the circle of spectators, and seized the contestants by their necks. With a display of undeniably great strength he brought their skulls together with a crack, then sent them both flying to the ground with a push and a kick for each.

"Damn yore eyes fer makin' sech a ruckus a gentleman cain't enjoy his licker!" he shouted. "Got me up from a jug of whiskey when I hadn't no more'n drunk half of it, an' had to leave the other half mebbe to spoil!"

The attack was unprovoked and unwarranted. But the two youths scrambled to their feet with no thought of fight, and with frightened faces hastened to lose themselves in the crowd.

Hooten glared around menacingly. "Anybody have somethin' to say?"

Nobody felt moved to comment.

The bully was not satisfied. He began to walk around in a circle, swinging his huge fists, meantime speaking, at first in a low growl, but with a voice gradually rising until he was bawling at the top of his lungs, and punctuating his words with whoops. Mike Hooten was working himself up, "making his brags," inviting anyone who dared to come to grips with him, in the curiously conventionalized manner of frontier challenges to fight.

He proclaimed that he was a "hoss, a team, a rampagious combination of b'ar an' yalligator." Next he volunteered the interesting information that he was a "bobcat with bristles on my belly," and assured his listeners that he could "outjump, outrun, throw down, drag out, an' stomp inter the ground any man in this yere county."

At this point he leaped into the air, cracked his heels together, and gave vent to a loud whoop.

Now he announced that he was a "thunderbolt an' a cyclone all wropped up in one." As if this were not sufficient, he added in stentorian tones that he was the "damnedest, hell-fired, rantankerous, he-panther that ever clumb a tree or clawed a man's guts out."

Here he paused and glanced about him expectantly. When nobody made the slightest move, his stubble-bearded face took on an expression of disappointment.

"I'd ruther have a scrimmage than eat!" he yelled.

When there still were no takers of this implied invitation, he flapped his arms and crowed insultingly, like a rooster.

Next he assumed an imploring, almost piteous tone.

"Look at me—*look* at me!" he pleaded. "I'm so plumb hongry, a-sufferin' fer a fight, that I'm a-fallin' away—gittin' so pore an' thin I almost gotta lean ag'in a saplin' to cuss!"

With that he let out another whoop.

Hooten's description of himself as "falling away, poor and thin," was hardly borne out by his wide and powerful shoulders, bull neck, square-jawed brutal countenance bristling with a week's growth of black beard, and eyes that glared evilly out from under bushy brows.

His next offer was to fight any man, any *two* men, in the sound of his voice, "fer fifty dollars—fer a dollar—fer a drink of whiskey—fer a chaw of terbaccer—fer *nothin'!*"

Another whoop.

"Anybody—*anybody*—want to accommodate me?" he asked beseechingly.

His yells had brought scores hurrying to join the circle about him and see what was going forward. But all the men eyed him with faces carefully expressionless, each taking care to avoid drawing upon himself undesired attention.

For a moment Hooten grumbled deeply in his throat like an ill-tempered dog. Then he fixed his eyes on a spectator who chanced to be standing in the front row of the crowd.

"What's so funny? What're ye laughin' at?" he demanded.

The man he addressed was plump and slovenly, with a good-natured, vacant face on which was an almost perpetual, rather pointless grin, which he wore in his anxiety to be at all times on the friendly side of everyone. He was Alec Moss, a ne'er-do-well who existed on odd jobs, scrounged his drinks, and was entirely harmless. Hooten knew him well, had long been accustomed to his foolish grin; but now he chose to take it as a personal affront.

The grin faded from Alec's face.

"Me?" he said, startled. "Why—Mike—I wasn't laughin'——"

"Meanin' I lie?" Hooten seized him by the front of his shirt. "Call me a liar to my face?"

"Oh, no—not me—shore not!" came a hasty, bleating protest. "Nobody knows better'n me that yore word's rock-bottom, Mike. I wouldn't even *think* it—let alone say a thing like that. No, sir! Not Mike Hooten!" Alec glanced hopefully at the other's scowling visage but caught no answering gleam of friendship. "Good as gold—Mike Hooten's word's as good as gold, I allus say," he went on wheedlingly. "Don't I, fellers?" he appealed to the crowd. "Ye've heard me say it, ain't ye? A dozen times, if I said it once! I'm proud to know Mike Hooten—allus been proud. It's a honor, a mighty important honor——"

Hooten was not mollified. He kept a firm grip on his victim's shirt front.

"Then jest what *did* ye mean?" he growled.

"Why—why——" Alec was floundering again. "I only jest meant—that—that ye was mistook—didn't understand——"

"Didn't *understand?*" roared Hooten. "Ge-reat Caesar's ghost! I'm stupid, ye mean? Implyin' I'm weak-minded, mebbe?"

The other gave a howl of denial that was cut short.

"By the je-humpin' Jehoshaphat!" the bully bellowed. "I'm a patient man, but this hyar's too much! Too *damn* much! A chap might spit on me, an' mebbe I'd overlook it, thinkin' it was a accident. But when it comes to *rubbin' it in*—thar I draw the line! Yessir! I r'ar up an' won't stand fer it!"

He dragged the terrified fool to the center of the ring and viciously slapped the flabby face on both cheeks. Alec only cringed and whimpered.

"I oughta kick yore ribs in!" snarled Hooten. "But ye ain't worth it." An idea seemed to occur to him. "Know what I'm gonna do, fer you makin' them uncalled-for insults?" he demanded. "Yore gonna eat dirt! Right hyar, before all these gentlemen, yore gonna lay on yore fat belly an' eat dirt!"

He tripped his victim and hurled him to the ground.

"Begin eatin'!" he commanded.

Poor Alec looked up at him with an expression so woeful that it might have melted the heart of a wolf. But Hooten only took a threatening step forward. With a wail of fear, Alec took a pinch of soil and put it in his mouth.

"I said *eat* it, not jest taste!" cried the tormentor. He gave the prostrate figure a kick that brought a wince and a howl. Then he leaped astride his victim's back, and grasped a handful of horse dung from the ground nearby.

"Oh, no, Mike—please—not that—" begged Alec.

"Dainty, are ye? Wall—ye'll eat it, an' like it!"

Hooten twisted the fingers of his free hand into the other's hair and forced his head around to cram the filth into his mouth.

Alec uttered a strangled squall of nausea and despair.

Thus far not a voice had been raised, or a movement made, to stop the senseless and cruel badgering of the harmless fool. Mike Hooten, ugly with drink, was too dangerous to interfere with.

But now, suddenly, someone said, "Let him up!"

At the same moment a hand seized Hooten by the shoulder and wrenched him off his victim.

In ludicrous haste Alec scrambled away and hid in the crowd.

The bully came to his feet, face contorted with rage. Confronting him was a very tall, bareheaded youth, in a faded shirt of flowered calico, buckskin breeches shrunk by rain and sun until they were far too short for his long legs, and moccasins of Indian make.

Hooten glared at the lean length, the deeply tanned face, the blue-gray eyes, and the wide mouth inclined to humor but just now sternly set. Then a look of contempt came into his face.

"Wall, now," he sneered. "If it ain't Injun Sam!"

The other did not reply.

Hooten's sneer deepened. "How come ye left all them leetle squaws in the Cherokee Nation?" he inquired. "Did their saddle-colored relations run ye off fer screwin' too many of 'em out in the bushes?"

Still the youth did not answer.

Hooten ran his eye disdainfully up and down the long figure.

"Grown some, ain't ye? Laigs like a sand-hill crane. Think yore a man, mebbe. Wall, it's time ye learnt not to poke yore nose in other folks' business." With an air of amusement he glanced around the circle, then fixed his eye on the youth again. "Tell ye what I'm agonna do, boy. I'm jest gonna make ye eat that hoss-shit in place of Alec Moss!"

The tall boy's eyes did not flicker, but he spoke at last.

"I heard you make your brags, Hooten."

"So?"

"You bragged you could outrun any man here. *I dare you to a whip race!*"

Something like a gasp arose in the circle of onlookers. The whip race was known on the frontier, but it had aspects of cruelty so savage that it was rare.

Hooten stared. Then he said, "Ye'll fight fust—then if ye kin still walk on two laigs, I'll race ye."

"My dare come before yours."

"Skeered to fight—ye yeller-bellied Injun lover?"

"If you want a fight, I'll fight you—*after* the whip race!"

In the ring about them, men nodded. Some of them said, "That's right. Fair's fair."

By frontier custom, which had almost the force of law, the first dare took precedence. Not even Mike Hooten could with impunity flout such tradition.

He scowled. "Wall, ye asked fer it. An' yore gonna get it. I'll skin yore back ontil they kin see the bare rib bones in it. An' after that, I'll give ye sech a beatin' yore own mammy won't know ye from sausage meat!"

Chapter Two

May the Lord have mercy on you both!

SQUIRE WILLIAM TOOLE

1

It was at this moment, unnoticed in the delirium of excitement surrounding the sudden furious altercation, that two newcomers rode up: General Jackson and Captain Reid. Without speaking they sat their horses, looking over the heads of the crowd, while three judges, apparently chosen by common consent but without vocal nomination or election, consulted with the antagonists.

The visitors had no way of knowing that the judges were the members of the "welcoming committee" which had completely forgotten its duties in the present all-absorbing interest: Squire Toole, Captain Cusack, and the Reverend Mr. Moore.

The distance for the race was quickly agreed: from a stake driven into the ground before the tavern, to one set before the log academy building at the other end of the village, perhaps a quarter of a mile. As principal of the temple of learning, the Reverend Mr. Moore betook himself with long, storklike strides to the academy, there to act as judge of the first leg of the race. Captain Cusack accepted the office of judge at the stake before the tavern which marked the finish of the return leg. Upon Squire Toole devolved the duty of acting as starter.

Men, and many of the women and children, hurried to line the course on both sides, forming a sort of lane bounded by avid faces, down which the runners were to race. In their carriages ladies wearing coal-scuttle bonnets stood up, the better to see. Some of the gentlemen in beaver hats mounted horses for the same purpose. Every neck was craned, every eye eager to witness the peculiar punishment this sort of contest provided.

Jackson and Reid experienced the curious and unaccustomed sensation of being lost in this crowd; but whereas the aide felt annoyance, the General knew only the keen interest which any kind of a sporting event aroused in him.

Sporting? The adjective might be used, if rules so elemental and brutal could define sport.

One runner was to take his place at the starting post, with, in his hand, a cowhide whip—a five-foot length of braided and cured rawhide that would cut a man's skin wide open at a slash. The other would receive a head start of five paces—fifteen feet.

Both would be stripped to the waist.

At the signal to start they would race to the opposite end of the course, and throughout that quarter of a mile the man with the whip was privileged to cut up his adversary as often and savagely as he could.

Places would change at the other end, and the pursued, now the pursuer, would have the whip, seeking in the return race to retaliate for his smarting back. Out of such contests both men usually came with their backs raw and bleeding—something very appealing to the lust for cruelty in some natures.

Grandiosely, Squire Toole stepped forward, a silver coin in his hand.

"Gentlemen," he announced in a stentor's voice, "I will toss up this shilling. You, Hooten, are the challenged party, so you may call it, heads or tails, while it is still in the air. Winner of the toss may elect whether to take the whip first or last."

Up flashed the coin, spinning.

"Heads!" said Hooten.

It fell, rolled, came to a rest.

Over it stooped Squire Toole. "It is—tails," he announced, picking it up. To the youth he said, "The choice is yours."

The boy looked at him grimly. "Give Hooten the whip first."

A yell of surprise from the crowd. This was an advantage not usually accorded, for often the front runner was so bloodily punished that he was weakened for the return race.

Now the contestants pulled off their shirts. Comparing them, Jackson observed that the youth's body was smooth, whereas Hooten's was rough and hairy. The younger was exceptionally tall—four inches over six feet at a guess—and long-legged. But Hooten's speed and prowess evidently were well known here in Maryville.

In the crowd bets were being offered: on who would get in the most "licks"; on who would win the fight following the race. The General noticed that nobody seemed willing to bet against Hooten for the fight, and few even had money to wager on the youth for the race. Many even offered odds that the bully would win both race and fight.

To Reid he said, "I like that boy's style, John. He steps like a blooded horse. He may be a poor bet in the fight, but if I'm any judge, he has a chance in the race. Here's my purse. Get down, if you will, and cover some of those two-way bets."

The captain dismounted, took the purse, and mingled with the crowd.

Already Hooten was at the starting stake, giving a surly grunt, and with the cowhide whip cutting the air with keen whistling sounds.

Five paces ahead of him half-crouched the youth called Injun Sam.

A few yards in front of the two, Squire Toole faced them, holding in his lifted hand a large blue silk handkerchief.

"Keep your eyes on me, gentlemen," he said. "When I drop this handkerchief—go. And," he added, "may the Lord have mercy on you both!"

The crowd held its breath. Down fluttered the blue handkerchief.

With a leap both runners burst forward. Hooten slashed viciously at the bare back in front of him. But the other fled like a deer, and the stroke missed by inches.

A mighty roar arose from the crowd, in which individual voices could be heard:

"Git him, Mike!"

"Go it, kid!"

"What a wallop!"

"Jest missed!"

"It would a-cut him in two!"

"Look out now!"

"Ten more dollars on Hooten!"

Down the lane between the two rows of howling spectators hurtled the runners, gasping, faces twisted with effort, the cords of their necks standing out, legs flashing at topmost speed. No time here for either to "pace" himself. Each furious stride must be at the utmost, the youth straining to keep beyond the reach of the whistling whip, the man behind savagely striving to cut raw gashes in the fleeing back.

The bug-eyed crowd was out of its mind, the play of lust upon it, mouths open in one continuous wave of sound. So perfectly matched were the runners that the few feet of "law" given the youth at the start remained almost exactly that. Time and again Hooten, a really magnificent runner, put on an extra burst, but each time the boy in some manner called on an added desperate reserve of speed, and the slashing whip just failed to reach him.

A final supreme effort by the bully. From the crowd a vast yell as it seemed he must catch his quarry. But the tall sun-tanned figure ahead, with what seemed the last possible ounce of exertion, spurted on, just beyond the cruel cutting lash.

By that much and no more the youth was still in front when they pounded down the stretch and flashed past the stake that marked the end of the first leg of the race.

Gasping, the boy pulled up. There was not a mark on his smooth brown back.

But Hooten's rage overcame every other feeling. Disregarding the rules he rushed on. With a hiss and a crack he swung the whip, and it bit keenly across the other's shoulders.

A roar of protest from the spectators at this violation. With surprise and anger in his face, the youth sprang out of reach and evaded the furious bully, until the latter was restrained by the crowd. There were angry comments at the rupture of the rules. Clearly public opinion swung to the boy.

Without speaking, the Reverend Mr. Moore took the whip from Hooten. Injun Sam accepted it from him, then walked over to his enemy.

"You had no call or right to hit me," he said coldly.

Hooten's face went black. "Jest keep this in mind, ye long-laiged shitepoke bastard. Ye still gotta settle with me when this race is over. If ye so much as touch me with that whip, I swear an' promise that ye'll never git over bein' sorry when I git aholt of ye—if ye even live to be sorry!"

The youth turned his back. Blood was prickling to the surface of the angry welt across it from the treacherous whip stroke.

"Gimme a drink," grunted Hooten. He took a pull from a liquor bottle someone offered him, then sat on the steps of the log academy building, his hairy chest heaving.

Those who heard his exchange with Injun Sam gave each other meaning glances. Sympathy was one thing: a bet something quite different. Men hurried away to lay new wagers. After Hooten's threat it was hardly likely that the lad, knowing he must face the ugliest fighter in the county, would dare lay a lash on his back—even if he caught him, which seemed none too likely after that very even first leg of the race.

2

Five minutes, by the Reverend Mr. Moore's turnip-shaped watch, were given the runners to "blow." Then they were again called to their places.

Down fluttered the signal handkerchief. Again they went speeding, this time toward the distant tavern—Hooten ahead now, the youth after him with the whip.

But this time the race had hardly started when all at once the tall figure behind careered forward and the whip flailed. Hooten gave a leap as if burned by a hot iron, his face twisting with pain.

From the crowd shouts of amazement:

"Looky yonder!"

"Why—the kid caught him!"

"Gave him a lick!"

"A definite lick!"

"Hell's ka-toot! Another!"

"An' *another!*"

"Damn me, he's called Hooten's bluff!"

"Je-*roo*-salem! Lookit that—an' *that!*"

The shouts blended into a single scream, a crazed pandemonium of excitement, as it dawned on the spectators that the youth not only had ignored the bully's threat, but that on the first leg of the race he had played with his adversary in a manner unexpectedly cunning.

He had *seemed* barely to keep beyond Hooten's reach; inducing his pursuer to extend himself in a continuous but futile effort to catch him. Not once in the entire first flight had Injun Sam drawn so far ahead that the bully did not feel that with just one more little extra access of speed he could close the gap and flay the fleeting, tantalizing back.

Now, however, it was apparent that the youth had kept well within himself. Not only was he the faster of the two, but far the fresher.

With eyes almost glazing with effort and breath coming in great sobbing gasps, Hooten strained for the distant tavern. But again, and yet again, the youth came storming up behind, and the bully felt the fiery bite of the cowhide on his back. To everyone—to Hooten most of all—it was clear that his adversary had him at his mercy, overtaking and punishing him at will.

It was not the pain so much as the humiliation that the bully could no longer abide.

Of a sudden a new and different roar came from the crowd.

In a deadly rage Hooten had halted halfway to the finish stake, and turned, crouching, on his pursuer. So sudden was this reversal that the youth collided with him. The shock threw them both to the ground.

The wind was almost knocked out of the lad, who was unprepared for the collision. Before he could gather himself, Hooten sprang on him with surprising agility and threw a great hairy arm about his neck. A moment later they were rolling over and over on the ground.

Andrew Jackson, sitting in his saddle at the tavern, tightened his mouth.

"Foul play, by God!" he exclaimed. "Hooten didn't run his race—he jumped the boy without warning!"

At once he spurred his horse and joined the rush of spectators to the spot where the unexpected conclusion was being fought out.

3

Hooten was in a murderous mood, hot to employ every trick and device, foul or fair, to maim, cripple, even kill his man.

He was on top, locking the youth's head to his sweating chest with one arm, while with the other hand he felt for the gullet, and failing that, jabbed viciously with his thumb at an eye—to gouge it out, one of the terrible inflictions of a rough-and-tumble fight like this.

The other fully knew his peril. Grasping Hooten's free hand with both of his own, he strove to wrench himself loose. But the bully's powerful wrist broke away from him, and now his ugly nails clawed for a corner of the boy's mouth—to tear it open—then felt for the eye again. To save himself from being blinded, the youth turned his head, until his face was pressed beneath Hooten's sweat-dripping, hairy torso.

He was almost smothered. But suddenly he somehow jackknifed his knees up, pushing the bully's hips to one side, and with a twisting, eel-like movement, freed himself from the headlock and came to his feet.

Hooten rose more slowly, but with his murderous purpose evident.

In an ecstasy of excitement the crowd now formed a dense ring about the fighters. Here, suddenly, had developed a combat of skill and strength and brutality, with deadly rancor behind it, much to the taste of the frontier.

Huge-shouldered, bull-necked, great-armed, his chest and back covered with hairy bristles like a wild boar's, Hooten made the youth appear almost frail by comparison. The youngster was taller by five inches, his figure agile and symmetrical, with wide shoulders and compact hips; but without question the bully was the more powerful of the two—and also the more experienced, unscrupulous, and cruel.

For a moment they crouched, circling warily, knees bent, hands half-extended to clutch and grapple. Neither closed his fists, for in such fighting as this the object was to seize the opponent, overthrow him, and disable him. Blows were struck after contact, not before, and then at the belly—or lower. To break bones, to blind, to maim, were the objectives, and there were no rules save that the fight must go on until one or the other could no longer continue.

Gazing over the heads of the crowd from his horse's back, Jackson saw that combat seemed to transform the features of the youth, sending all color from his face, narrowing his eyes, which never left the eyes of his opponent, making tense and grim his mouth.

It was as if combat—*this* combat—was to him an overmastering rage; yet a rage held in the leash of a cold, pulsating logic, which by the very force of its passion gave to his face an almost dispassionate cruelty. It was a look that somehow, on the instant, impressed itself not only on the General, but on all others, with the terrible seriousness of the will behind it.

A few panting breaths thus: then the crash of meeting bodies.

It was the heavier man who took the initiative with a sudden, bull-like, squattering rush, his clawing hands reaching for his foe.

The youth made no attempt to dodge or retreat. Instead, amazingly, he hurled himself straight forward. Low, and right under the clutching hands he drove, catching the bully about the knees, and lifting him bodily in a terrific tackle.

Caught off guard by this onslaught, his footing taken out from under him, Hooten, with all his mighty strength, was for the moment at a loss.

Then the gap-jawed crowd saw the youth, with his man off his feet, suddenly put all his power into his back, as a wood-chopper swings an ax. An instant later he brought the bully down over his shoulder with a fearful crash, executed with every ounce of savage fury in him.

With appalling violence Hooten's head and trunk struck the ground together. He lay still, as if he were dead, not seeming to breathe.

The onlookers, eyes almost starting from their heads at the sudden and unexpected turn of events, looked for the youth to leap on him, do some ferocious damage to him.

But the boy stood back, only watching his adversary narrowly.

After a time Hooten stirred, raised a knee, groaned, and rolled over on his face. His back, covered with mud mingled with the blood from the lacerating whiplashes, heaved.

Then he groggily lifted his head. His whole body was shaken by the terrible fall, and he was dazed. But dimly he saw the figure of his opponent leap toward him.

In that moment Mike Hooten knew in his innermost soul that he could not withstand such another fall as he had just suffered.

He dropped his head back on his arms in abject surrender.

"N-nuff," he gasped.

Chapter Three

*Once we bite we take hold and hang on
like a bulldog!*

ANDREW JACKSON

1

Andrew Jackson swore deeply and exultingly. A partisan always, the triumph of his favorite against what seemed impossible odds lifted him out of himself.

But his voice was lost in a great yell of applause and relief, for the secret wish of every heart in the crowd was placated. The town bully, hated and feared, had been overthrown, cowed, forced to capitulate.

When Hooten at last rose and limped away, he went alone.

In Maryville he was forever finished.

And now, the great central focus of excitement dissolved, men began to look about them, at their neighbors, smiling and talking, paying and collecting bets. Someone suddenly noticed, for the first time, the spare figure on the tall bay gelding.

As if unbelieving, a voice cried out, "By thunder, it's *him*—it's the General!"

People turned and stared.

Then there was a shout: "Hooray for Old Hickory!"

Now came the belated ovation as they cheered and pressed around to see more closely the hero of all Tennessee. Thin and strange as was his appearance, Andrew Jackson in that moment seemed to dominate everyone about him, the whole town, as if he owned it.

The portly gentleman who had acted as starter for the race pushed through the mob, removing his hat from his polished bald head.

"General, sir—I'm honored to address General Jackson," he said. "You perhaps do not remember me—I served with you in the territorial legislature, sir, and the statehood convention. The name is Toole, Squire William Toole, at your service, sir."

"I do indeed remember Squire Toole," said Jackson, with quick cordiality. "We stood together, I think, on the question of the universal vote for all citizens, as against the vote only for propertied men?"

"Together—yes, sir. Though it were better said that where Andrew Jackson led, I followed—and would follow blindfold, sir."

The General accepted the tribute with a nod and brushed aside the apologies that followed it, saying he was by no means offended because he was not greeted formally. Captain Reid came up and was introduced.

"How did we do, John?" asked Jackson.

"I managed to get down a hundred, sir, at two for one. You are two hundred to the good."

"Excellent," said the General, dismounting. "Now, gentlemen, it's been a cold ride. Is that the ordinary? If it's not asking too much, I'd like something to take the chill out of my blood."

"By all means, sir, and it's a pleasure," said the squire. Eagerly men took the horses of the visitors as the squire led the way to the tavern.

2

Behind the bar Russell, the innkeeper, a large man with a bald head and a smooth countenance, poured three glasses full, and stood back, awed by the honor of having such a personage in his place.

"Compliments of the house, General, sir," he said.

Jackson gave his fleeting smile. "Thank you, sir. And your most excellent health."

He lifted his glass and drank, as did the others.

"Ah!" he said, with the pleasure of a connoisseur. "An excellent bourbon! Twenty years in the wood if it's a day, or I'm no judge."

"Indeed, sir, you're a rare judge. That whiskey was kegged in '92," said Russell, delighted.

He lifted the demijohn to pour again, but Jackson shook his head. "No more for the present, thank you," he said.

Now, belatedly, the other members of the "welcoming committee" came hurrying in, to receive their introductions. The General spoke to each a courteous word or two.

"I'm at your service, gentlemen," he said.

"Then, sir, if you'll be so kind, let's cross the street," said Squire Toole. "I apologize for our accommodations, General. Maryville's just a pup yet, as they say. Lacking a proper rostrum, we've arranged to use the courthouse porch as a sort of reviewing stand, if you'll so honor us, while the soldiers give a display of drill for our people. At the conclusion of that, all of us would be profoundly obligated to you, sir, if you'd say a few words. The drill is for the purpose of getting enlistments for the army, and anything you might say to that end will be appreciated, I'm sure. Afterwards, we've arranged a dinner in the tavern, with yourself and Captain Reid as honor guests. And there are some other events projected, if you'll graciously indulge us."

Jackson nodded. "Lead the way, sir."

The dense crowd, gathered outside the inn, parted respectfully to allow the party to cross the street to the courthouse. Jackson mounted the steps, turned and faced the people, and received another cheer. Making a sweeping gesture with his hat, he indicated the soldiers, who had taken formation. At that the onlookers fell back to make room.

With the rattling of the drum and the shrilling of the fife to the tune of "Rocky Times," the infantry squad, the sun gleaming on their bayonets, the sergeant at their head and the music on their flank, swung into action.

Jackson held himself stiffly erect during the half hour the exhibition lasted, striving not to show his renewed weakness and weariness. He appreciated that the crowd was entranced by the marching and countermarching, the manual of arms, and the fife and drum, but to him they were an old story. He wished he could find a seat, and perhaps another glass of that good bourbon, and a chance to rest.

To John Reid he ventured one low-voiced grumble: "Muskets! I'd arm every man with a rifle. My volunteers always carry rifles. They shoot closer to the mark."

At long last, with a final squeal of the fife, the soldiers halted in line, facing the spectators at the foot of the courthouse steps.

Squire Toole stepped forward on the porch. His voice rose, orotund and far-carrying. Jackson hardly paid attention to the words—the usual, banal, stereotyped words—of all such introductions.

"My great pleasure and honor . . . man known to everyone . . . a judge incorruptible as Brutus . . . senator . . . record an honor to the

state . . . soldier . . . name feared by redskins and redcoats alike . . .
first citizen of Tennessee . . . I will go farther and say, in my humble
opinion, first citizen of these United States . . . General Andrew Jackson."

At that final salvo, "first citizen of these United States," Jackson
mentally winced. It seemed such a ridiculous overstatement with men
like Thomas Jefferson and John Adams still living, to say nothing of
younger, more active men, like James Monroe, James Madison, Henry
Clay, John Quincy Adams, John C. Calhoun, and Daniel Webster, all
of whom he considered superior beings and admired from a distance.

But the Tennessee crowd saw no exaggeration or discrepancy in
Squire Toole's introduction. They greeted it with a yell of applause.

Jackson removed his hat and stepped forward to speak. As he did so
he could not help comparing the rich, stentorian tones of the squire
with his own voice, high-pitched, shrill, and harsh. Always it was painful
for him to undergo this sort of unfavorable comparison. But he set himself to do as well as he could.

"My friends," he began, "I am here because our country faces a desperate crisis."

In a brief exordium he described the mighty power of Britain, her
enormous fleet, her veteran armies, her wealth and prestige, her victories
over Napoleon, whose surrender since the disastrous Moscow campaign, he predicted, was now only a matter of time.

"That fleet, those soldiers, who have faced and beaten the best that
the French emperor could hurl against them, soon will be able to turn
their full attention upon our devoted land!" he exclaimed.

Then his voice lowered as he gravely recited the reverses already sustained by American arms through the incompetence of commanders,
and the British raids on the Atlantic seaboard, defeats only partly re-
deemed by fighting American frigates on the high seas.

"I would be less than candid," he went on, "were I to tell you that
the future is bright."

Nevertheless, he added, he confidently expected victory before this
war was finished.

"My confidence," he said, his voice rising, "is based on what I know
about the American people. Slow to fight we perhaps are, and ill-
prepared for war, as any republic invariably is. But once we bite, we
take hold and hang on like a bulldog!"

A mighty cheer at that, which he quieted after a moment by lifting
his hand. Quickly he concluded his short speech.

"We face the gravest of crises—but I declare to you that we can sur-
mount it if we will! Brave men—loyal Tennesseans—patriotic Americans
—join the colors! I myself will march with you! Tennessee to the front!"

In the roar of applause that followed, he forgot momentarily his
physical disabilities. He had won these people; they cheered him with

almost frantic enthusiasm. For a little time he stood gazing out upon them, his blue eyes blazing, then he waved his hat and stepped back.

The crowd hushed as the sergeant, with the drummer beside him, marched to the front of the line of soldiers. Unslinging his drum, the drummer placed it, head up, on the ground, and returned to his post. On the drumhead the sergeant poured a little heap of silver coins from a leather pouch.

"You've all heard what the General said," he bawled in a parade-ground voice. "Here's your chance! Enlist with the regulars! Arms and uniforms furnished! Pay every month! Barracks and supplies! Be *real* soldiers! Step forward, men, if you wish to join up, and take a silver dollar from the drumhead! It's a gift to you from the government!"

In the crowd there was momentary hesitation. Then a tall figure in a calico hunting shirt stepped forward, and Jackson recognized the youth of the whip race and the fight. He stooped to take a dollar from the drumhead, then stood aside. At that others hurried up to follow his example and accept the bounty for enlistment.

"That boy," said the General to the squire, "I heard him called Injun Sam. Why?"

"Because, sir," said the squire, "he spends most of his time living among the Cherokees."

Jackson frowned. He had no love for Indians.

"His real name," continued the squire, "is Houston. Sam Houston, sir. Good family—Virginia people. His mother, Widow Houston, owns land near here. His brothers are steady, work hard, but this fellow's a wild jack—only thing he does hard is drink. I fined him awhile back for disorderly conduct. Work he despises. He did come out of the woods and teach school a few months—seems he was in debt. But he was soon back in the wigwams again."

"Taught school? Then he's well-read?"

"You might call it that. Went to the academy here awhile, but demitted—didn't like anything that took study, I reckon. Prefers reading—poetry, mostly. And wasting his time loafing and hunting with the Indians."

"If he learned that trick he served on Hooten from the Cherokees," observed Jackson, "his time wasn't entirely wasted."

"No, sir. I reckon not." The squire stared. "I reckon some good did come of it."

Captain Cusack came up the steps. "They're waiting for you, General, sir," he said, "at the tavern."

"We mustn't keep them," said Jackson. And then to Squire Toole: "That young fellow—Sam Houston, you say? Please send for him. I'd like a word with him."

3

Jackson sat wearily at a long table and the village dignitaries dined with him, waited upon by the women of Maryville. He had no appetite, and he was jaded, answering but briefly the remarks and compliments addressed to him. John Reid, sitting beside him, watched him with a look of concern.

All at once the General lifted his head. A figure in a calico shirt had just entered, stooping to pass through the door, and halted, gazing at him with a respectful question in his eyes.

"Our young friend of the whip race," said Jackson.

Squire Toole beckoned the youth forward. "General Jackson," he said, "this is Injun—er—that is—Sam Houston. At your request I sent for him."

The young man towered over anyone in the room, and Jackson, himself an inch over six feet, liked tall men.

He rose and offered his hand. "Samuel Houston, eh?"

"Sam Houston, sir," the boy corrected respectfully.

The General mentally ticketed the fact that this young man preferred the shortening of the full name. It told him something—the youth must possess a certain independence of mind.

"I heard you called Injun Sam," he said.

"Yes, sir." No change in the brown face.

"I'm told you've been living with the Cherokees."

"Off and on for three years, sir."

Like a whiplash came the question: "*Why?*"

The youth felt the criticism in it, but answered without apology.

"Because, sir, I find in the Indians much to admire. They live freely. They have a code of honor. Their pagan mythology is in many ways as poetic as that of the ancient Greeks."

"You're familiar with Greek mythology?"

"The *Iliad* is not unfamiliar to me, sir."

Jackson gave the youth a keener appraisal. His use of words was unusual—he talked like a gentleman. And the boy was handsome—no question of that—in spite of the ugly scratches on his face where Hooten had clawed him. His chestnut-colored hair was wavy and his face very tanned. On his lip was a soft down as yet untouched by the razor. In his clear gray-blue eyes was an undeniable look of admiration. The General found it difficult to resist admiration of this kind.

"Sit down, Mr. Houston," he said. And when they were both seated, he asked, "If you're so fond of the Indians, why are you here now?"

"Because I think there's going to be an Indian war, sir. The tribes will rise against the frontier."

"Too dangerous to remain in an Indian village, was it?"

"No, sir. Not for me. The Cherokees won't take part in the war——"

"How do you know this?" Crisp and sharp the query. A military officer now, questioning an intelligence source.

"A Creek chief came as ambassador to the Cherokees at Hiwassee. I saw on his breast a silver medal the width of a man's hand. It bore the picture of the British king."

"Ha! How did you know it was the British king?"

"Because of the legend surrounding it: *Georgius III, Dei Gratia Britanniarum Rex F.D.*"

"You have Latin?"

"Enough to translate that."

"And your translation?"

"George III, by the grace of God, king of Britain."

"Good. But those letters at the end—F.D.?"

"*Fidei Defensor*—Defender of the Faith—a title of the British king."

Andrew Jackson was not easily impressed, but he found himself not a little so now. A lawyer himself, at times a judge on the bench, he had some Latin, but this youth seemed steeped in it.

"This is important!" he exclaimed. "What you've just described is a British treaty medal. I've suspected some devil's work was afoot among the southern tribes, ever since Tecumseh, that British-loving Shawnee, was down there." To Russell, at the door of the barroom, he said, "Landlord, if you please, sir, a glass of bourbon for my young friend here."

Open-mouthed, the people who had crowded in to stare saw the greatest man on the frontier, ignoring them all, even Squire Toole, engage in conversation earnest and even confidential with the youth they had often derided.

"This Creek ambassador," Jackson was saying, "you know his name?"

"Yes, sir. Lomochati—Creek for Red Eagle. By the whites he's called Bill Weatherford, and he's far more white than Indian in blood. Yet he's a Creek of Creeks, a thorough member of the tribe, hating the white men and preferring his Indian name."

"He was stirring up the Cherokees in behalf of the British?"

"He didn't succeed, sir. The Cherokees loaded him with presents and sent him away."

"But there's an infernal volcano ready to erupt!" Jackson turned his long face toward Reid with a look of serious excitement. "Haven't I been predicting something on this order, John? An Indian war in the making—no question of it! The British are arming six thousand Creek warriors to do their bloody work for them."

He rose and the others rose with him. "Squire Toole," he said to that gentleman, "I do hope you'll accept my sincerest apologies if I depart at once. Captain Reid and I must lay this matter at the earliest moment before Governor William Blount at Knoxville."

"Why, of course, sir. Our regret and all that, but——"

Jackson interrupted the squire by turning his piercing blue gaze on Sam Houston. "I thank you for this information," he said, lingering for a moment. "By the way, I witnessed your contest with Hooten."

"Yes, sir."

"I admired your strategy. You could hardly have beaten him at rough-and-tumble had he been fresh—now could you, young man?"

"I might not, sir."

"So you maneuvered him into the race, and when he had blown himself you were able to overthrow him?"

"Something like that, sir."

"You appear to think ahead. We're at war. I could use a man like you in my Tennessee Rifles."

"I—I've already taken the dollar from the drumhead, sir. The regulars."

"But you're Indian-trained—you'd make a superior scout and rifleman. Why in the blazing blue thunders did you choose the musket-packing regulars?"

The youth's eyes fell, and he colored with embarrassment. "To tell the truth, sir," he said sheepishly, "it was those shakos—and—and—the white pantaloons—I think they look—so—so—splendid——"

From the General there came for the first time a shout of laughter.

"I'll wager you'll be heard from," he said, clapping the boy on the shoulder. "And as a soldier always remember the tactics you used on Hooten. When your enemy's superior to you in strength, extend him—lead him a chase until he exhausts himself—then close suddenly for the decisive blow!"

"Yes, sir." Sam Houston never forgot that precept.

Late that afternoon, riding back to Knoxville with Reid, to confer with the governor over the Creek situation, Jackson gave a chuckle.

"Remember that young fellow that fought the bully, John?" he asked.

"Yes, sir."

"He enlisted in the regulars. Know why?"

"No, sir."

As if savoring it over, Jackson said, "He just couldn't resist those white pantaloons!"

And laughed more heartily than he had in months.

Chapter Four

*I would have killed him had he shot me
through the brain.*

ANDREW JACKSON

1

The Hermitage.

Name chosen because of the isolation of the place?

Or because of the bald plainness of the place?

The house had something of the awkward appearance of a fortification; which was hardly a matter for wonder, since it was built originally as a blockhouse when the Indians were bad in Tennessee. It had since acquired a sheathing of white-painted clapboards to cover its log walls, and a shake roof. But these improvements failed to add measurably to the symmetry or congruity of the place.

Yet it was a home, a well-loved home, where people lived, and went about their daily tasks, and knew their joys and sorrows. And though there were in Tennessee many finer houses, this home was the most notable in the state, because it was the dwelling of a man nobody really knew or quite understood, an unpredictable man; a man full of secret violence, violence of the mind and violence of the body; a volcanic man; a man who by the very force of his personality, and without making any special effort, turned the thoughts and speculations of other men toward himself—Andrew Jackson.

The year had grown later since the General's visit to Maryville. March had passed into April, and April into May. The summer months followed, heavy with heated days and nights, still skies, still woods, the winding lanes of the countryside almost without the sound of a traveler between the ripening fields. Now it was September—the fourth day of the month.

Though it was early in the morning and the sun hardly risen, Jackson had finished his scanty breakfast at the long table, and now sat brooding in a wing chair by the window, with a small child, hardly awake, nestling in his arms. The dawn light could not disguise the crude plainness of this large room, which occupied the entire lower floor of the house, and was only partly relieved by a rag carpet and a harpsichord, a velvet settee, parlor chairs, and the long table from which the breakfast dishes had just been cleared. Nor could it disguise the melancholy in the face of the Master of the Hermitage.

On this early morning the man was oppressed by his age, and his graying hair, and a sense of futility and failure that hung like a weight on his heart.

He was forty-six years old. At forty-six, he considered, a man's best years are behind him. If he hasn't made it before then, the chances are slim that he will do much of anything important afterward. A gambler by instinct, he gloomily weighed the odds against him—his age, his ill-health, his enemies.

The Hermitage was his: true. Most men might have been satisfied at the attainment of such a plantation, with its fields, its barns, its slaves, its horses and cattle, all from nothing; for he had started with only his enormous energy and his wits, and built this property out of a strenuous practice of law, sundry land speculations, and hardheaded good management.

But Andrew Jackson was—and this was specially a part of him, a dominant trait—eaten with ambition, savagely eager to accomplish, savagely unhappy that he was here, accomplishing nothing.

All summer long he had sat idle at the Hermitage, while all summer long an unending succession of bad news came from the war fronts. He had humbly pleaded for a command in the Canadian theater, where there was fighting against both the British and the Indians.

He hated both the British and the Indians. That scar on his cheek was an everlasting reminder of the British—a saber slash from one of Banastre Tarleton's drunken dragoons when Jackson, only thirteen years old, refused to shine the trooper's boots. Such, at least, was the story, which he never denied. And his mother died of smallpox nursing his brother in a British prison camp, leaving to her son as a final injunction: *Never tell a lie, nor take what is not your own, nor sue for slander. Settle them cases yourself.*

And this injunction he had striven to carry out.

The long weeks of disappointment and frustration frayed his never easy temper. The plea for a fighting command had not even received the civility of an acknowledgment from Washington.

For this he blamed his enemies: the scoundrelly James Wilkinson, who plotted with Aaron Burr to erect an independent inland empire on American soil, and Henry Dearborn who conspired with him. When the plot failed, Wilkinson betrayed Burr; and Dearborn, using as a pretext the fact that Jackson had once entertained Burr at the Hermitage, tried to lay on Jackson the onus of the affair.

A pleasant but visionary little gentleman, Burr, as Jackson remembered him; but too obviously the cat's-paw of others in the grandiose scheme that came to nothing.

Though Dearborn was Secretary of War, and Jackson a mere militia general, that did not prevent him from writing a note which he still remembered with grim satisfaction:

Henry Dearborn, Sir: Colonel Burr received at my house all the hospitality that a banished patriot was entitled to. But, sir, when proof shews him to be a traitor, I would cut his throat with as much pleasure as I would yours on equal testimony.

It did not make for friendly relations. Burr was acquitted of treason, and Jackson was glad of it. But Wilkinson and Dearborn—to his belief —had since revenged themselves by working against him through politics and behind-the-back whisperings, to prevent him from having any chance to prove himself against the enemy.

Wilkinson and Dearborn both had disgraced themselves in their subsequent military operations, but their stupidity and blundering concerned him too much to give him any satisfaction.

With such men as those—men in broadcloth and beaver hats, men with smooth deceitful faces and strong connections through wealth, blood, or politics, men with political ambitions and the cunning to further those ambitions—he felt ill at ease. He was not one of them: only an upstart Tennessee backwoods lawyer-soldier who lacked prestige of family or fortune, and whose tastes were for military rather than political advancement.

It was with the lanky frontiersmen that he felt secure—men to whom the rifle stock, ax helve, or plow handle were equally familiar. The backwoodsmen considered Jackson their own, and believed in him with a faith that made him at times feel unworthy. They did not know his weaknesses: but he knew them full well.

His temper for one thing—a red-hot iron on a tensed spring with a hair trigger. Sometimes a mere touch might send it leaping out, searing what it encountered, with results often as disastrous to himself as to anyone else.

The man sitting by the window with the child in his arms did not indulge in self-analysis, or try to reason out why this was so with him. It did not, indeed, occur to him to do so; and if it had, he would have considered it unhealthy to be prying into his own inner motivations: an evidence of a mind that had not enough to occupy it, and so must examine, and feel, and manipulate itself.

He only knew that, admittedly, he had a reputation as a hotspur, contentious and dangerous. It was not a thing of which a man could be proud; yet, in cold truth, it was justified because of his many altercations.

At this very time he had one on his hands: and so senseless a thing that he could hardly understand it. Thomas Hart Benton had done him a favor. Back in Washington he had somehow induced the paymaster to restore the money Jackson borrowed for the Natchez campaign, making him once more solvent.

And yet with Thomas Hart Benton he had a quarrel; a quarrel arising

out of Benton's enormous self-esteem and his own incorrigible inability
to placate. Benton's brother, Jesse, had disgraced himself in a duel and
Jackson witnessed the disgrace. Benton held Jackson responsible. It was
as simple as that. Benton was bombastic; Jackson stern.

Bad blood. But at least Benton had remained in his own bailiwick
at Franklin. So long as he did so, trouble might be averted.

2

Above the General's head he heard the puncheons creak. That was
Rachel's room upstairs, and she would be coming down now, having
not yet eaten breakfast. Of his wife he thought with a sort of pitying
affection, tender and sad, like that which one feels toward a child that
is sickly, or not very bright, or otherwise stricken by misfortune. Rachel
. . . poor Rachel . . .

There was a time—before she became heavy and clumsy and over-
flowing with tears and self-pity—when he loved her with intense passion.

He still loved her; but no longer as a lover toward a woman.

It was a love more remote, having nothing to do with sex, which long
had ceased to have any meaning between them; something created out
of trouble, and hates and resentments, and injustices and slanders, and
his own sense of guilt; and also out of his deadly determination to protect her, and to justify her and himself after the sorry trick fate and
Lewis Robards had played on the two of them.

He remembered the day, twenty-five years before, when he first saw
Rachel. He was twenty-one then, a fledgling lawyer, redheaded, with a
reputation for wildness—considered, indeed, something of a rakehell.
But he forgot about every other woman as soon as he set eyes on her.

All the Donelsons were handsome, and Rachel, a year younger than
he, was the youngest and loveliest of the Donelson girls, with deep dark
eyes, a dimpling smile, and a form to make a man dream.

She was not smiling or dimpling when he first saw her, for she had
just been separated from her first husband, to whom she had been married for three unhappy years.

From the time she emerged from childhood there was that about
Rachel Donelson which spelled disquiet and longing in men, and caused
frequent jealousies among them. She was beautiful, and her playful way
of using her eyes was pure instinct. She did not plan it, she could not
help it, but she was born to be a challenge to every male she encountered; and she found it well nigh impossible not to laughingly coquet
with her pursuers.

Suitors came long distances to try their luck with the prettiest of the
Donelson girls: so many of them, and so importunate, that before she

was eighteen she surrendered to one of them and was borne off to Kentucky as his bride by Lewis Robards, of Harrodsburg.

As young Mrs. Robards, Rachel later told Jackson—and he believed her—she tried to be modest and circumspect; but men would not let her alone, and in spite of herself she continued to have admirers. Her husband was of a mean, suspicious, and jealous disposition. They quarreled frequently, though she declared that she never consciously encouraged any of the young gentlemen who clustered about her at dances and parties, and kissed her finger tips, and whispered in her ear bright nothings. It was after one of those quarrels, a culmination of many bitter scenes in which he made groundless accusations, that she left Robards and returned to her mother's home near Nashville.

When Andrew Jackson met her there he knew she was married; but married or no, he could not help falling under her spell. She seemed to him pathetic, with woe and pain in eyes that were meant for playfulness and mirth, and his heart went out to her. And she? Though she remained subdued, it was not in her nature to be insensible to the kind of friendship he offered her.

Perhaps, he now thought, it might have been better had she never felt his admiration. She might have gone back and lived out her life with Robards. Unhappily, of course. But he wondered if she would have been as unhappy as now.

He felt deeply culpable for her unhappiness; yet how could he have done differently then? He was bemused in her presence, trembled at the mere touch of her hand. He thought of her as all beauty, all purity, all wonder—the self-deceiving phrases with which a young man seeks to convince himself that what actuates him is not the hot, raw, insolent demand in him for the furious enjoyment of her body, but something much higher and nobler and more poetic.

So he continued his "friendship," which in reality was a courtship, though never open or even admitted by either of them.

After a time Robards, a self-assertive, sullen, though handsome enough young man, came from Kentucky to get his wife. Jackson and he quarreled almost on sight, but it came to no conclusion. Then, after a reconciliation was tried and failed—and Jackson did not dare ask himself how much he, himself, had contributed to that failure—Rachel left her husband again and fled downriver to Natchez, fearing, actually fearing, bodily harm from Robards. In the same flatboat flotilla, though not on the same flatboat, on excuse of business but really to keep guard over her, and watch after her, and be near her, rode the redheaded young cockerel known as Andrew Jackson.

It was after they reached Natchez that the word came to the effect that Robards had obtained a divorce from Rachel by enactment of the Kentucky legislature. Jackson broke the news to her. He never forgot that day, or her despair, or the way life seemed to go out of her, for she considered divorce the blackest of disgraces.

"I expected he might kill me," she said brokenly, "but this is worse."

Tears brightened in her eyes, beautiful with pain. It was then that he asked her to marry him.

An impulse: yet not altogether one of the moment. He had sometimes allowed himself the secret thought of what it might be like to possess Rachel; even, guiltily, while she was the wife of another man. That he denied himself any of the coarser imaginings concerning her was a proof of his will power, for he had fully known the meaning of sex and women since his fifteenth year.

The impulse, prompted by a wish to dry the tears in her eyes, became a permanency. Rachel accepted him without any great hesitation . . . a cynic might have said that she appeared not wholly unprepared when his offer was made. But Jackson was no cynic.

They were married by a Natchez magistrate; and Rachel, freed now of fear and despair, was radiant as he had never seen her, seeking to please her new husband with a myriad pretty ways, and mirth, and fervor in their nuptial bed. Jackson was lost in her completely; wrapped about her, enthralled and dizzy with delight and pleasure in her, hardly able to imagine such happiness as he was experiencing.

When they returned to Nashville there were two joyous years of wedded life: she the vivacious center of her social circle, he busy with law and land affairs, and with a sudden short campaign against raiding Indians, and with paying postgraduate courtship to her.

Two years—and then the thunderclap!

Even yet Jackson found it difficult to dwell on it in his mind.

The supposed divorce of Robards, it developed, was no divorce at all. It was merely an enabling act—whereby he was empowered by the Kentucky legislature to obtain a divorce, *if he could show sufficient cause.*

Robards permitted false information to be given out, and then for two years waited in scoundrelly silence. At the end of that time he at last showed his "cause"—to wit, that his wife was living, and had been living, "in adultery with another man," namely Andrew Jackson!

At first stunned, then furious, Jackson searched the lawbooks. It was only too true. Technically, because of Robards' treachery, he and Rachel were not, had never been, legally man and wife. Those nights of love and passion they shared were by this foul plot robbed of all the poetry and beauty with which his thoughts surrounded them. Instead they were reduced—at least in the eyes of the unfriendly world—to the sullied lecheries of an abandoned woman and her paramour, gratifying together a forbidden and unholy lust.

Rachel . . . *an abandoned woman?* Why, she was innocent of any thought of wrongdoing; and so was he!

But the fact that they believed they were truly and lawfully married did not change the legal status of the case. Blazing with fury, Jackson would have taken his pistols, sought out Robards, and shot him down. But Rachel's tears dissuaded him. In such an act she could see only further disgrace and woe for herself.

At first, even after Robards obtained the real divorce, Jackson refused to consider another marriage ceremony, feeling it would be an admission of the illegality of their union, which he, against all logic, still insisted was lawful. But she, poor creature, wept and pleaded so pitifully, hoping it would restore to her some shreds of respectability, that at length he consented. Once again he and Rachel went through the marriage ritual, fulfilling the exactions of the statute to the last humiliating letter.

But by that time everything was spoiled. Rachel had become a different woman.

Gone was his bright, joyous bride. A creature broken in heart and spirit took her place. She never laughed. As one oppressed by a burden almost too great to bear, she crept about, all pleasure gone out of her; her beauty fading, too, for she took on weight as in her woe over her disgrace she grew careless of her appearance.

Fire and ecstasy were lost in her, as if some wind from the caverns of evil had blown out her inward flame. Her soul was sick, as if it were blackened, sullied, destroyed forever: as if an unclean hand had been laid on her soul, from the touch of which her soul shrank.

Whose was the unclean hand? Her husband's? She never uttered the thought if she had it, but her body no longer responded to him, she seemed dead inside, the superb sex mate no longer, until at last he gave over all effort to rouse her. Yet even in this state she seemed to cling to him more, depend on him more, hold him more to account for her existence, for any hope of happiness she might yet know.

He changed also. Fiercely he dedicated himself to defending and shielding her from the world. For speaking less than respectfully of Rachel, General John Sevier, then governor of Tennessee, narrowly escaped with his life when he and Jackson exchanged pistol shots. For the same offense, Jackson caned that busybody, Thomas Swann, in a public place. And for that offense, unforgivable in his eyes, he met Charles Dickinson on the dueling field.

3

In the backward arch of his mind he seemed to see again the mist rising from the river bottom among the trees, on that early morning nearly seven years ago. To one side clustered the seconds and surgeons. Twelve paces away from him stood Charles Dickinson, the sneering elegant, his heavy pistol held muzzle down and cocked, awaiting the signal.

Jackson's own pistol also was cocked and ready. He intended to kill Dickinson, even though he was fully aware that the other was a far better shot than he.

He had a reason. Dickinson, bitter over a horse-racing loss, had slandered him. Jackson let that pass. But later, in a drinking crowd, Dickinson made a snide reference, with a nasty grin, to Rachel and the irregularity of her marriage, a sneer at her very character.

It reached Jackson's ears: the challenge followed.

That morning by the river he was sure Dickinson would hit him, perhaps mortally. But as if no other thing in all the world mattered, he concentrated his whole being on killing the detractor of his wife, even if at the moment he pulled the trigger he was himself dying.

He heard the voice of General John Overton, the referee: "Gentlemen, are you ready?"

Dickinson's voice: "Ready."

His own: "Yes, sir."

From Overton: "Fire!"

An instantaneous puff of smoke from Dickinson's weapon, and with the report Jackson felt a heavy shock in his side.

For a moment he swayed in the vertigo of wound sickness. Then, summoning all his will, he straightened his form.

He heard Dickinson's horrified half-whisper: "Great God! Have I missed him?"

The man recoiled a step.

Overton's stern voice: "Back to the mark, sir!"

Almost in a daze, Jackson saw his enemy step back to his place and stand with folded arms, his eyes averted.

He raised his own pistol.

Even now, years later, he remembered the futile click as he pulled the trigger and the hammer stopped at half cock; and also his intense annoyance at the misfire. Blood was trickling down his lank body inside his clothes and he felt lightheaded and weak.

Someone cried out, "Hold, sir——"

But remorselessly he drew back the hammer, sighted, and fired. Dickinson staggered, uttered a moaning cry, and pitched to the ground, surrounded at once by his seconds and surgeon. The ball had torn a hole through his bowels and he died that night.

When, later, the doctors examined Jackson, they told him that Dickinson's quick shot had almost been deadly true. Only the set of his loose coat on his spare frame saved him, for Dickinson misjudged the position of his heart. The ball passed under his thin ribs, breaking two of them, and lodged in a corner of his right lung, probably carrying shreds of cloth and splinters of bone with it, too near the heart to risk removing it.

For nearly seven years now he had carried that leaden ball, and he had never been the same since. He suffered recurring attacks of fever, spells of coughing, sometimes blood in his sputum. An abscess in the lung? Quite probable, and the medicine of that day had no cure for it. His whipcord constitution alone kept him continuing his active career, in the periods of comparative relief as the lung abscess periodically broke and rid itself of the pus which he coughed up.

His remark at the time he was wounded was remembered and quoted: "I would have killed him had he shot me through the brain." An evidence of indomitable will, his friends said; of reptile malignancy, declared his enemies.

His foes criticized him for deliberately recocking his pistol to shoot down his adversary after it seemed that fortune had spared him. But never for one moment did Jackson regret it. That man had slandered Rachel. If any other did the like, Jackson stood grimly ready to shed blood again, and the world knew it.

Yet after all, the pity was that none of this saved Rachel from the spiteful tongues: tongues of women, avid to flay one of their own sex; of men to whom her real sin was that she was the wife of a man they hated. Whispers . . . forever whispers . . . behind the fan or behind the hand . . . not open, but never ceasing.

Rachel knew of the whispers. She became a recluse from society, seeking the solace of religion, expending herself in meaningless activities, an old woman before her time.

There was for her another deep well of sorrow: Rachel had no child. She believed that the fault was hers, since she had never conceived during her three years' marriage with Robards either, a seeming proof that she was barren. This she accepted as another spear plunged into her heart, almost as if she welcomed the added sadness over which she could weep at times.

Jackson sought to comfort her by bringing the children of friends or relatives into their home; and finally by legally adopting the little boy lying in his arms at this minute—a son of one of Rachel's brothers who had suffered misfortune—so that she could have a baby of her own.

But though she gladly received the child, it was not quite the same. In her heart remained the secret gnawing frustration that neither this nor any other child was hers by motherhood's pristine right.

Poor, poor Rachel . . . she represented perhaps the greatest failure in all Jackson's life; a ruin he had caused and could not mend. A ruin for which he blamed himself, and which shadowed his whole outlook, blameless though he really was.

4

He heard her foot on the stair, descending.

In his arms the child stirred and his graying head bent over it. This man was a curious combination of concern over the momentary comfort of the little one, and perfect lack of any consciousness of comfort for himself.

He rose from the chair, still holding the little boy, whose eyes opened, fresh and round from sleep, and gazed about him.

Rachel reached the foot of the stairs: a large, unwieldy woman, vast-bosomed, yet with a hint of the beauty long past. Her hair was still black, hardly a thread of white in it, carefully combed with puffs at the sides of the head and surmounted by a lace cap, quite pretty. Though her cheeks were overplump and flabby, her eyes were large and might have been brilliant in her youth.

The General pulled a bell rope.

"Good morning, my dear," he said to his wife.

A Negro woman entered, and to her he gave the child.

Then he put his thin arms around Rachel's ample body, and kissed her on the cheek.

"You've had breakfast?" she asked. "I didn't hear you get up."

For years now they had occupied separate rooms because of his restlessness at night; and she made that same comment almost without fail each morning of all those years. Rachel was a heavy sleeper, and there always seemed a faint accusation in her voice when she spoke of his early rising.

"I was wakeful and heard little Andrew," he said. "I got him out of his crib and we had breakfast together."

"What did Noomy give him?"

"We had the same. Gruel and milk."

She gave him a sharp glance. "Your trouble again?" She was referring to his dysentery.

"Oh, not bad," he said.

"You ought to have the milk boiled. It's good for that." Like most women of her age, Rachel considered herself an expert on all diseases, and was willing to state her theories, which were positive, at length and on any occasion.

"I said it wasn't bad. Not bad enough to concern anybody."

"It concerns *me*. Have you taken your calomel regularly?"

"It upsets me worse."

"You must take it. And I ought to send for Dr. Hogg to physic you again with rhubarb or squills. Maybe bleed you. This has gone on too long. I can't understand what that doctor's thinking about, not to get at a case like yours and do something about it! I ought to give Dr. Hogg a piece of my mind——"

Jackson interrupted, because this could go on a long time.

"What will you have for breakfast, my dear?" he asked.

It changed the direction of her thinking, for she always had an appetite, an almost greedy pleasure in food, which served to appease some of her other frustrations.

"Noomy," she said to the nurse woman who stood still holding the baby, "tell Saphrony to fix me some batter cakes, and fry a slice of that smoked ham we took out of the smokehouse yesterday, and—oh—two eggs, she knows how I like them, and some of the grape conserve, and coffee, and some for the General—you'll take coffee, too, won't you?"

Jackson nodded and the nurse woman, with the child in her arms, departed on her errand.

They sat, and when the food came Rachel uttered a lengthy prayer during which Jackson dutifully bowed his head. He was not much of a religionist, but he respected his wife's feelings in this regard.

She began to eat with hearty enjoyment, as was her habit, and he sipped a cup of coffee, black. To him the cream and white sugar with which she loaded her coffee cup made it distasteful.

Between mouthfuls she talked continually, and rather complainingly. It was time for the annual fall house cleaning, and she told him how it bothered her and tired her to oversee the house servants while they took all the carpets up and beat them outside, and scrubbed the floors, and set the linen out to sun, and washed and ironed the curtains, and renovated the mattresses, and polished the silver, and did all the other things which she considered were a bounden duty both fall and spring, and then put everything back again where it was before. To all this he listened, having heard it countless times, his mind wandering, but striving to seem interested and to pay attention to the recital of trivialities. For he knew that in talk, as in eating, Rachel lost herself and was for a time content, and he wished to contribute as much as was humanly possible to the few happy moments she had.

In the midst of this, Aaron, Jackson's body servant and butler, a small, wizened bowlegged Negro, who had in his younger days ridden as a jockey for his master, hurried in and said, "Gin'ral, suh, I do believe Gin'ral Coffee is ridin' up to the house."

Jackson rose with shining eyes. Of all his friends he considered John Coffee, a brigadier general in the militia and a fellow planter, the least selfish and most loyal. A fighter, too, who knew how to lead horsemen in battle.

Coffee, forever careless of his appearance, entered a moment later, wearing an ill-fitting pepper-and-salt suit of clothes and a badly tied cravat. His boots were conspicuously in need of polish, and the wide planter's hat he held in his hand was stained with sweat. But there was about him something so strong and honest that people instinctively trusted him. A stranger looking at Jackson might have been reminded of tempered steel; Coffee would have made him think of granite.

The two men clasped hands.

"General," said the visitor, "and Rachel, good morning."

"Welcome, John!" exclaimed Jackson. "You'll have breakfast, of course. I'll ask the kitchen to fix it at once——"

"No, thankee," said Coffee. "I had a snack at Nashville." His big face crinkled in a smile. He was a huge man, a giant almost, with a booming deep voice.

"How's things been going, General?" he asked Jackson.

"Well enough, I suppose," was the answer.

In that long heated summer Jackson, chafing every minute at the inaction, had paid close attention to his plantation, watching the work of his field hands, building a new barn, overseeing the care of his stable of blooded horses. All this with a view of guarding his behavior, striving to discipline himself so that he could not be criticized, hoping still for some crumb from Washington.

Coffee knew what this cost him, and he had something of a private nature to impart to him. He looked at Rachel, then at Jackson.

"I brought a mare over," he said.

By this the General knew that the mare was in season, though Coffee would not mention that before Rachel. He had some time before promised his friend a service from his famous stallion Truxton, the most notable racer in Tennessee, when Coffee had a mare whom he thought worthy of such a distinction.

"Let's go out and look at her," he said. "You will excuse us, my dear?"

Rachel, perfectly understanding, nodded and went on with her eating.

5

Horses—fine horses—were the chief outlet for Jackson's pent spirits. His stable was famous, and he himself the chief figure of the turf in Tennessee. Though well past his youth, he had backed and ridden every animal he owned, even the fiercest stallion, for the sheer excitement of it. Always he entered horses in the county races and wagered heavily on them. In his younger days he had even ridden as a gentleman jockey, and one reason for his fondness for Aaron, his body servant, was that Aaron had more than once brought in winners for him as a race rider.

"Where's your mare?" he asked, as with Coffee he left the house.

"Down in one of your paddocks," said the somber giant.

At that moment the pealing neigh of a stallion rang out, answered at once by a mare's eager whinny.

Jackson gave his slight smile. "Sounds as if the courtship is beginning already. That's good. Some of these ladies are mighty coy."

They walked toward the barns. In the paddock a black groom was leading about a bay mare. No better judge of horseflesh existed in the country than Jackson, and he looked her over closely.

Quite pretty. Bay, with black points. Sensitive head and alert small ears. Clean-limbed and graceful, yet strong.

"She looks peart," he approved. "What's her name?"

"Bountiful," said Coffee. "Good blood, if I do say it. Her pedigree goes back to Colonel Hoomes' stallion, Bedford."

"This ought to be an interesting mating," observed Jackson.

Now, screaming his eagerness, and answered by peals from the mare, the stallion was brought from his box stall.

Truxton, now thirteen years old, had in his career beaten over the kingly four-mile course such celebrated horses as Francis Gordon's Jack-of-Clubs, Lazarus Cotton's Greyhound, and Joseph Erwin's Plough-boy—the last leading directly to the quarrel and duel with Dickinson—as well as many others.

Now retired from racing to the stud, he was still full of fire and fury, an imposing beast with a powerful muscular frame. His eyes blazed and his teeth flashed, and he made known his eagerness with shrill imperative buglings.

As he approached the mare, restrained by the groom at his head, he seemed a spectacle of almost ungovernable madness. The mare switched her tail and laid back her ears—coy, as Jackson had said. But Truxton, his bay coat gleaming like burnished metal, pranced, reared, pleaded, caressed her with little nips, blandished her, and used every art at his command to seduce her.

The lady's reluctance did not long continue in the presence of his magnificent display. She, too, gave a frisk and a whinny, by her actions betraying her willingness.

A moment later the great stallion reared mightily behind her and mounted her. The mating was complete. In his paroxysm the huge beast seemed almost to collapse on her, and when he dropped off, languid from his orgasm, one huge foreleg still remained across her back, as if he were unwilling to let her go, until she was led out from this odd embrace by the groom.

"That ought to bring a fine colt for you, John," said Jackson as the drama of procreation was finished, and the animals led away to their respective stalls.

"Yes, sir," said Coffee.

But on the way back to the house, he turned his broad, damp face to his friend, and placed a hand on his shoulder.

"Got something I want to tell you," he said in his usual half-diffident manner.

"What is it?"

"The two Bentons and some of their friends are in Nashville."

Jackson halted in mid-step. At first he studied the ground, making no reply, for the statement explained itself and needed no elaboration.

It meant trouble: trouble that had worried him for some time, since the regrettable affair that summer. Against his wishes he had been induced to act as second in the duel between Colonel William Carroll and Jesse Benton, Colonel Tom Benton's younger brother. Both Carroll and Tom Benton were favorites of his, and Benton had done him favors, but the outcome of the duel made an enemy of the orator, whose self-esteem was touched by it.

Coffee shifted his huge feet and looked at the sky, and then at the distance.

When Jackson spoke it was with a curious note of half-apology.

"So they dare me in my own back yard," he said. And then, "I protest it was none of my doing, John. I did my utmost, as the correspondence will show, to bring a friendly reconciliation between Billy Carroll and Jesse Benton. But Jesse is a fool as well as a poltroon. I thought I had matters smoothed over until Joe Erwin and Thomas Swann, who have no love for me, crowded Billy until he had to accept the challenge. Why, they even rattled the bones of Dickinson—I was the one they were aiming at, and they knew I knew it. What else could I do but back Billy?"

He paused and Coffee wondered why the General felt impelled to explain himself. It was never his habit to explain his actions to any man, and certainly there was no need to do so to this friend.

But Jackson's explanation arose out of his own feeling of guilt. He had made good resolutions and promises to John Coffee, and then had gone back on them. Well, he might as well say the rest.

"Carroll himself will tell you," he went on, "that I refused at first to second him, on the ground that I was too old to take part in such an affair. But they had me in a corner, John. They would have said I was side-stepping. I tell you, sir, my hand was forced."

Still Coffee remained silent. He did not condemn Jackson, he was too loyal and understanding for that. But Jackson, knowing it, condemned himself.

"You know what happened," he continued. "After that puppy, Jesse Benton, shot first and nearly took off Carroll's thumb, he failed to abide the return shot. Instead he doubled up like a sheep with the colic, and turned his hindquarters—I assure you he fills out his breeches bottom roundly. Carroll's shot cut across both cheeks and left a damned wholesome furrow without doing any serious damage. Of course Jesse couldn't sit down for a while and had to lie on his belly in bed. Folks took it up with considerable laughter, ringing all the changes you can easily imagine on a wound like that."

Coffee nodded. "And Tom Benton blamed you."

"My enemies got to his ear as soon as possible. They convinced him that the Benton name was everlastingly disgraced." The General sighed and shook his head. "I tried to forgive Tom Benton when he began his bombastic and ranting denunciations of me—busybodies always bring matters like that to your ears. I wrote him a letter, a conciliatory letter, sir. He replied in a toplofty and bitter manner, blaming me for the whole affair—as if I personally arranged that damned duel!"

Now Coffee could see the danger signals.

"I sought to forgive," Jackson said, his voice hardening, "but this invasion of Nashville has just one purpose. It's a throwing of the gauntlet in my teeth, John. And everyone will know it. I have to call that bluff by riding to town myself and confronting them, or lose the respect of every man, my own most of all."

He had spoken thus far in a quiet, almost contemplative tone, but now his voice rasped with passion.

"If I see either of the Bentons, by the Eternal, I'll horsewhip them!"

6

He tried to avoid Rachel, but she was in the hall and saw him take a pistol from the gun room.

"General—where are you going?" she faltered.

"On business," he said shortly.

But she knew her husband, that look on his face.

"Business?" she cried. "No—it's something dreadful. I know it is—don't go—I beg of you—Mr. Coffee, tell him how wrong it is—what a mistake——"

Her eyes welled with tears, and she put her arms about him, her heavy bulk hanging on him as she put her face against his shirt ruffles and wept. He felt profoundly sorry for her, but he was abrupt, almost rough, as he freed himself from her arms and strode out with Coffee, leaving her collapsed in a chair, crying into her handkerchief.

More and more these days Jackson felt impelled to seek refreshment in the outer world, away from the home he once loved. He was not self-discerning, and he did not understand his reluctance to remain for any length of time at home, his instinct being to breathe fresher air, a freer atmosphere, so that he plunged eagerly into any kind of a venture that took him away.

It might have astonished him, perhaps made him furious, had anyone suggested that he fled from Rachel—her tears, her self-pity, her banalities. To others, to himself, he maintained that his love for her was as it always had been, would ever be.

He was true to her: no other woman had ever caused his heart to swerve. And yet . . . he felt a downright relief, whatever the difficulties that might lie before him, when he mounted his horse and set out with Coffee on the road to Nashville.

Chapter Five

History will never record how many men
have performed great deeds because they
were driven out of their homes by some
unbearable trait of their wives, from
which they fled, almost joyfully, to face
as an alternative peril and even death.

MAJOR JOHN REID

1

It was nine miles to the town and in that ride they scarcely spoke.

Coffee, though he had considered it his duty to warn his friend, and foresaw the contingencies that might arise, was deeply worried.

He knew Andrew Jackson perhaps as well as anyone did. But when he was with him he felt as if he was with fire. There was the restlessness of fire in Jackson; the intensity of fire.

He could be, and was, often reserved, even cold in appearance. But Coffee always felt that within was an explosive force, a white heat that might at any time burst forth. Yet Jackson was watchful of himself, with an immense personal charm, a native courtliness and consideration for others, a human storm kept under iron control most of the time, a man fearless to the point of rashness, not selfish yet passionately eager to do something beyond the ordinary, an ambition that was like an avarice in him. He was a source of self-replenishing energy, like the sun. If only that energy, that ambition, that courage could be harnessed and set in the right direction there were almost no limits to what it might achieve. But harnessing the furious force that was Andrew Jackson . . . to John Coffee it was like trying to harness the tornado or the tidal wave.

When they reached the Nashville Inn, they tied their horses and entered together.

"No," said the clerk at the desk, in answer to Jackson's question. "The Bentons are not in this house, sir." Then he added, "I understand that they're at the City Hotel."

A young man, fresh-faced, wearing a wine-colored coat with fawn-colored trousers, and carrying a cane, appeared in the lobby—Stockley Hays, one of Rachel's numerous company of nephews and nieces.

"I stopped at the Hermitage a few minutes after you left, sir," he said. "Aunt Rachel was afraid something might happen, so I followed."

Jackson grunted, and Coffee swore beneath his breath. If there was one thing necessary to make trouble certain it was the arrival of this boy eager to see "something happen." The General was sure to be on his high horse now, with one of his younger relatives watching to see how he conducted himself in an affair touching his honor.

"Let us walk over to the post office," said Jackson after a moment. "I'd like to get my mail."

Coffee knew that the post office stood diagonally across the square and that between the post office and the Nashville Inn was the City Hotel. He said nothing. Matters had passed beyond his control. But he felt for the pistol he carried in his pocket.

Across the square the three men marched, in the General's hand a small riding whip. All at once Coffee saw a tall, heavily framed figure standing in front of the hotel. Black, curly hair and side whiskers, Roman features, double-breasted frock coat, it was Thomas Hart Benton himself. He appeared to be watching them.

"Do you see that fellow?" Coffee asked in a low voice.

Jackson slapped his riding boot with his whip. "Yes. I have my eye on him."

They entered the post office and took the letters awaiting them.

"The scoundrel stood where he was, inviting encounter!" said Jackson savagely.

Coffee regarded him anxiously. The vein of wrath pulsed in his forehead and his eyes were fiery. It was evident that he was in one of his passionate moods, and nobody could predict what might happen when he was like that. Young Stockley Hays, standing by the door, gazed out on the square, fiddling with his slender ivory-headed walking stick. He half drew the ivory head out—the cane contained a slim steel sword-blade.

"They've gone back into the hotel," he suddenly said.

At that Jackson led the way out of the post office. No cutting across the square this time. Straight toward the City Hotel he walked, a pace ahead of his companions. Coffee thought to himself that even from the rear, the high-shouldered figure of the General seemed to express sheer blazing fury. Gravely alarmed, but knowing that remonstrance would avail nothing, he quickened his pace to catch up and walk side by side with his friend, while young Hays remained a step behind.

Not a word was spoken. The tramp of their feet sounded unnaturally loud. The hotel was reached.

A surprise here. Tom Benton stood, as if waiting, just inside the entrance. Glancing past him, Coffee thought he saw Jesse Benton in the comparative darkness of the interior, also with that strange attitude of expectant waiting.

Whip in hand, Jackson walked ahead, as if to pass the building; then made a sudden, sharp, military turn and strode straight for the portal.

He lifted his whip and his voice rose, shrill with passion.

"Now, you damned rascal! I'm going to punish you! Defend yourself!"

Coffee saw Benton's hand go into his coat bosom for a pistol, but Jackson's weapon was out first, cocked and aimed directly at the other's breast. He dropped the whip to the ground.

Back stepped Benton. Jackson advanced.

To Coffee it seemed that they were performing some grotesque and horrible slow dance, keeping perfect pace as Benton backed and Jackson followed him.

Down the length of the corridor continued the slow, silent march, neither man speaking, maintaining their strange deathly pace, Jackson's gun at Benton's bosom, Benton's face white with horror.

They reached the end of the corridor. Benton, staring with dread at the black muzzle of the pistol aimed at him, did not realize that he had reached the head of a stair that pitched steeply down to the alley outside at the rear of the hotel.

Too late Coffee saw the treacherous move of Jesse Benton.

Not daring to face Jackson, the younger Benton slipped through a doorway until he was at the General's back, aiming his pistol.

"Hold that!" cried Coffee.

But the report of the pistol, double-shotted, made an ugly shattering roar within the narrow walls of the corridor.

Forward pitched Jackson, his own weapon discharging harmlessly as he involuntarily pressed the trigger.

Tom Benton, unhurt, drew two pistols from under his coat and fired both of them at the long form lying prostrate at his feet.

Through the powder smoke that now choked the interior Coffee's huge figure strode, and his pistol also crashed out.

He missed in the hurry and confusion, but clubbing his weapon he charged Tom Benton.

The black-whiskered orator stepped back to avoid him. His foot found air—he had forgotten the stair. Down he went, plunging and rolling the full length of the steps into the alley.

Jesse Benton swung about just as Stockley Hays pulled from his walking stick the hidden blade like a short rapier, and closed on him.

A thrust—with all the young man's fury. But the blade snapped.

By some incredible chance it struck a metal button which caused the steel to break.

Yet Hays pressed forward.

Jesse Benton drew a second pistol, thrust the muzzle against his body, and pulled the trigger. The hammer struck sparks from the flint but the weapon misfired.

Hays struck at Benton with his cane. The other retreated, leaping down the stairs to join his brother, who had risen, bruised by his fall but not seriously hurt, to his feet below.

In the smoke-filled corridor Coffee, his only concern for Jackson, bent over him. From the prostrate man's left side blood was gushing.

"My friend—my dear friend!" exclaimed Coffee. "How is it with you?"

"Take care of yourself," gasped Jackson. "I—can't—get up."

"Lie still. I'll see to it——"

But the fight was over. In those few instants it began and ended. The Bentons had withdrawn from the battle.

2

They had wanted his arm. The surgeons told him they must take off his arm.

In his agony, lying on his bed, he scarcely knew how he fought them away.

He remembered the dreadful anguish when he was lifted and carried across the square to the Inn. The stream of his life was running out of its natural course, and his shoulder was choked with aching heat. He could not rightly breathe.

Somehow he lived out the night. Next day they told him his blood soaked through two mattresses before the flow was stanched.

In the room a sobbing, weeping presence. Rachel . . .

The sobbing irritated him, made him impatient in his sickness. Then his conscience pricked him. He felt like a Judas, resenting her presence; yet he could hardly bear her near him, the reddened face, the vast breasts quaking under the lace fichu, the pathetic but reproachful looks she cast at him now and then, for getting himself—and her—into this trouble which she had begged him to avoid.

His left shoulder was shattered. One lead slug had splintered the shoulder bone. Another lodged against the bone in the upper arm. It could not be removed because it lay next to the wall of the main artery of the arm.

But he had been strong enough to utter a stony "No" when the surgeons explained to him that they must amputate to avoid gangrene.

"Amputate, hell!" he swore. "I'll keep my arm!"

He had heard how the Bentons, after the fight, stood in the square and shouted defiance and revilements. But that was a small matter now, compared to things far greater.

Rachel rose from her chair and began moving about the room, dabbing at her swollen face with her handkerchief. He knew he should be grateful for her solicitude, but he wanted only to be alone. To be mewed up with her in this room was almost more than he could stand.

To his relief she came over presently to his bed and said, "Are you more comfortable, dear? I have to be gone for a time."

He tried to smile. "Comfortable. Yes." But his shoulder pained damnably. "Go on, I'll be all right."

After some stirrings and hesitations—her usual way—she departed.

Now he could think. And the thoughts were bitterly painful.

That damnable temper of his again! He had allowed his temper to trap him into a hotheaded, thoughtless, needless brawl as the culmination of an utterly senseless series of events.

A brawl. Just that. It could be given no better name. He repeated the word to himself, wincing inwardly, because he considered it an expression of his besetting weakness.

Weakness . . . Andrew Jackson did not willingly associate the word with himself. He despised weakness. Yet now that he was confronted by the fact of the episode in the hotel and his own actions, he perceived his own weakness.

A strong man, he told himself, would have ignored irritations such as drove him into the bootless fight with the Bentons. He thought of John Coffee, his heavy, steady face. Coffee, under the same provocations, he was sure, would have ignored them.

But he had not John Coffee's self-control. Instead he had his cursed pride, and his thrice-cursed temper, and his lack of self-control . . . and together they had come near costing him his life.

Probably they had already cost him something he valued more than his life. The story of the brawl would reach Washington as soon as his enemies could carry it there; and it would be embellished with every detail, real or fancied, that could be conjured up to make it appear more disgraceful. The tale of the brawl was the one thing needful to make the interdict of the administration final against him.

Andrew Jackson, alone in his sickroom, gave a groan. Nobody heard it, and nobody could have eased the pain that brought it forth. It was no torture of the body that wrenched that moan from him. His torment was of the soul.

3

He was back at the Hermitage, in his own bed. Slowly the days passed. In his shoulder still sat a core of pain. The ball against the bone of his upper arm probably would be there the rest of his life. But lately Dr. Hogg, when he examined the wound daily, clucked encouragingly.

Perhaps no gangrene after all, he said. To the doctor it looked favorable.

But to Jackson nothing looked favorable. The future was dead for him. He would live out a life of mediocrity, in the dull round of planting, with perhaps a little law practice on the side . . . a failure in all the things he had prayed to achieve. Death would have been better.

John Coffee came to his bedside one day with a strange bit of news.

"General," he said, after a kindly pressure on his friend's thin hand, "this'll interest you. By the holy poker, sir, the Bentons have skedaddled!"

Jackson stared at him, uncomprehending.

"I reckon they discovered there was a sight more people in Tennessee that was friends of Andy Jackson than they ever dreamed," continued Coffee. "When folks found out how you come to be shot—in the back —they hissed the Bentons off the street. I understand they've left the state. For good." Coffee chuckled. "Maybe they found out they were out on a limb—Old Hickory's as tough as his name, and might soon be about looking for an accounting."

He meant to cheer the sick man, but to Jackson it was a confirmation of what he believed was the general opinion of him—a frontier bravo with a streak of murder in him. As usual he could find no words to express this, even to a good friend like Coffee.

Friend? Maybe Coffee was the only true friend he had left in the world.

"Ease me over, will you, John?" he asked.

He did not want Coffee to see how near he was to having tears in his eyes at the thought of that selfless friendship. It was another weakness, growing out of his condition, but still weakness, he told himself. After Coffee gently turned him with his face to the wall and was gone, he conquered the unmanly feeling and returned to his thoughts.

So the Bentons were gone from the state. That yellow puppy, Jesse, was only contemptible. But Tom Benton was more of a man.

Jackson was, had always been, a good hater. But here, in the quiet of his room, he found somewhat to his surprise that he hated neither of the Benton brothers. Jesse was not worth it. Tom had done him a favor, and had been pushed into this quarrel. They need have no fear that he would go hunting for them.

The thought caused him to wonder if he had learned a lesson about unprofitable animosities. He truly hoped so. And yet even if he had, he told himself, it had come too late. A man who was turning gray ought to have learned that kind of a lesson twenty years ago.

Fitfully and without peace his mind continued to work. The war was being fought on many fronts, and he could be no part of it.

Disgrace, disgrace everywhere! Hull's pusillanimous surrender of Detroit, Van Rensselaer's defeat at Queenstown, the cowardly and sluggish tactics of his old enemies Wilkinson and Dearborn along the

Niagara front, the horrible disaster suffered by Winchester and the massacre of his captured troops by the Indians who were allies of the British at the Raisin River—they heaped up into a pyramid of shame for the United States.

None of the American commanders seemed to want to fight, or to know how to fight. And he, Andrew Jackson, who would have fought most joyously, given the chance, could only fret himself into greater thinness and weakness.

The doctor told him that even if he had a command, he had lost so much blood that it would be months, perhaps, before his system could make enough new blood to replace it. He did not, however, have a command. He would never have one. He wondered how he could spend the interminable years of monotony which he foresaw extending ahead of him.

Once more he wished that Jesse Benton's cowardly shot from behind had claimed his life instead of leaving him to lie crippled in bed, gnawing over the raw bones of his despair.

4

Rachel could not be said to be happy: she never allowed herself to be that. Unhappiness, self-created, a feeling of martyrdom, had by a strange paradox become a sort of happiness to her, a state so accustomed with her that she felt lost without it. The disgrace concerning her marriage was now a quarter of a century in the past, but she still conceived that the world was preoccupied with it, in the manner of small natures who cling to anything, whether good or bad, that may give them some distinction in the minds of others.

Yet, with her husband home—and, for the time being at least, safe in bed—she was measurably content. At least, weak from his wounds as he was, he could not at present leave her, and to have him near her had become to her a besetting need.

As a symbol of stability, of tardily won respectability, her prudishly puritanical soul clung to Jackson's near presence. His stern manner and strange inward strength caused everyone to treat him, and by consequence her, with deference that was pleasing to her. When he was absent, as he so often was, she thought that she could notice a change in this manner, a lessening of regard by others.

In this there was perhaps a certain degree of truth, for she lacked much of the charm and pleasantness which women use in creating about themselves an aura of glamour. She had had this once, but it was as if she had forgotten, or put far behind her, all the qualities which had once irresistibly drawn Andrew Jackson to her.

The General was undeviatingly kind to her. His impatience in being bedfast never manifested itself in her hearing. He was at pains to be grateful for everything she did for him, even when his voice was almost too weak to utter his thanks.

Rachel, feeling that for once her husband depended on her, was in this interlude as near to peace as it was possible for her to be.

5

Word of the hideous thing was brought by galloper to Nashville.

Within an hour Jackson heard of it from Stockley Hays, who rode posthaste to the Hermitage.

It made him start up from his pillow, causing such a flash of anguish that he went paler than usual and clamped his teeth to keep back the groan. But it was no time to consider his pain. He listened with growing excitement as his nephew unfolded the story.

He had expected it; wondered why it had not happened before, warned the governor of the state against it.

Down in the Alabama country, the fierce Creek Indians had exploded suddenly in a war of massacre and destruction that surpassed in brutality and horror any Indian war of which he had knowledge. A stockade called Fort Mims, at the head of Mobile Bay, felt their first fury. They surprised it, and in the dreadful holocaust that followed men were hacked to pieces, little children nailed to the walls by arrows, women outraged and then ripped open and scalped. A score who took refuge in a block-house became a living funeral pyre when the log building was locked from outside and set on fire. In all, four hundred and thirty-seven, of both sexes and all ages, lost their lives.

Jackson knew well the terrible aspects of Indian warfare. He had fought Indians; had seen bodies of their victims worried as if by a pack of wolves; had found the fire-blackened trunk of a comrade after he was tortured to death at the stake and then thrown to the dogs. Rachel's own father, Colonel John Donelson, had been murdered by Indians.

This red fury would spread; something must be done.

But that evening old Dr. Hogg, the family physician, found him fuming in bed, shook his head, and gave orders that he should not move.

Jackson obeyed that order for one night.

Next morning three men rode up to the Hermitage, and Rachel was too awed to refuse them admission to the sickroom. They were General John Overton, a veteran of the Revolution, who had been Jackson's second and acted as referee in the Dickinson duel; Judge James Trimble, dry as a cornhusk and keen as a razor, Nashville's leading lawyer, who handled the legal business of the Hermitage; and huge, rumpled General John Coffee.

Overton, tall, gray, and serious, was the spokesman. "We've been named, sir, as a Committee on Safety," he said.

Rachel saw how eagerly her husband, propped on his pillows, greeted his visitors, and also how sadly thin and hollow-eyed he looked. But she knew her place in this kind of discussion and withdrew from the room, a stricken look of helplessness and foreboding on her face.

At the bedside Overton went on to say that he assumed General Jackson had been informed of the Indian trouble to the south.

"Yes, sir," said the gaunt man on the pillow. "Just yesterday, sir."

"The situation is pretty bad," said Overton.

"Sir, it's worse than that!" exclaimed Jackson. "It's critical, sir! I've been forewarned of this, and warned Governor Blount. The British are behind it—someone told me of seeing a Creek chief with a British treaty medal—a young man at Maryville. Name of Houston, I believe. That means British guns, and we've known smuggling has been going on for some time."

Overton nodded solemnly. "Then you can guess the occasion of this call on you?"

Jackson could: they wished to see for themselves how his physical condition was. He was glad that Aaron had shaved him that morning, but even with that he knew his appearance was not reassuring. So he remained silent.

"The Creeks are reported moving northward," Overton continued. "We hear that they're already bushwhacking homes in the remote southern areas of Tennessee."

Jackson's reply was explosive. "Those people," he cried, with his favorite oath, "must be saved!"

Overton agreed, and added that there was a general panic. The committee had come to discover what it could do, inasmuch as the General himself seemed hardly in condition——

"Do?" Jackson's voice rose shrill with excitement. "By God, sir, *I'm* the commander of the Tennessee militia! And by God, sir, *I'll* muster them! And by God, sir, I'll lead them—*in person!*"

The committee departed, two of its members noting with misgivings that the General was too weak to leave his bed. But great John Coffee lingered behind for a moment.

His huge paw swallowed Jackson's thin hand and he grinned down at his friend.

"I knew what you'd say, Andy," he said. "I'm already forming up my mounted rifles."

"Help me, John," said Jackson. "Get word to as many of my captains as you can reach—Gibson, Cannon, Hammond, Cocke—the rest. Tell Billy Carroll to come here with all speed. John Reid ought to be here by now. And—thank you, old friend."

As Coffee departed, plans already were leaping in Jackson's mind—

plans as wide as his sickroom walls were narrow. Everything depended on speed. He saw a great hope, if he acted with sufficient celerity, that he might have the military command he had longed for after all. But the thing must be accomplished before the news could reach Washington, and officialdom there get around to countermanding it. Not an hour to waste.

He called for Aaron, and had his body servant lift him so that with the pillows at his back he could sit up. With Rachel's bedboard, on which she sometimes took breakfast, across his knees, paper on the coverlet, and Aaron anxiously holding the inkstand and extra quills at his elbow, he scribbled letter after letter as fast as he could write.

Before noon John Reid, now a major, appeared after a hard ride from Gallatin.

"Take this," Jackson said. He handed the major a sealed envelope addressed to His Excellency, Governor William Blount, Knoxville, Tennessee. "Get a good rider, John, a *trusty* rider. Have him take that to Willie Blount, and tell him to *wait for the reply to me.*"

Other letters went out, chiefly to officers of his militia companies. At midafternoon Lieutenant Colonel William Carroll appeared. For an hour they were deep in talk of stores and transport and rations and beef on the hoof and remounts and ordnance and ammunition, and all the other details which Carroll, as chief quartermaster, must see to.

After this Jackson lay back in his bed, cold sweat on his face, sick from very weakness. Yet even as he lay, as if bound down to the bed by lack of strength, his mind was racing along the lines of calculation, precaution, even audacity, which this hour of action demanded.

Next day he insisted on getting out of bed.

Rachel was alarmed. "You can't, General!" she cried. "You'll do yourself a hurt! The doctor said so! You mustn't even think of such a thing!"

Jackson's patience was badly frayed, but he kept control of himself and reasoned with her.

"How can I get strong lying in bed?" he asked. "Why, just lying here, even if nothing was the matter with me, would make an invalid out of me." And then, as winningly as he knew how: "My dear, this need for action is like an elixir of life to me."

She turned her eyes up to the sky, and gave a sigh, but in the face of his determination, she gave up. With the aid of Aaron she helped him to rise weakly in his long white gown. He noticed how his shrunken legs would hardly uphold him even when Aaron supported him, but by sheer will power he reached a chair by the window. There he sat, a light quilt across his lap, and presently when food was brought he forced himself to eat because he knew he needed the strength.

A different kind of strength arrived next day. Willie Blount, a politician not noted for aggressive speed in action, was so alarmed by news of the Creek uprising that for once he moved with promptitude. He had, of course, no conception of the physical condition of his commander of militia, but by return courier he sent a letter granting gubernatorial authority to Major General Andrew Jackson to raise twenty-five hundred men and "suppress the enemy."

At the last words Jackson almost chuckled. He would get the men—his riflemen already were gathering at his call. But the enemy would require quite a little "suppressing." Nevertheless, with this authority he was launched on his adventure. Orders went out for his men to mobilize at Fayetteville, near the border south of Nashville.

Now Jackson bent his will to gaining strength. It came more rapidly than he had any reason to expect, partly because of the burning intensity within him. In a day or two he was able to hobble out in the yard, with Rachel or Aaron at his elbow. His journeyings grew longer, and he ventured as far as the stables and paddocks, to look over his horses and talk to the grooms. A white gelding, of the get of Truxton, with good shoulders and trim legs, spirited but tractable, caught his eye. He ordered the grooms to get that horse into condition for him.

Impatience grew in him, fretted him. He must be away, launched on his campaign, before the people at Washington could stop him. He ran over in his mind the names of political favorites they might appoint in his place—any number of them. And he was sure that not one of them would be capable of facing and defeating six thousand bloody-minded Creek warriors.

Each time a letter arrived, he looked at the envelope anxiously for the dread Washington postmark that might tell him he was superseded. But for once he found reason to be thankful for the dilatory habits of the government. Washington had not yet taken cognizance, or had been too slow to act, when almost exactly a month after he was shot, he one morning announced that he was ready to ride.

His parting with Rachel was distressing as usual. Major Reid, who as his aide was to ride with him, witnessed it and felt sorry for the poor woman, who did not seem to understand that the man she had married was of some unusual metal; and that she could never hope to keep pace with him; and perhaps even that she should not try to hold him back.

She wailed sadly when she clung to Jackson at the cost of anguish to his wounded shoulder, as he showed by a twist of his face. When Rachel cried, her face had a habit of curling up in thick fleshy folds that might almost be mistaken for laughter, were it not for the tears leaking through her tightly closed lids.

She implored him, knowing it was useless, not to leave her. This was followed by her usual pleadings and broken sentences about a man's duty being at home with his family. At last:

"But you're going! I know you've made up your mind to go! Nothing can change you!" She was a tearful accuser now. "You're going in spite of anything I can say. I know how reckless you are. You'll get killed, I know it! And then what will happen to *me*? Oh, there's nothing left for me but to take my refuge—my *only* refuge—in prayer. It's my only, my sole, consolation. Oh, why, why, was I ever born?"

Reid watched the General try to comfort her, and knew that she had succeeded in making him feel like a traitor to her. But he observed that for all her reproaches, in this one thing Jackson would not yield. He humored her in almost every other matter, but when it became a question of what he conceived to be his duty, to the country, to the people of the frontiers, he was decisive and settled on his course.

At length he made his escape from her and mounted his horse with some help from Aaron, for he had not yet regained all the strength he needed. When he rode away from the Hermitage, with Reid at his side and black Aaron trotting his horse and leading a baggage animal a few yards in the rear, Jackson turned. Rachel was still standing where he had left her, staring after him. He waved his good arm.

She did not wave back. Slowly she turned and moved back to the house.

6

Reid took all this in silently. But he had literary ambitions and kept a journal. That evening, when they stopped in a wayside tavern on the way to Fayetteville, he wrote in his diary the following observations:

The influence of women in the destinies of men, and therefore of nations, is beyond estimation. Inspiration is often their gift; but history will never record how many men have performed great deeds because they were driven out of their homes by some unbearable trait of their wives, from which they fled, almost joyfully, to face as an alternative peril and even death.

The well-worn saying that behind every great man there is a woman is perhaps true: but it fails to stipulate how often the woman, consciously or unconsciously, was an enemy to the man, and rather than inspiring him she instead unwittingly forced him to the course that led to greatness as a relief from her harassment.

Perhaps it is even well for the world that some men are not happy in their marriages. It requires a nature both strong and in a measure lonely to break the bonds of mediocrity. The excessively doting or submissive husband too often declines into insignificance even though his gifts may be worthy of loftier things. Heroes are not hen-pecked.

Andrew Jackson assuredly was not henpecked; and had he seen those paragraphs he would have rejected fiercely any hint that he was not happy in his marriage, or that he could face bullets and tomahawks more easily than he could face Rachel's unremitting whining.

Yet young Major John Reid, diarist, was not entirely lacking in penetration.

Chapter Six

Some of the army has took a notion to go home and leave us holding the bear by the tail. Old Hickory's got a different notion.

GENERAL JOHN COFFEE

1

March again—March 6, 1814. In the chill predawn, with the stars still keenly sparkling in the frosty night sky, Andrew Jackson rose from his cot and lit the candle in his tent.

The tiny flame, a flickering brightness within the canvas walls, revealed his littered camp table, rumpled cot, scattered baggage, and also his ravaged face with its deep lines and hollows.

As usual he was ill this early morning. He suffered continually, either from the chronic dysentery that preyed on his vitals, or from the fever and coughing caused periodically by the abscess in his lung, sometimes from both at once.

His crippled arm and shoulder had not done well, either. On this morning he wondered, as he often had wondered before, if his arm ever would be of use again. Each time the surgeon dressed it, he looked at it with renewed apprehension. It had not healed properly; still was suppurating, pus on the bandage each morning. The surgeon, Dr. Shelby, believed there might be foreign matter in the wound, perhaps bits of cloth or shattered bone, but it was beyond his skill to find it, even if Jackson could have borne the probing.

Often with this combination of ills he was unable to sleep at nights, and to ease his pain spent hours propped erect, standing with his good arm hanging over a sapling spiked across two posts, to support his sagging body.

The army had been in the field since October. It had marched, and built a road of sorts through the forest, and fought some skirmishes at places with outlandish names like Tallushatchee and Talladega. But no decisive results had been obtained.

Jackson still felt a sensation of surprise that he was permitted to command here for so long. He had forestalled orders from Washington, and now perhaps he was beyond them. But in so doing he had taken upon himself full and complete responsibility for the conduct of the war.

It was a dirty war, an ill-omened war, a war of sniping and scouting, in which he and his army groped rather hopelessly for the enemy, never quite getting home to him. It was a war doomed to obscurity in the public mind when compared with the larger scene against the British; a war in which he stood to gain little and had everything to lose, for if he encountered disaster his name would be linked with Wilkinson and Dearborn, whom he despised, or even with Benedict Arnold. He knew these things. And yet he knew he must fight and somehow win just this war.

Outside he heard the early morning sounds of the army—insistent coughing, throat-clearing, and spitting, without which men seemed unable to awake; growling phrases of talk, complaints, obscenities, stirrings of camp cookery, and necessary visits to the bushes. A squad tramped past the tent to reinforce the outposts, for in an Indian war dawn always was an hour of danger.

A scratching on the canvas.

"Who is it?" Jackson asked.

"It's me, Gin'ral," said Aaron's voice. "Some hot coffee, suh, an' a li'l breakfuss?"

The bowlegged little servant entered. He was wearing a homespun smock and breeches, and he bore a steaming tin cup filled with coffee, and a tin dish on which were some oddments of food.

"Won't yo' set yo'self, Gin'ral?" wheedled Aaron.

Jackson inwardly bristled at being mothered by the slave, but then he remembered Aaron's devoted loyalty, and that he probably was following to the letter orders given him by Rachel. So he seated himself at the table. The food looked unappetizing—scraps of salt pork raked up from somewhere, and a brown pone. But he knew it was better than the army had that day. His men were near starvation, and he faced a problem worse than a battle: he might lose his entire army by mutiny or desertion. It was this that deepened the lines of worry in his forehead and about his mouth, more than any privation or personal danger could have done.

He sipped at the scalding black coffee and it made him feel somewhat better.

"Eat a li'l suthin', suh," pleaded Aaron, concern on his wizened face. With distaste Jackson swallowed a few mouthfuls of the mess, then pushed the dish aside.

"That's all I want," he said in a voice that was final. Aaron took the unfinished food away and Jackson knew he would eat it himself and be glad for it.

For a moment the General sipped his coffee. Then his eye lit upon the heap of letters on his table. One had been brought the previous night from Nashville, and although he had read it before, he now read it again:

My Dearest Life, I received your Letter by Express. How it feels, I Can never disscribe it. I cryed aloud and praised my god For your safety. how long o Lord will I remain so unhappy. no rest no Ease I cannot sleepe. all can come hom but you. I hope the Campaine will soon end the troops that is now on their way will be sufficient you have done now more than aney other man ever did before you have served your Country Long enough. you have been gon six months. oh Lord of heaven how Can I beare it. Colo. Hayes waites. our Dear Little Son sayes maney things to sweet papa. your faithfull wife until death.

Rachel Jackson.

Thus Rachel, in one of her more tearful moods. Deficient it might be in spelling, grammar, and punctuation, but it nevertheless was the wail of a wife, not only expressing her loneliness, but reiterating her long postulate that her husband's duty was first to her, and second, if at all, to the rest of the world; woman's eternal assertion of her property interest in the man she has married.

As always, when he read a letter from Rachel, Jackson's conscience stabbed him. Her nearest approaches to happiness were when he was with her. She depended on him absolutely; was afraid of the world, afraid of other people, distrusted friendship even, looked for hidden slurs beneath compliments.

And here he was, on this far-flung desperate effort to reach the heart of the bloody Indian empire. Rachel was not subtle, but she somehow managed to hold up the mirror to him as the cause of her lifelong woe.

He laid the letter back on the table. It must be answered, but other matters were at present more pressing.

Another communication: Governor Blount was advising him to retreat, since the enlistments of most of his volunteers had expired and reinforcements and supplies were hard to get and harder to transport.

Retreat? In the face of Weatherford and his Creeks?

Weatherford . . . Weatherford. The name echoed in the chambers of his mind. Weatherford . . . Red Eagle. Weatherford, seven-eighths white, no ordinary Indian strategist.

Retreat before Weatherford would mean relentless pursuit by red warriors armed with British guns. Perhaps rout and massacre like that which overtook St. Clair and Winchester. Retreat at this time would at once bring into Weatherford's ranks five thousand additional warriors—Cherokees and Choctaws now wavering and watching the turn of events. Retreat would expose five hundred miles of frontier to the sickening savagery of massacre, torture, fire, and rape. Retreat was unthinkable.

Jackson seized his quill pen. It fairly stabbed the paper:

Arouse from yr lethargy—despite fawning smiles or snarling frowns—with energy exercise yr function—the campaign must rapidly progress or yr country ruined. Call out the full quota—arrest the officer who omits his duty, and let popularity perish for the moment. Save Mobile—save the Territory— save yr frontier from becoming drenched in blood. What, retrograde under these circumstances? I will perish first. Yr ob'dt serv't, etc.,

Andrew Jackson, Maj. Gen. Tenn. Militia.

This to the governor of his state. He poured sand over the sheet of paper to dry the ink, then carefully funneled the sand back into its container. That letter would go by special courier, and he hoped it would put into the heel of Willie Blount a thorn of rectitude and decision.

A stab of anguish in his bowels—the dysentery again at work within him. He gripped the edge of the table until it passed.

Pain in no wise diminished the activity of his mind. In the dimly lit tent, even while the pang still gripped him, he groped for answers to his problems. His mind pounced on the smallest details that were of any importance, yet thought at times in wild, almost outlaw terms. Smash the Indian confederacy, rescue Mobile. Beyond that—and this exceeded any orders he might possess—raid Pensacola, across the border in Spanish Florida, and destroy the depot of supplies from which the hostile warriors received arms from the British.

Almost ferociously he sought to accomplish what he had set himself to do, demanding, insisting that fate obey him.

2

A shadow, cast by a flickering campfire, darkened against the canvas.

"General, sir, it's Reid," came a voice.

"Come in, John."

Major Reid entered, his face very serious.

"I just got word, sir. Hall's Brigade has voted to go home."

Jackson's heart seemed to give a spasmodic leap. This was what he had expected, dreaded. His men had the legal right, since their enlistments had expired, to go back to their homes. Some already had done so, and he could hardly blame them. They were volunteers, boys for the most part, away perhaps for the first time in their lives from the clearings and backwoods villages which were their homes. For weeks they had been starving. They were cold and uncomfortable, they were poorly equipped, and they lacked discipline and training.

Yet if he allowed them to go, if he could not somehow hold them, he was finished, the campaign was finished, the red hordes from the south the victors, blood by rivers the payment. Everything he had labored and suffered for, gambled and defied authority for, seemed to be collapsing in his face. He could picture himself before the court-martial, and how his actions, some of them admittedly impetuous and high-handed, would be solemnly brought forth to his everlasting condemnation.

Yet he took care to keep his face expressionless. It would never do to let his subordinate know how this news shook him. His voice betrayed nothing of his feelings as he gave an order without even replying to Reid's statement.

"Be so good, Major, as to send a messenger to General Coffee, with my compliments, and ask him to report here at once."

"Yes, sir." Reid saluted and turned to go.

"One moment."

The major halted, a question on his face.

"What about Colonel Hall himself?"

"He's waiting to report to you, sir, at your convenience."

"Ask him to do so."

"Yes, sir." Reid was gone.

Jackson felt another spasm of sickness, but it was not as painful as his thoughts. Hall's Brigade—it was part of the old Tennessee Legion that had marched to Natchez with him. These men once had been intensely loyal to him; it was they who gave him the affectionate sobriquet "Old Hickory." What had changed them?

Constant privation and discomfort, of course. But he had suffered them also. The long strain of warfare with a foe who never came to grips? But he, too, had undergone that strain.

Malcontents must be at the bottom of this. Men who had not received promotions for which they had schemed, or had been disciplined for infractions, or merely belonged to the scurf of humanity which always stirs dissensions. The malcontents must have been busy with the backwoods hunters whose sworn term of service was at an end, suggesting to them over and over thoughts of home, and comfort, and women. . . .

He rose. Whether he had a legal right or no, he must somehow stop those men.

The tent canvas was brightening with the early dawn. Soon the sun would be up. If Hall's men were going to leave it would be right after they ate their scanty breakfast.

Then Coffee came with lumbering haste, followed in a moment by Reid and Hall.

"What's this I heard, Colonel?" rasped Jackson.

Hall, lank and lantern-jawed, in old blue-and-buff regimentals, looked at the General dumbly, almost beseechingly.

"I cannot understand, sir, how you allowed your men to get so out of hand," continued Jackson sharply.

Hall began an apology. "It's four days, sir, since they've had what you might call a real issue of provisions——"

"No excuse!" cut in Jackson. "A good commander's men are loyal to him if they die of hunger!"

Hall drew himself up. "I'm loyal to you, sir, if they burn me at the stake!"

Jackson cleared his throat. Events were moving rapidly. Outside, sounds in the camp indicated that men were gathering their equipment and preparing to form a column.

"General," he said to Coffee, "how many of your cavalry can you gather?"

"Perhaps fifty, sir."

"You know the one-mile clearing?"

"Yes, sir."

"Go at once, take all the men you can muster, and ride around through the woods to that clearing."

Coffee plunged out of the tent.

Jackson spoke to Hall and Reid. "I'll ask you gentlemen to mount and prepare to accompany me. Those men will be marching in a few minutes."

They saluted and departed.

"Aaron!" called Jackson.

The servant popped into the tent.

"Help me into my best uniform coat!"

Aaron brought the newest blue coat, the one with the epaulets, which the General rarely wore because the weight of the bullion hurt his crippled shoulder, and assisted his master into it. One sleeve hung empty over the left arm in its black sling. Jackson was ashamed of that arm and sling because of the shabby affair of which it was a memento. He had the empty sleeve pinned up as neatly as possible.

"Now get my horse—and be quick about it!" he commanded.

A moment later he passed out of his tent. The sun was just tinting the tops of the trees with gold. He saw a disorderly mob of men, in buckskin and butternut, long rifles on their shoulders, tramping down the military road which had been cut through the trees. Others were preparing to fall in the column—Hall's Brigade, all of it.

Aaron brought up the white horse, saddled. The very act of mounting was painful, but Jackson did not wince.

Hall appeared on a big black which he brought to a plunging stop, and Reid rode up from another direction.

Without a word Jackson led the way. He did not take the road; instead he went through the forest in a wide detour to the right, dodging encumbrances, trotting his mount where possible in the trees and undergrowth.

Ahead, he hoped, Coffee would be waiting with his cavalry. One way or another the critical decision on which hung everything must very shortly be made.

3

Coffee was prompt as usual. He went straight to the part of the camp where his men were and spoke at once and to the point.

"Boys," he said, "hark an ear."

They rose from their breakfast fires and gathered about him in a casual half-circle, lounging easily, some with frying pans still in their hands. Though they stood in no military array, they were silent and attentive. He estimated that about fifty were here, the number he had told the General he could gather.

"Some of the army has took a notion to go home and leave us holding the bear by the tail," he told them. "Old Hickory's got a different notion. He wants us to back him up."

Nobody spoke.

"Get your horses right quick and come with me," said Coffee.

As silently as they had listened to him, the men turned, laid down their frying pans or whatever cumbered them at the moment, and went to the horse lines. Hardly five minutes had lapsed when they were threading through the trees behind their huge commander.

They were bunched in the small clearing through which the military road slashed its way when Jackson, breaking out of the woods with Hall and Reid, rode up to them.

For a moment he studied their faces. Would they stand? Hall's Brigade must number some nine hundred men, and many of them were friends of these lean riders. When the column reached this place, might not the handful of mounted men simply join their fellows and ride away?

John Coffee brought his horse alongside. "This here's what I got left," he said, "but they'll follow orders."

"Line 'em across the road," said Jackson.

Already he could hear the sound of the approaching column, the tramping of many men, talking, coughing, swearing, complaining, an indescribable blending of many separate noises into a sort of overriding guttural rumble.

Coffee's riders swung into line across the clearing just as the head of the column appeared. The leading men in the column seemed to hesitate, then advanced a little farther into the clearing, gazed uncertainly at the line of horsemen, and came to a halt. Behind them their fellows piled up, spreading out on each side, like a crowd trying to jostle for room to see a spectacle of some kind.

Alone, on his white horse, Andrew Jackson spurred forward.

"Men!" His voice sounded high and almost uncanny in the silence that fell. "March back at once to camp! That's an order!"

Not a man moved.

Riding across the front of the sullen mass, Jackson reached out his good arm and snatched a rifle from one of the soldiers.

Every eye was on him as he backed the white horse, with truly great riding skill since his left arm was in a sling and he managed both bridle and rifle with his right hand, until he confronted the mutineers.

Then he rested the weapon on the horse's neck and cocked it.

"I swear by Almighty God that I'll shoot the first man who moves in the wrong direction!" His shrill voice rose.

The moment was electric.

If even one of the mutinous riflemen had started forward, disaster would have exploded. But nobody moved.

The man who sat his horse alone, midway between the rebellious soldiery and his handful of loyal riders, with his blazing eyes and the strange force of his will, dominated everyone in the clearing.

The backwoodsmen had no spokesman and no commander. They looked at him gloweringly, shifting their feet. Presently some of those in the rear ranks began to turn and amble off, back toward the camp. The movement grew. Before many minutes the whole brigade, following its rearward party, was marching sullenly back to camp.

John Reid gave a deep sigh of relief. As he rode up to the General, Jackson handed the rifle to him.

"Why, sir," said Reid in surprise, "this piece is out of order. You couldn't have shot it if you tried!"

4

Crises continued, never ceased.

How long he could hold his army together, even though he had prevented the wholesale desertion of Hall's Brigade, became a day-and-night preoccupation and concern to Jackson. Desertions could not be stopped and the morning muster showed fewer men reporting for service each day. The militia were restive, officers found it difficult to compel obedience, only one man continued to receive instant attention to his orders, and that was the General himself. No man yet dared brook his white-faced wrath.

But the morale of the army was bad, chiefly because there was no way of enforcing discipline. To make matters worse, the Creeks, as if sensing this condition, grew continually bolder, and there were one or two minor battles, indecisive repulses of Indian surprise attacks.

Then, at last, fortune changed. His letter to Governor Blount had been effective. Two regiments, one of regulars, came marching up the military road to join him.

Regulars! Here, at least, was discipline!

Jackson had worn himself out trying to lead and keep together a horde of undisciplined men through force of personality alone. With this new strength he issued an iron order:

The extreme penalty, under the articles of war, will be invoked against any man guilty of desertion or insubordination.

There came a night when he lay awake in his tent, in that sleeplessness which he had come to expect. But this time there was a different cause for it.

A man was to be executed in the morning before a firing squad—a boy, rather. John Wood was the name, one of the undisciplined militia, though he was one of the least disciplined of all. Wood had refused to obey an order, resisted an officer. He had been found guilty of insubordination by a court-martial.

He must die, to put the fear of God into the others.

That long night was an agony to Jackson. When at last daylight came into the fortress which had been a pool of blackness, the drums began to beat.

Reid appeared at the door of the tent. "The troops are falling in for assembly, sir," he said.

Jackson turned to him a haggard face. "Report when the execution is completed," he ordered.

An hour, an endless hour. He and he only could save the life of the condemned man, and the man who was to die hardly comprehended why he was doomed, which was the pity of it. He was ignorant, the unlettered ways of the backwoods were his. He had cursed an officer it was true, but he scarcely realized it was Authority he was cursing and not a mere man whom he considered officious.

Yet where many men must risk their lives in battle, discipline, the instinct of obedience to Authority, must be deeply ingrained. So Jackson could not intervene or the force of the object lesson, terrible as it was, would be destroyed.

An hour, an endless hour. Then he heard the sudden sharp volley.

Poor John Wood, a gawky backwoods youth, was dead. The regiments would be marching back now from witnessing execution. By some, Jackson's name would be execrated. But in no soldier's mind would there now be left any question as to the grim determination of the man who commanded them.

It was necessary to give the army a task, to take its mind off the execution and any debates that might arise over the justice or injustice of doing a man to death for insubordination. On Jackson's table was a dispatch he had just penned to Governor Blount:

A private having been sentenced to death by a court martial is now in the act of execution. I have ordered the line of march to be taken up at 12 o'clock with seven days bread rations and two of meat, direct for Emuckfa.

Emuckfa was a creek on the way to the Horseshoe Bend of the Tallapoosa River. It was at the Horseshoe Bend that John Coffee's scouts reported a "citadel" had been built by the Creeks.

Just what this "citadel" consisted of was not clear. But one thing did appear clear from the reports. It was the capital of Weatherford, the war chief. If fate permitted, Jackson would there pin down and shatter the Creek confederacy.

He took another sheet of paper and penned a brief sentence on it, the Order of the Day, to be read to the troops:

Any officer or soldier who flees before the enemy without being compelled to do so by superior force shall suffer death.

Chapter Seven

*You boys gonna catch hell. Them Injuns
don't give a damn who they hit!*

ONE OF JACKSON'S SCOUTS

1

In the middle of the morning on the tenth day of the march, the Thirty-ninth Regular United States Infantry doggedly trudged through the woods, a long river of men, bristling with bayoneted muskets.

Since dawn, this 26th of March, the regiment had been on the move, feeling its way through the trees and thickets and fording creeks and swamps. But except when someone fell out of ranks occasionally to answer a necessary call of nature, the men stayed well closed up. Even those who dropped out, quickly rejoined the column.

There were no stragglers, for the forest held a pervasive menace. Even though Coffee was supposed to have a fringe of cavalry out as flankers, nobody knew where the Creek Indians were. They might be anywhere, right at hand perhaps, behind those nearest trees. A man caught off alone by them would be killed and scalped for certain.

In the Thirty-ninth one long-legged young ensign marched with an especial swing and high carriage of his head. His name was Sam Houston, he had been in the army a year, had held his commission only a month, and he was boyishly proud of his platoon, which he thought the best in the regiment, his regiment the best in the army.

One small shadow clouded Ensign Houston's pride. The army supply department was in chaos, and instead of the white pantaloons and blue uniform coats with brass buttons that once had charmed him, the soldiers of the Thirty-ninth were outfitted in rough gray kersey. Only their white crossbelts and tall shakos distinguished them as regulars. He had, however, become accustomed to this, and he was, according to every report, about to see action, and his excitement and the thousand speculations chasing themselves through his mind fully occupied him now.

A horseman trotted up along the column, gazing at the men. That was Major Lemuel Montgomery, dark-faced and only a few years older than Houston, who was acting commander of the regiment since fat, clumsy old Colonel John Williams, that typical politician-soldier, had been left behind by General Jackson as unfit for active duty.

"Look smart, men," the major was saying. "The General is coming by."

Ensign Houston turned, and walking backward, shouted an order to his platoon. "Attention! Sergeant, see that those men march at attention!"

There was a hurried huddling forward of the rear ranks. The soldiers straightened up, their muskets stiffly aligned at the carry.

From the tail of the column trotted a handful of horsemen, led by a thin, gray-haired man with his arm in a sling, on a white gelding: General Jackson. He rode by, his eyes straight ahead, as if the regiment did not exist.

When the General and his staff were past, Houston barked an order for his men to march at ease. He had not expected that Jackson would know him, but he was slightly disappointed that the General's eye had not even rested on him.

Jackson, he said to himself, looked thinner, the lines more deeply bitten in his face than when he had visited Maryville a year ago; and Houston well remembered his impressions that day. With all the talk he had heard about the hero of the frontier, he had expected to see a man about ten feet tall, wide as a door, with a voice like a wave on the shore. Instead he beheld a lean, homely, sickly-looking man, who spoke in a shrill, piping voice. Yet almost at once he forgot his disappointment over how the man looked and sounded in a sort of strange captivation, as the General's mighty spirit somehow made itself evident through his words, his blazing eyes, the electric personality he possessed. That captivation had lasted ever since for Sam Houston.

Up ahead the column was halting. From somewhere, far out to the right, came the flat, solitary report of a rifle.

It was followed by two more quick shots, then silence.

The men came to a stop, leaning on their muskets, waiting listlessly, making poor jokes, and wondering what the shooting meant. Comments ran up and down the platoon:

"Some of Coffee's hoss-sojers bushwhacked by the Injuns?"

"More likely some of them saddle boys tooken some shots at a deer."

"Deer, hell! A rabbit'd bring a volley from them."

"Or a possum. Or one of them leetle red-tail squirrels."

"It's ag'in orders to do any shootin', 'thout it's at a redskin."

"Mebbe so. Still, a man with a instinct fer huntin' would find it mighty hard to keep his finger off'n his trigger, if'n game showed up."

Another contingent of horsemen, twenty or so, came jingling by from the rear: barbaric, buckskin-clad, shining black hair bound by red kerchiefs, a deer tail hanging from each scalp-lock.

One of them, passing, called out, "Hai—Co-lon-neh!"

Houston saw a flashing grin of white teeth in a dark face and grinned back.

"John! John Rogers!"

They were Cherokee scouts, the deer tails being Jackson's special insignia to show that they were friendly allies, and John Rogers had been one of Sam Houston's boyhood friends when he lived in the Cherokee village on the Hiwassee. They rode on past, one behind the other, and every one of them looked at Houston and grinned.

2

Co-lon-neh—the Raven.

The Cherokees had called Sam Houston that, and he had been one of them once, an athlete and a hunter. Almost wistfully he now recalled the Hiwassee village, and his life there as the adopted son of Oo-loo-te-ka, the chief.

The village stood on an island at the place where the Hiwassee River rushed down from the mountains and poured its flood into the Tennessee River. The Indian lodges were of logs, with the great council house in the center, and fields on either side of the river, tilled by Negro slaves of the Cherokees. Bear wallowed in the canebrakes and there were deer and other game in the forest to hunt, and the Cherokees were happy and content.

John Rogers was a son of a half-blood subchief, and one day he imparted to Houston the information that his younger sister, Tiana, would dance the maiden dance at the spring festival. This was a clean-grained evidence of friendship and respect, for the maiden dance had high significance, being a ceremonial in which girls ready for marriage were

presented to the tribe. Advance word of this kind gave a possible suitor
an inside track if he desired it.

At the time, however, Houston gave it little thought, for the spring
festival also was signalized by another event, the great game of ball-play,
called by the French *la crosse*, from the heavy racket of hickory webbed
with deerhide thongs, in which the ball of deerskin stuffed with grass
was thrown or carried. Houston was to participate in it with the chosen
team of Hiwassee against a picked team from the Chickamauga village
sent over for the contest. The game was ferocious, more a combat than
a sport, a training for warriors. Rackets were used more often as weapons than to handle the ball; and men tripped, smote, and kicked each
other. Broken bones, cuts and bruises, other injuries, even deaths, were
not uncommon.

On the day of the game Houston, tallest man in the village and the
fastest, was like a wild horse in the riot of the play. The Hiwassee star,
he raged through the field, eyes flashing, snorting, dangerous, bursting
every restraint, like a furious stallion, until the Chickamauga invaders
were fairly routed, and the Hiwassee onlookers thundered their acclamation of the victory.

One who watched him in the wild melee with a growing light in her
eyes was Tiana, John Rogers' pretty sister.

Later it was turnabout. This time it was Houston who watched Tiana,
also with a new light in his eyes.

The maiden dance in the council house that night was beautiful. All
the nubile girls of the village, graceful and slender in their clean white
doeskin dresses, moved about the central fire in rhythmic step to the
roar of the drums, sometimes joining hands and chanting musically,
sometimes looking up toward the skies in symbolic search for lovers of
their own, until all the young men watching grew heated with excitement.

Now Houston remembered John Rogers' friendly word about his
sister. When he had heard that word he had paid little heed to it, considering Tiana a child, unformed, nothing for a second glance. But on
this evening he perceived how suddenly a miracle had taken place in
her. She was no child now, but wondrously shaped, with grace and
beauty that he felt in his very blood.

Next day, after the dance and the feast, he looked upon her when he
met her as he had never regarded her before; and saw her eyes fall, the
color come into her cheeks. She did not speak.

Other days came when they met and passed on as if she did not see
him. But it was as if her reticence and her averted glances themselves
took hold on him.

One morning he encountered her with a basket of clothes in her arms.
She looked down demurely, not at him, and he did not speak. But this
time when she had gone by he heard from her a gurgle of laughter.

He turned and saw that she had taken a side path, which went down among the trees by the river, evidently to wash her clothes. Almost as if without any volition of his own, but irresistibly drawn, he followed her.

He found her alone, kneeling by the river's verge with her washing ready for labor. She must have known he was coming after her, for she showed no surprise, but rose and stood still, looking downward. On impulse he reached out, took her hand. It was soft, warm, and after a moment it tried to get away.

The little escaping movement aroused in him a capturing instinct. Hardly knowing what he did, he drew her to him. It was like a game, her smothered laugh, her lithe body twisting in his arms. She was fragrant of sweet grass.

Then, in tumultuous excitement he lay with her under the bushes by the river, her washing neglected on the bank. He could not now remember any words they said, save that she made a few small protests, not loudly.

Instinct directed matters, for they were both virgins. At the end she was as eager as he . . . they were young, and healthy, and their blood was heated by thick red vapors.

This might have led to marriage gifts and a lodge of his own in the Cherokee village, had not war intervened; for she had aroused in him that which caused his thoughts to shape themselves about her. It chanced, however, that on the very next day Weatherford, the war chief of the Creeks, appeared at Hiwassee. Co-lon-neh, now become Houston again in his own thinking, left the Cherokees to carry news of the threatening war to Maryville; and by fortune strangely mixed, to fight Hooten, see and talk with Andrew Jackson, and become a soldier.

He wondered about Tiana. Perhaps she had a husband now; there were plenty of young men in Hiwassee who were after her. Some not so young, too. He hoped that in his first essay of love with her he did not get her into trouble.

Then he remembered John Rogers' friendly grin. No hint there of resentment, as toward one who had deflowered and then deserted a sister. It must be that nothing untoward had happened, and that Tiana had kept secret to herself her tryst with him.

More than ever he thought well of the girl.

3

Orders came relaying back from up front. Once more the column went into motion. As yet there was no explanation of those far shots, but now there seemed to be a new alertness, a mounting tension among the soldiers.

A soldier . . . with a whole year of tedious garrison duty and drill behind him, and promotion from the ranks first to corporal, then to sergeant because he had a far-carrying voice and made it his interest to learn every detail of the manual of arms and close-order maneuver, and at last a commission, the lowest commissioned rank in the army, an ensign, already beginning to be called second lieutenant in some units of the American forces.

Ensign Houston suddenly realized, with a sharp thrill, that after all those months of preparation he at last was going into battle; as a leader, too, at least of his little platoon.

He wondered what it would be like—battle. And he marched in a small trance of imaginings. A boy still, with a boy's unreasonable dreams, he began to picture in his mind a gallant figure—himself—leading a charge with his sword grandly waving, the enemy retreating, his men cheering him. Perhaps General Jackson would witness this heroism. Noble work, Ensign Houston. I only did my duty, General Jackson. I promote you on the field of battle, *Captain* Houston. I thank you, General Jackson.

He aroused himself from this with a wry half-grin. Ridiculous to carry on that way in his mind. General Jackson did not even know who he was.

But, after all, why not have hopes and ambitions?

He told himself he was twenty years old. At twenty the Marquis de Lafayette was a major general in Washington's army. At twenty Alexander of Macedon had sacked Thebes and was preparing for the Persian conquest whereby he earned the title of the Great. At twenty another Alexander—Alexander Pope—gained fame with his first poems.

Pope's verses were a passion with Houston. He had carried the poet's mighty translation of the *Iliad* into the Cherokee camp with him, and in those years at Hiwassee he all but memorized it. Enormously it influenced his thinking, his imagination. Lines from the epic now leaped into mind.

Unwept, unhonored, uninterr'd he lies . . . Pope's—and Homer's—epitaph to mediocrity. Desire to rise above mediocrity was a hungry longing in young Sam Houston's heart.

Another line from the *Iliad*:

Ajax the great . . . himself a host . . . that was something like. Heroisms spurred him.

Shouts from the rear brought him back to the present.

"One side—one side! The guns are coming up!"

The column veered to the right through the trees, and he was again aware of the sounds of men's tramping feet, clink of accouterments, voices mingled in speculation, bickering, talk about women and liquor, such as forever pervades a body of marching men.

Then the pounding of horses' hoofs and the rattle of wheels. Jackson's two cannon, a six pounder and a three pounder, trundling past. Four horses hauled each, a rider to each team. Two riders sat on the caissons and more gunners were in the ammunition wagon that followed.

An officer in a fore-and-aft cocked hat went by on a gray mare, his cold eyes searching right and left.

"Carroll," men in the column said. "Billy Carroll. Colonel Carroll."

Houston had heard of Carroll. He was one of General Jackson's favorites and had distinguished himself in the earlier fighting. The tall ensign remembered those cold eyes, eyes calculating and secret.

Soldiers in the column were speculating:

"Them guns means somep'n."

"Injun fort must be ahaid purty clost."

"Looky out, we're gonna git it."

Major Montgomery came riding back, coasting along his regiment, his dark face earnest.

"The party's about to begin, boys," he said.

4

The Thirty-ninth came out of the woods into an open flat from which all the trees had been cut. Ahead of them the men could see what looked like a disheveled heap of logs, spanning a narrow peninsula which was made here by a wide loop of the deep-running Tallapoosa River.

A wild chorus of high gobbling whoops and the reports of a hundred guns greeted the appearance of the regiment.

Houston and the other officers busied themselves forming the regiment into a double rank facing the enemy.

"Stand easy, men," said Major Montgomery, riding along the front. "We're out of range. A few spent balls might get this far, but nothing to bother."

Houston dressed his platoon and took up his position in front of it. Behind him he could hear the comments running back and forth along the line.

"That there the Injun fort?"

"Yeah. Cain't ye see the smoke of their guns?"

"Looks more like an almighty big beaver dam than a fort."

"Ever see Injuns do anything shipshape? They got them logs laid like a snake fence, with a lot of brush in the corners."

One man said doubtfully, "I dunno, it may be catawampus, but it looks kind of impressive to me."

"What's the matter?" gibed another. "Ready to run? Them Injuns ain't even shootin' at us. It's the skirmishers down amongst them stumps they're a-poppin' at."

A long brown rope of men crawled out of the woods and ranged in a ragged file toward the right, where Billy Carroll's guns already were unlimbering on a small rise by the river bank, somewhat forward of the battle line.

"Them's the Tennessee Rifles," said someone. "Hope to Gawd them boys is as good on the fight as they is on the brag."

The sudden heavy reports of Carroll's guns took precedence over all other sounds. Houston could see the gunners leaping at their work, swabbing out the cannon, ramming in new charges, to fire again.

Once more the guns crashed out.

Men in the ranks craned their necks to see what damage the artillery was doing, and Houston could hear their remarks.

"Them round balls don't seem like they bother the Injuns much."

"Jest sink into them logs."

"Don't even splinter 'em."

"Looks like we're a-gonna have to claw them reds out of their hole ourselves."

"Hyar comes the skirmishers back."

The Indians had transferred their fire to the gun crews, and one or two of the artillerists were down. Taking advantage of this the scouts who had been up ahead were falling back on the main body. One or two figures lay still in the stump-dotted clearing before the fort, and here and there men were helping wounded comrades along.

"You boys gonna catch hell," one of the scouts said. "Them Injuns don't give a damn who they hit!"

A cry: "Thar's the General!"

Houston turned and saw Jackson threading his white gelding among the trees, bending his head this way and that, to avoid the branches. A half-dozen mounted officers, his staff, followed him.

The small cavalcade halted just behind the Thirty-ninth, and every man dismounted, except Jackson himself.

It was general knowledge throughout the small army that the commander carried that arm in a sling because he had been shot up in some kind of a gun fight back in Nashville.

Houston thought, looking at him: Must hurt him to get up and down on that horse.

Major Montgomery rode over and joined the group. He saluted the General and dismounted also. Two men from the rifle regiment took the bridles of the riderless horses, and had trouble holding them, as the animals sidled and pulled back restively, nervous because of the thunder of the guns.

Chapter Eight

When Andy-by-God-Jackson gives an order, he means it.

SERGEANT LEE ROONEY

1

Andrew Jackson lifted a telescope with his one good hand and studied the Indian breastworks. How many enemies were behind it he had no way of knowing, but judging from the noise there were a good many, and they were well protected. Even from this distance he could see that.

After a moment the telescope swung around toward where Carroll's two guns had just shrouded themselves once more in smoke and sound. It was evident the small cannon were doing little execution. Two or three men lay sprawled near the guns, showing that the Indian marksmen knew their business; and Jackson observed that the other artillerists, in serving their pieces, crouched and almost crept forward to load and fire.

In this lay a heavy disappointment. He had hoped the guns might breach the log walls, but that hope seemed lost. Furthermore, he could not well leave those pieces in their exposed position much longer.

But this created a dilemma. If he withdrew the guns, it would greatly encourage the enemy, and might dishearten some of his own men.

He glanced down the irregular ranks of the Tennessee Rifles. Most of them were raw recruits, he considered, though apt enough with their weapons. They had no battle experience, and neither did most of their officers. If the fighting grew hot they might, at any show of weakness by their commander, "retrograde," as he phrased it. He could afford no lessening of the morale of his troops, but on the other hand he could not leave Billy Carroll and his poor devils out there much longer.

His eyes ranged to his left. There was the Thirty-ninth—the regulars. Discipline in those ranks at least.

His instinct was all for fighting; but to attack that bristling fortification head on, with a force of men of whom half hardly understood orders, meant taking a fearful risk of repulse and perhaps disaster. He must make the decision, and at the thought a sick wave of apprehension or perhaps excitement swept over him. Yet his mind did not cease calculating the possibilities as well as the risks involved in whatever course of action he took.

A horseman, in buckskin breeches and naked to the waist, came careering through the woods from the rear. One of Coffee's Indian dispatch riders.

Without dismounting, saluting, or any change of face, he handed a folded paper to the General. Jackson took it, noting mentally that Coffee did not trust verbal reports. He read:

Am in position with my cavalry across the river at rear of enemy position. Most of the Indian women and children have crossed to this side, but the men remain in the fort. Will await developments here.

Coffee.

P.S. My Cherokee scouts have got most of their canoes. They cannot escape from this side.

Jackson gave a nod. John Coffee, following orders, had somehow found a ford fifteen miles or so to the rear and posted himself behind the Creek position to cut off retreat. The comment about the women and children showed that an earlier warning to the defending braves to send away their noncombatants had been heeded. Very likely this meant that the defense would be more desperate.

He glanced at the dispatch rider.

"How did they get the canoes?"

"Creek squaw bring some. Swum over for rest."

Jackson turned to his staff. "Gentlemen, you're going to see the damnedest fight you ever saw. Get back to your commands, your boys may need a little stiffening up."

His decision had been reached. He would attack, and at once; and because his men had never been tried in a full-scale assault he would lead the attack himself. He would lead it mounted, so that they could see him. Personal example was important, especially with raw troops, and he intended to furnish it, because once the order to advance was given, the course of the battle would be out of his hands, to be fought out by the soldiers and their foes.

He gave an order. Major Reid sailed into his saddle, whirled his horse, and went pounding off to the right, scattering some of the Tennessee Riflemen who were in his way.

"Almighty hurry," one of them grumbled.

"Headed for the guns," said another. "Them Creek sharpshooters is keepin' the artillery boys too clost to the ground to git much work done."

Major Montgomery left his mount with the horse holders and sauntered on foot down the line of the Thirty-ninth.

"How do you feel, boys?" he called out.

A chorus of replies:

"Fine!"

"Fit as a bobcat!"

"We're ready!"

"You're going to get your chance," said Montgomery. "We engage as soon as the General's cease-fire order gets to Colonel Carroll. We don't want his peashooters throwing round shot into us when we advance, you know."

A half-nervous laugh from some of the men.

Lemuel Montgomery had spoken with elaborate casualness, to conceal his own immense inward excitement. This was his first battle too. A far call, this, from the quiet lawyer's desk in Nashville, which he left to accept a commission in the army. Although the day was not warm, he found that he was perspiring, his palms damp with excitement. He removed his hat to wipe his face with a large kerchief.

General Jackson rode out to a place between the regiments, and raised his arm.

The drums of the Thirty-ninth began the rolling signal to advance.

Montgomery replaced his hat on his head. "*Fo-o-or-ward!*" he shouted, prolonging the command to give it greater force.

The regiment reacted to the order, in which it had been drilled for months, and stepped forward in fair alignment.

Ensign Houston, marching ahead of his platoon, heard above his head a high, piping sound.

Rifle ball, his mind told him seconds later. So that's the way they sound.

With a species of shocked surprise he suddenly realized that the rifle ball probably was aimed at him: that malignant savages were shooting at him, trying to kill him. He felt his stomach tighten, but he continued to stride forward, and the accustomed action seemed to give assurance, released the tension in his body.

Behind, he heard a gasp and a thump. He turned his head. One of his men lay doubled on the ground, while three or four others were gathered about him.

"You men, there—back into line!" he yelled. "File-closers, see to it!"

A sergeant ran toward the little group. The men looked at him with staring, trance-like eyes. This was death; the first time they had seen violent death close at hand in battle.

"You can't help him! Git goin', you bastards!" shouted the sergeant.

They left their prostrate comrade and went shambling forward, glancing sidewise at each other with dull, animal eyes.

The Indian breastworks were almost hidden by powder smoke, while the roar of muskets and rifles ahead, and the constant whine of bullets, grew in volume.

Houston glanced back again. Here and there other figures, stricken and left behind the advancing line of the regiment, were scattered prostrate, or in some cases sitting or trying to rise.

"Dress on the right guide!" he shouted to his platoon.

But his voice seemed lost in the din of battle, and the order was ignored. The men made no effort to dress their ranks, but at least they continued to go forward.

At first Houston felt annoyance. Then he told himself that this, after all, was no parade ground; and with that he discovered that he had almost forgotten he was in a battle, in imminent danger of his life, in his preoccupation with the alignment of his ranks.

At the discovery he felt a sudden inflowing of confidence, almost happiness. He was not particularly frightened, not as frightened as most of his men seemed to be. He felt strong, stronger than he had ever felt in his life before.

Thus far the Thirty-ninth had not fired a shot. Muskets, thought Houston, our guns are outranged by the Indian rifles. This is the worst of the regulars.

He suddenly remembered a voice, it seemed a lifetime ago: *Why in the blazing blue thunders did you choose the musket-packing regulars?*

Oh, yes. General Jackson. At Maryville that unforgettable day, and it was only a year ago.

An order, repeated down the line:

"Halt! Make ready to fire!"

With the other officers he fell back behind the firing line.

"Hold your fire, men, until the command! Hold your fire—hold your fire——"

Officers repeated it crazily, as if it were some magic formula.

Directly in front of Houston a man spun sidewise, clutching his thigh. The soldiers on either side of him glanced down at him.

"Eyes front!" snapped Houston.

A cry came. "At the command—*ready—aim—fire!*"

The Thirty-ninth's first volley raked out, a vast searing gash of sound. White fog hid the front of the regiment.

He heard himself, the mechanical orders: "Handle cartridge—bite cartridge—load——"

The men were going through the actions of recharging their pieces.

From the right came a rippling crash as the Tennessee Rifles cut loose with their own ragged volley.

A wild shout: *"Hold your fire, men!"*

Powder smoke was blowing away. Through it Houston could see a gaunt man on a white horse riding before the regiment.

"General!" Montgomery's scandalized expostulation. "You must not expose yourself in this manner, sir——"

"You will charge those breastworks, Major Montgomery!" shouted back Jackson, his eyes blazing.

The major turned to the regiment.

"Here we go, Thirty-ninth!" his splendid voice soared. "You see the General! Come on—clean them out!"

Drums roared the charge, and the regiment lurched forward.

2

Andrew Jackson swung his horse toward the Indian palisades. He knew that volley firing would never drive the enemy back from the protection of that log breastwork. Attack was his only chance to win this battle.

The white gelding under him was on edge, feeling peril. But he moved forward, tossing his head, foam flecking his bridle bits, compelled by the will of his rider.

Only once the General glanced back, to be sure the army was in motion. Then he fixed his pale eyes on the enemy position. Behind him his men followed as if drawn by invisible wires.

He had dismissed Montgomery's remonstrance; but he knew that what he was doing was perhaps foolhardy—riding into battle at the head of his lines, mounted on a *white* horse, a shining mark for Indian rifles. Yet he rode forward, his depression, physical discomfort all forgotten, caught up in the strange exhilaration he always felt when the waiting was over and action began.

In his mind now was no concern for himself, for anything. His army was moving forward and he was a part of the whole, no longer an individual. He and his men were one, welded into a unit by the ragged jabs of flame and smoke, spurting singing lead from the unsightly breastworks ahead.

The log bastion shrouded itself in a cloud of white, and even above the multiplied clatter of their rifles the Indians could be heard howling shrilly like a thousand ghosts. Bullets sighed in the air, and in the ranks advancing behind the General men were checking and falling more and more frequently.

"Close up! Close up! Keep those lines dressed!" came the insistent orders, repeated over and over. Men were shouting the commands at the top of their lungs, but they were futile.

The soldiers went forward half-crouched, stooping to offer smaller targets to the enemy rifles, holding their muskets in any manner most convenient, alignment gone as some advanced more rapidly than others.

Jackson's horse started sidewise and half-reared. He brought the animal under control and leaned forward. A red streak glared on one side of the white neck, beginning to trickle blood. Grazed by a bullet. How close did that bullet come to himself, and how could it have missed him?

It shook him from his high mood. Instead he began to feel a blazing rage, hatred of the savages who were shooting his men down, trying to hold his army back, to hold *him* back.

Nothing could possibly hold him back. Above everything in existence he was furious to strike those savages, to maim and kill them as they were maiming and killing his men, as they had maimed and killed the women and children of Fort Mims, as they had maimed and killed helpless settlers on the border.

The Thirty-ninth still rolled forward, but its line now had lost any semblance of regularity. Without any command the pace began to quicken. To walk forward at a march step into the teeth of the Indian fire was unbearable. Men began to hurry. Get it over with. Get in where we can shoot back at the red devils.

Glancing backward, Jackson saw the movement and understood his men. He must release them and drill regulations be damned.

Raising his hat he waved it right and left.

By instinct the men interpreted the signal. All at once the regiment was on the run—roaring forward, bursting past the General, hurling itself toward that wall of logs.

Gaps appeared in the ragged line as men dropped. But the others rushed on, running awkwardly, muskets held across their bodies, faces set but oddly filled with wonder at what they were doing, their attitudes singularly unheroic, but never hesitating. From their throats came a babel of sound—curses, yells, barbaric whoops, growling imprecations, even prayers—as terrible as it was incoherent.

Houston, outracing the running, roaring regiment, felt that the Indians were shooting and howling more loudly as he neared their breastwork. In addition to the bullets, arrows now began to glint in the sun like a flight of grasshoppers.

He ran in a battle daze, with one thought only—reach that parapet and get over it, among the painted fiends behind.

Suddenly, with a shock of surprise, he found himself confronting a tangle of logs in the powder smoke.

So disheveled was the breastwork that in the white fog his first impression was that he had come on a windfall of timbers felled by some past storm. Then he knew it was the Indian fort, that somehow, miraculously, he had reached it.

Soldiers caught up with him. They crowded against the parapet, trying to shoot through the loopholes at the defenders.

A mistake. The savages within had the advantage. Men were dropping, falling to the ground kicking, as the Indians blasted them at close range.

Houston glanced up at the top of the parapet. Over it—they must get over that barrier.

Suddenly he saw a man scrambling over the windfall. Montgomery!

For a moment the young major stood on top of the breastworks, wildly beckoning to his men to follow him. Then, in a flash of rifles from below, he dropped backward, thudding to the ground, gone limp and dead.

Sam Houston felt sick. Then fury filled him. Major Montgomery—the finest man in the regiment—killed by those damned savages!

Impulse and instinct worked together. A foot in a chink between the logs, a hand grasping above. Carrying his sword he began one-handedly to clamber.

All at once he was up.

Up and alone.

As if dreaming it, he gazed down at a crowd of savage faces, smeared with grease and paint, staring up at him. Then guns were uplifted. He leaped down among them.

He was in a wild melee, enemies all about him. It resembled the fierce contest of the Indian ball-play, but no hickory rackets were being wielded here. In the hands of his foes were deadly weapons, in his own hand a steel sword.

His muscles, his whole body reacted instinctively. Once again he was the wild horse of the Cherokees, laying about him like a madman at the snarling, shrinking savages. By sheer raging violence he made room for himself in the press. He was conscious that his sword blade was dripping red.

A searing pain shot through his thigh.

Then his men came, plunging down from over the parapet to join him. Bayonets lunged and skewered painted bodies. The melee receded. The Creeks were being driven back from the breastwork.

Houston braced himself against the logs of the parapet and gazed down at his hip. A thin stick with a feather frill at the end seemed to grow out of it.

Arrow. An Indian arrow in his thigh.

He called to a soldier. "Pull it out!"

The man seized the slender stick and pulled, but not strongly enough. The arrow was barbed, fast in the wound, and it sent a thrill of anguish through him.

"Pull, damn it, or I'll cut you down!" Houston screamed, frantic with pain.

The soldier looked at the scarlet-stained sword, bit his lip, and pulled heavily. With a hot gush of blood the arrow came out.

Houston felt faint, and the man helped him sit on the ground at the foot of the palisade. Blood soaked hotly in his pantaloon leg.

They were still fighting on the peninsula. Driven from their breast-work, the Indians took refuge in log shelters they had prepared, and resisted furiously, their yells and the continual reports of guns creating a hideous uproar.

Jackson dismounted when he reached the palisade. His men had passed him in the charge. With some difficulty he climbed over it, un-comfortably aware that he was awkward and slow. He was nothing of an athlete, and he was handicapped by his wounded arm, and by the time he reached the ground on the other side he was breathing heavily.

But a mighty thrill of elation filled him. They had carried the parapet. The battle was as good as won, the enemy would be crushed.

He glanced about at the wastage of battle. Among the scattered bodies, Indian and white, a bareheaded youth sat with his back against the logs, trying to bind a white rag about his leg.

Jackson's tall figure stood over him.

"Doctor," he called. "Help this man. Can't you see he needs help? Take care of him."

Houston was too intent on his hurt to look up. A man knelt beside him, and he felt his clothing pulled down, an unaccustomed exposure. From the bleeding wound shreds of torn muscle protruded, pulled out when the barbed arrow was drawn. Sharp anguish as a broad thumb, none too clean, pushed back this extrusion into the laceration. Then a bandage was wrapped about his upper thigh, through which presently spots of blood began to soak.

"What's your name?" It was the surgeon who asked.

"Houston, sir. Ensign Houston, Thirty-ninth Infantry."

"Well, Ensign Houston, that's about all I can do for you now. You're lucky. No major blood vessels ruptured. The quadriceps muscle is in-jured, but maybe you'll be all right—if that arrow wasn't poisoned. Re-port to the hospital tent as soon as you're able."

A voice, high-pitched like a neighing mare, broke in.

"Ensign Houston? I believe you're from Maryville—am I mistaken?"

Houston glanced up. Mane of rust-red hair turning almost white, bril-liant blue eyes, deep-lined fighting face—the General himself.

He struggled to rise.

"Sit still," said Jackson.

He sank back. "Yes, sir," he replied faintly, to the question. "From Maryville, sir."

"I remember you. It's Sam, rather than Samuel, isn't it?" The odd Jackson half-grin.

"Yes, sir." That the General would remember such a thing!

"Houston, I saw you first over the breastwork," said Jackson. "After we root out this vermin I'll have something to say to you. Take it easy now."

An arrow sang through the air and struck with a rapping sound, quivering in the logs close beside Houston's head.

"What the devil!" exclaimed the General.

He strode off in the direction of the fighting, his shrill oaths cleaving the air as he berated some men who showed signs of falling back.

Houston used the log bastion to pull himself awkwardly to his feet. His head was swimming, but in a moment it cleared somewhat and he looked around. Hospital tent? Where in hell was any hospital tent?

Limping, hardly knowing where he was going, he started away.

The shooting and howling still continued as the Indians fought desperately from numerous coverts. Houston's leg hurt damnably, but he found that he could walk after a fashion. Some men were over there; he headed in that direction.

Uniforms of the Thirty-ninth. Though his brain still reeled, he made out that soldiers of his regiment were firing from behind stumps and trees down into a ravine.

He found that he had lost his sword, but he picked up a musket from the ground.

A soldier from his own platoon turned and recognized him as he hobbled up.

"They're down in there, sir," said the man. "It's like a blockhouse— the way they've got the logs piled."

From a little beyond, Jackson's high, strenuous voice.

"I want that rat's nest taken! Volunteers to storm it!"

Houston looked over. The General stood, tall and thin, his empty sleeve over the wounded arm, his curve-bladed sword, somewhat like a scimitar, in his hand, stretching his neck as he gazed down into the gully.

All at once, and for the first time, the ensign grasped the full significance of the episode back by the rampart. The General had taken personal interest in him . . . directed a surgeon to give him special treatment . . . remembered his name, even to the shortening of the first name . . . promised to say something to him later. His head had cleared now, and he could hardly believe his own great honor in having been so noticed. A sudden exaltation uplifted him. At that moment he worshiped Andrew Jackson as if he were a god.

He limped forward, looking at the men of the Thirty-ninth.

"You heard what the General said!" he cried. "You—Hobson, Gard, Cornwell, Boleen—the rest of you fellows—follow me! Charge that blockhouse!"

A moment later, without looking back to see whether the men were with him, he went half-bounding, half-hobbling, down the slope into the brush-choked ravine where squatted the Indian redoubt.

A few of the men began to run after him. The bushes hindered them, clutched at their legs, switched across their faces.

For a moment they lost sight of their leader's tall figure. Instinctively they began to slow down, creep forward, take concealment in the undergrowth. When they saw him again he was at the bottom, almost beside the crazy log structure in which the warriors crouched.

When he reached the bottom of the ravine, Houston for the first time saw how impossible it was to capture the place with a few men. The logs lay thick-laced and slovenly, but he could not even make out an entryway through them.

He shouted back over his shoulder, supposing his men were following him.

"Come on! Shoot 'em through their loopholes!"

No cry answered him. He knew all at once that he was alone, and his leg was paining him dreadfully again.

A movement and a rasp among the tangled logs before him. Almost fascinated, hardly realizing at first what it meant, he saw the barrels of guns appear, two—three.

Round black muzzle holes.

His heart gave a leap of apprehension. Half-leveling the musket he carried, he pulled the trigger.

No report. The gun was not loaded.

Smoke of Indian rifles blinded him and the shock of reports so close almost deafened him. A blow, as if he were struck by a gigantic club.

His legs seemed to die.

With a feeling of stunned surprise he found himself lying flat in the dust and stones at the bottom of the gully. An instinctive effort to rise, but his left arm gave way.

At first there was no sensation but numbness. Almost at once, however, came blazing pain. He gasped for air, clutched at the earth.

One thought was in him: to get away, somewhere, anywhere, so that he could lie at ease.

A tiny corner of his mind wondered why the Indians did not shoot him again. It brought clearer consciousness. He lifted his head and saw that where he lay, in the very bottom of the ravine, they perhaps could not see him.

Like a stricken animal he began to drag himself away, one arm hanging useless, his wounded leg an agony every time he used it.

Sickness overcame him and he fought against fainting. And nobody came to help him.

He did not know in this moment of despair that up above General Jackson himself was directing a rescue party to bring him in.

After he had crawled for what seemed aeons of time and pain, hands at last grasped him. A great bolt of savage anguish shot through his shoulder, and he was half-carried, half-dragged up a slope, his heels trailing.

Night closed thickly about him.

4

A voice said, "He's shot, but not gut shot."

Another voice, "Find Dr. Shelby. Ask him to report here at once."

Something in the second voice was familiar. With enormous effort he opened his eyes.

For the second time that day the General stood over him, looking down at him.

Jackson looked away and shouted an order. "Have the Cherokees go over there—the far side. They can get their fire arrows in on the redoubt better from there."

For a moment he watched the effect of the arrows, with flaming tow wrapped about their heads, as they struck on the log protection of the Creeks below. Already the flames were breaking out among the dry logs. When the Indians inside were forced out by the fire, the riflemen on the ravine's edge would finish them off.

This was what he should have done in the first place. He was sorry he had ordered the log bastion attacked. But that young ensign, at his call for volunteers, went limping down the slope as if he would take it all by himself.

When he saw that, Jackson vainly hoped the boy would perceive for himself the impossibility of what he had started to do, and fall back. But he had the pure grit in him and went forward until he fell.

He returned his gaze to the ensign at his feet. A handsome young man, even as he was, covered with dust and blood. And he had charged that casemate alone!

"Here, Dr. Shelby," he said as the surgeon appeared. "Take a look at this man."

The surgeon began an examination of the now unconscious figure.

"What about it?" asked Jackson.

"Arm's shattered, General, and there's an ugly wound in the shoulder. He's lost a lot of blood there and with the hole in his thigh."

"See that he has the best of care."

"Yes, sir," said the surgeon.

But the General knew without being told how little chance the boy had, what with clumsy frontier surgery and frontier medicine. Too bad. Given time this youth might have amounted to something. It appeared that he might not have too much time now.

It was, however, all that could be done for the present. Jackson felt regretful, but this was part of the inevitable butcher's bill of battle. And there still were Creeks to be fought.

He turned away, leaving Houston and the surgeon. The peninsula seemed to be owned by the dead who littered it, the ghastly detritus of conflict. Their castoff weapons and scattered garments made a scrofulous confusion about them.

He stepped over dead men, and realized suddenly that the shooting had stopped. It must be that the last of the Creeks down by the river were finished.

But a sudden clatter of rifles and the yelping of the Tennesseeans rose behind him. It ceased almost at once.

He thought to himself: That's the end of it. The Indians in that bastion made a break. None of them escaped.

Major Reid, a smear of dirt on his face, his handsome uniform torn and awry, was before him, saluting.

"The field is cleared," said Jackson.

"Yes, sir," said his aide.

"Have you any notion as to our casualties?"

"Only a partial reckoning, sir. As near as the officers I've talked to can make out, we've lost better than two hundred—at least fifty of them dead. The regulars suffered most."

"Of course. They led the charge. The Indians?"

"The count isn't full there either, sir. But there must be better than five hundred Creeks killed."

"How many wounded?"

"All dead, sir."

All dead . . . the measure of the ferocity of the attack and the hatred of the frontiersmen for the Indians. The Creek confederacy was crushed. It could not recover.

Strangely, he felt no particular elation, only a scorching thirst. A dirty job done—that was the best that could be said for it. So grimed and dry was his face that it seemed it might crack if he stretched the skin in any kind of an expression.

"Order camp made in the clearing outside these palisades," he said to Reid.

"Yes, sir."

"See that the men have supper and the wounded are attended to."

"Yes, sir."

"Notify company commanders to tell off burial parties to bury our dead tomorrow."

"Yes, sir. And the others—the Indians?"

"Just roll them into the river. They'll be carried downstream by the current to their friends—a notice that the war is over for themselves, at least."

"Yes, sir." Reid saluted and departed.

Jackson was intensely weary. He thought he would go to his tent as soon as it was pitched, and have Aaron bring him a sip of brandy. After that, maybe a bite of hoecake.

Then there was that letter to write to Rachel. . . .

5

Cold rain was falling, but young Sam Houston was heated by the fever of his body. One shoulder and side were rigid with unceasing anguish. He could not rest.

He knew he was in a cart, with a wet blanket over him, and that it must be days since the fight at the Horseshoe Bend, which still dwelt like a confused nightmare in his mind.

Vaguely, now, he remembered something of the securing of the cart in which he rode the night after the battle.

A voice had said: "We're from Cocke's Brigade, an' we want that there cart."

Another voice: "Ye cain't have this cart. This here cart b'longs to the commissary."

First voice: "An' what was the commissary doin' all the time we been starvin'? Come down off that!"

A thump. A struggle. Second voice, pleading: "No—don't—take the goddam cart—lemme up, boys——"

First voice: "Andy Jackson told us to take this man home. An' when Andy-by-God-Jackson gives an order, he means it. Git up. If ye wanta make somethin' of it, now's yer time."

"No—no, fellers—I don't want to——"

"Then help us put him in. An' be damn keerful. If ye bring a groan out'n him, we'll bring one out'n you."

There followed lifting, and pain, and Houston, half conscious, repressed his groan.

First voice: "Drive."

Second voice, protesting: "I cain't. I gotta report——"

First voice: "Report, hell! Ye done reported—to *us*. Want us to teach ye again?"

The cart began its long jolting progress. Days and nights followed.

This much Houston remembered. He heard men walking near him, and scraps of talk, grumblings, curses at the weather, one asking for "a chaw of terbaccy."

He sank again into semiconsciousness. Sometimes in this state he almost found ease, did not feel the pain so greatly, or the fever, or the cold rain. But he could not remain in this quiescence. More and more now his mind fought to clear itself, to take hold of impressions, to know what was going forward.

He half opened his eyes, and heard his own voice, a weak mumbling of words. A long-nosed face, bearded and coonskin-capped, bent over him.

"Who . . . ?" he whispered.

"Lee Rooney, sargint. This here squad of men's from Sevier. Goin' home. If it warn't rainin' ye could see the big Smokies now."

"Tennessee . . . ?"

"Yeah. The Gen'ral give us orders to deliver ye home. We'll be at Maryville—that's whar ye live, ain't it?—in one more day."

"What happened . . . the war . . . ?"

"The Creeks got a whippin' like they never dreamed of. Old Hickory wiped out the best of 'em at Horseshoe Bend. The rest is beginnin' to beg for peace. So the war's over an' the army's goin' home."

Sam Houston scarcely understood, nor did he care. This Sergeant Rooney, whoever he was, evidently was to take him home, but this seemed far away and unimportant. His body, dulled and drugged with weakness and pain, had no vitality either to protest or hope.

Darkness covered him again.

6

At last there was rest. He heard a clicking sound, and his mind faintly wondered what it was. He opened his eyes and he was in his own home.

His mother sat beside the bed. The clicking he heard was made by her knitting needles. Her gaunt face was intent, her mouth pursed over her work.

The clicking ceased and she arose, the knitting sliding to the floor.

"Sam?" she said. "Are you awake? Did you call me, Son?"

"How did I come here . . . ?"

"They brought you. Some scamps I don't know. And in such condition—never bathed you, starved you, I'd never have even known you, if it wasn't for your eyes. I gave them a piece of my mind, I can promise you!" His mother's tongue could be acid when she wished.

"Mother——"

She stopped talking to listen.

"They saved my life."

She regarded him doubtfully. "Maybe. But the *way* they saved it. Well, you mustn't talk any more just now. I've got some chicken broth hot and good. You'll eat something——"

In the days following she watched over him, hungrily nursed him, her most handsome, most wayward son. And as the weeks passed he grew stronger under her care, until at last he could rise alone, and walk about, sometimes sitting long hours, as if in silent thought, or dozing in the sun on the porch.

In those days Widow Houston perceived that her son was changed. His brothers, who once regarded him as a wild ne'er-do-well who lacked industry and the qualities that make for success, no longer patronized him when they visited him. They spoke instead with respect, and listened to his replies with gravity and attention.

Other people came from the country about to see him, once he was well enough for the widow to permit it. He had as visitors persons as notable as Squire Toole and the Reverend Mark Moore of Porter Academy, together with others of lesser eminence in the community, all of whom inquired most politely as to his health, as if they considered him worthy of their solicitude and attention.

One reason for this new respect was a packet received at the Maryville post office, addressed to *Lieutenant* Sam Houston. Later it became known—through the widow, who was bursting with her pride—that the packet contained a letter from General Andrew Jackson himself, written by his own hand, and in a most cordial and friendly vein, as one who addresses someone well and highly regarded. The letter contained a commission as lieutenant in the regular army, and a request from the General that Sam Houston join the First Infantry, garrisoned at New Orleans, as soon as he was in sufficient good health to do so.

This was akin to being touched by the stars, and Maryville discovered a sudden pride, almost awe, for its new favorite son.

Lieutenant Houston could not obey the mandate at once, nor was he able to be with his General during the mighty events of the campaign against the British about New Orleans, which immediately followed the Creek War, and of which he learned only by report. But sitting in the sun on his mother's bench, with a shawl about his shoulders, his wound healing very slowly because the rifle ball had not been taken from it, he thought long and deeply.

It was not his way to tell others what was in his mind; but visitors noted how he spoke with a new measured courtesy, a manner that impressed even those who knew him of old. When he was alone, his thoughts took their time, dwelling upon one thing until it was fully turned over in his mind, then taking up another for equal consideration.

He weighed his previous acts and perceived that until this time he had behaved as a boy rather than as a man. The needless and vainglorious charge he led against the Indian redoubt—it was heedless and headstrong. A real leader first would have made sure of his following, then would have aimed his attack at a place where there might be some chance of success. Instead, he rushed impetuously forward, and only a few followed, these soon falling back and leaving him alone as a target for the Indian bullets. For this rashness he paid the penalty.

The letter from General Jackson, and the promotion in rank, in some measure alleviated his feeling of failure. At least the General remembered him and inquired after him kindly. Perhaps the episode was not wholly wasted after all.

Nevertheless, he resolved in the future to try to think before acting. It was apparent to him now that a leader must think not only for himself but for other men. If he does not think he can be a blind follower only, in the train of a greater mind.

But one who thinks, he came to perceive, as Andrew Jackson thought, causes the thoughts of lesser men to fall away before his more powerful thoughts, his brain using their efforts to think in order to feed itself. Thinking is hard, and it is a relief to the mediocre not to think at all. Yet thinking is that which creates the difference between great men and nonentities.

General Andrew Jackson, Sam Houston was sure, was a great man, a very great man. He could be a follower of Jackson, and be proud in following; but he would seek to serve the General better in the future. Such greatness as that which surrounded Andrew Jackson, he reasoned, came only to one loftier and mightier than all other men because of some special alchemy of the soul.

Sam Houston was not religious. But Andrew Jackson became his faith, his creed, his worship.

New Orleans,
*** 1815

*T*here was Bill Weatherford—the Red Eagle. Jackson had sworn to hang Weatherford when he captured him. But one morning, after the Horseshoe Bend, a tall, light-colored Indian, unarmed, naked to the waist, in moccasins worn and ragged, walked into camp. He was instantly seized and taken before the commander.

"General Jackson?" he asked in good English.

"Yes."

"I am Bill Weatherford."

In spite of himself, Jackson was startled. But he quickly recovered, glared at the chief, and gave him a tongue-lashing.

The Indian did not quail. "You can speak to me like that now," he said. "I could have answered you—once. I could animate my warriors in battle; but I can't animate the dead. I have nothing to ask for myself. But I beg you to send for the women and children who have been driven into the woods without an ear of corn. They never did any harm. As for me—kill me, if the white people want that."

Jackson stared at him. Such raw courage he respected even in an enemy. His vengeful spirit faded. After a moment he poured for Weatherford a cup of brandy, and took one himself. Silently they drank together, and shook hands on a promise that Weatherford would bring his people to peace and Jackson would help the women and children.

Thus, quickly, the Creek War came to an end.

Then, August 24, 1814, the British captured and burned Washington. It was a national humiliation, yet out of it came inspiration; for an obscure young lawyer named Francis Scott Key, detained on a British warship, watched the brave defense of Fort McHenry which saved Baltimore from sharing Washington's fate, and was moved to write on the back of an old envelope a poem entitled "The Star-Spangled Banner," which was destined to become the national anthem.

But America, in that hour, needed something more than a song. Out in the West, haggard-faced Andrew Jackson lifted his head at news that a great British force was being gathered for a new attack—somewhere.

Men, thereafter, long remembered and discussed his movements. He knew, had known for months, that Spain, supposedly neutral, allowed to Britain the use of her Florida city and port of Pensacola as a base of operations. In a single week Old Hickory made a lightning march from Mobile, stormed Pensacola, forced the British to blow up their Fort Barrancas, and was back on American soil.

It was an act of sheer daredeviltry, performed without orders, and it created a serious diplomatic incident. But it delayed British plans, made his troops fanatically loyal to him, and gave the nation, in need of something to buoy it up, a surge of pride.

Victory-starved in that fall of 1814, the American people began to look toward the West, where it appeared there was a man who could and would fight.

Chapter Nine

One recognizes in him the habit of command. He may indeed be a soldier.

GENERAL JEAN ROBERT MARIE HUMBERT

1

A tall, sallow man, with a pursed-up mouth and a long nose, sideburns to the angles of his jaws, and a few wisps of hair twisting down on his forehead in the style supposed to be Napoleonic, sat behind his desk staring at his visitor. He was Governor William C. C. Claiborne, and he was no fool. A man who had been governor of the Louisiana Territory for eleven years had need for a head on his shoulders to deal with the touchy Creoles of New Orleans, especially if he was an American.

"The battle will be fought at this point," Andrew Jackson was saying, returning the stare.

Claiborne knew Jackson. They had served together in the Tennessee constitutional convention; and Claiborne, an appointee of Thomas Jefferson as governor after the Louisiana Purchase, had sided with Jackson in his fight to gain universal suffrage for the citizens of the state. Yet he half distrusted the General. His recollection of the Jackson of those days was of a wild man, redheaded and red-tempered, uncertain and unpredictable.

"But why New Orleans?" he asked. "You come to me and ask me to prepare for a siege. This will require extraordinary expenditures and exertions, and will create dislocations among a people who are already difficult. General Jackson, your reasons for your assertion, if you please."

Jackson sat straight up in his chair, his pale eyes boring into the governor's. "I am military governor of the Seventh District, sir," he said. "Since this nation is at war, it's enough that I state the situation and demand your co-operation."

Claiborne made a deprecatory movement of his hands. "There's no question, sir, of my co-operation. Remember that I'm an American, too, and a former Tennesseean."

The General relaxed, and the cold light in his eyes softened.

"It's only fair to you, Governor," he said, "to take you into my confidence, since I must place great dependence in you. I'm here ahead of my army, with only two aides—Major John Reid and Captain Jack Donelson—for this very reason, to enlist your help."

Claiborne nodded, remarking to himself that since the old convention days this man had evidently changed greatly. But he did not speak.

"I was at Mobile when I received confirmation of the heavy British troop concentrations at Jamaica," went on the General. "It's an invasion force, Governor, with a fleet to back it up. It's even certain that regiments in it come from the veteran army of the Duke of Wellington, direct from the Peninsular War against Napoleon. If so, they're the best in the world. Now, where would you say they would strike?"

Claiborne shook his head, unable to answer.

"This is December," said Jackson. "To my mind that narrows the field of speculation. A British invasion at this season can hardly be aimed at the Atlantic Coast in the teeth of winter gales and storms. The Gulf Coast is the only alternative, and that's my immediate responsibility. The problem is, at what point on the Gulf will the enemy make his attempt?"

"That's my very point," said Claiborne. "It seems to me that Mobile is the logical place. Mobile Bay is the most important harbor on the Gulf Coast. It's close to Pensacola, where the invaders could revictual. A landing force there could gather hundreds of Indian allies from disaffected tribes." He paused, and for a moment considered his hands, finger tips placed together, which he held before him. "On the other hand," he continued, "New Orleans would be most difficult to reach, particularly by an amphibious operation. The enemy knows these things as well as we do."

Jackson gave a bleak smile. "You perhaps think, as some of my officers do, that I'm insane for marching away from Mobile toward this city, against all apparent logic? Then I must tell you my reasons. They may seem flimsy to you, but to me they seem impelling."

"I'd be most interested, sir," said Claiborne guardedly.

"I talked to the captain of a coasting vessel at Mobile," went on the soldier. "He told me of the great fleet of warships and transports gathered at Jamaica under Admiral Cochrane—the same who devastated Washington City."

Claiborne picked up a snuffbox, took a pinch, and offered it. But Jackson shook his head, took a pipe from his pocket, filled it, and lit it.

"I didn't give my officers the full particulars," he continued. "They might have been daunting. The sea captain, a Dane, and evidently a close observer, told me that the British had between nine and ten thousand veteran troops with requisite artillery, fifteen hundred marines, and nearly ten thousand seamen. Against such a force I can, at this present time, oppose no more than fifteen hundred, half of them raw recruits."

Claiborne gave a low whistle, his long face growing longer. "But—I still don't understand your reasoning that brought you to New Orleans."

"There was another bit of information offered by the sea captain," said Jackson, puffing at his pipe. "He gave it incidentally and as of little importance. But it was important to me. On that shred I based my movements which appear so illogical to you—and others."

"And that information?"

"The British are so confident of easy victory, the sea captain said, that many of the officers' wives, with their luggage, pretty wardrobes, and ladies' maids, are sailing with the fleet as if they look forward to a pleasant holiday."

Claiborne seemed puzzled. "I admit I do not follow——"

The soldier's blue eyes gazed shrewdly at the governor.

"Officers' wives . . . pretty wardrobes? Don't they mean anything to you, sir? A trivial detail it is, perhaps, and yet to me most significant. There's only one place on the Gulf where ladies of quality may expect gala times. And assuredly that place is not Mobile with its mud flats."

"New Orleans!" exclaimed Claiborne.

Jackson nodded. "Society in New Orleans is high-toned. The Mardi Gras season is especially celebrated for its gay revels. Exactly what officers' ladies would anticipate with pleasure." He paused. "That's why I ordered my army to march and rode hard to precede it here."

Claiborne, now fully convinced, sat forward with excitement.

"How soon do you think——?"

"The bit about the feminine contingent with its furbelows on the fleet even gave me a clue as to time," said the General. "The Mardi Gras—it comes before Lent, doesn't it? And New Orleans is Catholic, so during Lent it will be sober and pious. British officers' wives must be expecting to be safely installed in time to take part in the round of pleasures preceding that season."

"Ash Wednesday, the beginning of Lent, comes in March," said the governor.

Jackson nodded. "Yes, I had it looked up. So . . . we have a sort of timetable, don't we? The British attack must be projected for some time within the next six weeks. I can only pray that it will be delayed until I can take such measures as lie in my power to meet it."

"What measures *can* you take? Fifteen hundred men—against ten or twenty thousand——"

"I've called for reinforcements. Colonel Carroll of my staff is in Tennessee now, and I hope he'll bring me two thousand riflemen. I have a regiment of regulars on the way from the north, and another following

from Mobile. I've even asked Kentucky—although it's out of my district
—for volunteers."

"So you'll gather—how many? Five thousand?"

"Perhaps, at the outside."

"And they're raw levies, while the British are professional veterans?
What chance have you?"

"We'll do what we must. Militia haven't been trustworthy, I'll grant
you. But remember that my men are Western men—hunters and Indian
fighters. I'm Western myself. We'll not meet the British on their own
terms—with columns of bayonets. We'll meet them on our terms—with
the American long rifle. I have my own ideas as to how best to utilize it.
I don't doubt that, under the right conditions, my men will fight
stoutly."

"Tell me what you want me to do, General," said Claiborne, more
impressed than he had ever been in his life.

2

New Orleans was . . . New Orleans. Hardly eleven years under the
American flag—and then unwillingly—in that December of 1814 it was
not yet American. Rather it was a curious extension of Europe on the
American continent, partly Spanish, mostly French, with various other
nationalities and many Negro slaves; a polyglot city, a hybrid city, with
foreign customs and ideas and languages.

As to Americans—and things American—New Orleans knew them
chiefly from the flatboatmen, boorish, drunken, and smelling atrociously,
who came floating down the river with whiskey, corn, livestock, and
other produce to trade.

The city, therefore, was in no vital way concerned over the arrival of
General Jackson, or even the report (ridiculed by many) that there
might be fighting somewhere in the vicinity.

Haughty Creole ladies sniffed contemptuously at such talk. This
Jackson, for example: they heard that for beating a tribe of wild Indians
he had been made a major general and military governor of Louisiana.
And when they had a good look at him he was altogether a disappointment.

On his first day in the city he made a speech from a house balcony
on the Rue Chartres. Only a small crowd heard him, for it was raining.
Mayor Girod, indeed, brought a snicker, when in attempting a flowery
address of welcome he used an ill-chosen metaphor: "The sun is never
shining more brightly than when you are among us!" And at the time
the heavens were weeping.

The American general did not smile. He said something; a few words in a high, shrill voice, that had to be translated. He did not even speak French, this general—what an ignoramus!

He was, it was agreed, excessively gaunt and tall; homely, too, with a complexion sallow and unhealthy; and strange, very light blue eyes. His apparel, moreover, was enough to cause a smirk: nearly threadbare, a dark suit covered by an old Spanish cloak, and high boots long innocent of polish and smeared with mud.

New Orleans was accustomed to the epaulet, the sabretache, the ribbon, and the gold braid with its military uniforms. Why, a common soldier of one of its own militia companies—say, for example, the *Carabiniers d'Orleans*—made this "general" look like a clodhopper by comparison! How could such a man fight the *élite* British regiments? One highborn Creole lady put the common impression into a phrase: "An ugly old Kaintuck flatboatman." When you spoke of a Kaintuck flatboatman in New Orleans, you reached the last degree of disparagement.

The rank and file of his "army," when it arrived, bore out the general opinion of its commander. With curiosity women of New Orleans gazed down from their iron-grilled balconies when a contingent marched through one of the streets.

Tall, yes, one admitted that. But how ungainly! Shock-haired bumpkins; whiskered, every one of them; in dingy woolen hunting shirts and copperas-dyed pantaloons; with caps of coonskin or fox on their unkempt heads. They did, to be sure, carry their long rifles with a certain assurance; and it was observed that they had bold eyes for any woman. A snigger and a nudge in the ribs of the next men when a quadroon girl went by, hips gracefully swinging, a basket of fruit on her head. The tangled beards split in meaning grins and the hunters winked at each other, as much as to say, wait until we get leave in town!

They seemed fascinated also by the taverns and grogshops they passed, licking their chops at the thought of rum or brandy. One wondered how long it was since any of them had bathed, or washed their dirty shirts.

A wrinkling of a dainty nose, and a shrug of a pretty shoulder in the balcony. So these were American soldiers? At least give us something civilized!

The Creole ladies turned their thoughts to the British expedition now being rumored. Officers of the British army were frequent visitors in New Orleans, before this war. At least *they* knew how to dress and conduct themselves in polite society.

One remembered, with a sparkle of the eye, the splendor of the British uniforms, scarlet and gold and white, and Wellington boots polished until they shone again. And also how beautifully the gallant young men in the brilliant uniforms danced . . . and also in what a delightfully urbane fashion they flirted. The world knew they were brave

—think of Napoleon! And the ladies of New Orleans knew they could make love. . . .

Pretty Creole women gazed contemptuously under their lids at the backwoods yokels tramping the muddy street below. Assuredly these barbarians could never stand against real soldiers! And when the British soundly beat them, the men in scarlet naturally would occupy New Orleans in triumph.

An inward thought at that, and a hidden smile: the old, lawless instinct of woman to go over at any time to the stronger side. Has not this been history?

3

Jackson was painfully aware of his lack of a speaking knowledge of French, and also that the beautifully dressed Creole ladies looked askance at his shabbiness. For these reasons he took up his headquarters at the home of an American, bluff old J. Kilty Smith, on the Rue Royale. Without intending it, in so doing he offended the sensitive feelings of a very notable Creole, Senator Bernard de Marigny de Mandeville, who had also offered his home.

The General was not entirely lacking in tact, but at this moment he was too terribly involved with problems that multiplied themselves to be concerned with delicate matters of protocol.

There were problems heavy enough to bring further lines to his face: personal problems such as Rachel, and the politicians at Washington; the great all-absorbing problem of the British.

He had promised to send for Rachel when he thought he would be stationed at Mobile, and he had been forced to rescind that promise. Forever he seemed to be disappointing her, and though he wished sincerely to make her happy, events continually arose that made it impossible to do so. Not for months had he been home, and the old sense of guilt gnawed at him as he pictured her woeful disappointment when she learned that her journey to him was canceled.

As for Washington, the government still was upset over the Pensacola affair, and he continually received nagging, inquiring, critical letters because of that unauthorized raid.

Well, Pensacola, assuredly was in Florida; and Florida, at least nominally, was Spanish territory; and Spain, technically, was neutral. But realities cut deeper than the nominal or technical. When Spain allowed the British to use Pensacola to arm the disaffected Indians, and as a base for an armed invasion, he alone fully realized the peril.

Let the politicians rave. The responsibility was his; and his brief campaign had, for the time being at least, eliminated Pensacola as a point for enemy operations. They might call him before a court of inquiry. But just now he had something so important on his mind that every personal consideration, even his wife's unhappiness and his own professional future, were unimportant in comparison.

First, he must place under control a half-hostile city; and further than that, enlist if possible its support. Claiborne, quite haggard now from his worries and apologetic over not having his city in a better state for defense, was helpful. He brought to Jackson three Americans who held key positions.

One was Commodore Daniel T. Patterson, compact and stiff in his neat blue navy undress uniform; a second was Edward Livingston, a lawyer with wrinkled clothes and disheveled hair, but a keen legal mind; and the third another lawyer, John Randolph Grymes, impeccable in fine broadcloth and a black stock. The latter two were reputed to be attorneys for the pirates, headed by Jean Laffite, in Barataria Bay; but Jackson would use anyone if he needed him.

His first interview was with Commodore Patterson, who had recently destroyed the Barataria pirates' roost.

"Available maps show at least six water routes by which New Orleans might be reached," he began. "What ships have you available?"

"The armed schooner *Carolina*, sir, and the sloop-of-war *Louisiana*," replied Patterson. "Both are now anchored in the river opposite the city. On Lake Borgne are five gunboats under Lieutenant Thomas Ap Catesby Jones."

"Gunboats? You mean those flat-bottomed, one-gun affairs?"

"Yes, sir."

"Hum. Well, they may do for scouting. What of the crews of your ships on the river?"

"They are shorthanded, sir."

"The water-front lodging houses are full of sailors. Recruit them."

"They will not serve, sir."

"Impress them!"

"The state assembly will not grant authority, sir."

"Hell and damnation, this is *war!* I tell you, sir, that *I'll* grant you the authority! By the Eternal, Commodore Patterson, I want you to take a detail of marines and comb the dives. Get 'em drunk, bribe 'em, hale 'em—but fill those crews! I'll face this assembly for you!"

A voice, calm and smooth, intervened. It was Livingston, the lawyer.

"A word from you, General, might solve this difficulty."

"Eh?" Jackson stared at the lawyer. "And what word is that?"

"The Baratarians are sailors, sir. They might make up the crews."

"Those hellish banditti? I can do damnably well without them!"

"With respect, General, I have a letter here which might be of interest. It was written by Jean Laffite himself."

"Let me see it."

The letter was written in a Frenchman's flowery English:

MonSieur: I address myself to you with confidence for an object on which can depend the Safety of the State. I offer to Return to this State many Citizens Who perhaps have lost to your eyes that sacred title. I offer Their Efforts for the Defense of the Country. This point of Louisiana that I occupy is of Great Importance in the present situation. I offer myself to defend it. . . . I am The Lost Sheep who desires to return to the flock . . . for you to see through my faults such as they are. In case, Monsieur Le Gouverneur, that your Reply should Not be favorable to my ardent wishes I declare to you that I leave immediately so Not to be held to have Co-operated with an invasion. This can not Fail to take place, and puts me entirely at the judgement of my conscience. I have the honor to be, Monsieur le Gouverneur,

Laffite.

"When was this written?" demanded Jackson.

"Before Commodore Patterson, on Claiborne's orders, destroyed Barataria," answered Livingston.

"Then the temper of the pirate must have changed."

Now Governor Claiborne himself intervened. "On the contrary, sir," he said, "I've had my difficulties with Laffite, but I consider him a man of his word. I have, in fact, a trustworthy report that he received an offer from the British to join them, and refused it."

"Hum," said Jackson. "Why?"

"He has a certain loyalty to his friends—and they are almost all in New Orleans. Furthermore he has a sworn personal war with Spain, and an alliance with Britain would force him to cancel that vendetta."

The General considered, then shook his head grimly. "I place no confidence in him."

4

It rained steadily, a downpour that made a bog of the *Pláce d'Armes*. The tramping of the marching men sounded soggy and dismal as the five militia companies of New Orleans assembled. In the ranks and even among the officers there was muttered cursing at the stupidity of an order that brought them out in such weather for a mere inspection.

Yet they came, though the band played the "Marseillaise" rather than "Yankee Doodle"—Captain Plauche's *Carabiniers d'Orleans*, Captain St. Geme's *Dragons à Pied*, Captain Hudry's *Francs*, Captain Guibert's *Chasseurs*, Captain Maunsel White's *Louisiana Blues*. These were the *élite* organizations, composed of sons of planters, merchants, bankers, and professional men, with a few French refugees of undoubted quality, including a handful of seasoned soldiers, some of whom had served under Napoleon himself. Their uniforms were as flamboyant as their names, for they existed chiefly to provide military pomp for notable occasions. Now the reds and greens and blues and golds of those uniforms were sadly soaked by the downpour, and the twelve-inch plume with which Captain St. Geme sought to enhance his five-foot figure, sagged in an ungraceful droop. Nevertheless their sense of honor forced them to come out, even in this rain; it must not be said that the soldiers of New Orleans were afraid of the weather!

The commanders of the battalion formed a small knot of horsemen in front of the ranks as they were marshaled in the soggy *Plâce d'Armes*. Chief of these was a large man with fiercely outthrusting mustachios, a leonine head, and a huge nose the color of a ripe strawberry. Major General Jean Robert Marie Humbert had once commanded a division in the Napoleonic armies, and with distinction. But he had made a mistake. Sent as second in command to General Leclerc, who sailed with an army to put down the uprising in Santo Domingo, he succeeded to the command when Leclerc and half the French army died from yellow fever; and also succeeded in making Leclerc's widow his mistress. The widow happened to be Pauline Bonaparte, Napoleon's favorite sister, whose beauty and sensual tastes were rather widely celebrated. When the emperor heard of the scandal, he was outraged. Humbert narrowly escaped a firing squad, and was confined in a prison in Brittany. His sweetheart was taken from him and married to an Italian count. After a time the amorous general managed to bribe his guards, succeeded in escaping to New Orleans, and now divided his time between seeking new feminine conquests, keeping himself well warmed with rum, and playing at soldiering by commanding the New Orleans militia.

With Humbert were Major General Jacques Villeré, a very wealthy planter who commanded the militia horse; and Major General Garriques Flaugeac, also a Napoleonic veteran and an artillerist of renown. Each of the three considered himself the equal, if not the superior, of the upstart American general who presumed to command them, although none of them had as yet met him.

"Our commandant is overdue," grumbled Humbert, with an ironic emphasis on *commandant*. "The rain appears to be growing heavier, and the men grow restless."

"You have met him?" asked Villeré.

"No. That honor has not yet been accorded to me." Again Humbert spoke with irony.

"From reports, we will find him, let us say, an *original*." Villeré's lips twitched in a half-smile.

"We'll see," growled Humbert. "Let him show the soldiers of New Orleans what qualities as a leader he possesses."

"Ah," said Flaugeac, who had been silent, "can this be the American general now approaching?"

It was Jackson, and his advent was disappointing in its lack of pageantry. He was without military escort, accompanied only by two civilians—Governor Claiborne and Edward Livingston. The General was swathed in the old blue Spanish cloak, and on his head, because of the rain, he wore a leather cap. As he rode up he exchanged salutes with the waiting officers.

Humbert was the first to speak. "General Jackson," he said, "I am General Humbert, commander of these troops. This gentleman is General Villeré, and this is General Flaugeac."

Jackson inclined his head. "Your soldiers are handsomely uniformed," he said, glancing toward the five companies of militia.

"Yes," said Humbert complacently. "I believe in smartness. A soldier takes pride in the amenities and colors of war."

Jackson looked at him coldly. "The men I have brought here lack the gaudy garments and plumes for the crowds to admire and stare at," he said. "But they can fight. Will these?"

The chill blue stare he bent on the three generals had a force almost hypnotic and daunting. Each of the three felt the impact of a personality such as they had never before experienced.

Humbert cleared his throat after an awkward silence. "Yes—I believe they will fight if called upon to do so," he said. "Are you ready to review these troops, General?"

"First I'll inspect them. Company by company. Rank by rank. On foot." Jackson fairly bit off his short phrases.

In wonder and not a little awed, the three generals, who had never planned to get their boots muddy, dismounted and followed him as he marched toward the companies.

Not soon did the Creole militia forget the experience when Andrew Jackson walked down their files. Genius in a leader lies in part in his ability to create emotion in others. Every man in those ranks for an instant or two felt Jackson's eyes pierce his own. A glance from the thin, cold-faced General was a spine-tingling thing which brought a soldier to his full height, chin up, with a feeling in his heart that he was here in the presence of someone greater than ordinary men.

The inspection finished, and he did not neglect a man, Jackson mounted again. His voice lifted, thin, high, and far-carrying:

"Soldiers of New Orleans! Military service is a right, as well as a stern duty of citizens! Your city is in danger from the power of the invading Briton! The peril is great, the fight will be for house and home, for America and liberty! That is all, but it is enough!"

When later the companies passed in review, they appeared, in spite of the dripping rain, to march with a step and carriage they had never shown before. Clearly the new commander had made a mighty impact on them.

"I confess," said Humbert after Jackson bade them farewell and rode back to his quarters, "that I am impressed by him. One recognizes in him the habit of command. He may indeed be a soldier."

Villeré nodded. "I think it would be unwise to trifle with him."

Flaugeac had another observation. "This General Jackson, my friends, is a leader. He may not be showy in his attire, but thinking back on the glorious days in France, do you not remember that the Little Corporal himself was not much for display, either? Especially in the field he looked almost drab in that long gray coat, among his brilliantly uniformed, medaled, and plumed marshals."

Speedily, New Orleans received this viewpoint. Soldiers in the ranks of the *élite* companies, as well as officers, proclaimed their enthusiasm for General Jackson with Gallic flourishes, and announced their willingness to "follow him to the death."

Endorsement such as this from young men of family, as well as from their sober seniors, measurably altered public opinion. Even the ladies, always slowest to accept one who was careless in proper grooming, spoke with a new interest of the American General.

5

The inspection of the militia, even in the rain, had been a necessity of his situation, Jackson felt, but his ailing body could ill withstand the exposure.

After a difficult night, he awoke the following morning with a high fever, and a throbbing in his shoulder. That morning he coughed so severely that he spat up blood. While this did not overly concern him, since it had happened before, the new pain in the wounded shoulder, which had been much better of late so that he no longer wore his arm in a sling, caused him such trouble that he sent for Dr. Shelby, the surgeon who was on his staff.

"Look at this damned arm, will you Doctor?" he asked.

Shelby, who had dressed the wound more than a hundred times, did so. The scar left by Jesse Benton's bullets was raw and angry, and he noticed that a red and threatening swelling had developed.

"How long has this been going on, sir?" he asked.

"I noticed it was beginning to throb yesterday," said Jackson.

Dr. Shelby pressed gently at the swelling with supple fingers, and to the General the pain was like that of a sore boil.

"It's there, isn't it?" said the surgeon, noticing his patient's face twist slightly.

"Yes."

"Morbid swelling. Febrile." Dr. Shelby glanced up. "General, we have an abscess. I recommend the lancet. Can you stand being hurt?"

"If that's your professional recommendation, yes."

Dr. Shelby fumbled in his medicine case and brought out a thin, sharp knife. He called for hot water and cleansed the instrument.

"Now, General," he said.

Andrew Jackson could stand pain, and he would not have allowed his face to show it even if the pain had been great. But the small cut made by the lancet was immediate and not as severe as he had expected.

"Ah," said the surgeon. "As I thought—pus. But I think laudable pus. Formed to discharge unhealthy humors. Wait a minute——"

A cloth in the doctor's fingers pressed the swelling and at the same time absorbed the matter forced out. Reaching into his bag again he drew forth a pair of tweezers with which, looking closely into the wound, he probed.

Slight moment of pain, then relief.

"There!" exclaimed Dr. Shelby triumphantly. He held up between the small pincers a wet sliver, two inches long. "Bone! A fragment sloughed off where it was shattered by the bullet that wounded you. Infection, of course. I'll bandage it, and you'll feel better, I promise you."

"Keep that piece of bone," said Jackson.

"For what reason?"

"I want to send it to my wife."

The surgeon stared.

"I intend no piece of gruesome humor," Jackson explained. "I know my wife. This, and a letter I shall write with it, will do more to prove that I'm still alive and improving, and thinking of her, than anything I could do."

Afterward he ate breakfast with a rather better appetite. Aaron, waiting on him, thought fit to offer a piece of information.

"Gin'ral, suh," he said.

"Yes, Aaron."

"Yo' baggage done come in. Las' night from Mobile."

Jackson was pleased. He had agreed to attend a dinner party that night, given by his new friend Edward Livingston, at which he was to meet some of the Creole aristocrats. It would be, he knew, an occasion of some importance. The Creoles wanted to look him over, to decide for themselves what sort of a boor had come in their midst. A good impression might do wonders in his effort to win the city, so that he might better defend it.

A new uniform would help mightily, and he told Aaron to unpack his best and see that it was pressed and ready. Major Reid, of course, would accompany him to the Livingstons', and Reid always looked superb. Jackson, with little personal vanity, yet envied his aide the fine figure and bearing he displayed, and wished that his own bony body, six feet and an inch tall, but weighing little more than one hundred and thirty pounds, was less scrawny and angular.

6

Edward Livingston, with the kindest feelings, nevertheless awaited his guest of honor that night with some apprehension. It was to be, as Jackson supposed, a testing in a manner of speaking. He had invited a choice company, although the Marignys had pleaded another engagement.

It was raining again and Jackson and Reid arrived in a coach. Livingston himself was at the door when his major-domo admitted them, and at his first glance some of his concern vanished.

He was honestly astonished at the change in the General's appearance. Heretofore he had seen him only in his worn and careless campaign uniform. But Jackson entered looking almost resplendent. His blue coat, with gold buttons and epaulets, seemed to fit his lean body perfectly. The tight-fitting trousers were snowy white. His Wellington boots were new and shining. And he wore at his side the curved sword with its scabbard freshly polished.

"General!" exclaimed the host. "You're most welcome in this house, sir, and you appear to be in better health than yesterday."

"A small operation this morning relieved a minor disability," said Jackson, inwardly smiling at the other's evident surprise at his new garb. Livingston, meantime, mentally compared him with Reid. The major was the younger, certainly the more handsome man of the two. And yet such was the General's magnetism that one hardly looked at anyone else when he was present.

"Let us go to the salon," he said. "The other guests are eager to meet you."

A company of a dozen or more couples rose in the room, well-lighted with candles, as the General entered.

Livingston conducted him to the center of the floor.

"Mesdames and monsieurs," he said, "I have the honor to present Major General Jackson of the Army of the United States."

A graceful young woman, with a lovely oval face, luxurious hair, magnificent eyes, and a slender and charming figure which was flattered by the white silk empire gown she wore, came forward.

"General," said Livingston, "this is my dear wife."

She extended her hand. "Our house is honored by your presence, General Jackson," she said, smiling delightfully.

He took the slim extended hand and bent over it.

"This house," he said, "could not possess a higher honor than the presence of so beautiful a mistress."

It was well said, thought the onlookers, and every lady present mentally told herself that his smile was charming. Madame Livingston was from that moment his friend, and turned to present him to the others.

As he bowed and spoke a pleasant sentence or two to each, Livingston, watching, thought to himself that this strange man could win ladies as well as men, that he had indeed two sets of manners, one for headquarters where he dealt with the problems of war, the other for the drawing room where he met femininity in the etiquette of polite society.

Jackson now presented his aide, and Madame Livingston led them into the dining room.

At the table she seated the General on her right, and next to him Mademoiselle Chotard, a pretty young Creole who spoke English easily. Across sat Reid, with Livingston of course at the head.

In that repast Livingston marveled at the way his guest seemed completely at home in this rather glittering circle. The women in particular seemed delighted with him, and he was delighted with the company.

To his hostess and his companion on his right he was smilingly attentive, but he by no means neglected the others. Once he raised his wine glass and said to Livingston, "This is the finest old Madeira I've tasted since Burr's dinner in Philadelphia in 1797. Do you remember that occasion?"

"Indeed I do," said Livingston. "You were a senator from Tennessee then, and I a member of Congress from New York. It was," he explained to the company, "when Aaron Burr was a senator from my home state, before he fell under a cloud."

Pretty little Mademoiselle Chotard smiled up at Jackson. "You must have known Mr. Livingston a very long time."

"Indeed yes, my dear," he smiled back, "I had the honor of knowing Mr. Livingston before the world was blessed by your beautiful existence."

The girl blushed with pleasure at the compliment, and the whole company smiled.

And so the dinner progressed, with Jackson the center of all attention, conversing with a grace that truly surprised them, although it was natural with him since he lacked any self-consciousness. When the evening ended and he said his farewells and was gone with Reid, the ladies turned on their host, laughingly.

"Is this your savage Indian fighter?" they demanded. "Is this your rough frontier general? Shame on you, Mr. Livingston, to deceive us so! Why, he is a veritable *preux chevalier!*"

Edward Livingston smiled, well satisfied. His friend had scored a triumph of no small value in New Orleans.

7

The news next morning was like a lightning bolt.

The British fleet actually was near at hand to New Orleans! It had been sighted in Chandeleur Sound, just off the coast to the east!

Buzzing with excitement, the townspeople did not know that the General's subordinates looked at him with suddenly enhanced respect. Some of them had been more than a little skeptical of his sudden move from Mobile. Yet he had come to New Orleans like a bee to a tree, not hesitating, and summoning all his forces to concentrate there. How had he so amazingly guessed the enemy's intentions?

Then a shock came to New Orleans. Jackson issued a proclamation of martial law. Nobody was allowed to enter or leave the city, by water or land, without an official pass. Anyone found in the streets after nine o'clock was subject to arrest. This, in a city where night life was the only worthwhile part of existence!

New Orleans seethed and Jackson's nascent popularity fell very low.

But a day later the city had something else to chew over. The Baratarian pirates, who had offered their services, had been rejected by Jackson. Yet in some manner Jean Laffite, the Baratarian chief, had obtained an audience with the General. Sheer audacity this, because Jackson's views of the pirates, whom he called "hellish banditti," were well known.

New Orleans chuckled. Just like Laffite, that daring and unpredictable rascal, to do such a thing! A real flourish, a snapping of the fingers!

But the surprise of the piece followed. Jackson accepted Laffite and the Baratarians into his army!

Quite evidently the American commander had reversed himself. And quite evidently he did not care who thought so.

A few, a very few, marked in this a deep-running consistency which made light of apparent surface inconsistencies. Jackson would employ anyone or anything that would serve him . . . and Laffite had mentioned cannon, and a supply of gunflints needed by the army. The one thing the General most sorely lacked was artillery.

He, too, could snap his fingers—at public opinion.

Jean Laffite was the darling of New Orleans. His sleek figure and lean dark face, in which one eye was always half-closed due to an injury to the lid, were engagingly saturnine, and he was elegant and debonair in his manners. He sold smuggled goods to luxurious ladies at prices far below the market, and even though he was not *quite* received in the best homes, he associated freely with men in the highest business circles. Full of pranks, too—New Orleans still relished the joke when Governor Claiborne posted a $500 reward for Laffite, and the pirate countered by posting a $1500 reward for the governor. A rogue, yes, but a pleasant and clever sort of rogue!

When Laffite and his people joined the American forces, Jackson's popularity received a new impetus in the city. A few even cried, "*Vive Jackson!*" when he appeared, stern-faced, riding by in the streets.

Two regiments of American regulars, the Forty-fourth and Seventh Infantry, arrived and camped north of the city. A day or two later a long flotilla of flatboats came floating down from upriver, all the way from Tennessee, bearing three regiments of riflemen, brought by Colonel William Carroll. It was said that these men were drilled, too, after a fashion, for on the way down the Mississippi they took turns rowing, and those not at the oars were put through the manual of arms and short evolutions on the decks.

On the heels of this came a new alarming report. The British fleet had smashed the five small American gunboats on Lake Borgne, which was an arm of the Gulf reaching perilously close to New Orleans from the east.

What next? Lake Pontchartrain perhaps? *Mon Dieu*—the British were almost in cannon range!

A new panic in the city, and rumors of defection. Down from the headquarters of the American General came a grim warning, which was posted on the streets:

The rules of war annex the punishment of death to any person holding secret correspondence with the enemy.

Provost guards marched constantly on patrol.

But what, the people asked each other, of those who might have "treasonable thoughts," yet held no communication with the enemy? It was well known that the Louisiana state assembly was controlled by the Creoles, and that the Creoles were controlled by Bernard Marigny.

Marigny, of the highest aristocracy, despised all things American, and personally detested Jackson.

No telling what Marigny might do.

Chapter Ten

By the Eternal! They'll not sleep on our soil!

ANDREW JACKSON

1

December 23, 1814, and Christmas only two days away.

The first panic in the city had passed, and knowledge that the British were somewhere in the vicinity hardly detracted from the seasonal merriment of the lighthearted people of New Orleans. Streets were gaily decorated, and in the homes pre-Yule celebrations already had begun.

In the festivities not a few Americans were taking part. By one means or another some of the Tennesseeans from Coffee's and Carroll's commands managed to obtain leave from their camps outside the city. The grogshops were filled with them, and the sound of their boisterous laughter and roaring songs pervaded the streets of the Vieux Carré. Women were available, too. Pretty quadroons and white *filles de joie* forgot their aversion toward these giants in homespun or buckskin when there was silver to be paid. With a girl on his knee and a pewter cup of rum in his fist, a rifleman had little thought of war, or anything but pleasure.

But the General thought of nothing else but battle. That day he dined at the home of Kilty Smith with John Coffee, Billy Carroll, John Reid, and Jack Donelson. Young Captain Donelson, one of Rachel's numerous brood of nephews and nieces, had virtually been brought up at the Hermitage, knowing it in some ways better than his own home. His full name was Andrew Jackson Donelson, but it was shortened to Jack, and this was his first military campaign, and he was very proud of his uncle, his uniform, and his chance to be in the hub of great affairs.

In the course of the dinner Smith, a resident of New Orleans for many years, with extensive property and mercantile interests, expressed his concern over the prospect of an immediate British invasion and the flimsy forces available to oppose it.

"In war," Jackson replied to him, "it's the commander's head and his men's hearts that count. Unless the combination is good, success can hardly be hoped for."

"I have no doubts about the commander's head," said Smith. "But what about your men?"

"Of close-order drill my men know little, but they have other qualities.

British military training—all European training—aims to make automatons of men, so they will not think and therefore will not make mistakes. My men must use their heads and act for themselves. Because they're resourceful we may have some surprises in store when the enemy comes."

Kilty Smith sat back, hardly half convinced.

"I've spent the last several days reconnoitering the environs of New Orleans," Jackson said. "It furnishes some interesting problems. There are, for example, at least six water routes by which this city can be approached. Which way do you gentlemen think the British will come?"

After a little silence, Carroll spoke up:

"They're in Lake Borgne now. That gives them a water passage to Lake Pontchartrain. My guess is they'll attack from the north."

The General shook his head. "Up there everything's woods and bogs. I'm not overlooking any possibility and have guards posted at each foreseeable avenue. But woods and bogs! Fine for Indian fighters and deer hunters like your long-shanked boys, Billy. But try to imagine a British regiment of the line keeping formation in such country! Close-order drill's their strength, and they've got to have open ground for it. Now the Plain of Gentilly, downriver from here, is flat. Cane fields mostly, cropped down at this season. A few shallow ditches. Nothing to prevent a regiment, or a brigade, or even a division, from keeping its alignment and maneuvering."

He paused. Jack Donelson, looking at him, saw how hollow-eyed and emaciated he was, as if worn to a skeleton by his physical ailments and his ceaseless labors. And his mane of hair had grown even whiter since coming to New Orleans. Yet there was a fierce gleam in his eyes, and his manner was almost gay. Assuredly this man was born for battle. He seemed to grow exhilarated as the prospect of fighting drew nearer; even when the odds were all against him.

"Now, how will they reach the Gentilly flats?" resumed Jackson. "They hold Lake Borgne, of course, but from there, what? Will they try to fight their way through the bayous and marshes from there? I think not. And if the men I've posted are reliable, we should have warning so that we could catch them in transit, where of all places they'd least like us to catch them."

"Then," said John Coffee in his slow rumble, "they'd have to come up the river. The enemy's warships will try to reduce our two forts downstream so their transports can sail up and land. In that case, also, we'd have plenty of warning."

"Just so," said the General. "But what if they don't come by the river——?"

Voices rising in the entry interrupted his question. A moment later the Negro butler came in, ushering three men.

Jackson recognized them. One was Dussau de la Croix, a friend of the Livingstons and loyal to the American cause. The others were Colonel de la Ronde, another planter, and Major Gabriel Villeré, son of General Villeré, wearing the somewhat fantastic uniform of the Creole Light Horse.

Villeré, in his twenties and greatly excited, broke into a torrent of French which none of the American officers understood.

De la Croix interpreted: "Major Villeré is saying that the British are in force at his father's plantation, ten miles below here!"

"*What?*" Astounded, Jackson sprang to his feet.

"Major Villeré was at his father's house when he saw the British arrive and capture a picket there. Fortunately he was able to mount a horse and escape by leaping a fence—followed by a volley of musketry which luckily did not injure him. He rode hard to bring the news here."

"Damn and blast them to hell!" swore Jackson.

But he was thinking rapidly. The British had surprised him, no question of that. But how did they come without warning to Villeré's plantation? It made his gray thatch bristle.

He had predicted that the enemy would seek the Gentilly flats for a battleground. He had ordered every possible route to that plain guarded. Yet in some manner they had made their way over the morasses from Lake Borgne.

Rather than spending time in seeking answers to enigmas or in unprofitable self-blame, his instinct was to act. Someone had blundered but plans already were forming in his head.

"By the Eternal!" he cried. "They'll not sleep on our soil!"

To the others, in that moment of confusion, he seemed tinged with a desperate fatalism, refusing to concede even the possibility of defeat in spite of being thus outmaneuvered so early in the game.

His orders began to rap out, and orderlies scurried as he touched off an explosion of human energy that transcended all ordinary considerations. Those men in the bars and bagnios must be gathered by the provosts and sent to their commands. Troops camped north of the city must march to its south. The Creole militia must be alerted. Coffee, Carroll, and Donelson, each with separate instructions, left, to gallop to their respective stations.

Alone with Reid, Jackson had a new idea, a moment of inspiration. "The ships!" he exclaimed. "The *Louisiana* and the *Carolina*! I have a plan for them. Take an order for Captain Henly of the *Carolina* and one for Commodore Patterson, and see that they're expedited as fast as boats can row them!"

He dictated the orders. Half an hour later he and Reid left the house and mounted. They had done everything that could be done up to this point. The larger arena now lay before them.

In the city, where at first there was a new panic at word of the British arrival, people had quieted as American troops began marching through the streets. Some of the soldiers were Creoles, some regulars, but most were hickory-hard hunters from the forests of Tennessee.

Evening was falling when Jackson and his aide reached the downstream limits of the town. Threatening clouds darkened the sky and cast an early gloom soon deepened by a fog which began to creep across the cane stubble of the plain and out over the river.

They reached the road which ran along the top of the levee, and in a moment a group of horsemen showed dimly ahead.

"General Humbert!" exclaimed Jackson. "Take your men down the left of the levee, and form them with the regulars at the De la Ronde plantation."

"*Oui, Général!*" Humbert saluted, gathered up his escort, and rode down the escarpment of the levee and off into the night.

Jackson gazed anxiously out across the river toward the *Carolina*. Darkness and the thickening mist made visibility difficult but he thought he could make out men clambering up the rigging. Captain Robert Henly, a good officer who had commanded a brig in McDonough's victory on Lake Champlain, evidently was acting on the orders Reid had dispatched to him. Presently the little ship cast off and began drifting slowly down the current into the deepening darkness.

"Henly's to drop down abreast of the enemy position and open fire at seven-thirty," said Jackson. "I'll attack half an hour later."

He and Reid swung their horses aside, as both regiments of regulars tramped down the levee. Dim ranks of Carroll's Tennessee Rifles would extend the left of this advance, and far out across the plain, invisible in the darkness, Coffee presumably was riding with his five hundred horsemen and special orders.

On the field Jackson computed that he had a few more than two thousand men. That was it, and it was all. With these, some of whom hardly understood orders and were almost unacquainted with their commanders, he was undertaking the most difficult of all military actions, a *night* attack against an enemy of superior force and discipline.

Literally, he must feel for his foe in the darkness and fog. All the dangers and problems of night battle in which irregular troops are engaged, swept through his mind. Wrong orders, wrong directions taken in the gloom, fears easily accentuated into panics among raw troops in the darkness—the possibilities of disaster were infinite.

But the gaunt, gray man, sitting his horse in the darkness on the levee road, thought only of success. And in some manner that night he seemed to infuse his own implacable determination into his poor makeshift army.

2

The *Carolina's* dim bulk disappeared in the night fog, and Jackson rode forward with Reid to where the troops had taken position behind a row of oak trees on the De la Ronde plantation. The General could hear the hoarse growl of men talking together, and his pulse beat faster with excitement.

"Isn't it almost time, John?" he asked, anxiously staring off through the darkness. Reid rode over to the house, where light from a window allowed him to see the face of his watch.

"It's just seven-thirty, sir," he said, cantering back.

At the words a sudden great red glow appeared for an instant in the night fog downstream, and faded. It was followed by a rolling thunder and an echo.

"Right on the minute!" exclaimed Jackson. "I knew I could depend on Henly! He's loosed a broadside of grape fair in the middle of the British camp!"

Orders began to sound up and down the line of troops, as by platoons the soldiers moved forward in the darkness across the stubbled field. Downstream another red belch showed that the *Carolina* had got her guns into action again.

Jackson was chafing with impatience. After a few moments he could no longer resist his nervous anxiety and spurred forward, followed by his aide.

Far out on the left, winking flashes were followed by a stuttering of rifle shots.

"Coffee's engaged!" cried the General. "That old Indian fighter knows every trick of taking advantage of darkness and cover! So far, everything's going beautifully."

Just ahead red pencils of fire, a half volley, burst out.

There was cursing in many voices, and someone howled: "Them milishy is shootin' into us!"

From its position he judged the cry came from the Seventh Infantry, and he galloped his horse over to the militia.

"Hold your fire, damn you, until you're sure where you're aiming!" he yelled in rage and excitement.

"*Oui, mon Général!*" came a reply from the darkness.

So it was the Creole militia. He cursed them roundly and sulphureously.

"*Oui, mon Général!*" came the reply again. It had the sound of good humor and an understanding of the commander's irascibility.

Jackson checked his swearing and half grinned. No use to scold these men. He tried a little of his broken French.

"*En avant—mes enfants——*"

It delighted the Creoles. A voice sang out:

"*Vive—Ol' Heeckoree!*"

He could hear, rather than see, the militia sweep forward to form a line in the darkness with the regulars. The men went slower now, not firing but looking for enemies.

Again and again the ship downstream blasted the shore. By Coffee's rifle flashes Jackson calculated that the mounted command, after riding far out to the left, was making a rapid sweeping movement toward the river.

"The *Carolina's* justified herself!" he exclaimed. "The British are likely taking refuge behind the levee to escape those broadsides—and Coffee's closing in on them like a door on its hinges!"

For a moment he even experienced a wild hope that he might smash the enemy here and now, by a single blow.

But immediately he knew the impossibility of that. Steady British troops would not panic or be routed easily. He would not smash them this time, but at least he hoped to teach them a lesson.

"Look at that!" cried Reid.

The *Carolina* had ceased fire, because of the danger of hitting the advancing Americans, and now a long flare of flame with a crashing explosion of sound came from the British position. Just as Jackson thought. Already the enemy had taken formation, and that first volley was fired with the disciplined precision of veterans.

Now the advancing Americans began to shoot back, aiming at the gun flashes of the British. The rising roar of musketry showed that Jackson's main body along the river was at last heavily engaged.

Shouts and the clatter of bounding wheels from the rear. Two pieces of artillery—guns he had brought up from Mobile—came up behind galloping teams of horses.

"Unlimber here!" Jackson shouted, riding over and indicating the height of the levee.

Gunners scrambled to obey. Almost incredibly soon the first flashes and thundering reports of the cannon added to the fiery confusion of the night.

But the artillery gave the British an objective for attack. Very soon Jackson was aware, solely by the wavering and retreating of the continual gun flashes of his men ahead of him in the darkness, that his lines were falling back.

He spurred forward, his voice rising high: "Save the guns!"

To him it was a point of honor, and his near presence was felt by the soldiers. The retreat slowed, ceased. He heard a French shout:

"*A la bayonette!*"

The Creoles were doing better than he had ever thought, and now the American lines moved forward again, the regulars driving along the levee.

A thousand yards out on the night-shrouded plain, the flickering of Coffee's rifle flashes showed that he was still advancing in his encircling drive toward the British camp.

"The firing on our immediate front seems heavier," said Reid.

"The enemy's being reinforced during the progress of the battle," Jackson exclaimed. "Ride over to the left, John, and find Billy Carroll. Tell him not to be drawn in too far. We've given the British a taste of fire. Maybe it will hold them for a while."

3

At midnight, after five hours of fighting, Coffee appeared with his men. He had dismounted them and made that entire sweeping attack on foot.

"The boys could shoot a lot better on the ground," he explained half apologetically to his chief.

"What did you do with the horses?" asked Jackson.

"Sent 'em back with a guard."

"Good," approved the General.

"We cut through the British camp and brought in some prisoners," Coffee continued. "I never saw anything like it. Couldn't tell a friend from a foe. We just cut down on anybody in front of us."

Young Jack Donelson, who had been with Coffee's advance, came up to where Jackson and Coffee were talking, and saluted his uncle.

"We got to their commander's headquarters," he said, trying hard not to show his elation and excitement. "I heard the enemy shouting they were General Coffee's men—having somehow learned the general's name. But in ten steps they ordered us for damned rebels to lay down our arms. I answered them to be damned and ordered my men to fire right into the thick of them."

It was the boy's first taste of battle and Jackson was pleased with him. "You'll do, son," he said.

But it was high time he withdrew his men. This could be an operation even more difficult than advancing in the darkness.

Donelson, Reid, and others went riding off to find detachment commanders and give them the General's orders. In all that night's operations, nothing perhaps so well showed the army's confidence in its leader as the steady manner in which it fell back.

The British did not pursue. They had been roughly handled by the *Carolina's* broadsides and the surprise attack. Firing gradually died down, until it ceased entirely and the field was black and quiet.

Dawn found Jackson at the Rodriguez Canal, an abandoned dry

waterway, once used as a millrace but now shallow and grass-grown. Just behind it was a large house with a group of smaller buildings about it.

"The Macarte house," Major Villeré told him.

Jackson nodded. To Coffee he said, "Keep some of your horsemen out there on the plain to watch the enemy. As the retreating units reach this place, halt them here. I'll await the pleasure of the British at this point."

To nobody did he communicate fully his intentions; but to himself they were as sharp and keen as a sword blade.

He would fight the British here below New Orleans. If driven back he would fight in New Orleans itself—street to street, house to house. If beaten there he would fight above New Orleans—fight as long as he had a man left, or life was in him.

Chapter Eleven

*If I thought the hair on my head knew
my thoughts on that subject, I'd cut it off
and burn it!*

ANDREW JACKSON

1

Jackson had not yet slept. It was late afternoon, and he stood watching the fury of activity that went forward, as his men labored at fortifying the Rodriguez Canal position which he had chosen. Clear across the plain, from the cypress woods on the left to the river on the right, lay the raw weal of fresh soil, torn up to make the trench and the embankment in front of it; and the trench was growing deeper every hour.

But a continuous feeling of urgency and apprehension surged in him. If the British were alert enough to strike before he was prepared for them, he would be hard put to it to know how to fight them.

The gaunt, gray commander spared neither himself nor others in this race against time. Every tool that could aid in making entrenchments which could be found in New Orleans had been requisitioned. He had organized a supply-wagon train to bring up rations and ammunition and other necessaries to this vital point.

There had been difficulties among the men. Soft-handed sons of rich planters, for example, while willing enough to march into battle, considered plying a shovel in the mud as demeaning.

For this he had an answer. Down the line went a warning:

Any man who ceases work without orders will be summarily dealt with under the provisions of the laws governing mutiny.

The sons of planters considered. Laws governing mutiny . . . that meant the firing squad. Something about the grim figure of the General persuaded them that he meant exactly what he said. So the sons of planters returned to their toil, side by side with American hunters, bayou pirates, and Negro slaves, a leveling of classes very strange to New Orleans gentry, and productive of stiff backs and blisters on the palms.

When Jackson rode his horse along the earthwork, his mere presence seemed to infuse new vigor and activity into his trench diggers. By sheer will power he threw off not only his own weariness but his chronic illnesses, and his nervous, pulsating energy infected others.

Uncomplicated in his thinking, he knew only his great single-minded purpose, to defeat the enemy before him. And he did not depend on coercion to keep his men at it; he knew far better than that how to handle soldiers.

He moved among them, sometimes joking with them, sometimes scolding them, sometimes praising them, sometimes beguiling them. One look from his gaunt visage was enough to make a man tingle. Approval from him became a matter for rivalry. So the men toiled and sweated in the muddy trench not only willingly but even with enthusiasm, carried forward by his tenacity and a sort of electric magnetism of which he himself may not have been entirely conscious.

In the middle of the morning General Humbert, vast mustachios newly waxed, ventured to compliment him.

"My congratulations, *mon Général*," he said, in an expansive manner that told of recent studious attention to the bottle. "Do you know, sir, that in last night's action you achieved something so rare in history that I do not know a name for it?"

"No name? How do you mean?" asked Jackson.

"Surprised by the enemy, you managed to surprise the surprisers themselves. In fencing, it perhaps most nearly resembles the *riposte*— yet it is not that, either, for the *riposte* is a return thrust after the parry of a thrust expected and taken into account. You by no means expected the enemy's pass. Yet your return thrust was a clean *touché*. And by night with green troops! *Quelle audace!*"

Slightly tipsy Humbert was, but he was an old soldier and a shrewd one, who had seen war in the grand manner, and the praise warmed Jackson. Nevertheless he deprecated it:

"A risk had to be taken, General," he said. "And we must remember that a night operation is, after all, the one department of tactics in which the undisciplined man has an equal chance with the trained soldier."

"You are far too modest, General. You gave the enemy the sort of sharp reverse that blunts any immediate forward movement."

"Pray that is so." Jackson gazed across the plain toward the distant enemy camp. "We need every minute of time to prepare for them." Then, half-musing, "But the British *do* seem to be nursing their wounds this morning."

Yet nobody, not even Humbert, knew the heavy problems confronting him: problems of logistics, and personnel, and diplomacy, as well as strategy. First and most important, he must weld this "army" of his into a real fighting force, actually, here on the very field of battle. And its elements were as motley as had ever been assembled—Creole aristocrats, backwoods hunters, two companies of free Negroes from Santo Domingo, pirates, French refugees, sailors of a dozen nationalities from the water front, American regulars, even a contingent of Choctaw warriors. They spoke a babel of different tongues, and many of them did not even possess the concept of patriotism to spur them.

In that day of hard labor on the entrenchments, as the tall, thin man with the whitening hair and compelling blue eyes went up and down the works, the men grew to know him, to speculate on him, to take pride in him. In that day—a mighty tribute to him—the strange material became fused into an army, which, whatever its differences, was bound to Andrew Jackson by a fierce personal loyalty not often won by any man. Even those who cared not a snap of their fingers for the flag under which they fought, became eager to show their devotion to the General in battle.

Nightfall came. The British during the day had made no movement, and already a considerable rampart had been raised behind the Rodriguez Canal.

At dark Jackson listened to casualty reports. Twenty-four of his men had been killed and one hundred and fifteen wounded or missing as a result of the night fight. But it was certain that the enemy had suffered more heavily; and there was a disconsolate band of prisoners, sixty-four all told, which had been lapped in by Coffee's circling movement. He questioned some of these.

The British army reached the Plain of Gentilly, he was informed, by way of the Bayou Bienvenue, where an American picket was expertly captured, forestalling any alarm. It was a brilliant movement, as Jackson mentally conceded.

Further: four of the British regiments were of the army that defeated the Americans at Bladensburg, Maryland, burned the Capitol at Washington, and looted Alexandria. The rest, almost all, were battle-tested veterans from Wellington's Peninsular forces, direct from victories over Napoleon's armies in Spain.

The name of one regiment Jackson noted with especial interest: the Ninety-third, called the Sutherland Highlanders. A famous regiment. It was sure to fight like the Scots always fought, with wild and deadly fervor. Jackson was of Scottish blood himself.

He learned something else: Major General John Keane commanded the enemy during the night battle, but he was being superseded by a still more formidable figure, Major General Sir Edward Pakenham, brother-in-law of the famous Duke of Wellington, a notable soldier. Pakenham was the hero of the great British victory over the French at Salamanca, Spain, and his veterans of Salamanca were with him now.

That night, to forestall wild rumors which might affect morale, Jackson made the name of the renowned British general a matter of official announcement. And he added something else he had culled from the prisoners: the British sneered at the Americans as *Dirty Shirts*.

A shrewd touch. Small things sometimes outweigh important ones. The "Dirty Shirt" gibe had enough truth in it to gall the army so that it forgot to be awed by the reputation of General Pakenham.

Just behind the growing entrenchments stood the house of Augustin Macarte, a planter—white-pillared, pleasant, with a railed gallery running around it at the second floor. The family was alarmed and with good reason.

Hat in hand, Major Reid bowed at the door.

"A battle is certain to be fought here," he told them. "It will be most perilous to remain in the vicinity. An unhappy situation for you, which I deeply regret, but the fortunes of war. General Jackson has provided wagons to convey your effects, and carriages for yourselves, if you desire to withdraw to a place which may be more safe——"

Reid's tact was rewarded. The Macartes left in a small disconsolate caravan, and the house became the headquarters of the commanding general.

In the darkness of night, about the time for the night tattoo, Jackson stood on the gallery gazing out across the black plain. A mile and a half away he could see glowing spots, the campfires of the enemy.

All at once there was a twinkling of sharp flashes: rifle fire.

He nodded, and turned into the house.

That was a continuation of his night tactics; an old Indian trick. Tennessee riflemen had been told off to creep forward in the darkness and open fire on the British camp.

One enemy soldier was killed near a campfire by the night fusillade. Drums rattled and troops hurriedly formed columns, expecting another full-scale attack in the darkness.

But the Tennesseeans had slipped off somewhere in the gloom.

The British columns were recalled, the men returned to their bivouacs. But hardly had tranquillity been restored when another volley of rifle shots lashed out from the black plain.

Again the weary troops formed ranks. Again no enemy could be discovered.

Over and over these maddening gadfly tactics were to be repeated that night and in the nights following. There was no way in which the British could find their tormentors, and even when they did not form ranks they could not sleep. Sentinels were shot at their posts; men found it dangerous to sit near a fire, even to light a pipe.

Andrew Jackson was keeping his promise that the British would get precious little sleep on American soil.

2

All that night of Christmas Eve the work on the entrenchments continued, one rank of weary men sleeping while another toiled.

Christmas morning dawned, crisp and frosty, and Jackson, for the second successive night, had not slept. His eyelids felt as if lined with gravel and his thin body sagged at times, but his inexorable will kept him at the task of constant supervision even when it seemed he could not take a single step farther.

An elegant figure strolled up to the headquarters.

"Laffite!" exclaimed Jackson.

From beneath his thin dark mustache the pirate's teeth flashed in a smile.

"*Joyeux Noël*," he said. Then, "General, if one might make a suggestion——"

"Very well."

"Many cotton bales are stacked on the wharfs of New Orleans. They would form good emplacements for your cannon and strengthen this mud rampart."

"Hum. Thanks," said Jackson. "Please, Captain Laffite, step into my headquarters."

Within he poured the pirate a glass of wine and took one himself.

"The claret is excellent," said Laffite, tasting it.

"It should be," said the General. "It's from your own cellars."

"So I suspected. A fine Bordeaux. I took it from a Spanish ship—it was intended for the viceroy of Mexico."

"It was confiscated—before we became comrades in arms."

Again the flashing Laffite smile. "Permit me to compliment you, General, on your good taste. And I drink to your sentiment—comrades in arms."

He sauntered out, and rode away to the station which Jackson had assigned him—with his company of Baratarians, expert bayou men every one, to watch the northern approaches of the city.

That day carts trundled up from the wharfs carrying bales of cotton with which the men labored to strengthen the rampart.

And still the British remained in their camp.

3

Dawn of December 27. Jackson, sleeping in his clothes, exhausted after three nights without closing his eyes, was almost propelled out of his bed in an upper room of the Macarte house by an immense thunder that fairly shook the building.

Knuckling his eyes, he hurried to a window. On a table lay an old battered telescope. He snatched it up and clapped it to his eye.

For once the landscape was not fogbound. All too clearly he could see what was happening. In the night Pakenham had mounted a battery of heavy naval guns near the levee, and in the river, anchored and becalmed, unable to return to her berth upstream because of lack of any wind, lay the *Carolina*.

The naval guns were blasting at her. Their first salvo sent geysers of yellow water leaping up all about her.

"Hell's blood and bones!" swore Jackson bitterly.

He had further plans for the *Carolina* and for her consort, the *Louisiana*.

But at the second discharge from the battery, debris flew from the little ship. A moment later a jagged hole appeared in her side and her foremast sagged. As the barrage continued, Jackson saw flames licking up her rigging.

No way to help her. Teeth set, he watched. On the side of the ship opposite from the battery two boats were taking off such of the crew as could escape.

None too soon.

A vast quaking explosion. The brave little *Carolina* was gone.

A moment before she had been there. In a single instant she no longer existed, blown to bits by her own magazine which the fire had reached, her flaming fragments splashed the river from bank to bank.

Toward the far shore her two boats rowed frantically for safety. They might have gone more leisurely. The British guns were after bigger game.

The *Louisiana*, though farther upstream, also was in range of the naval battery. Sudden leaping splashes appeared about her.

Patterson, her commander, was taking the only possible means of saving her. While the *Carolina* was meeting her fate, he put out boats with tow lines. In them men tugged desperately upstream with their oars.

Almost sick at heart Jackson watched the struggle in which he could take no part. If the *Louisiana* were lost, a key part of his whole plan would go with her.

In the boats the coxswains were urging their crews to greater efforts. The men at the oars had to combat not only the river current but their vessel's own sluggish inertia.

He could see the coxswains standing in the stern sheets, bending tensely forward, could almost hear them shout cadence to the oarsmen. Slowly the *Louisiana* began to gain a little headway. But now spouts of yellow water were all about her.

Once he saw splinters fly up from her hull. Then a great splash seemed to obliterate one of the towing boats. But a moment later he drew a deep breath. The boat was still there, its crew putting every ounce of their strength into the oars.

A slight breeze stirred the sails which Patterson had shaken out in hope of just such a contingency. Though a ragged hole suddenly appeared in one of them, the sails swelled, the *Louisiana* moved more easily, drew near the American lines.

The British battery, with the range grown too great, ceased fire. Patterson had saved his ship. Though she had shot holes in her sides and her deck was ripped up, she could still fight.

Jackson nodded in relief. Then he put down his telescope, washed his face in a basin of cold water, and drew on his coat—a gingerly process still, for though he no longer wore a sling his shoulder pained him at any twist.

As he started down the stairs, he heard from the outside cries of surprise or alarm.

Down the steps he fairly ran, burst out of the house, and stepped clear of it to look toward the enemy position.

From the distance a long shower of sparks soared towering toward the sky, then plunged downward. There was a shocking explosion fifty yards in front of the parapet.

Men were calling to each other:

"That ain't no shell!"

"What in hell them people doin'?"

Another missile rose and plunged downward, this time detonating heavily far behind the rampart.

"I know goddam well I don't like this," wailed a voice, high-pitched with alarm.

Jackson walked along the top of the trench looking down at the men.

"Congreve rockets, boys," he said. "Pakenham may set store by them, but I don't. Keep on working. Nobody gets hurt by 'em, except maybe it's an accident!"

Never before this moment had he seen the rockets, a new instrument of war, though he had heard of them. But his smiling confidence re-

stored the confidence of his men. They began to notice that the rockets
—if that was what the beastly things were—did appear to be highly inac-
curate. As they went back to work in the entrenchment, they were even
able to give derisive cheers as each of the recurring missiles fell with a
harmless explosion.

"Lot of smoke an' racket, but no damage," they told each other.

Jackson returned to the house and mounted his horse. The rocket
bombardment might be a prelude to something. About midway along
the line he saw Colonel William Carroll, cold-eyed and collected as
usual, sitting his mount.

"There they come, now, General," said Carroll.

Jackson already had seen. From the British camp two columns of
red coats and white breeches, glittering with bayonets, were advancing
across the cane stubble.

The great test at last? And he was hardly ready.

In the trench a musket banged.

"Stop that!" he exclaimed. "Pass the word up and down the line,
that no man is to fire until the command is given. Why, the enemy's way
beyond even long-rifle range!"

The British seemed to be sending their heavier column against the
American right, at the river flank. There was a wide gap between this
column, and the one on the extreme left of the American position, which
advanced close to the cypress woods on that side. Both maneuvers bore
out Jackson's earlier prediction that these troops preferred level and
open ground for their operations.

A courier sped away toward the position occupied by General Coffee's
dismounted riflemen and Indians where the trench plunged into the
woods, bending back in the swampy ground there. For Coffee, Jackson
had some new instructions.

A great cottony cloud of smoke, with a crashing report, rose as the
first of the old rusty cannon Jackson had managed to gather, fired. The
scarlet columns advanced steadily.

The General glanced over toward where the *Louisiana* lay, anchored
in the river a little upstream from the Macarte place. It would soon be
her turn now.

One after another his pieces of artillery, most heavily massed on the
right, let go.

Then the *Louisiana's* broadside blasted out, sending a storm of grape
into the head of the nearer, heavier column.

Red coats lay scattered on the earth, but the British flattened out from
column into a wide battle front and continued to advance.

At Jackson's elbow appeared a plump, pink-faced man in broadcloth
and a beaver hat, riding a sweating roan horse.

"General!" he exclaimed excitedly.

"What is it?" snapped Jackson without taking his eyes off the ad-

vancing enemy. He knew the man—Abner Duncan, a busybody New
Orleans lawyer, always endeavoring to push into things.

"I bear a message from Governor Claiborne!"

"What does Claiborne want now? I hope you see that I'm a little
occupied!"

"Sir, the state assembly is about to surrender the city to the enemy!"

That brought Jackson's immediate and intense attention.

"I don't believe it!" he exclaimed.

"The governor expects orders what to do!" said Duncan.

"Tell him to make strict inquiries, and if they persist, blow them all
to hell!"

Jackson swung his horse away, and galloped along the works toward
his left, where the battle was growing hotter. Duncan, he considered,
was a nuisance with his silly twaddle while fighting was in progress.

From the cypress woods, near which the British far column was advancing, came a sudden spiteful crackle of rifles. Scarlet figures were
down.

"Good, by God!" he said.

Coffee was following orders. His men, expert forest fighters, must be
flitting among the trees there, shooting to kill.

The British array near the woods, like the river column, came to a
halt and began to extend its line laterally.

4

Bernard de Marigny de Mandeville was twenty-nine, darkly handsome,
and wealthy. He was New Orleans' foremost elegant; spoke both French
and English but preferred French; was known in the salons of both
Paris and London; possessed all the graces of conduct and conversation;
and as leader of the Louisiana assembly had thus far kept that body
from being anything but Creole in its make-up and interests.

This morning Marigny paced the floor of his library, feverish with indecision and anger. He had received two reports that were enough to
unsettle any man.

First a rumor: "General Jackson has said that he will follow the example of the Russians at Moscow and consign New Orleans to the
flames rather than see its rich stores fall into the hands of the British."

New Orleans in flames? A holocaust to sweep away his city, his home,
his property, the property and homes of all his friends? Incredible! And
yet—that madman Jackson . . .

Almost on the heels of this came word that was more than mere
rumor: Governor Claiborne had ordered the doors of the assembly hall
locked.

The furious Creole leader made up his mind. He left his house and called for a horse. Within a few minutes he was galloping out toward the battlefield, from which the thunder of artillery could be heard clearly in the city.

As he approached the battle line he could see its extent by the clouds of powder smoke; and the heavy thunder of big guns was almost deafening. Out on the river a ship-of-war was slamming broadside after broadside toward some target on the shore.

Marigny was a man of resolution. He was willing to undergo whatever risks the battle might offer, and he brought his snorting horse to the rear of the Macarte house, where he understood General Jackson made his headquarters.

As he swung out of the saddle and began to fasten his sidling, panic-stricken horse to a tree there, he saw a man hurrying across the back patio carrying a bucket from which water splashed in his haste.

"Where is General Jackson?" he asked.

The man spat. "Dunno. Ain't hyar," he said over his shoulder, and hurried on.

The door at the rear of the house stood open, and Marigny entered. Nobody there. The family was gone—evicted by this hellish barbarism of war. He looked about at the furniture, disheveled and overturned, and the floors from which the carpets had been torn up—ripped to pieces for cannon wadding, he presumed.

Raging inwardly at this desecration, he climbed the stairs to the upper floor. A disheveled bed there, and a table on which lay an old brass telescope. He seized the telescope and gazed out on the field.

Immediately in front of the house a couple of cannon let loose, quivering the boards under his feet with their thunder. Up and down the line other big guns crashed.

Through the smoke cloud Marigny made out a line of red near the river, halting, apparently confused. Another, near the woods to his left, also seemed to be hesitating.

In midstream the ship still blasted deafeningly.

He glanced below him. In the deep trench which ran across the field from the river to the woods, men stood or sat idle, guns leaning against the parapet walls, with here and there a watcher on the fire step, craning his neck and screwing his eyes toward the enemy. Muddy and torn as they were, Marigny recognized the uniforms of some of the New Orleans companies, and he wondered at their apparent lack of excitement.

Then Jackson came leaping up the stairs, two steps at a time.

"Ha! Senator Marigny!" he exclaimed.

Marigny laid down the telescope and turned quickly.

"General Jackson," he said without any preamble, "I wish to know your reasons for closing the assembly."

Jackson raked his visitor with a furious eye. "Because, sir, I understand your damned assembly has a notion to take things into its own hands and offer surrender to the enemy! That, sir, is *treason!* I'll have you to understand that New Orleans is under martial law! And by God, sir, I intend to enforce it! If it takes some hangings to do it, sir! Nobody will make traitorous advances to the British while I'm here to prevent it!"

The General's wrath, leaping out like a sudden searing flame, almost took the breath of Marigny. The Creole ordinarily was himself inclined to the hot retort, but it seemed highly politic now to speak calmly.

"You are misinformed, sir," he said in a moderate voice. "The assembly has taken no such action. My word of honor on that."

"Well, then?" Jackson controlled his ire, his voice became less strenuous.

"One question, General, from the assembly. What are your plans in case this battle goes against you?" said Marigny.

In an instant the remarkable individual he addressed went from fire to ice. Jackson's eyes grew as chill and gray as iron filings.

"If I thought the hair on my head knew my thoughts on that subject, sir, I'd cut it off and burn it!" he said.

Marigny stood silent.

"Return to your honorable body," continued the General, in a voice of deadly meaning. "Say to them for me, that if I'm so unfortunate as to be beaten from these lines and compelled to retreat through New Orleans, they'll have a very warm session!"

To Marigny, almost aghast, it seemed a confirmation of the very rumor he had heard earlier. But in the presence of this overpowering personality, the elegant Creole again was at a loss for words.

Jackson seized the telescope and swept the field.

"Look there, sir!" he cried. "Go back and tell the city that the British are beaten—and for the second time!"

Marigny did not need the telescope he offered. With his unaided eyes he could see that both scarlet columns were in retreat. A few sprawled bodies lay on the ground near the levee; and some men crouched in ditches or behind ruined buildings, but these soon fled.

The Creole looked at the gray-haired soldier with ungrudging admiration.

"General, my compliments," he said.

With his own eyes he had seen the supposedly invincible British driven back. He would return to New Orleans with a story of victory.

5

But Jackson had no false illusions.

"They were just feeling us out," he told John Coffee, when the rough old giant came riding up to headquarters from his post far out on the left. "Good move by you, John, sending those riflemen into the woods. Teach 'em a lesson. But the enemy's major effort's still to come. I hope, and believe, that he's learned something useful—useful to us, that is."

Together they rode to inspect the defense from end to end.

On the extreme right was a redoubt, defended by two companies of the Seventh. Next came the rest of the Seventh, and the uniformed companies of New Orleans, under the command of General Humbert. Two companies of Dominican free Negroes followed, under Captains Lacoste and Daquin. The Forty-fourth Infantry, a steady regiment of regulars, occupied the center of the line. But the entire left half of the works, clear to the cypress woods, was held by the backwoods riflemen of Carroll and Coffee.

Jackson's thirteen precious cannon received especial notice. Two on the extreme right were Captain Humphrey's army fieldpieces which had figured in the night battle. A few yards farther, two naval guns peered through their embrasures. A freckled young man in a navy undress uniform saluted crisply. He was Lieutenant Henly, with some of his crew who escaped from the lost *Carolina*.

"How is it, being a sailor on land?" asked the General cheerily.

"At least it simplifies some gunnery problems," said Henly. "Just let me get these two pieces trained on the people who sank my ship, sir!"

"The *Carolina* has paid for herself already," said Jackson as he and Coffee rode on.

Another pair of guns, one of them a huge, old-fashioned thirty-two pounder. Their crews, red-shirted and smoking long twisted cigars with the air of desperadoes, were making coffee.

Jackson halted his horse on the bank above. "That smells like better coffee than we can get," he said with a twinkle. "Smuggle it?"

A short, rotund figure rose by the fire, a red kerchief about his head, the sleeves of his red shirt rolled above his elbows. He was Dominique You, one of Laffite's pirate captains, reputed to be the best of the Baratarian gunners.

"Mebbe so, General," he grinned, and passed up a cup to his commander and one to Coffee. They sipped the scalding black liquid.

"I wish I had fifty guns like yours in the butts," Jackson said, "and five hundred such devils behind them."

The inspection continued, the commander exchanging a pleasant word here and there, sometimes advising, sometimes praising. At one of the farther guns a harsh-faced veteran in a fore-and-aft hat stood heels together saluting palm out. Jackson returned the salute with equal courtesy. The man was General Flaugeac, who had commanded a division under Napoleon in the Egyptian campaign. An old artillerist, he had volunteered to serve in this battery to be near his beloved guns. Jackson treated him as a respected equal.

"Come dine at my mess, John," he said as he and Coffee turned back to headquarters. "The boys found a loose shoat wandering in the military purlieus of this army and they sent over a pork roast. I also have some of that Laffite claret."

That night he and his friend talked until late. At the end Coffee spoke a word of caution against overweariness.

"You may be Old Hickory," he said, "but I've seen hickory bend, yes, and break. It would be most powerful sad for people who hold you in affection——"

"A man lives his span, and sometimes the span is shortened by war," replied Jackson with odd, slow reflectiveness. "As for mine, it's unimportant compared to defeating the enemy."

After a pause, he added: "Man is the only animal willing to fight and die for an idea. The idea we're fighting for is liberty and country. Time and circumstances so far have favored us. Our men have gained confidence. They're beginning to believe they can beat the British."

"The trench and embankment help," observed Coffee.

Jackson turned on him a slow smile. "Self-preservation is not a bad foundation for victory," he said. "My men will fight from cover; the British must attack in the open. I care not how disciplined a man is, he does not fight for the love of fighting; he fights to win. The will to fight wanes when victory seems snatched from his grasp. It is our task to break the spirit of our foes. Mere unimaginative professionalism, John, would never accomplish that, for Pakenham has every possible advantage of numbers, battle training, ordnance, and discipline, all working for him."

Coffee stared at him. This man already had displayed fabulous audacity in an age of formal and calculated warfare, and had somehow by sheer power of personality made a fighting machine out of the incoherent elements he could gather. What would he do next?

"Against my opponent's advantages," went on Jackson slowly, "I can oppose only one thing in our favor: my soldiers know how to shoot. They do not volley blindly. Each time they pull a trigger they aim to hit a mark. I must use that one military asset to its best advantage when the enemy comes again—and he will come, a-roaring, next time!"

When Coffee rode back to his own headquarters that night, Jackson was still sitting, chin in hand, looking broodingly into the flames of the fireplace in the Macarte house while his body servant cleared away the remains of their supper.

Chapter Twelve

Tell 'em to cut the V!

ANDREW JACKSON

1

That night of January 6, in the very dawn of the new year of 1815, Major General Sir Edward Pakenham entertained as his guest a gray-haired, weather-beaten man, in his headquarters at the Villeré house, which stood some distance behind the British camp beside the Mississippi River. The garb of the visitor, donned for the muddy journey through the swamps from Lake Borgne, singularly differed from his usual splendid uniform of blue, white, and gold.

Vice-Admiral Sir Alexander Cochrane, commander of the British fleet, as hard-bitten a sea dog as the King's Navy boasted, already had made the eastern seaboard of America feel his wrath. Now he was in serious, even angry conversation with Pakenham, his host.

"With respect, sir," the general was saying, "the position occupied by the enemy is very strong."

"For British troops to carry? I'm astonished to hear such words from you, Sir Edward," retorted the admiral.

"My demonstration in force, the twenty-seventh of last month, revealed that the Americans are very cunningly entrenched, with some artillery, and a ship on the river for enfilading fire——"

"Mud ramparts!" interrupted Cochrane testily. "And behind them a chaw-bacon rabble!"

Pakenham slowly reddened at the sneering tone.

"What in God's name do you propose to do?" insisted the admiral.

"The position our force occupies here was injudiciously chosen," said the general. "Mind, I do not criticize Keane, who selected it. He was, as you know, attacked that very night and had tuck-and-go of it. Say what you will of them, the Americans have shown themselves nimble at night fighting, and have harassed us continuously. I have a casualty list of over three hundred——"

"Who spoke of night fighting?" broke in Cochrane.

"I referred, sir, only to *their* attacks. As for ourselves, we should be better off at almost any other point but this. I have even considered a withdrawal and new landing——"

"In the face of those miserable Dirty Shirts?" The admiral's scorn was open. "Why, your army, sir, should blast them off the face of the earth!"

"It might take more doing than you surmise, sir."

Cochrane gave Pakenham a bitter, even contemptuous look.

"If you are unwilling to take the risk, Sir Edward," he said, "perhaps I can bring over a few stout lads from my ship's crews to take that rampart of mud." And then he added, sneeringly, "Your soldiers might then make themselves useful bringing up the baggage."

Pakenham leaped angrily to his feet. Nobody had ever in his life accused him of cowardice, and this slur, undeserved as it was, made him furious. Had not Cochrane outranked him, there might have been a glass of wine in the face.

When he spoke, his voice shook with passion. "Sir Alexander," he said, "my soldiers need nobody to defend their courage, and this very closely touches my personal honor. We will assault that position—tomorrow. Or at the very latest, the day following!"

2

Andrew Jackson had hardly slept at all, and he had been awake continuously since three o'clock that morning of January 8. It was Sunday and in New Orleans the faithful were attending early mass.

Daylight had come at last, but a fog hung over the field, and from his lookout in the Macarte house he could make out nothing of the enemy. Nevertheless, he had been aware throughout the night of the sound of sledge hammers from the direction of the British lines—new artillery batteries being emplaced, very probably.

Just an hour ago a disturbing report had come from Commodore Patterson that men were crossing the river in boats at a point below where the *Louisiana* lay. That might mean a flank attack on the newly built "Kentucky Bastion," over on the far side of the Mississippi.

Those Kentuckians! He had looked forward most hopefully to their coming, but when they arrived two days before they were almost unarmed.

"I can't believe it!" he exclaimed in bitter disappointment when this was first reported to him. "I never, in my whole life, saw a Kentuckian without a pack of cards and a bottle of whiskey and a gun!"

But it was true. Of the twenty-three hundred men in the contingent, only seven hundred carried firearms. The others were enlisted militia who looked to the government to supply them with weapons—and the government, with its customary dilatoriness, had failed to do so.

Jackson expressed his opinion of the government and all politicians, in an eloquent, sardonic, searing, blasphemous condemnation such as only his tongue could fashion.

"I'll confront them with this!" he finished. "On my honor, I will! Some day I'll make those damned lily-livered, pusillanimous, time-serving, treasonable, cock-a-hoop sons of bitches in Washington sweat for this, or my name isn't Andrew Jackson!"

But after he thus expressed himself he tried his best to provide the weaponless with some kind of arms. Every gun that could be found in New Orleans was requisitioned—antique muskets, fowling pieces, even old Spanish *escopetas*, so far out of date that men had to be shown how to load and fire them. Yet not enough arms, even of this almost worthless sort, could be obtained to go around. It was enough to make a commander's head ache.

He sent the Kentuckians across the river to the bastion under the command of a brigadier general named David Morgan, and gave them some of Patterson's naval guns to support them. They were to guard against a flanking movement, and such a movement might now be in progress.

Yet he believed that the major blow of the British would be delivered directly at his front. Caught up in the unreasoning intensity of his dedication to the young nation he was defending, and filled also with the exaggerated passion for combat which was natural in him, he awaited the assault almost trembling with eagerness, or anxiety, or simple desperation. All the concentrated hopes and fears of the weeks were at last coming to an awful culmination.

Steps on the stairs. He had called a conference of his chief officers this morning for last-minute instructions in the plan he had prepared for the coming battle. He put down his excitement, and it was as if a vertigo had left him. When he turned to his staff, he was the cold, deadly-sure Jackson again.

He looked at their faces, one by one: Coffee's vast, granite countenance; the cold assurance of Carroll's eyes; Humbert, huge-mustachioed and a little drunk but an old soldier, ready; Villeré, young and just now subdued; Reid, handsome but very grave.

"Gentlemen," he said, "this may be the day the enemy has chosen for his grand assault." He repeated to them the message from Patterson. "If there is an attack on the Kentucky Bastion," he went on, "it will be no more than a diversion. Here—right here—will be the line where the British will smite with everything they have."

He paused. Nobody spoke. There was a slight shuffling of feet.

"I have given you your instructions," he resumed. "I repeat them once more."

Genius sometimes shatters military values and reassembles them in terms of the future. Jackson had thrown aside all military pedantry, and was preparing to fight as his own genius dictated.

He knew savage Indians at war, and how they often lay in wait for an unsuspecting enemy, hiding behind trees. Jackson, a product of the frontier, imagined nothing less than a gigantic ambuscade, in which a deadly force was to be hidden behind *an idea,* a sheer creative innovation much more decisive—if it worked—than any physical concealment and surprise.

"The rifle must be our hope," he said. "At one hundred yards, which is the battle range of the British musket, only forty per cent of hits can be expected from that weapon. But the American rifle will account for *fifty per cent at three hundred yards.* And at two hundred yards—twice the musket's battle range—our border marksman aims with certainty at an enemy's head or his heart. We have, therefore, the advantage of our riflemen. We must give the British every opportunity to accomplish their own defeat."

To General Humbert, who still thought in terms of war as it was taught him by Napoleon's armies, the novelty of the idea was difficult to accept at all, and especially as Jackson was proposing to put it into effect.

"But the rifles—even if they are as superior as you say, *mon Général*— hold only the left half of our front," he said.

"Very true," said Jackson. "But let me remind you of the enemy's reconnaissance in force a week ago. He came, remember, in two columns, the heaviest by the river. He will come that way again. His first demonstration was to feel us out and discover the weakness of our defense. He believes that two columns will seize us between them at a disadvantage. But his two columns, I promise you, will never act in unison. I will beat them one after another."

They listened with rapt attention, none lifting his voice.

"What did the British learn in their reconnaissance?" he continued. "The main discovery was that our greatest artillery strength is on our right, near the river, with the *Louisiana* to back it up. Continental battles have been decided by artillery fire—you well know, General Humbert, that Napoleon's concentration of guns has been his greatest tactical asset. Therefore, I firmly believe, the enemy will again advance a column along the river, much of the way protected from the *Louisiana's* enfilade by the levee. But this will be, gentlemen, more of a threat than the full assault. The column which attacks our left, near the woods, will this time be far heavier than the other, containing the best troops, the real assault."

He paused and looked them over, his eyes alight with his inspiration.

"And there," he finished, "is where my surprise awaits. I have purposely massed my rifles on that side, so thickly that they must fire by turns. Gentlemen, I confidently expect that we may see something new in war today."

A rocket suddenly soared upward through the fog into the clear air above, from the enemy position.

"I believe that is a signal of some kind," said Jackson.

Almost at once the men in the group could hear through the misty gloom a distant mutter of drums and the thin squealing of fifes.

"By God, gentlemen!" cried the General. "I think they intend to attack us under cover of the fog! Return to your units at once, and have your men stand to their posts! And may God help us this day!"

They needed no prompting. Leaving beside him only Major Reid, they clattered down the stairs to mount and ride to their respective sectors of the battle line.

Jackson stood staring, almost as if in a hypnotic trance, or as if he sought by sheer will power to see through the shrouding fog. It was the gravest moment his life had known.

However well he had laid his plans, they might be all nullified by the heavy mist. Hidden by it the British could approach within fifty feet of his rampart before they became clearly visible. The whole basis of his strategy—the far-killing power of his riflemen—would be lost. If the enemy, approaching within fifty yards, broke suddenly into view they might receive a single volley from his men, no more. Then their bayonets would be at the throats of his people.

It was a contingency he had feared but hoped prayerfully would not occur. Standing there, looking out from the gallery, his fists clenched so tightly shut that the nails cut the palms of his hands.

Presently he turned. He did not speak to Reid, but the aide followed him down the stairs and just behind him stepped out of the house.

The dense fog which hid everything was frosty. A heavy rime lay on the ground, and Jackson's breath was like steam before his face.

Painfully he stared through the white murk, listening to the sounds which told him of heavy concentrations of marching troops, now definitely coming nearer.

An actual feeling of nausea came over him. He had hit upon his improvisation, based on the shooting ability of his Tennessee hunters, which he hoped and believed would counterbalance the weight of the British battalions. To have the weather render his plan useless before the battle even started—it was too tragically disheartening!

Reid, glancing at his General's tense face, understood the turmoil going on within him. Then he noticed something that gave him a momentary thrill of hope.

"I believe, sir," he said, "there's a breath of air beginning to stir."

He pointed at a tree, green even in this midwinter season, and Jackson followed his gaze. A few leaves, sure enough, fluttered slightly.

"Pray God it does," said the General. And it *was* a prayer, a supplication to heaven from one who knew little of praying.

The stirring leaves began to dance, a cold whiff of air touched his cheek, and as he looked, the blanket of fog suddenly began to shred away.

Then, dimly at first, but growing clear as solid blocks of scarlet, the advancing British columns appeared.

Striking through the mist as it rolled apart and dissipated, the January sun shone on a field that looked as if it was of polished silver. A heavy frost had settled on the cane stubble, and the brilliant red tunics of the oncoming army contrasted vividly with the white earth underfoot.

"Just in time!" exclaimed Jackson. "Thank God, just in the nick of time!"

All indecision, all weakness left him. Something hot and alive seemed to flow back through his veins, sending its strength and vitality into his body.

"Major," he said to Reid, "send an order up and down the line. Every officer is to warn his men again, according to instructions given, making sure each soldier in his unit understands to which rank he is assigned, and at what commands he will take position on the fire step."

It had come. At last he was face to face with the dread British attack, fearsome because of the iron discipline and the natural courage of the British soldiers. He knew his only chance was to break the attack before it reached him. If those red columns ever came to his wretched mud rampart, their numbers and training could hardly fail to clear the works and make a butchery of the defenders.

"Aaron!" he called to his black servant. "Bring my horse!"

The wizened little Negro knew his master. At the call he led up the bay hunter his master had chosen, already saddled and bridled.

Jackson mounted, settled himself in the saddle, struck in his spurs. The bay leaped forward, thudded across the yard, and rose under him to skim over the fence. As he rode he felt keen, alert, filled with savage anticipation.

In a moment he curbed the animal to a walk, and went slowly down the fieldworks, on the escarpment behind the trench, looking down at the long rank of his men already on the fire step of the rampart, their rifles lying on the parapet ready to be used. Below and behind them in the trench, out of the line of fire, stood two other ranks, each equaling the first, one behind the other, making a triple array.

This was the acid moment for his plan. At the word, which would be given by himself when he believed the enemy was in sufficiently good range for execution, the men on the fire step were to fire. But this would be no mere haphazard volley, such as was the custom of European troops. Each of his riflemen was to choose a picked target.

Having fired, the first rank would step down and reload, the second rank mounting the step to send their rifle bullets singing toward the British with the same careful aim. This rank would in turn be succeeded by the third rank, and by the time that rank had given its volley, the first would be reloaded and ready to take its place. If the thing worked as well as he hoped and planned, the stream of fire from his parapet would be almost continuous.

As he had predicted, the British were advancing in two rivers of red, with a glittering froth of bayonets, spiked with ensigns, flowing far back into the distance. Jackson tried to estimate their numbers. Ten thousand? He had fewer than four thousand, of whom a half only were riflemen. He could only hold a last-minute hope that they had been schooled well enough in the past few days to obey the simple commands on which everything depended.

With a rolling concussion the British artillery opened. Yes, they mounted new batteries during the night, Jackson told himself. Eight hundred yards, perhaps. Navy guns, by the sound.

A new barrage of Congreve rockets soared toward the rampart.

Jackson thought: They seem to have the range somewhat better.

A mighty explosion shook the ground.

Ammunition wagon, said his mind. Over to the right of headquarters. Direct hit by one of those damned rockets.

Slowly he continued to ride on the level ground behind the trench, where he and his horse were in full view of the enemy.

Just above his head a howling fiend passed, and an artillery horse fifty yards in the rear seemed suddenly to fly apart.

Reid, now mounted also, overtook him. "They're using red-hot shot," he said. "Some of the cotton bales in the rampart are burning."

Jackson's few guns began to respond to the enemy bombardment with belching roars. A choking, blinding cloud of smoke mounted.

"That's worse than the fog!" he cried impatiently. "Major, get back to the house. You can see better from the room above. When the enemy gets within four hundred yards, pass the word up and down for the artillery to cease fire."

"Yes, sir." Reid was almost shouting to make himself heard in the din. He hesitated. "Sir, with all respect, you're too exposed up here."

Jackson turned to him with the odd half-grin. "I've reached an age where my blood's not so hot that it tempts me to expose myself out of vanity," he said. "However, example is the greatest inspiration to men. I must not exempt myself from danger."

"Sir," said Reid, "the men have no doubt of your courage. By your leave, sir, they'd do much better if they weren't afraid *for* you."

Some logic to this. Jackson nodded, rode back to the house with his aide, and dismounted.

Across the frosted field the scarlet columns had appreciably narrowed their distance from the American works.

He descended to the wide bottom of the trench. Slowly he walked down it, speaking to his soldiers.

"Remember, boys, one rank at a time. Fire on the order, not before."

"Yes, sir, General."

"You bet, General."
The men's faces were serious. A few saluted awkwardly.
He passed on.

3

The big guns behind the rampart suddenly ceased fire and the breeze cleared away the powder smoke. The British artillery, however, continued to thunder in the center, between the two advancing columns.

Young Captain Jack Donelson, dark-eyed and thin-faced, judged the enemy's guns were concentrating on the American cannon, over toward the right. He understood there had been some losses over there, but nothing to shake the men.

The British were in rifle range now, he thought. Tense in the sharp frosty morning, he glanced up and down the trench at his own company of men, proud of his command. Then he mounted the fire step to watch the oncoming enemy.

The sight was impressive. British drums rolled, every man marched in step, every musket was at the same exact angle, every bayonet gleamed, whetted to a razor edge. All at once the column near the cypress woods, to the rattle of the drums, fanned out with well-drilled precision. By squads Donelson watched the red uniforms wheel to left and right, forming an extended front reaching from the trees out toward the ruins of the Chalmette house, a plantation home burned during the earlier fighting, about half a mile from the American parapet. For a moment the scarlet ranks stood stationary while more troops came up from behind, widening out, forming a second, even a third, front.

"When we goin' to shoot?" said a bearded Tennesseean near Donelson. "I reckon I could hit a runnin' deer from here."

"Not until the order comes," said the captain.

He heard a hoarse voice cry, "Hooraw fer Ol' Hickory!" Then a cheer. The General was coming down the ditch, bareheaded, his face pale with determination, his eyes blazing. To Donelson he seemed at that minute a straight sword of fiery courage.

At the place where his nephew stood on the fire step, he halted and glanced up.

"How're you doing, Jack?" he asked with a twinkle. "Rather be home with Aunt Rachel?"

"Not by a million, sir!"

"We'll smash 'em!" said Jackson. And every man within hearing believed him absolutely.

The General climbed to the fire step beside his nephew.

"I was afraid the fog would hide them," he said. "Give our boys daylight to see their front sights, and they've got a target no real Tennes-seean can miss."

A sudden idea occurred to him. Frontier targets usually were cards with V-notches cut in them, rather than round bull's-eyes. The marksman aimed to strike the point of the V, and "Cutting the V" was an expression meaning a perfect shot.

"Boys," he said, "I'm going to give you a V to shoot at! See those white crossbelts the redcoats wear? They make a V right above the cross-plate. Pass the word up and down the line to aim for the V—at the cross-plate that marks the point of the V. Tell 'em to cut the V!"

"Yes, *sir!*"

The homely thought appealed to every man of them. Jackson could hear his words, meaningful to the backwoods riflemen, caught and carried on in a ripple of phrases, the length of the rampart in either direction.

He descended from the fire step with his half smile on his face and walked back toward his headquarters.

Young Donelson waited, listening to the din of the British artillery, and he thought the order that would set all the rifles blazing would never come. The red ranks had resumed their advance, and it seemed irresistible, as if by its very momentum it would roll over any defense or obstacle.

Then he saw, far down the trench, the General lift his sword and bring it down. At once along the line came the command.

"*Make ready!*"

He echoed it to his company. And added, "Remember, men—by ranks, at the command!"

On the fire step hunting shirts crowded close to the rampart and brown Tennessee faces lay close to brown curly-maple rifle stocks. Flintlock hammers clicked back, and keen eyes squinted through sights on the long octagonal barrels.

"Remember," cautioned Donelson again, "*above* the cross-plates."

Far off to the right a thundering broadside burst from the *Louisiana* as she raked the British column near the river. An answering roar came from the enemy batteries.

Why doesn't that order come down? Donelson thought.

The long scarlet rank, marching smartly, bayoneted muskets stiffly at the carry, swept forward. Now the British artillery ceased fire for fear of injuring their own troops, and for a few moments a strange, chilling quiet seemed to hang over the field, in which the roar of drums and the shrilling of regimental fifes, and even voices of officers shouting orders, came suddenly clear and near.

"Look at them bastards dress their lines!" someone cried.

Far away, it seemed, a voice cried the signal.

"Aim your pieces!" shouted Donelson, and he heard the order echoed in each direction.

"*Fire!*"

With a tearing crash the parapet seemed to blaze a sheet of flame, followed instantly by a billow of smoke.

"Second rank!"

Already men were leaping up from the trench bottom to the fire step as the first rank descended to reload.

"*Fire!*"

Another flaming blast of death from the mud rampart.

The third rank replaced the second on the fire step.

"*Fire!*"

And now the first rank, rifles reloaded, was ready to keep up the furious pace.

"*Fire!*"

Jackson had waited with almost quivering anxiety to hear his first volley lash out. He watched as a second, a third, a fourth succeeded it almost without cessation. And by that time he knew that his innovation was working better than he had dreamed.

"We can keep it up forever!" he exulted. "Give 'em hell, boys! Give 'em hell!"

Through the acrid smoke haze he saw the British line suddenly grow ragged as it rolled forward with its dread precision. Gaps opened wide in it here and there, as if men had stepped aside from each other.

They had not stepped aside. The soldiers who had filled those gaps reddened the frosted field with their scarlet bodies.

4

Tall and gaunt, Major General John Keane, commanding the British river column, saw his front ranks smashed by the *Louisiana's* broadside. At once he ordered a halt, and his men sheltered themselves behind the levee, which just there formed a substantial embankment.

Beyond this shelter a crushed swath of redcoats littered the open space, where the guns of the American ship had caught the first platoon. A few of the prostrate figures writhed and screamed, but grapeshot from a warship's broadside did not leave many living among those it struck down.

In spite of this preliminary loss Keane had his column well under control; and his halt was not due to any hesitation on his part to continue the advance. It was in line with Pakenham's tactics.

Over toward the cypress woods, the opposite column, commanded by Keane's friend, Major General Samuel Gibbs, was to deliver the main assault. It was the strongest column, numerically. According to Paken-ham's information the enemy's left was the weakest part of his line, having almost no artillery, which instead was massed on the right, in front of Keane.

It was Keane's duty to deliver a second blow, after the main attack reached its objective and the Americans were compelled to throw part of their force over to that flank in an effort to repel Gibbs. A rather well thought-out plan of battle, thought Major General Keane.

The naval batteries in the center, which had been brought up during the night, began a new hammering barrage. They had changed their target, Keane saw, and were directing their fire at the American ship on the river. Presently the *Louisiana* could be seen getting up sail and taking advantage of the breeze that had cleared the fog, to work her way up-stream out of range. That placed her where she could no longer bring her guns to bear on his column when it advanced again. The naval guns began once more to play on the enemy fieldworks, concentrating their attention on the emplacements of the American artillery.

Keane's column was out of musket range, and the men were allowed to rest easy until it was time to call them into action. He looked across the field toward the woods on the far side, and nodded with approval as he saw Gibbs deploy his men into battle front. Napoleon, who clung to the old column formation in his assaults, had learned to his eternal cost how the British extended lines could cut his heavy battalions to pieces with smaller loss to themselves.

It was just then that the first American volley blazed out. Major General Keane experienced a stunning surprise. The range was far greater than was permitted for usual musketry, and yet it was dropping men. Furthermore, he had expected after the volley the usual pause, while weapons were reloaded. Instead a second volley blasted forth almost immediately, followed in quick succession by a third, and yet a fourth . . . it seemed an almost ceaseless sheet of flame and lead.

With a sense of horror he now gazed over at Gibbs' ranks and saw the execution wrought there. Never before had Keane, or indeed any of the British, faced frontier riflery, and he did not at the moment under-stand Jackson's radical expedient of three ranks of men, each taking its turn on the fire step to maintain that deadly blaze which transcended anything in his military experience.

Gibbs, very plainly, was in serious trouble. Not even British veterans could go forward under this kind of fire. The first lines simply wilted down. Those behind wavered. Some of the men, in spite of orders, came to a halt in disorderly little groups and raggedly fired small volleys of musketry that could do no possible damage to the enemy.

"My God!" exclaimed Keane. "They're giving back!" But in the enormous din of the battle, his voice was lost.

A scarlet-clad figure on horseback careered out in front of the line, sword lifted. Gibbs himself. Keane could not hear him in the multiplied racket of the guns, but he saw his friend's chin lift, his body tense, as he shouted something—a command, an appeal.

Two other riders spurred forward. Looking across the field, now littered with red uniforms, Keane recognized General Pakenham. The other must be his aide, Captain McDougal.

Even in the ear-splitting din, and at the distance, though Keane could not hear the general's voice, he could tell that Pakenham was raving.

Too late. The British ranks began stumbling back, the retreat gathered speed, fell into disorder.

Keane caught his breath. Down, crashing to a sliding fall, went Pakenham's horse. But a moment later the general was up and mounting the horse his aide promptly offered him.

"Thank God!" breathed Keane.

But the general's fall, even though he quickly rose, completed the demoralization of the men in the far wing. Completely out of hand now, they ran desperately to get out of range of those deadly rifles, carrying with them their protesting, cursing, imploring officers.

"Shame! Shame! A disgraceful shame!" cried Keane.

But he knew that the situation had become grave. Only leadership, example, would bring those routed regiments back to charge again. He could see that their officers gradually were bringing them to a halt out of range of the American rifles, trying to re-form them. The men were discarding their heavy knapsacks.

Near Keane, in the lee of the levee embankment, stood Colonel Rennie, the youngest officer of his rank in the army. The general called him over.

"I intend to go to the relief of Gibbs," he said. "You will command here. Press forward when you see the main column advance again."

Rennie saluted, his young face lighting up, and thanked Keane as if he were being given the rarest of gifts. A fine British fighting man. Almost with regret Keane looked at him, as he surveyed what he was calling upon him to do.

No time now, however, for sentiment. He glanced back down his column. Red jackets, tall black headgear, plaid kilts. The Sutherland Highlanders. It was his favorite regiment, though he himself was not Scottish. Every man in it stood six feet tall or more, a rawboned, fierce, half-savage mustering, Covenanters all, who prayed and fought with equal fury.

Keane cantered his horse back along the levee which sheltered his column. Colonel Dale, commander of the regiment, as Scotch as the heather, saluted him. He was a middle-aged man, with whitening hair, smooth-shaved, inclined to be plump-faced but with direct blue eyes and a firmly set mouth.

"Colonel," said Keane, "I'll ask you to oblique your men across this field to the aid of Gibbs' column. I will accompany you."

Dale saluted again. "Very good, sir."

He made a stiff military about-face, and shouted an order. At once the Scots swung out toward their right, barelegged, kilts swinging, bayonets fixed, muskets sloping over their shoulders.

The American rifle fire had ceased, but the artillery on both sides had gone at it again. A cannon ball from the American lines skipped and plowed the ground just ahead of the regiment. The Highlanders were, however, well out of rifle range; though they would not be out of that range very long, and every man knew it. They had all watched the decimation of the first attacking column.

Keane smiled a little grimly. For some reason he always experienced a sort of elation when he found himself going into battle; and this was a battle the like of which he had never seen or even heard of before.

Six hundred yards, he thought to himself, estimating the distance to the American ramparts. A smear of sprawled red figures on the ground up ahead showed the limit of the first advance.

From behind, rockets once more began their tearing sound overhead as they soared toward the enemy rampart, adding their noise to the reverberations of the big guns.

As Keane rode up, Pakenham was in consultation with some of his officers. Poor Gibbs, past his prime but still a stout soldier, was feeling the disgrace. Tears rolled down his face.

"The men won't follow me," he said brokenly. "I can't get them to come on."

"Thank God, here's the Ninety-third!" exclaimed Pakenham as he saw the Highlanders. "Rally on the Ninety-third!"

Keane observed that his face was flushed, and that he exhibited evidences of great excitement.

"I praise God that you've come, General," Pakenham said to him. "We'll go forward again, of course, as soon as we get these men into some kind of order. Those works *must* be taken."

"It was pretty hot up there," said Keane to Gibbs. "The American fire took your men by surprise. But they're British soldiers. They'll come again, be sure of it."

Gibbs refused to be comforted. "They ran! They ran like cowards!" he kept saying.

Pakenham spoke. "The Highlanders are fresh. Let the Ninety-third take the van."

Colonel Dale heard the order and turned to his regimental surgeon.

"Give these to my wife," he said.

To the surgeon he handed his watch and a letter, written the night before.

"I'll do it, sir, if you don't return," said the surgeon.

"I do not expect to, sir," Dale said calmly.

He turned to his men, who stood with muskets grounded. He was proud of this magnificent regiment, and in that moment as he looked at it, he wondered what would be left of it when this day was finished. But in his manner no hesitation showed.

"Sutherlands!" he shouted. "We are honored by being given the van of this advance! Forward! Scotland forever!"

Grim Scottish faces did not alter. Out in front strode the pipers and the pipes began their shrill, blood-stirring clamor. Dale felt an especial warmth toward the pipers. They went into battle without a musket, and they were expected to lead the others, their pipes skirling, to the very cannon's mouth.

Now he stepped out ahead, and with a flourish of his claymore indicated those deadly far ramparts.

Up and down the files went the orders as the regimental column flattened out into battle front. As a single man, the Sutherland Highlanders marched forward behind their colonel.

Three hundred and fifty yards from the enemy's sullen parapet prone red figures marked the beginning of the British travail in the first attack. Dale, his naked claymore on his shoulder, inwardly braced himself for the expected volley.

It did not come at once. He glanced back. His Scots were keeping a perfect line. And now other regiments, their ranks closed once more, followed, tier after tier of red uniforms.

All at once, with a searing crash, the sullen American rampart burst into flame and smoke.

A piper, marching at Dale's right, stumbled and went down, his bagpipe uttering a final despairing squall as the air went out of it.

No time to be concerned over a piper. Too many others were dropping in the ranks, going down sometimes with faces twisted by anguish, sometimes only with looks of dumb surprise.

Again and again the enemy entrenchments wrapped themselves in smoke, seamed and lined with streaks of fire.

Colonel Dale, calm and realistic, knew he was leading a forlorn hope, a suicide advance. He turned once again to his men, and walking backward without breaking step, surveyed his lines. It was shocking to see the gaps already torn in them. And still there were more than two hundred yards of this death plain to cross before the foe was reached.

The Scots did not falter. Shredded as it was, the regiment strode forward in order, bare knees flashing, kilts swinging in perfect step. One solitary piper survived, still skirling wildly, but hardly audible in the battle tumult. Eighty steps a minute, two and a half feet to a step, on and on.

The Highlanders did not know it, but at that moment Pakenham was dead behind them. Gibbs was dying. Keane was down with a bullet through his neck. Their own comrades, dead and dying, trellised the cane field with their scarlet-and-plaid bodies.

Colonel Dale expected death. But he did not know it when it came to him.

The lead slug from a Tennessee deer rifle made a small rapping sound as if hitting a wooden board. Then Dale was on the ground, a blue hole in his white forehead, the ground beneath his head growing red with blood from the greater hole which the bullet tore as it left the back of his skull.

5

In the midst of furious action it is difficult for most men to distinguish what really is going on. The mind tends to focus on one individual sector of the scene, so that the relationships of many other events, taking place simultaneously, appear only as a confusion.

Andrew Jackson, however, had the gift of viewing the battle with an odd impersonality, as if he were not of it, so that from his place on the balcony of the Macarte house he focused unerringly upon the critical points.

He lowered his telescope and turned to Major Reid a face almost terrible with its cold rage of combat, and the terrific seriousness of the will behind it.

"The Highland regiment is leading this time," he said, loudly to be heard in the deafening uproar. "They'll never stop as long as any are left to advance."

Reid nodded, as the guns below shook the floor with their bellowing. A crash at the side of the gallery opened a sudden ragged hole in the wall. Already the house had been struck more than a score of times by enemy cannon balls, yet the General would not leave this place of vantage for observation.

Jackson returned to his survey, peering with his telescope through the smoke at the grim line of red coats and dark kilts sweeping forward. The Scots were losing heavily, a slaughter terrible and chaotic, but they still advanced without breaking step, men who had never been beaten on any field, almost machine-like in their dedication.

The American rampart was a vast and lethal cloud of smoke, through which incessant lightnings flashed. The sound of the rifles was so continuous that it was like that of a vast tearing of threads in some gigantic fabric ripped apart, punctuated by the greater eruptions of the cannon.

On came the line of scarlet and tartan, bayonets glittering in front. Behind came other scarlet ranks: the regiments of Wellington, the veterans of the Peninsula.

A figure on a horse toppled from its saddle, and the horse remained standing beside it, while the red lines passed on beyond it.

Again and again, raw gaping holes appeared in the kilted front. Each time the Scots closed their ranks, kept cadenced step, came on with order aligned, their steel flashing before them.

"I never saw anything so magnificent!" exclaimed Jackson, lifted momentarily out of himself by sheer admiration. Then his face again went grim as his mind returned to the deadly necessities.

"If they don't stop now——"

They did not stop. Not a single officer was left to lead the Sutherland Highlanders, but with the magnificent courage of their fighting race they trudged inexorably forward, bayonets now level.

And behind the Scots flowed other regiments.

From the right a sudden hammering of musket fire. Jackson swung his telescope that way. The enemy's river column at last was in motion. And the *Louisiana* no longer in position to rip it with her broadsides!

Humphrey's battery in the levee bastion let go at the column, and Jackson saw the men leaping like maniacs to sponge and load and train their guns for a second discharge.

Fifty yards nearer a short, plump, important-looking figure supervised the loading and aiming of the great thirty-two pounder. Dominique You intended to uphold his reputation as a gunner this day.

"More powder!" he yelled. "Now my leetle bags of hornets!"

Almost to the muzzle he had the vast old gun loaded with musket balls in cloth sacks, which would shred at the discharge and send a hail of leaden missiles whizzing and scattering toward the target.

"Aside! I train heem myself!"

Dominique squinted along the huge barrel, and gave sharp orders as the trail was slewed around and the muzzle depressed to his satisfaction.

"Now!" he cried.

The thick advancing red masses seemed to pour directly across the line covered by the cannon.

"*Tirez!*" he cried, and pulled the lanyard, leaping aside at the recoil as with a thundering crash the old gun belched forth its hell's broth of screaming slugs.

Momentarily cut off by the smoke, Dominique did not at once see what execution he had done. But Jackson, above, saw it.

In that single dreadful discharge an entire platoon of the enemy was wiped out. The column, badly shattered, hesitated but then moved forward once more, not spreading out but coming on in a mass. At its head a young colonel held his sword on high.

But now the roar of battle beat louder on the left, and Jackson turned his glass in that direction.

On the long fire step of the rampart rank still succeeded rank, and the rifles never ceased their frenetic racket. Over toward the cypress woods the flank of the British who were coming behind the Scots showed distress as Coffee's hunters, stealing through the trees, picked off marching soldiers.

But still the Highlanders came on.

Jackson found himself wondering crazily how human flesh and blood could stand it.

To the very edge of the canal before the rampart the few that were left of the kilted regiment marched, then halted there. The men who had been detailed to bring scaling ladders and fascines had failed to come up. Unable to go forward, too proud to retreat, although the regiments behind them had all fallen back, the Highlanders stood where they were, falling about their colors where the staff of the flag had been planted in the ground by a Scot who died to do it.

At length a mere handful of what had been the magnificent regiment slowly retired, still in unbroken order, still turning to face the foe.

From the rampart the Americans cheered them wildly. All rifle fire ceased.

The British attack was broken, smashed, the remnants of the scarlet array in full retreat.

Almost with awe Andrew Jackson looked out across the stricken field at what he and his army had wrought. On his right the regulars and massed guns had beaten Colonel Rennie's late attack, and young Rennie himself lay dead.

The General could hardly believe that he was gazing at the wreckage of a defeat so disastrous that British troops never before had experienced its like, not even when facing the great Napoleon.

His men were yelling themselves hoarse, but he turned away.

Somehow he did not feel like cheering over the gallant soldiers who had died so vainly.

Besides, a new flood of tasks now awaited him. The enemy retreat must be made complete with their retirement to their ships. The city he had saved must be restored to order. The dead must be buried, the wounded cared for. The thousand and one details of administration must be attended to.

Just now, however, every fiber in his body cried for sleep.

The Greater Arena,
*** 1827

Miracle victory though it was, the Battle of New Orleans was fought uselessly insofar as the outcome of the War of 1812 was concerned. Already, before that bloody action, peace had been concluded, though because sailing ships crossing the Atlantic were so slow with the passage, the nation did not learn of the Treaty of Ghent until after Jackson's incredible feat.

Save for Jackson's part of it the war had been badly fought. Only sheer good fortune brought the young country out of it as well as it did. Three factors entered into this: British sentiment at home regarded the war as "a pestilential nuisance"; Britain's greatest soldier, the Duke of Wellington, considered it a military operation so difficult and costly it might never succeed, and so informed his government; and the British knew they must have their hands free to prepare for a new titanic struggle with Napoleon.

Nevertheless, New Orleans served to restore the national pride, sadly shaken by previous events of the war. And it made of Andrew Jackson, who had proved himself the best general on either side, a national hero, where before he had been only a regional hero.

As for Jackson, his turbulent career continued, though the war was over. In April 1818 the second "Florida incident" occurred, when the General waged war on the Seminole Indians, who came up from that Spanish province to murder and burn and loot in the settlements feeling sure of safety as soon as they retreated south of the international boundary.

To Jackson, the frontiersman, however, the myth of the "border" was evident. Without hesitating he followed the Indians into Spanish territory, soundly defeated them, executed two Englishmen whom he proved were agents stirring up the Seminoles, and with his army occupied most of northern Florida.

The storm of these acts echoed and re-echoed through the political halls of America. A protest from Spain and a demand for "the punishment of the general [Jackson]," were formally placed before President James Monroe. But the net result of all this was only to prove to the world, most of all to Spain herself, that she could not even police Florida, much less defend it; and for the sum of fifteen million dollars the United States purchased the province and added a new state to the union.

An effort, led by Henry Clay of Kentucky, to censure Jackson for his Florida adventure, was soundly defeated on all counts by Congress, for by this time the man had become not only a hero but a symbol.

America was not yet a homogeneous nation. The original states, once separate colonies, differed in background, beliefs, feelings. New England, the Puritan stronghold, was almost a separate entity from the Cavalier-bred South. Louisiana and Alabama possessed French and Catholic customs and ideas.

The political mind of the nation was chaotic. Personal feuds cut across it, and so did personal ambitions. Demagogues could rally their followings, sectional prejudice could have its voice.

America was like a concert orchestra without a director, a blaring clang of lusty sound, an immense creative impulse, but yet without leadership or plan. The moment was at hand for a man of clear ambition to create of these disparate elements a united nation; and such a man already had stepped on the scene.

Andrew Jackson had become the symbol of the common people. Hitherto national government had largely been in the hands of the aristocracy of wealth and privilege. But Jackson was of the West, a plain man who spoke a plain man's language, one of the people, who thought of his nation as a whole, rather than as a composition of many parts.

Chapter Thirteen

*Mandate? What does that mean to the
boys who are after the big swag?*

WILLIAM CARROLL

1

Washington shivered all those early days of February 1825. Cold
and dismal rains during the week had been followed by a light snow
that soon turned into an ugly, muddy slush on all the roads, which were
cut by hub-deep ruts, running with half-freezing water.

The nation's capital, so ambitiously planned by L'Enfant in straight
geometrical patterns, as yet consisted chiefly of wet and snowy flats on
which a few shivering cattle picked miserably at whatever poor forage
they could find in the wintry fields. Muddy wheel tracks with little re-
semblance to streets or avenues crossed the wide-open spaces here and
there in erratic, rambling fashion. There were a few small huddles of
houses, such as those about the Navy Yard, the Arsenal, and the Capitol
itself, and these seemed to form separate little villages rather than being
parts of the same city.

From the Capitol building—still under construction after the British
arson of 1814—the expanse of sticky mire known as Pennsylvania Avenue
stretched cheerlessly northwest, past the Executive Mansion, and on to
Georgetown. For most of its length it was lined with houses or tene-
ments, usually with shops on their ground floors.

Georgetown, with its cobblestone streets and fine old homes, looked
with some contempt on its crude young neighbor, and most distinguished visitors to the nation's capital sought lodgings there. But it was
in Washington itself that the important events were moving, the evening
of February 8, 1825.

In the White House two men sat up late that night, going over business both governmental and personal. One of them, tall, long-necked and
long-nosed, with a slight sedentary stoop and an expression of per-

petual diffident inquiry on his face, was the President, James Monroe. He was a kindly man, who wished to be friendly to everybody; yet he knew his own shortcomings intellectually, so that his speech was usually colorless, sometimes even halting.

The other seemed his absolute opposite—short, portly, with a huge bald head which he always carried lowered like a bull about to charge. His features were grim, the mouth wide and thin, set in deep lines of determination, even stubbornness, the blue eyes constantly searching from under heavy gray brows. A cold man, a difficult man, but a man of ability and force, was John Quincy Adams, the Secretary of State.

Monroe had no especial liking for the New Englander, but he often depended on him for difficult decisions. It was an open secret that the Monroe Doctrine, chief history-making act of his administration, was more Adams' doing than his. He even hoped that Adams might be the next President—a choice of the least objectionable, to his view, for the most apparent other possibility was General Andrew Jackson. Monroe, a Virginia aristocrat, was horrified at the thought of the wild man from the West in the White House. As Secretary of War in Madison's Administration, he had dealings with the General, and gained some knowledge of the brusque, impatient character of the man.

Both Monroe and Adams were thinking of the morrow, when a historic event was to take place. Upon Congress had fallen the responsibility of choosing a President.

In the national election the previous fall there had been four candidates, and amazingly Jackson had received a plurality of the popular vote, though no majority. In the electoral college the count stood for Jackson ninety-one, for Adams eighty-four, for William H. Crawford forty-one, and for Henry Clay thirty-seven. Therefore the election was thrown into the House of Representatives—something that had not occurred since Thomas Jefferson's first election.

The vote in Congress would be by states, each state having but one vote, regardless of its population or the number of its representatives. Gravely and somewhat gloomily Monroe and Adams considered the prospect. In the election Jackson had carried eleven states, Adams seven, the remaining six divided between Crawford and Clay. But Clay was out of it, since only the leading three candidates could be considered by Congress; and Crawford, the Secretary of the Treasury, also was out of it, felled by a paralytic stroke and helpless in bed. It was therefore between Jackson and Adams, and since there were twenty-four states in existence, only thirteen were required for the majority—of which the General, presumably, already had eleven.

Yet undercurrents existed of which even Monroe, who strove to keep aloof from political wire-pulling, was aware. There was, above all, Henry Clay, the Speaker of the House, a man of many secret subtleties, who lately had declared himself as favoring Adams. Monroe knew Clay and his political sleight-of-hand from years of close experience. That knowledge moved him to ask an outright question at the end of the evening's conversation.

"Mr. Adams, what do you think—of tomorrow?" He spoke in his rather hesitant manner as if hardly expecting an answer.

"Sir," John Quincy Adams seemed to chop off his words, "I can only say this: if that man Jackson should win, it will be *vae victis* as the old Romans had it."

He departed abruptly, hardly pausing to say good night.

James Monroe was left alone in his office, looking worried. *Vae victis* —woe to the vanquished—sounded like trouble. The President hated trouble.

2

A tall man with prematurely gray hair, a long homely face, high forehead, small eyes, and a wonderfully expressive mouth, entertained a group of friends with wine and a late supper in his rooms on Ninth Street, midway between the White House and the Capitol.

Henry Clay, nicknamed "the Cock of Kentucky," was as proud as Lucifer, and as ambitious. As bitter, too—bitter because he had wanted the Presidency, had counted on the Presidency, had hoped to the last for the Presidency, which was to climax his life's plans and ambitions. The sudden spreading ground-fire of Andrew Jackson's popularity had upset all his careful calculations.

Clay had conceived a hatred for Jackson: primarily because he was a nonpolitician who had entered a field in which he did not belong; secondarily because he disputed with Clay the popularity of the West. The gaunt General had not made one speech or lifted a hand in his own behalf, doing no more in fact than simply not refusing to allow his name to be placed on the ballot. And yet he had led the ticket. It was unheard of, a paradox in politics.

The Cock of Kentucky's bitterness was perhaps understandable. Yet to him the game was not yet over. He was still Speaker of the House, with all the enormous powers of that office, and he knew every political trick and stratagem. By using tact, cajolery, and promises, with just enough pressure, he might still so manipulate the House that the man he chose would receive the final, decisive vote.

Sitting there, smiling pleasantly as he listened to his roomful of supporters debating, suggesting, talking endlessly in the manner of politics and politicians, his mind was busy with a train of thoughts in which there was no real place for a smile.

The surest road to the White House, considered Henry Clay, was through the Portfolio of Secretary of State. Had not Thomas Jefferson, James Madison, and the present incumbent, James Monroe, provided the precedents? And now John Quincy Adams occupied the office . . . denied the Presidency, Clay was determined to have the Portfolio.

No man but he knew the subtle inquiries and suggestions that had been made looking toward this end. A discreet approach—later disavowed by Clay—had even been made to his arch rival, Jackson. The reply not only was discouraging but infuriating:

"Before I'd reach the Presidential chair by such means, I'd see the earth open up and swallow Mr. Clay and his friends, and myself with them," Jackson was reported as saying.

It was after that that Henry Clay announced he would support John Quincy Adams on the grounds of "superior fitness"—grounds, he felt, which were well nigh unassailable, since Adams had all the experience that Jackson lacked. The step might even be interpreted as courageous, in view of the General's popularity over most of the nation. Its real motive Clay preferred to keep to himself.

On this evening he appeared to be taking matters far more lightly than those in the room with him. At length, growing weary of long-winded discussions, he proposed a few hands of whist, at which he was an expert. As attractive in personality as he was enigmatical, he devoted the rest of the evening to entertaining his guests with witticisms and amusing stories.

Yet in spite of his apparent frivolity, the hour was to Clay one of portent. During the past several nights he had slept little; but now at last he felt that he held the winning political cards for the great play he intended to make. Even though his own state, Kentucky, had memorialized its Congressional delegation, including himself, to support Andrew Jackson, and many Crawford adherents were reported swinging to the General, Clay, keeping his plans to himself, believed that John Quincy Adams would be the eventual winner in the balloting on the morrow; and for the very best of reasons—the management of Mr. Adams' battle would be in the hands of the cleverest political manipulator in the nation, Henry Clay himself.

3

At best, as William Pinkney had once remarked, Washington was no fit capital for a nation. At worst—as on this dark evening, with the snow still spattering and equipages on Pennsylvania Avenue splashing mud and dirty water—it was doubly uninviting.

A very tall man dismounted from his horse at the Franklin House, a popular inn operated by a certain Major William O'Neale (military title by courtesy), and gave over the animal to a black boy serving as a groom.

In spite of the unseemly weather without, warmth and cheer seemed to radiate from within the tavern itself, and the newcomer made haste to enter. For a moment he glanced about him. The bar was crowded and so was the lobby. He heard the sound of many voices, and coming as he did from the fresh outdoors, the combined smells of damp leather and wool, whiskey and brandy, strong tobacco smoke and stale breath, seemed to him to hang heavily on the air.

An undercurrent of excitement also pervaded the place, for the inn was the headquarters of General Jackson and the Tennessee delegation. The man who had just entered was in fact a member of Congress from that state, Sam Houston.

One who knew him in his early days would have said that this was a Sam Houston vastly different from the youth who, twelve years before, caught the attention of Andrew Jackson by his wild courage against the Indian rifles at the Horseshoe Bend. The weedy boy had become a powerful giant very arresting in his appearance. Some tall men are merely long-legged, but Houston, who stood a splendid six feet and six inches in his woolen socks, had the proportions and limber grace of a finely conditioned athlete.

He had come far in twelve years. Though his wounds prevented him from fighting with Jackson at New Orleans, the General did not forget him. Major John Reid died of a sudden fever, to the grief of Jackson, who was fond of his aide. But the death left a place to be filled on his staff, and the appointment went to Lieutenant Sam Houston. When, after a year or two, for a very personal reason, the young man wished to resign from the army, the General spoke to him like a father:

"We have peace now, Sam, but it's only part peace. We've opened a lot of new country, into which is pouring a mob of land-seekers. The biggest share of them are squatters, and red-necks, and ne'er-do-wells—settlers in a new country always have a surplusage of that sort. Some are downright outlaws. We've got to make citizens of these people, and that requires law and leadership. In a democracy the leaders are men elected to public office. Now, boy, I've got plans for you. To get into politics, get into law first, because law and politics naturally lead to each other. Back in Nashville, I have an old friend, Judge James Trimble, a damned good lawyer. If you read law with him, he'll make a damned good lawyer out of you, too. And once you start practice, and maybe get into public office, no matter how unimportant, do your damnedest to conduct it well."

Jackson did not suggest; he commanded. Sam Houston read law under dry, gruff old Judge Trimble, passed the bar examination, and hung out his shingle. He was a frequent visitor at the Hermitage and more and more he became a favorite of the General and his wife, whom Houston called "Aunt Rachel." Presently he found himself elected attorney general of Tennessee and major general of the Tennessee militia, both at Jackson's nod. The next step was election to Congress from the General's own district.

Sam Houston owed everything to his patron. His great concern at this moment was the outcome of the balloting in Congress on the morrow. As he drew off his rain-dampened cloak and wiped his tall beaver hat, he heard his name called.

"Congressman Houston!"

"Governor Carroll!" he replied.

They shook hands. Each could write "General" before his name, and back in Tennessee they commonly addressed one another as Sam and Billy; but here in Washington protocol seemed to require the use of political titles.

William Carroll, who had served so well under Jackson in the Creek War and New Orleans campaign, had grown stout since the old army days. His face was bland and smooth, his smile ready. But the blandness and the smile somehow were belied by his cold, steel-gray eyes. Under the General himself, Carroll held the political strings in Tennessee, and he and Houston on the surface were allies. But beneath the surface distrust was latent between them. In Carroll, Houston smelled a self-seeker and possible turncoat; Carroll saw in Houston an overmastering rival.

"You're late," said Carroll, quite pleasantly.

"I've been over at the Clay headquarters," said Houston.

"Learn anything?"

"Not much. The Cock of Kentucky's too damn cocky to suit me."

"If Jackson holds the states he carried, he needs only two more to prevail."

"But Clay's declared for Adams."

"He's declared," said Carroll, "but can he even hold his own delegation? It's been memorialized by the Kentucky legislature to vote for Jackson."

"Henry Clay is Speaker of the House," said Houston.

Carroll lowered his voice. "We'd have it in the bag, if our man wasn't so hard to handle. I could have Clay with us——"

"You have to admire the General for sticking to his principles," said Houston shortly.

The other was coldly practical. "You've got to make promises to win in politics. John Quincy Adams may be a Puritan but I don't think it hurt *his* conscience to make a trade with Clay. I'm convinced the State Department's the bargain, and that's why Clay's supporting him."

"Do you think Congress would dare ignore the popular vote the General got in the election?" exclaimed Houston. "Why, sir, it's a mandate from the people!"

Carroll's lip curled. "Mandate? What does that mean to the boys who are after the big swag? I look for a long session and a lot of ballots. And if our man finally wins, it will be by forgetting some of his notions and letting us make the deals he seems to despise."

Even implied criticism of this kind concerning the General was distasteful to Houston. He excused himself and moved away through the crowd to ascend the stairs to his room, which was on the second floor.

4

At the railing of the balcony above stood a girl, looking down at the crowd. She was Margaret Timberlake, daughter of Major O'Neale, the innkeeper. Usually she was called Peggy, and though for some time she had been married to a navy lieutenant named John Timberlake, almost everyone spoke of her as Peggy O'Neale—perhaps a curious evidence of the whispered stories concerning the lightness with which she was said to take her marital state, what with her seafaring husband gone so much of the time on his cruises.

Peggy was pretty—more than merely pretty. Glints of red gleamed in her rich brown hair, her eyes were wide and blue, her figure supple, alluringly proportioned, and slender. She had the power of drawing the secret thoughts of men to her, and she knew it, and felt a triumph in it which made her sometimes audacious and not always scrupulous in her dealings with men.

Inevitably gossip built about her. It was whispered that though she was just past twenty she had already experienced enough romances to satisfy a dozen women. Various names had been coupled with hers, but of late she was linked most frequently in gossip with Senator John Henry Eaton of Tennessee, who was wealthy, and a widower, and who assuredly had displayed extraordinary interest in obtaining for her husband a berth on the frigate *Constitution*, aboard which Lieutenant Timberlake was now—conveniently?—away at sea.

Eaton, however, was not on the floor below, and as the girl's eyes fell on the figure of Sam Houston, she smiled to herself. She was a born huntress, and knew the handsome congressman was not invulnerable, and willful feminine vanity was inherent in her.

Perhaps it was more than mere vanity. Once she had been received at the White House, and a First Lady, Dolly Madison, had pronounced her the prettiest girl in Washington. But the years passed, and Peggy may have been less than discreet on occasion, in her flirtations with guests at her father's inn who were young enough, susceptible enough, and of enough position, to be worthy of her coquetry. A second First Lady, Elizabeth Monroe, sent her a note asking her not to call at the White House. Whereupon the other ladies of Washington society likewise refused to receive the "tavern girl."

So Peggy had reasons for resentments. She was, in the manner of her sex, completely secretive in her intimate thoughts. But did she perhaps spread her net for gentlemen of society, deliberately to revenge herself on ladies of society, by showing them that she could take their men away from them? She never said; but as to other women, she came to ignore them, devoting herself entirely to the world of men, where she received no insulting snubs, but instead a continuous admiring interest.

When she saw Houston leave Carroll and move toward the stairs, she stepped back a little. Presently he came up the steps, whistling to himself. He glanced up and saw her, standing there, looking at him with a smile which nobody but he could possibly see. It was therefore for him.

Houston stopped on the landing, with a slight bow and an answering smile. Everything in him appreciated the charming feminine picture she made, in her white silk gown, caught under her breasts and falling smoothly to the floor, flattering every curve of her figure.

"You're going to be at supper tonight, aren't you?" she asked.

Her father had planned a special private occasion for General Jackson, and Houston was invited.

"I wouldn't miss it," he said, "and I'm a little late."

"Where have you been—over at—Arlington?"

It was a light stab from her, because she knew that he had on a few occasions ridden across the Potomac bridge to pay his respects—fruitlessly—to Miss Mary Parke Custis, daughter of George Washington Parke Custis, owner of the huge-pillared mansion and direct heir of George Washington.

Houston grinned at the smiling dig. Custis did not consider that a frontier congressman was a suitable match for a daughter of so distinguished a line as his. In point of fact, Miss Mary already was promised to a cadet at West Point named Robert E. Lee, of a very aristocratic tidewater family. When Houston learned this it did not especially dash him, for the Custis girl had a nose too long for beauty, and he liked beauty in his women.

"No," he said, "I was just politicking."

"What is happening?" she asked eagerly.

He knew that the girl was interested in politics, having lived in the midst of it, so to speak, all her life; and that like her father she was a partisan of General Jackson.

"I hardly know how to tell you," he said seriously. "Something's going on, but I can't quite put my finger on it."

"You mean Clay and Adams and Van Buren, and all those people?"

As if politics was all that interested her, she slipped her arm intimately into his and began to walk slowly down the hall with him.

"Those, I reckon, and some others." He nodded.

He found it pleasant to have her thus close to him, the light pressure of her hand on his arm, even the touch of her skirt against him; and politics, just then, seemed a dry subject to concentrate upon. He had known Peggy for some months, and they were on a basis of a laughing semiflirtation, with little teasings, and small private jokes, and occasional moments of semiserious personal talk.

The girl looked up at him, and she felt very tiny beside him, and accordingly very precious. She was not the first woman who had been taken by the way he carried his fine head with its thick chestnut curls, and his strong face with those strangely attractive gray eyes, and his truly magnificent figure and stature. Her mind, like his, was not overly occupied at the moment with politics. The huntress in her suggested that here was a rarely splendid quarry.

His room was far down the hall, and her apartment was on the way. When they reached her door, he paused while she opened it.

Her eyes met his with a veiled smile. "Come in?" she suggested.

Houston was past thirty and unmarried. A pretty woman was a challenge to him as well as a temptation, and an invitation like this could hardly be misinterpreted. He glanced up the hall: nobody was in view. Then he looked down at the girl again. She seemed, assuredly, most enchanting. Was she really John Henry Eaton's girl? It is the kind of a thing that is always interesting to learn when it concerns a pretty woman —especially if she is a pretty married woman. Infinite possibilities are suggested . . . if she will yield to one, why not another? A faint feeling of discretion warned him; and discretion was something Sam Houston rarely felt in situations of this kind. He ignored the feeling of discretion and entered.

At once she closed the door and for a moment stood with her back and her two bare arms pressed against it, half as if she were ready to open it and flee, half as if she would bar his escape; a tantalizingly bewildering yet graceful attitude.

A fire burned brightly in the grate at the opposite end of the room and her eyes seemed brilliant in its reflection. He thought her beautiful, but again he felt the vague sensation of disquiet.

"You were asking about politics," he suggested.

"Was I?" she smiled. She took his hat and coat and placed them on a table.

He glanced toward the door of the next room, which was her bedroom.

"There's no one here," she said. "The baby's downstairs with Mother."

So they were alone; for the first time really alone together.

He felt his throat swell, and became speechless. She came to him, and for a moment placed her small delicate hand on his arm. In that moment his senses were captured by a fleeting impression of her fragrance, her light touch, the upward tilt of her face, the highlights in her eyes.

"Do you *really* care about politics—just now?" she breathed.

He did not. As if he could not resist it, his hands went about her, crushed upon her shoulder blades. Her lovely head was lifted, her slim back curved, her eyes wide, dark, deep with some hidden emotion.

Still as a bird in a serpent spell she went—until his strength brought a throaty, breathless gasp from her . . . upon his lips.

Almost without volition but guided wholly by imperious instinct they moved together to an insanity he had not contemplated.

5

Somewhere downstairs a bell jangled.

Andrew Jackson, sitting in his room, said to his wife, "That must be dinner."

The General took no part in the political hubbub below, preferring to sit with Rachel. He was in Washington not as a candidate but as a senator from his state, an honor he had accepted rather unwillingly; and in absolute truth he was less interested in the outcome of the morrow than were almost any of his advocates.

Jackson, now in his fifty-eighth year, was even more gaunt than before. His hair, roan-gray during the New Orleans campaign, was now snow-white, but it still flared back thickly and stubbornly from his brow like the plume on a dragoon's helmet.

He had been writing a letter to his old friend John Coffee, and at the sound of the bell he glanced up over the square steel-rimmed spectacles he wore these days to aid his failing eyesight, and regarded Rachel with an expression curiously akin to concern.

She, too, had grown older. Her hair now was shot with gray, her figure was a dumpy quaking lump, and she sat in her rocking chair, rocking ceaselessly back and forth, wearily gazing at nothing.

Her husband knew what ailed her. She was trying to break the habit of smoking, a lifetime addiction with her, and with all her family; indeed with most frontier women. He remembered a paragraph in a letter written by her sister Jane Hayes only a short time before, which Rachel gave him to read:

How does my sister Jackson do? I cannot take up my bonnet and meet you at sister Betsys or Marys, smoke our pipes, laugh and talk over occurrences of former days, each taking the word out of each others mouth. . . .

The pipe was an innocent consolation to Rachel, and until recently nobody had thought anything of it. Yet now she was trying to give it up, and only because she thought it would make her appear better in the eyes of the world, and thus perhaps help him.

Because she was the wife of a candidate for the Presidency, Washington society had freely and cruelly discussed her awkwardness and backwardness in a drawing room, the unhappy details of her marriage.

But the *pièce de résistance* of the spiteful chatter was the fact that Rachel smoked a pipe—a corncob pipe! What *gaucherie!*

There even had been an open reference to this in a pro-Adams newspaper:

How can the voters justify themselves and posterity to place such a woman as Mrs. Jackson at the head of the female society of the United States!

The slur made the General so wrathful that he was with difficulty dissuaded from challenging the editor, by his friends who convinced him that a duel would be unseemly in a candidate for the high office of Chief Magistrate of the nation.

Rachel knew of the hostility and backbiting. She almost never went out in public these days, and her face was heavy with unhappiness. Jackson's heart smote him. It was he that insisted she accompany him to Washington, believing the sights and events of the capital would divert her. Instead the entire experience had been sad for her.

He should have known, too. She was unhappy even in the limited society of Pensacola during his brief tenure as governor of Florida, which he soon resigned, chiefly because of her.

And there was the time when she went to him at New Orleans, after his defeat of the British. She came by keelboat, with happy expectations, to bask in his glory, bringing her little boy, Andrew, Junior.

Jackson met her at the wharf, and though he had not wished it, several of his New Orleans friends with their ladies were there also—he suspected out of curiosity.

"Oh, Andrew, there's Papa!" Rachel screamed as he advanced toward her down the gangplank. Her stout figure seemed to trundle toward him, and she tugged the child along so that he lagged behind with outstretched arm, nearly tripping.

"Welcome to New Orleans, my dear," said Jackson. He put his lank arms about her and embraced her, and she released the little boy's hand to hug him, with tears in her eyes.

When he freed himself to speak to the child, she wiped away the tears and carried on a stream of ecstatic conversation.

"How good to see you! You look so thin! And tired! I heard your name spoken everywhere! Such a great battle it must have been! Thank God you came out of it safely! Now you can come home, can't you, and let me put some meat on your poor bones? Hasn't little Andrew grown?

You'll never believe the smart things he does! He talks of nothing but you! Speak to Papa, Andrew!"

All this in a loud, excited voice, and Jackson felt that he detected amusement in the party on the pier. The child, far from speaking, seemed backward and shy, as if he hardly recognized the tall gaunt man who stooped over him. This was a small embarrassment which Jackson covered by turning to present his wife to the elegant gentlemen and ladies of the party—the Claibornes, the Livingstons, the Villerés, the Grymeses, even the Marignys, for now that he had become the hero of the city the feud between him and the most prominent of the Creoles had ceased to exist.

The ladies, elaborately and modishly attired, made Rachel seem dowdy in her provincial sack dress. To each introduction she gave a little countrified bob, and a "Pleased to meet you." She seemed unaware that they surveyed her from head to foot with a sort of pity, noticing especially her stoutness, which brought to their minds the French saying, "She shows how far the skin can be stretched."

But Jackson noticed the looks and winced inwardly. Then he despised himself. After all, what difference was it how Rachel dressed or how she spoke? She was his wife; his loyal friend. He saw penetratingly that his own momentary feeling of a little shame concerning her arose from a motive as ignoble as self-esteem.

Every decent instinct in him, as well as his natural kindness, caused him thereafter to be more than usually attentive to her. With her and the child he rode off in his carriage to the home of Edward Livingston, who had offered them hospitality.

Rachel's admiration and amazement at her surroundings in the first large city she had ever seen were almost childlike. At first they amused pretty young Madame Livingston; then they aroused her genuine fondness. She had been the General's sworn friend since the first evening they met. Now she took the General's wife in hand and tried to provide her with a wardrobe suitable for society.

This was needful, for Jackson had received invitations which he could hardly refuse. In spite of the efforts of Madame Livingston and her friends, however, nothing really could make Rachel appear well-dressed. But he bore her to the affairs it was necessary to attend, and looked in so sternly questioning a manner at any who appeared to stare that even whispers died down; at least none came to his ears.

Then on Washington's Birthday they attended a patriotic dinner and ball given at the French Exchange. In her usual naïve manner Rachel was ecstatic over the gorgeous display of food and decorations, particularly admiring a gilded ham which was part of the banquet.

When she and her husband were seated together at the head of the table as guests of honor, she expressed her delight.

"I never saw a gold ham before," she said. "It seems almost too bad to carve anything as beautiful as that."

"It's not the outside decoration but what's within that matters, my dear," Jackson replied. She did not realize that he said it more for the benefit of the listeners at the table than for her, or that he was thinking of an honest and loving heart in an awkward body when he said it.

She ate heartily as usual, but he had little appetite and made a pretense of eating, being ill at ease and half angry with himself and the assemblage because of her. There were toasts, and he made response to one, neither wittily nor eloquently, he feared, but at least briefly.

Afterward, when the floor was cleared for dancing, he stood behind Rachel's chair, fidgeting and wishing there were some graceful way he could excuse himself and take her home. She had fallen very silent, and he did not ask her to dance since he was aware that she did not know the new formal figures.

Toward the middle of the dance program he saw Marigny approaching, elegant and graceful as usual, and with a slight smile on his dark high-bred face. He wondered if the suave Creole was going to offer a duty invitation to Rachel and hoped she would have the good sense to refuse tactfully.

But Marigny surprised him.

"Will you not, *Général*, and *Madame le Général*, treat this assemblage to a *pas de deux*, such as you enjoy in your own home?"

It was malicious and impertinent, and Jackson flamed inwardly. But there was another surprise. He looked into Rachel's eyes and saw that she recognized the malice too—and was angered by it.

"Come on, General, let's show them," she said, rising and taking his arm.

"I haven't danced a step in twenty years—" he began.

"Oh, but we must." For once her mind was made up. "They expect it," she added. And he recognized the courage it took for her to accept the challenge, and ungrudgingly admired her for it.

Marigny already was in the center of the floor announcing that General and Mrs. Jackson had consented to appear as partners in a dance number. What sort of dance? He turned to the guests of honor in inquiry.

The fat was in the fire and Jackson knew they must go through with it.

"I am a soldier," he said, "and know little of dancing. But if the company will indulge us, Mrs. Jackson and I will try a country dance such as I sometimes attempted long ago."

"The name of the dance?" asked Marigny. "And the music?"

"A—er—breakdown," said Jackson. "Any lively tune."

Then he and Rachel were alone in the center of the polished floor, with the others forming a circle all around. The fiddles began to scrape and Jackson, violently self-conscious, began to hop in time to it.

After all, Rachel did better than he. In her youth she had been noted for her lightness of foot, and even now that she had become fleshy she did not give a bad account of herself. He, on the other hand, was stiff and awkward. He knew that the effect of his performance on the watchers was the reverse of elegant, and his embarrassment grew.

Vincent Nolte, one of the city's *bons vivants*, afterward said of it: "To see these two figures, the General, a long, haggard man, with limbs like a skeleton, and Madame le Général, a short, fat dumpling, bobbing opposite each other to the wild melody of 'Possum up de Gum Tree,' was to say the least very remarkable."

At the end there was polite applause. Now Jackson, furious with himself and everyone concerned, did make his excuses and took Rachel to their lodges.

The affair made him rage within; but at the same time it had the effect of steeling his loyalty to his wife. She was Mrs. Andrew Jackson, and he told himself that her battle was harder than any he had ever fought. He felt shame, terrible shame, not for her but for himself, that he had ever, even in his own secret mind, questioned anything about her. Henceforth, he swore to himself—and it was no light oath he took —he would carry himself as if she were the only woman in the world; now, as in the past, and in the future, forever.

And yet, in spite of this, he brought her to Washington. Rachel did not know, never would know, how to dress herself for Washington affairs. In her despair she often complained drearily to him.

"I can never make anything look right," she would say. Or, "How I dread this evening! I'll be a perfect dowd among all those fancy women."

He could not comfort her. The art of bedecking a woman was beyond him. He supplied Rachel with enough money, he supposed, for any need, but she declared that she could find nothing to suit her in Washington, or even in Georgetown.

She employed seamstresses, but in truth nothing could really make Rachel appear well garbed. They told her she had "a difficult figure," by which they meant she was too heavy, and she had no style of carriage, and no flair for wearing clothes.

She would come to him with a new dress, delighted momentarily merely by its fabric, although the style might be hideous on her. He, knowing he had the power to hurt her horribly by failing to show enthusiasm, would go to the opposite extreme and flatter her unjustifiably. Yet she was not without perception, and she suspected that he did not really mean his compliments, and her face would fall as she turned away with the dress which she now hated.

About Rachel was something very childish and pathetic. In the familiar surroundings and routine of her home in Tennessee, she at times knew a certain placid happiness. But her mental inertia was basic and she lived only a fractional life, convinced that other women looked down on her, vainly wishing, but never expressing the wish, that her husband would stay at his home and venture forth no more.

Andrew Jackson, gazing over his spectacles at his wife, felt a helpless and bitter resentment. Why should she be deprived of the one thing that comforted her most—her pipe?

He sincerely regretted now that he had ever allowed his name to be brought forward for the Presidency; the more so since, though he had never offered a statement or made a speech in his own behalf, his political foes, sensing the surprising popularity his name evoked, resorted to personalities, growing more unrestrained as the weeks passed. "Brawler," "cock-fighter," "gambler," "incompetent," were only a few of their epithets. His supporters were labeled "Rowdies, the very dregs of the community."

Well, he could take their vituperation. It was not pleasant, even though his political advisers assured him that such intemperate statements only showed the desperation and fear of his opponents, but he could endure it.

With Rachel, however, the case was different. She had been dragged into this through no fault of her own, and against her desires. Jackson was fond of his wife, wished her to be happy, wanted to protect her. She was a habit of his life, a part of him, dependent on him, a duty and a cause which he assumed by instinct as well as desire. He was glad when he saw her smile; it lifted his own spirits. But it appeared that he could not protect her now. She never smiled these days.

Jackson's feeling toward his enemies—and Rachel's—had become a glowering hatred. He despised politics and politicians, but now that he had been dragged into the battle there was in him no instinct to retreat. However distasteful and degrading, he felt he must go on with it.

It was while these thoughts passed through his mind that he heard the dinner bell. He rose quickly, removed his spectacles, and stepped to the door. As he opened it, he could hear his wife moving to rise from her rocking chair.

"Wait a moment, my dear," he said.

He turned back into the room, closing the door behind him. He did not want Rachel to see what he had just seen: Sam Houston, down the hall, hat in hand, backing out of Peggy Timberlake's apartment, and closing the door behind him.

In these later years Andrew Jackson had become almost ascetic in his personal habits. His chronic illnesses had forced him to give up strong liquor. Never a hearty eater, he had become so abstemious that he scarcely touched meat and subsisted almost entirely on vegetables, which he fancied were better for his health. For every practical physical purpose he was a celibate, though he lived with his wife; and he had schooled himself in the sternest manner to think of women, though always with his ingrained chivalry, as creatures apart, almost impersonal to him.

Yet he was by no means naïve. Sam Houston coming out of Peggy's apartment, in a manner oddly suggestive of secrecy? That was what he did not wish Rachel to see. He knew that she would at once leap to conclusions; and he strove to keep himself from doing so.

To gain time he went to the washstand and again combed his white hair back from his forehead.

Rachel, to his relief, also went before the mirror to do some arranging of her hair.

He judged that sufficient time had elapsed when once more he opened the door. Sam Houston had disappeared from the hall.

6

Major O'Neale that evening had arranged a private dinner party in his small dining room for the General and some of his closest friends. Now he stood at the head of his table, an apron about his ample waist, whetting a long carving knife and smiling at his seated guests.

It was a goodly assemblage, surely: General and Mrs. Jackson, Governor and Mrs. Carroll, Senator Eaton, and Congressman Houston. Neither O'Neale's own wife nor his daughter had as yet appeared. One or the other would remain with Peggy's small daughter and have her dinner sent to her.

Following his usual custom, the major announced the excellences of his principal dishes, in a voice that could be heard over the conversation:

"Gentlemen and ladies, I have here a delicious quarter of venison, just brought down from the Blue Ridge Mountains. Let me send you a slice, Mrs. Jackson? And you, General, I remember you like it very thin. What of you, Congressman Houston, do you prefer it medium? Ah, Peggy, my darling, here you are at last. Please take your seat by Senator Eaton, and send up your plate for this beautiful slice. You, Senator, a well-done bit of the outer crust? Governor Carroll, I have here an excellent cut of the center round. I know that your lady does not care for venison, so I had the baked ham, as you see, placed before her plate, ready sliced. Would you, Congressman Houston, be so kind as to preside over that fine fat goose before you? The carving set is beside the plate. We also have an excellent sea bass, baked whole and to a turn, on the sideboard, along with a beef-and-kidney pie." He turned to a young Negro who waited on the table. "Boy! Pass around the candied yams and white bread! And look sharp for any who desire liquid refreshment. We have tea or coffee for those who wish them. The brandy and whiskey are on the table, and my guests all know my Madeira is of the best."

So, with a constant stream of hospitable discourse, and carving with great skill, Major O'Neale served his guests.

Sam Houston ate very little of the truly sumptuous meal. He had received one fathomless look from Peggy when she came downstairs, and thereafter not a glance from her. He wondered if she hated him, and he had just begun to realize the terrible danger of what they had done. Why, the door to the hall was not even locked!

He had no way of knowing that in Peggy there was a curious mingling of triumph and malice. The huntress had her quarry. The image of Peggy O'Neale, she was sure, would remain in him, the feel of her soft body in his arms, the fiery taste of her in his mouth, the memory of her way of love-making and the craving for her in his blood, a lasting mischief.

He sat near the General, who conversed on any subject except politics, which was uppermost in the minds of everyone in the room except the congressman and the innkeeper's daughter. At the thought of his patron Houston's feeling of guilt deepened. He knew that Peggy was a favorite of Jackson's. In company she was witty and gay, sometimes daring, and her very pertness had won for her the friendship of the fierce old General. Houston had heard the story more than once.

On a certain evening Jackson made a statement, rather pridefully, that he had never set foot on foreign soil.

"What about Florida, General?" asked Peggy.

The whole room sat aghast at such a challenge from such a source. Jackson himself broke the stillness. "That's so, my dear," he said, "Florida *was* foreign then." It seemed to his listeners there was a note of mortification at forgetting his campaigns in Florida when that territory still was a legal possession of Spain.

"Never mind, General," said Peggy, smiling as the consternation deepened, "Florida didn't stay foreign long after *you* got there!"

Like the bark of a fox on a frosty morning, Jackson's laugh rang out. The whole room, in sheer relief, joined in a shout of mirth.

"By the Eternal, Peggy!" vowed the General. "You're as smart a little girl as there is in all America."

Since that day she had been like a bright child to the veteran, allowed privileges nobody else enjoyed. Very sincerely Houston hoped that Jackson would never hear of his indiscretion with her.

The General, as usual, barely nibbled at his food. He had caught the glance passed between the young congressman and the girl, but it told him nothing. He kept assuring himself that he may have read a wrong meaning into what was a completely innocent episode.

Nevertheless he disapproved of it, whatever it was. Had someone besides himself seen the stealthy departure of Houston from Peggy's room, it might seriously have impaired the girl's reputation, to say nothing of the man's.

Chapter Fourteen

It was impossible to win the game, gentlemen. The cards were stacked.

JOHN RANDOLPH OF ROANOKE

1

Sam Houston that morning shaved with more than usual care, studying his face in the mirror and painstakingly trimming the edges of his sideburns, which came exactly to the lobes of his ears. Past thirty though he was, there still was a little of the romantic folderol of youth in him; and he had taken to affecting a Byronic disarray of his hair, even a Byronic open collar and loose cravat.

Byron, in fact, was a new passion, taking place beside his beloved Pope. He sometimes secretly thought of himself as somewhat of a Byronic hero—mysterious, lonely, defiant, slightly stained with sin.

The poet's *Don Juan* lay open and face down on the table, but lines from it made a cynically amusing cadence in his mind:

Let us have wine and women, mirth and laughter,
Sermons and soda-water the day after.

He thought to himself that he drank rather more than was good for him, gambled as he imagined a gentleman should, and his bachelorhood was from no disinclination toward women. His record with the sex, though hardly comparable with Don Juan's, had given him no inconsiderable number of conquests. The first was in the Indian village of Hiwassee. There was one—no, two—in Maryville. A sergeant's daughter at Knoxville, where he took his first army training. Various others here and there along the way. He took none of these affairs seriously, though some of the ladies did so with almost annoying assiduity.

And now Peggy O'Neale.

He fell to thinking of the episode of the previous evening. Was John Eaton in love with her? If he was, and had a prior claim, not legal but secretly agreed between them, it was rather disloyal to intervene with her. A man's mistress, gentlemen rakes usually considered, was even more sacred from his friends than his wife, who had the protection of law. Still, he had no positive knowledge that Peggy was Eaton's mistress.

She was hot-blooded: so much so that she actually invited seduction. Nothing was averse in her behavior—the contrary. His kisses had been returned, he remembered softness, and fire, and a smell of flowery musk, and a lushness crawled over his body. And then the surging fury of their passion together.

Thinking back, he could hardly call it a seduction. She led him into her room. She offered herself. She throbbingly responded to him, with abandon almost stunning, withholding nothing.

Why? Perhaps . . . she had designs. In the manner of young men after an affair that might breed complications, he damned himself. But then, he considered, there were no witnesses. . . .

At the moment there was a knock at his door. Houston laid down his razor, wiped the lather from his face, and opened.

To his surprise, General Jackson himself stood in the hall.

"May I come in, sir?" he asked.

"Why, most certainly, sir," said Houston. He wondered at the reason for this call. Ordinarily one was summoned to the General's presence for conference. He felt a sudden sense of uneasy guilt, even apprehension.

"Will you have this chair, sir?" he said. "It's my only piece of comfortable furniture——"

The General remained standing, dry and stern.

"I suppose you'll see John Randolph of Roanoke today?" he asked.

"Yes, sir." Houston was relieved at the tenor of the question. "At the Congressional caucus, sir."

"If opportunity arises, will you extend him my compliments? He's been most friendly in the present political occasion."

"With pleasure, General."

"Further, if you're speaking with him, say to him that I'd most cordially like to obtain from him a filly got by the great horse Sir Archie, of which I understand he has a few in his stables. She should be full bred on the dam side, of course."

"Of course." Yet Houston began to realize that all this was not what brought Andrew Jackson to his quarters.

For a moment the General stood silent. The errand concerning the filly was a pretext only. He felt diffidence in the more important object for which he came, because a gentleman did not by custom inquire into the private affairs of another gentleman. Yet there was something at stake. Presently he cleared his throat harshly.

"Sam, may I speak to you as a father?"

A pulse of apprehension went over Houston. But he nodded.

Jackson's intense blue eyes seemed to bore into him. Had he by some means learned of the previous night's episode with Peggy O'Neale? In that moment Houston remembered the kind of a man this was. An incorruptible idealist.

But Andrew Jackson, standing there, was himself experiencing one of the rare indecisions that came to him. He saw before him a man who had what seemed limitless possibilities, mentally brilliant, physically splendid, loyal, courageous, honest. He discovered suddenly that he did not want to ask the question he had come to ask: he did not want to know what took place in Peggy Timberlake's apartment. For once in his life he shrank, out of very affection, from carrying out a determination.

After a pause, he said, "A woman's reputation is a precious and delicate thing. For that matter, so is a man's, particularly a man in the public eye. Indiscretion is sometimes as dangerous as actual iniquity."

The hint was broad, and Jackson felt he had said enough. He would have gone, but Houston's eye held his.

"Sir," he said, "somebody has told you that I visited Mrs. Timberlake yesterday evening before supper in her rooms?"

"Nobody told me. I myself chanced to see you departing." The coldness had returned to Jackson's voice. "I assumed then and do so now that the matter was easily explained."

In that moment Sam Houston demonstrated that he was of more than ordinary clay. He might have grown angry—certainly this was an invasion of privacy. He might have expostulated. But the man he was speaking to was Andrew Jackson. On the other hand, every rule of gentility forbade his saying anything to the detriment of a woman, and Jackson had said he "assumed" the matter was capable of explanation. He sensed that his friend and patron had suddenly decided he did not wish to know something that might be prejudicial and which would achieve no good purpose if he did know it. So Houston, speaking dutifully and respectfully, yet skating on the thinnest edge between truth and untruth, sought to do his duty both by his chief and by the girl.

"I am glad you saw me, sir, and no other, for I know you will understand what I will tell you," he said. "Peggy Timberlake invited me into her parlor because of a mutual interest—in you, General. I had just returned from the Clay headquarters, trying to pick up information as to the trend in town. She happened to see me, and invited me to come in, asking about the election."

"Ah!" Jackson's face cleared. "And what did you tell her?"

"I am bound to say, sir, that I confessed I did not know. We spoke only a few other words before I departed."

A few other words? There had been no need, no room for words, when need for action swept all words away before it.

Andrew Jackson was a fool in no respect. That something else lay behind this he must have felt. But a new feeling grew in him. Age looked on tumultuous youth in that room. An anchorite he was, but not by choice. Certainly he was no Puritan, and the soul of long denials understood the soul of tumbling passions. He was satisfied to let matters rest thus: satisfied to cast out from his mind any thoughts other than those he chose to retain about the young man before him, about the girl who so often delighted him. To Andrew Jackson, the slate was wiped clean.

"Sam," he said, "you are the only man in the world of whom I would have made such an inquiry. Or who would have accepted my presumption——"

"Nothing you could *ever* ask me would be a presumption, sir."

"Yes, it was presumption. And I am satisfied. Will you believe, boy, that I was more deeply concerned for you than for Mrs. Timberlake? Peggy is a child of whom both Mrs. Jackson and I are fond. But you——"

He broke off, and then: "Why, hell's blood and bones, I regard you as my very son!" His voice rasped, getting a little out of control with an emotion strange and unwonted.

Houston could not speak, could not take his eyes from the blue gaze of the General.

"I have no son of my body," went on Jackson after a moment, his voice steadying. "I've felt of you, boy, as the son of my spirit."

He offered his hand and Houston, more touched than he had ever been in his life, bowed his head as he took it, to hide tears that sprang to his eyes.

"General," he said, "if I can only—if I can only live up to that!"

They were awkward for a little time after this, both abashed by the show of emotion, both however feeling a new heart's warmth.

Presently Jackson said, "Well, you'll be going to the sitting of Congress." And he added drily, "I will not be present."

Though, as a senator, he had the privilege of attending the balloting, it would be unseemly for him, as a candidate, to appear.

They parted with another hard pressure of their hands. An unspoken something had passed between them. Jackson, Houston was sure, understood more than he revealed. Houston, Jackson was satisfied, had behaved as a gentleman and a man of honor in a delicate matter. Mutual respect had become something far deeper.

When Houston descended the stair that morning, he saw Peggy O'Neale in the foyer. She was in a pretty gown, and as if she had forgotten entirely the previous night, gave him her brightest smile.

He bowed to her. Said something of no importance. And was gone.

2

Long before the marble clock in the chamber of the House of Representatives indicated the hour of two o'clock in the afternoon, the place was filled. The day had turned out clear, but the roads were still muddy and most of those who went to the Capitol traveled by horse or coach or private equipage, depending on their personal tastes and pocketbooks.

On a fine blooded horse, which was taken away by a servant, rode up a strange and whimsical figure, tall, with an ill-proportioned body clad in a loose surtout, beneath which projected spindly legs in riding breeches and boots. A jockey's cap covered his small round head. John Randolph of Roanoke was an eccentric genius, who was said to drink two quarts or more of porter during a day's session of Congress, and was noted for his acid tongue and his enemies. Since he supported Andrew Jackson, his chief foes at this time were John Quincy Adams and Henry Clay. When he rose in session to bait his enemies, a crowd never failed to be drawn to hear the virulent abuse of which he was capable, uttered in a high, piercing voice like the shrill scream of an angry vixen, and indiscriminately sprinkled with classical apostrophes and pungent stable language. His characterization of Clay was well remembered: "So brilliant, yet so corrupt, which, like a rotten mackerel by moonlight, shines and stinks!"

As Randolph marched up the steps of the Capitol he greeted with a cold nod another striking personage, Senator Thomas Hart Benton of Missouri. A burly man, heavily framed, with black curly hair and side-whiskers, in a full-length greatcoat and black hat, he was celebrated for his immense conceit. He had been likened to a "wild buffalo" in debate, and people still talked of his bloody fight with Andrew Jackson years before. Yet Benton was a man of high abilities, a sincere patriot, and he and the General had become fully reconciled because of their mutual interest in the expansion of the nation. In the Senate they sat side by side, and Benton shared Randolph's detestation of Adams and Clay.

Scarcely had these two entered the doors at the top of the marble steps when Henry Clay himself dismounted from a carriage and followed them. The Cock of Kentucky, so-called because of his high-stepping airs and willingness to battle, was known to be the Adams faction's leader in the coming balloting. A bitter phrase he had originated was much quoted by opponents of Jackson: "I cannot believe that killing two thousand five hundred Englishmen at New Orleans qualifies a man for the various difficult and complicated duties of the Chief Magistracy."

Shortly after Clay passed up the steps, and as the crowd going into the Capitol thickened, a man as much discussed as any of the foregoing appeared—John C. Calhoun, Vice-President of the United States. Without an ounce of superfluous flesh, his lank coal-black hair and luminous eyes making more striking his dark, unsmiling countenance, he had been described as looking "like an arch conspirator waiting for the time to come when he could strike the first blow." All men knew that Calhoun had Presidential ambitions which had received a severe reversal in the recent campaign, in which he was forced to accept the Vice-Presidential seat. But no man knew what thoughts he held in his secretive head.

Now with others hurrying to the climactic session, great-shouldered Sam Houston approached the marble steps. He was greeted by two men, either of whom would have attracted attention anywhere by his remarkable appearance.

One was stalwart and dark, with a massive head, a vast triangular breadth of jaw, and fiercely bristling black eyebrows overhanging cavernous eyes of extraordinary brilliance—the famous Daniel Webster, congressman from Massachusetts, already accounted by many the greatest orator of his day, greater even than Clay, and a member of the Adams camp. With him was a personage almost equally celebrated, his boon companion Junius Brutus Booth, intemperate and eccentric but the greatest stage tragedian of his time, a short dumpy man yet with majestic features resembling those of a Roman emperor.

After they exchanged greetings with Houston, Webster glanced at him shrewdly. "How think you, friend Houston, matters will turn out?" he said.

"General Jackson will be elected as he deserves," replied Houston. Though he and Webster and Booth did not find political kinship, they were old barroom friends and drinking companions.

"I trust you are prepared for disappointment," said Webster.

"General Jackson is at least an American," retorted Houston. "An American proud of his native land, believing in the American genius, and what is more important, the American destiny. We have a sight too many Anglophiles and Francophiles and Italophiles, and I don't know how many other kinds of philes, all aping some foreign country, adopting their manners, airs, and even thinking from that country, and looking down their noses at their own country, the United States, which feeds and nurtures and protects them. The day is going to come, believe me, gentlemen, when this situation will be reversed, and the rundown, decadent nations of Europe will be copying America, looking to America for courage, example, and hope."

"And how do you regard John Quincy Adams?" asked Webster.

"Mr. Adams is—I hardly know what to say. But consider this entrance. You'd never know it was the portal to the Capitol of the American nation by observing those figures on either side of the steps, which are foreign in conception and construction—due to our foreigner-loving Secretary of State, John Quincy Adams, who commissioned them, and who paraphrases the Biblical Nathanael by thinking—if he does not actually say—'Can any good thing come out of the United States?'"

Daniel Webster grinned. He had a fancy to hear what the Tennessee giant would say next.

"On your left," continued Houston, indicating one of the two colossal statues, "the stalwart gymnast with a profuse development of muscle and a benign expression of countenance, who is partially encased in Roman armor, represents War. On the right, the matronly dame, somewhat advanced in life and heavy in flesh, who carries an olive branch as if she wishes it to keep off flies, is Peace. Both are the work of one Luigi Persico, a subject of Italy, who happens to be a favorite of Mr. Adams."

The three reached the top of the steps and entered the Capitol rotunda.

"Here is more Italian work in an American Capitol," said Houston, indicating the bas reliefs on the four walls. "Mr. Adams appears to have a fondness for anything European—up to, and including, marrying his wife in England. These are by three more imported artists, Capellano, Gavelot, and Causici. No doubt they are intended to portray historical episodes but they fail ignominiously. How could it be otherwise? Their sculptors knew nothing of America, its ways, or its history. And they cared less."

He paused and glanced whimsically at his companions.

"I was present one day when a visiting Indian chief first saw those bas reliefs," he said. "The intelligent savage looked at the east doorway, above which is represented the Landing of the Pilgrims, and said, 'There Injun give white man corn.' Turning to the north doorway over which William Penn is depicted making his treaty with the red men, he said, 'There Injun give white man land.' Next gazing at the west doorway, where Pocahontas is saving Captain John Smith from the barbarian executioners, he said, 'There Injun save white man's life.' Finally, pointing to the south doorway where Daniel Boone is shown plunging his knife into the heart of one red man while his foot rests on the dead body of another, he said, 'And there white man kill Injun!'"

An expression of mock sadness came over Webster's face.

"Sam," he said, "I regret to say it, but I fear that in your diatribes you too closely approximate the style of Junius Brutus Booth in one of his more celebrated Shakespearian characterizations."

"And I," said Booth, "must with equal candor state that I fear you too nearly follow the delivery of Daniel Webster in his more eloquent passages."

Houston grinned and lifted his hat. "I couldn't be more highly flattered, gentlemen. To be likened either to the inspiration of a Booth or the eloquent fervor of a Webster is enough to satisfy a man for life. But to be compared to both, almost in one breath, is too much. I will stand the treats as usual this evening at Major O'Neale's, for all the world knows I am undeserving of either comparison."

3

In the domed chamber of the House of Representatives, the desks of the members stood in concentric curves before the dais of the Speaker. Upon each desk was a snuffbox, and beside each desk was a brass spittoon wherein members could practice their tobacco-spitting marksmanship. Above the dais a clock ticked off the minutes.

Already, as Houston entered, the hall was crowded and its lack of proper ventilation was evidenced by its stuffy atmosphere. The galleries were filled to standing room; and the openings between the marble pillars surrounding the Congressional seating space were occupied by sofas and chairs, in which were ensconced persons of special distinction, such as Cabinet members and foreign envoys.

At the stroke of two the senators, forty-seven in number, filed in and took seats reserved at the right of the dais. By this time almost all the desks of the representatives were occupied, but Houston glanced around with a speculative scowl. Where was Henry Clay?

That morning the best information had been that Jackson was sure of ten states; but just before noon Missouri's single representative, Scott, in the face of a blistering denunciation by Senator Benton, also of Missouri, announced he was for Adams. It was known that Maryland and Louisiana were undecided and might be swayed by the Speaker. Interest was great in New York, the delegation of which was exactly split, although its leader, Martin Van Buren, favored Jackson.

Thirteen of the twenty-four states were required to win, and it was freely predicted there would be a long succession of ballots. In such case it was considered probable that the eventual trend would carry Jackson to the Presidential chair.

Houston drummed his desk with his fingers in an agony of nerves. He could not down the fear that the master politician, somewhere in the cloakrooms or foyers, was using every resource of his wonderful persuasiveness to gain a slender, decisive majority, for Clay knew it must be the first ballot or never for his candidate.

Suddenly there was a stir. Houston saw the Kentuckian's not ungraceful figure coming down the aisle. He seemed damnably confident, smiling, nodding, speaking to friends as he made his way to the dais.

Henry Clay knew his dangerous position. Glancing over the assemblage, he mentally computed his strength. He had word that Daniel Webster had succeeded in winning over the Maryland delegation to the side of Massachusetts—and Adams—by a single vote. Louisiana, too, was safe for the moment; but the decisive vote there was in the hands of a timid, unsteady man.

New York, thus far, had been unable to break its deadlock. Clay needed every one of those delegations. Adams' firm nine states, with the addition of Missouri, Maryland, Louisiana, and New York, would be exactly enough for the vital majority.

The Speaker lifted his gavel and rapped on the desk. A hush fell over the chamber as the House came to order. The chaplain droned a lengthy prayer, during which members and onlookers alike fidgeted in their seats. After the "Amen," Henry Clay lifted his voice; a notably clear and pleasant voice, with which he could charm his auditors when he spoke.

"The electoral college having been counted, it was announced that John C. Calhoun is elected Vice-President," he said. "There is, however, no majority for any candidate for President. It therefore becomes the duty of this House of Representatives to select the man who will become the Chief Magistrate of this nation, from among the three highest candidates in point of electoral ballots. Those three are, in alphabetical order, John Quincy Adams, Secretary of State; William H. Crawford, Secretary of the Treasury; and General Andrew Jackson."

A pause, and at once the hum of conversation arose as the crowded hall was seized by excitement and tension. Crawford was out of it—lying helplessly paralyzed at home. It must therefore be between Adams and Jackson. Which?

Again the gavel descended, bringing silence.

"The vote," continued Clay, "will be by states, as stipulated in the Constitution. The chair appoints as tellers the Honorable Daniel Webster of Massachusetts, and the Honorable John Randolph of Virginia. Each state delegation will at this time begin to ballot. When the candidate of its choice has been determined by the majority of its members, the name of that candidate will be written on two pieces of paper. One of these will be placed in the box before Mr. Webster; the other in the box before Mr. Randolph. When all the states have voted, the tellers will then count the ballots and announce each the result he has received without consulting the other. The chair now decrees a recess, for the purpose of allowing the state delegations to ballot."

Down came the gavel. Instantly an uproar filled the chamber as delegations gathered in knots. Under the terms of this contest New York and Pennsylvania, with the largest delegations, had no more voting power than Missouri, which had only one representative.

Daniel Webster, with his swarthy imposing head and face, went forward and took his seat at a table to the left of the Speaker's dais. At the same time John Randolph grimly placed himself in a corresponding

chair at the right. Houston noted that Clay had chosen as tellers a supporter of Adams and a supporter of Jackson: a proper impartiality.

The excitement grew even more intense in the crowded chamber as
the onlookers saw leaders of state delegations, one by one, go to the
tables of the tellers, and drop into the box before each a slip of paper
with the fateful name of one or the other candidate written on it.

Through the galleries whispers and speculations ran:

"They say Clay's got twelve states for his man."

"There's a report that three are pledged on the first ballot to give a
complimentary vote to Crawford."

"Then Jackson couldn't win on the first ballot."

"On the second ballot the Crawford states will likely go to him."

"Louisiana might switch—Maryland, too."

"What about New York? There's where the whole thing may be
decided."

By this time New York alone had not cast its ballot, and every eye
was fixed on the delegation, where Van Buren was seen earnestly arguing, seeking to carry it to the General's side. If New York went for
Jackson, most men predicted certain victory for the General in the second, or at most in the third ballot.

4

In the furiously disputing New York delegation sat an old man, with
white hair and a worn face. He was General Stephen Van Rensselaer, a
good enough man and a veteran of the War of 1812 in which he had
served without distinction, but torn by indecision and the great responsibility placed upon him, for by this time his was the only vote uncast.
He knew that he must decide the ballot of his delegation, perhaps turn
the entire election.

Helplessly he looked at the partisans of both candidates, who were
storming at him, imploring, reasoning, almost threatening. After a few
minutes he dropped his white head forward on the edge of his desk on
his hands, as if in prayer for guidance, or to try to shut out the clamor
about him.

Then all at once he raised his head. His eyes for a moment had
rested on a piece of paper which lay at his feet.

Nobody in the entire chamber noticed the glance, but it was fateful.
The bit of paper was a discarded Adams ballot. Taking this as a sign,
the old general wrote the name of John Quincy Adams on his own ballot
and turned it in.

Now all attention turned on Martin Van Buren, with his high forehead, short figure, and almost dandified attire, as he counted his state's

ballots. It was seen that he flushed, and called to his side another member of the delegation to assist in a recount.

Sensation in the chamber.

Tension grew until it seemed it must explode as the New York ballots were enumerated for the second time. Then hundreds of eyes watched Van Buren write a name on two pieces of paper.

Was it Adams? Or Jackson? Some even tried to guess, by the length of time Van Buren took in writing, which name he was putting down. Adams was shorter than Jackson. Was that the name? Nobody could really tell.

The entire assemblage almost held its breath as Van Buren, with his two pieces of paper, advanced toward the dais and dropped one piece in each of the two tellers' boxes. At that the hum of excitement rose again, increasing in volume, until the Speaker's gavel once more called for order.

Henry Clay had watched the little drama in the New York delegation, but he could not decide in his own mind whether or not it augured favorably for him. Of all those in the chamber he felt he had most at stake on the outcome of the ballot; but his face seemed undisturbed as he made the announcement that the tellers, having counted the ballots of the several states, would give the results of their count.

Daniel Webster rose first. Perspiration beaded his great domed forehead. Over the hushed assemblage sounded his magnificent oratorical voice:

"Mr. Speaker, there are in this box the votes of four states for William H. Crawford—seven states for Andrew Jackson—and thirteen states for John Quincy Adams."

A cheer burst out. But the gavel at once descended. The second teller had not yet announced his result.

Lean and tall, Randolph rose and turned his head with its black Indian hair toward the dais.

"Mr. Speaker," he said in his high, piercing voice, "I find thirteen states for Adams, seven for Jackson, four for Crawford."

Now a roar of delirious triumph from the Adams supporters almost shook the domed ceiling. For minutes it continued in spite of the pounding of the Speaker's gavel. Among the cheers began to sound some hisses.

A member from South Carolina leaped to his feet. "Mr. Speaker," he shouted, "I demand that the galleries be cleared!"

Clay was seen to point with his gavel toward the sergeant-at-arms, though his voice could not be heard in the tumult. That official gestured toward the exits.

The crowd, unwilling but orderly, began to make its way out of the chamber. After some minutes the legislators were left alone.

Silence now fell as the gavel once more descended and the Speaker lifted his voice. Henry Clay announced the greatest personal triumph of his lifetime.

"The votes in the two boxes of the tellers are found to tally," he said. "This being so, and John Quincy Adams having a majority of the votes of these United States, he is thereby duly elected President of the same."

The mighty business was finished. The adjournment came. Stunned, Sam Houston trooped out with his colleagues. To him it seemed the end of everything.

"They will regret this!" he said darkly.

Outside, others echoed his feelings.

Thomas W. Cobb of Georgia stamped about furiously. "Treachery! Damnable false treachery!" he exclaimed.

"Wait till the people of America learn of this!" cried Senator Benton.

John Randolph's sallow face was bitter. "It was impossible to win the game, gentlemen," he said. "The cards were stacked."

Sam Houston, listening to him, at that moment remembered the errand concerning the filly of which the General had spoken. But assuredly this was no time to broach such a matter to Randolph.

5

Andrew Jackson was astonishingly calm and unruffled when he received them in his room—Randolph, Eaton, Benton, Houston, and several others. He smiled and soothed his friends.

"Thank you, gentlemen," he said, "for all your great services for me, and for your expressions toward me. But let us remember that Mr. Adams has been elected President by constitutional processes, and I was defeated by the same. I have no doubt that a great portion of the citizens will be satisfied with the choice. My one regret is that many persons were unpleasantly situated today, compelled to act either against Mr. Adams or myself. I further believe that it is of small moment to the people who is their President, so long as he administers the government rightfully."

He had wine brought up, but shook his head at a suggestion of a testimonial dinner to be given him by his supporters, saying, "It might be viewed as conveying a feeling of complaint which I do not feel, and which I sincerely hope belongs not to any of my friends."

Sam Houston thought to himself that the General's voice actually indicated some semblance of relief. Was he rather glad, after all, that the election now was over and he could return to the peace of the Hermitage?

After Jackson bade each of his visitors good night, and they had all filed out, he turned to Rachel with his curious little half smile.

"My dear," he said, "you can take up smoking again."

Her eyes filled with tears. He patted her on the shoulder and she seized his arm and pressed her head against it. Now at last they could return home. The nightmare was ended. Her tears were tears of gratitude at his kindness, of happiness for herself.

6

"President Monroe," said Jackson, "gives his regular weekly reception at the Executive Mansion tonight. I feel that I should make an appearance."

"Yes, General," said Houston. He glanced at Rachel. She was moving about the apartment, and for the time being, at least, her depression seemed to be forgotten as she already began to pack their effects for the journey back to Tennessee.

"Mrs. Jackson prefers to remain here," the General said. "She feels that she has much to do, to which I accede. Will you and John Eaton share a coach with me?"

On the ride to the White House the General was silent, and neither Houston nor Eaton felt impelled to break in on his thoughts. But at last he said:

"I am told that the Speaker of the House was very adroit at the caucus today, in his stratagems against me."

Houston said soberly, "I never saw anything more skillful—or more unprincipled."

"Mr. Clay detests me," said Jackson after a moment. "But he went to extraordinary lengths to elect Adams. You have heard the rumor?"

"That Clay was promised the Portfolio of Secretary of State?" asked Eaton. "It's all over town."

"We must not pass hurried judgment," said Jackson. "I honestly don't believe that either of the gentlemen would be guilty of such a compact in a matter as grave as the election of a President."

Neither of his companions replied, and by this time the coach was turning into the driveway of the White House.

Throngs of people, ladies and gentlemen well wrapped, for the night was cold, were dismounting from carriages and other vehicles before the pillared portico, which was illumined by torches held by Negro servants. Jackson stepped down out of the coach followed by his two friends, nodded here and there at acquaintances, and entered the open door of the President's dwelling.

The reception was in full swing and the East Room was well filled. Jackson glanced about the large and rather ornate chamber—the pier-glass mirrors on the walls, the rich draperies at the windows, the thick carpeting underfoot, the handsome furniture, the heavy chandeliers suspended from the ceiling and gleaming with a thousand candles.

In the center of the room a crowd surrounded President Monroe, who was acknowledging greetings with his customary half-apologetic, sheeplike expression. Another in the group was also receiving marked attention: John Quincy Adams. He would be there, of course, lionized as the President-elect.

Adams wore a blue suit, the high rolled collar of which almost seemed to support the back of his head within its voluminous folds. From this his face with its bald head gazed out. He acknowledged greetings with a chill expression, a scarcely perceptible bow of his head, and no smile. It was notorious that Adams had no intimate friends.

Jackson observed these things, but he gave little time to such reflections. As he walked forward to pay his respects to the President, Mrs. Cobb, wife of the Georgia congressman, appropriated his arm. She was immensely fat, not entirely humorless, and she shared her husband's indignation at the method of the election.

"It was criminal, General Jackson!" she exclaimed. "It was rigged, and the people of America have been cheated!"

He gave her his thin smile. "However it was arrived at, it will go down on the records as official. But thank you for your interest in my behalf, dear lady."

Houston lingered behind to speak with Billy Carroll and his wife, while Eaton wandered off in another direction. When presently Houston turned to follow the General, he saw something that caused him to quicken his pace through the crowd.

Because his height enabled him to look over the heads of everyone in the room, he observed that John Quincy Adams, who had left the company of the President, and General Jackson, who was proceeding in that direction, would almost inevitably meet if they continued as they were now moving through the crowd. Neither Adams nor Jackson saw it, being engrossed by their immediate surroundings, but Houston wished to hear what took place when the victorious candidate and his defeated rival confronted each other.

He was hardly in time. The surprise of the two men at the encounter was evident. Adams, with his polished bald head and his somewhat pompous manner, even seemed flustered. He almost turned away, but saw he must greet his late opponent and faced him.

The General behaved as if nothing of great moment had transpired that day. Extending his left hand, he said heartily and pleasantly, "How do you do, Mr. Adams? I give you my left hand, for the right, as you see, is devoted to the fair. I hope you are very well, sir."

Adams hesitated, then took the offered hand without warmth.

"Very well, sir; I hope General Jackson is well," he replied. His chilling manner was noticed by all about them, and he showed no sign of a smile to answer the General's smile.

They parted and Jackson, with Mrs. Cobb still clinging to his right arm, passed on to where President Monroe and Mrs. Monroe were receiving their guests.

"So," said Houston, to himself but loudly enough so that those near him glanced at him, "the military hero is genial and gracious, while the unamiable diplomat is cold as an iceberg."

He felt almost as if a personal affront had been given to him, and his dislike for Adams and all that Adams represented deepened. Evidently the New England aristocrat considered himself superior to the frontier soldier. Sam Houston had small use for aristocrats, New England or otherwise.

He looked for the General. Having paid his respects to the President and his wife, Jackson had left Mrs. Cobb with some of her feminine friends, and stood at one side of the room in conversation with John C. Calhoun.

The man whom Webster had called "the Carolina Cataline," seemed very earnest in whatever he was saying. Houston watched a moment, then turned away. He had a deep and abiding dislike for Calhoun, and for a reason that Calhoun presumably had forgotten. Years before, when he was a young subaltern in the army, he brought a delegation of Cherokee chiefs to Washington, to discuss an important land treaty. Traveling with his old Indian friends, to make them more at ease, he dressed like them in Indian garments. But to Calhoun, then Secretary of War, this was an affront. He called the lieutenant aside and furiously berated him for appearing out of uniform, even more for wearing "the garments of barbarous savages." His biting sneers constituted a humiliation which Houston never forgot or forgave. One day, perhaps, he might repay them.

In a few minutes Calhoun left Jackson, and observing the General glance around, Houston went over to him. At the same time he saw the General's eyes following the figure of Henry Clay, who had just crossed the room. It was noticeable that Clay did not return the glance, but moved off almost hurriedly in another direction, as if to make sure he would not have to exchange greetings with the man he had defeated. And yet it appeared to Houston that the Kentuckian's bearing as he passed through the crowd, nodding and smiling, showed elation, even jubilation.

"Let's go back to O'Neale's," said Jackson when Houston came up to him.

The younger man asked no questions. He could see by the General's face that some deep feeling stirred him.

He hurried to find Eaton, and the three called for their coach. On the way back to the hotel Andrew Jackson exploded.

"It's done!" he exclaimed. "Calhoun told me that he has it on the most trustworthy authority. It will not be announced until later, perhaps in a week or two, but Henry Clay has been appointed to the post of Secretary of State for which he bargained like a miser!"

For a few minutes he was silent. Then:

"Did you see Clay avoid me? The Judas of the West has closed the contract and will receive the thirty pieces of silver! His end will be the same! Was ever witnessed such a barefaced corrupt bargain?"

Corrupt bargain! Fighting words.

The old fighting Jackson speaking. In that moment Sam Houston knew that the easy acceptance of the result of the election which the General had indicated earlier, was now changed to the exact reverse. It was war. The musters were already beginning.

Chapter Fifteen

Our country! In her intercourse with for-eign nations may she always be in the right, but our country, right or wrong!

STEPHEN DECATUR

1

All that day long the General had labored in his office, his white hair rumpled, his spectacles on the end of his nose, striving to catch up with his correspondence. On the desk before him a heap of letters still required answer, though his fingers were ink-stained and cramped, and he had sharpened and resharpened his quills until he was weary of it.

It was a vastly changed Andrew Jackson who labored in the small one-room office building which stood a little apart from his house. The Hermitage itself, in that fall of 1826, differed markedly from the one from which he went forth to fight in the British war. The old, awkward blockhouse had been discarded, and in its stead stood a solid, two-story edifice of brick, painted white, built for Rachel on a spot selected by her, with a broad lawn shaded by fine trees, and a full acre of flower beds traced by brick-edged walks.

This September day was fair, even warm, so that the door of the little office building stood open to admit the air, and Jackson gnawed the end of his quill, seeking for the words which exactly would express his thought.

Before the day, a year before, when Henry Clay dragooned Congress into giving the Presidency to John Quincy Adams, the General had been a candidate who, if not actually unwilling, was at least inactive. He had expressed his position in the one statement he issued before the election of 1824:

I have never been an applicant for office. I never will. I have no desire, nor do I expect ever to be called to fill the Presidential chair, but should this be the case, it shall be without exertion on my part.

A strange declaration, when to be President of the United States was the supreme height of ambition; but one completely sincere. And yet, amazingly, he had come within an ace of winning without campaigning, without soliciting a single vote.

It was all different with him now. The "corrupt bargain" aroused all his fighting instinct. Within a week after the official announcement that Henry Clay actually was named as Secretary of State by Adams—first word of which came from Calhoun—Andrew Jackson was an open, avowed, and strenuously active candidate for the next election.

Since that day he had devoted all his fierce competitive spirit to the defeat of his enemies, Clay and Adams, in spite of the knowledge that it would be far harder to beat them in a race where the administration asked for re-election, than it would have been in the first campaign, had he but given to it then a tithe of the exertion he had devoted to the matter since.

He believed Clay and Adams were perfidious politicians who deserved retribution. He detested them because of the slur against his wife in the preceding campaign. But there was a reason more important to his present thinking than these personal ones.

Not until his actual defeat did he fully appreciate the miracle that had nearly been achieved. He had thought of going to the White House as he would have gone to the command of an army, to give the nation such ability and leadership as he was able, with very little new or constructive in the way of ideas except that he intended to see that there was honesty and efficiency in government.

Then came the awakening. Until the election of 1824 the political operations of the nation were in the hands of men of family, wealth, education, influence, but not of all the people. Beginning with George Washington, and continuing through John Adams, Thomas Jefferson, James Madison, James Monroe, and John Quincy Adams, a steady parade of aristocrats had gone to the White House. Federalists, anti-Federalists, Republicans, and Whigs politely exchanged the major offices of the country, blandly seeing to it that only those they considered to have "fitness for office" ever had a chance at those offices.

But with the rise of Jackson, the people for the first time spoke. He was of them, born in humble circumstances, self-educated, thinking their thoughts, fighting his way to the top without family or influence, except that which he created for himself. Disorganized, inarticulate, often unlettered, the common men rallied to this common man, ignored the party caucuses, and were prevented from sweeping him into the Presidency only by the smooth manipulations of Clay and his lieutenants.

Andrew Jackson thus had created a great responsibility, and in his deep concentration of thinking during the past year, this responsibility, which he accepted instinctively and without hesitation as he always assumed responsibility, led him to the study of many matters, the touchstone of his interest being the interest of the ordinary people of America as against privileged interest.

He was far from young, and still often ailing. But he labored endlessly. Letter after letter flew from his pen, to friends, to well-wishers, to political leaders of various kinds, even to enemies.

As to the last, there was, for example, the time when Jackson blew up at a paragraph in a letter from Senator John Eaton:

Southard, Secretary of the Navy, at a private dinner party, made the statement that James Monroe, who was Secretary of War when the Battle of New Orleans was fought, deserved the laurels for that victory, saying that Jackson abandoned the army and was on the way home when Monroe's peremptory order sent him back to the threatened city.

When he read that, the old man crumpled the written page in his fist, his white hair bristling, his blue eyes blazing.

"God damn the pusillanimous liar to hell!" he cried aloud.

Then he seized his pen and wrote hotly to Eaton. One paragraph in that missive typified the whole:

The War Department's support of my army was so tardy and ineffective that had New Orleans fallen, either Monroe or his ordnance officer should have been shot for negligence. Inquire of Mr. Southard if those were his very words. I shall call him to account severely, very severely, if this is true.

He signed his bold signature, put the letter on top of the heap of replies already completed, and reached for the next.

2

Plunged deep in his labor, he did not glance up when he heard a horse's hoofs in the driveway outside, until there was a little knock at the open door. Then he rose, and a pleased look dawned upon his thin face.

"Sam Houston!" he exclaimed.

The congressman, just back from Washington, was attired in a tall beaver hat, patent-leather military stock, ruffled shirt, bottle-green coat with long tails, and fawn-colored trousers, very tight-fitting, with straps beneath the insteps of his patent-leather shoes. The General's eyes twinkled. At times he was secretly amused by his younger friend's dashing taste in his garb.

"Come in, boy," he said heartily. Between them had grown a deeply affectionate relationship, a full understanding and trust.

When they were seated, Jackson lit his pipe while Houston bit the end of a long cheroot and set a flame to it with a paper spill which he touched amicably to the tinder his host had kindled. The old man listened eagerly as his friend related gossip concerning Washington. Not long ago he had despised politics, but of late he had come to understand it as a battleground as valid, often even more important, than the field of arms.

"You heard of the duel between Randolph and Clay?" Houston presently inquired.

"The barest report of it."

"The affair took place after I spoke against the appointment here of your old ill-wisher, Joseph P. Erwin——"

Jackson nodded. Erwin was his bitter enemy. He was one of the troublemakers who stirred up the duel with Dickinson. More importantly to the General, he was Clay's cousin, and editor of the Nashville *Banner and Whig*, a newspaper which fought Jackson and everything he stood for, right in his own home town.

"The Senate debated Clay's proposal to call a meeting of Latin-American nations," continued Houston. "As you know, John Randolph of Roanoke is in the Senate now. I knew his opinion of the Secretary of State might be worth hearing, so I was in the gallery. He opened by addressing Calhoun, who as Vice-President was presiding, as follows: 'Mr. Speaker! I mean Mr. President of the Senate, and would-be President of the United States, which God in His infinite mercy avert!' "

Jackson gave his short bark of a laugh. "Randolph has a mordant tongue. What did Calhoun do?"

"Nothing. Just sat there, his face pinched and black, while Randolph went on—you know how he screams when he's aroused. Toward the end of his attack on Adams and Clay, he spoke of 'the coalition of Blifil and Black George—a combination unheard of until now, of the Puritan and the Blackleg.' "

Jackson nodded, his eyes gleaming. He understood the reference to the two most unfragrant characters in Fielding's *Tom Jones*. Adams, of course, was the dishonest Puritan; Clay the unsavory Blackleg.

"The Senate was in an uproar," said Houston. "Clay challenged and they met in Virginia, at ten paces. Randolph fired in the air. Clay's shot perforated Randolph's coattail. They shook hands. 'You owe me a coat, Mr. Clay,' says Randolph. 'I'm glad the debt is no greater,' says Clay. They exchanged cards and parted amicably."

Jackson chuckled. "Someone ought to teach John Randolph not to waste good bullets. But Erwin was appointed after all?"

Houston nodded. "He seems aggrieved by some of the things I said about him on the floor of Congress."

"Has that boot-licking puppy made threats?"

"A few."

"I think he's too big a coward to challenge. Still, he might do it, he's a fool—anyone who follows Clay is a fool. If he does, it's my quarrel you'll be fighting. I've had some small experience in that line." A blue steel gleam from Jackson's eyes. "I'll turn my own pistols over to you and you can sharpen up your shooting right here on the Hermitage grounds. I'll make a pistoleer out of you, boy."

"Thank you, sir. But there's no challenge as yet."

"I trust there won't be. I'd hate to have anything happen to you, Sam. Do you know this will be your last term in Congress?"

Houston was astounded. "Why—what do you mean—sir?"

"Billy Carroll's finishing his third consecutive term as governor of Tennessee. Under the state constitution he can't succeed himself. I intend for you to stand for governor at the next election."

Houston's amazement grew. "You think the voters would be willing to give me such an office?"

For a moment Jackson's half-grin showed. "I think we might accomplish things even more surprising than that," he said, the grin departing. "There are matters of the greatest importance coming up, and I need every man's help. Look at this." He picked up a newspaper and indicated a paragraph. "The *Banner and Whig*. Your friend Erwin's newspaper. This is a pronouncement of John Marshall, Chief Justice of the United States Supreme Court, who is a damned Federalist, my personal enemy, and I think the enemy of his country. Read it, sir!"

Houston obeyed. The paragraph read:

A state is an organization of politicians who prey on society. Our fathers proposed to circumvent such roguery by establishing a government controlled by the intelligent, the cultured, the educated, the responsible, the propertied men—the upper half of the population. Liberty can only be preserved by excluding the ignorant and improvident from a voice in government through suffrage qualifications.

"Hamiltonian Federalism!" said the old General grimly. "For an aristocracy of birth they would substitute an oligarchy of wealth. To get rid of such we fought two wars with Britain. And speaking of war, in government there's always jeopardy of war. Which brings me to my point. I say to you, sir, that a poor man's life is worth as much to him as a rich man's is to him. And therefore a poor man has an implicit right to cast his vote on issues which may bring him into a conflict where his life and property are at stake. I led the fight in the Tennessee constitutional convention against putting just such a property qualification on the voter. I want to purge that so-called political philosophy from this nation." He paused. "Did you ever know Commodore Stephen Decatur, Sam?"

Houston shook his head.

"A brilliant naval officer and a patriot, who brought glory to the flag, but was killed in a duel by a man not worthy to latch his shoes. I shall never forget his toast: 'Our country! In her intercourse with foreign nations may she always be in the right; but our country, right or wrong!' "

Jackson uttered the sentiment with a peculiar ring. "That has metal in it, boy. The kind of metal those lily-livered silk-stockings of the East haven't got. I——"

He broke off and gazed out through the open door. "There's a coach coming up the driveway."

He rose and stepped to the door to look. "Why, if I'm not mistaken, that coach yonder belongs to Colonel John Allen, master of Allendale, over near Gallatin. I must welcome them."

3

The coach, drawn by four stylish bays, with a black coachman and footman in the high box, turned up toward the house as Jackson and Houston stepped out of the office. Rachel Jackson had seen it also, and she came to the door of the house so that the three of them were there to greet the visitors.

Nimble as a monkey, the footman was on the ground, opening the coach door with a bow. An austere personage in blue broadcloth, white silk stock, and gray bell-crowned hat, descended.

"Colonel Allen!" exclaimed Jackson, warmly. "Welcome, sir, to the Hermitage!"

The colonel took his proffered hand. "Thank you, General Jackson, sir. And you, Mrs. Jackson. It's a pleasure to see you both in such apparent good health."

He turned to hand out from the coach a girl, slim and frail-looking, but very pretty. In her blue eyes was a wide stare, the way her lips half-parted hinted of immaturity, and the curls of her yellow hair and the ruffles of her dress somehow suggested vanity. She was perhaps eighteen.

"General and Mrs. Jackson," said Colonel Allen in his stately manner, "it is my honor and pleasure to present my daughter, Eliza."

The old General bowed with stiff gallantry, and the girl looked at him with all her eyes. This was the greatest man in America, or so said her father.

She heard the General's voice:

"May I present my friend, the congressman from this district, General Houston—Miss Allen—Colonel Allen."

Houston's bow was always impressive.

"I'd have been over sooner," Colonel Allen was explaining, "but Eliza would come, so I took the coach instead of riding horseback."

"At least you're here now," said Jackson, "and we're delighted that you brought Miss Eliza. Let us sit out here in the shade of the trees for the present. The day has been oppressive, but with evening the fever in the air cools down. Aaron!" he called to his Negro butler, who came from the house. "Colonel Allen will have whiskey with a lump of sugar. General Houston the same. Mrs. Jackson and I, lemon squash. And," he turned his quizzical gaze on Eliza, "what will please this little flower of yours, Colonel?"

The girl smiled prettily. "I think I'd like a lemon squash, too, if you please, General," she said.

Rachel Jackson took her hand and led the group over to an arrangement of lawn chairs, where they seated themselves while the servant brought the drinks.

"I've given up liquor," said the General to Allen. "The old army trouble—it makes me careful these days. Limewater and squash are the limits of my indiscretions now. A penalty of old age."

"Pshaw, General, you're younger than most men half your age," protested the colonel.

The conversation turned to horses, an ever-present interest with the Master of the Hermitage.

"It's my hope to obtain a good filly got by your stallion Chandos, out of a mare with a strain from Jess Haynie's Maria," Jackson said. "A wonderful creature, that little Maria." He shook his head. "I never was able to beat her. Decatur, Dungannon, Doublehead, Western Light—she lowered my colors on them all." He gave a little rueful laugh. "At the end I was willing to join Jess Haynie, since I couldn't beat him, and offered to bet a thousand dollars that Maria could defeat any horse in the world."

"That's why I'm here," said Allen. "I received your letter. The filly I have in mind for you, Emma J., is exactly what you've described. Of course, she's not been proved yet."

"General Jackson," said Houston, "had hoped for some of the Sir Archie strain. But I fear I was a poor negotiator. John Randolph of Roanoke asks too high a price for his fillies."

Jackson smiled. "Don't blame yourself, Sam. John Randolph may be a little on the eccentric side—and this he's the first to admit—but he's a horse trader. I may get to him yet."

4

The talk ran on, and Eliza Allen, sitting still and upright like a lovely blonde doll, exchanged a few commonplaces with Mrs. Jackson, but she really listened to the conversation of the men, especially when they turned from horses to other matters.

She was not insensible of the honor of sitting in company with these important personages, and her eyes roamed about her. The plantation resembled a little village, with its great house, the Negro cabins, the two barns, the sheepcote, the blacksmith shop, the cooking house, the small office building, and a summer house in the middle of the flower garden. Thoroughbred horses grazed in white-painted paddocks. In the pastures were fat cattle and sheep, and the field hands were busy in the cotton and corn fields which stretched beyond. A beautiful, pleasant, and prosperous place, altogether.

But Jackson was speaking to her father. "No, I had no ambition for the Presidency. My name was advanced without my wish or permission. When I failed of election I was content—until I learned of the manner in which it was done. But now I'm in the race, sir, head, feet, and hocks, and I trust I'll have your support."

"You'll not only have mine, General, but you'll have the support of virtually every man in Tennessee, sir."

"By the way," said Jackson, with a new thought. "You may be interested to know, Colonel, that General Houston here will stand for governor when Billy Carroll retires."

"Were I not already convinced of General Houston's great qualities of mind and character," said Allen, "I'd nevertheless instantly be a supporter of any friend of General Jackson's."

"Why, sir, that's most handsome," said Houston. "And I do soundly agree with you that the friendship of Old Hickory is the highest recommendation any man can have."

Eliza, sitting to one side with Mrs. Jackson, was becoming bored, not so much because she found little to talk about with her hostess, as because she was accustomed to being herself the center of attention.

Sam Houston noticed it. Excusing himself, he rose, and came over to tower above her where she sat.

"Miss Allen," he said, "could you find a moment to converse with one of what must be a whole army of your admirers?"

Eliza smiled up at him, her afternoon suddenly become golden.

"Show her my flowers, Sam," said Rachel.

The girl rose and walked with him in the garden. Sam Houston could be very charming, and from that moment the hours passed most pleasantly for her. His voice was deep, his manners graceful, his words delightfully complimentary. She thought to herself that never in her life had she met a man so tall or so handsome.

The Allens remained at the Hermitage for the night. But Houston excused himself after supper, bowed over the hand of Mrs. Jackson— whom he addressed affectionately as "Aunt Rachel"—hesitated appreciably over the hand of Eliza, with a smiling look into her eyes until she dropped them, and rode back to Nashville.

As he left, Colonel Allen stopped him at the door.

"I trust you'll honor us by coming to Allendale soon, General Houston?" he said.

"I'd heartily like to do so, sir," said Houston.

The golden-haired girl heard the invitation given and accepted, pretending not to notice.

5

Sam Houston had spoken lightly of his quarrel with Erwin, but the matter was more serious than he indicated to Jackson. He rode back to Nashville that night because there would be a challenge, he was sure of it, and none must be allowed to say that he absented himself so he could not be found when it was delivered.

In his room at the Nashville Inn that evening he wrote a brief note before going to bed, and sealed it in an envelope with a superscription: *To be published in case of my death, Sam Houston.*

One paragraph expressed his credo:

My firm and undeviating attachment to General Jackson has caused me all the enemies I have, and I glory in the firmness of my attachment. I will die proud in the assurance that I deserve, and possess, his perfect confidence.

That done, he slept well. Next morning, while he was shaving, the expected happened. The manager of the hotel came to his door with an envelope in his hand.

"This was left for you, sir," said the manager. "I thought, since it might be of importance, I should deliver it in person."

"Thank you, sir. Come in," said Houston. "Will you wait a minute?"

He opened the envelope and read the note it contained, a stiff inquiry if a certain aspersion imputed to Houston was as represented. It was signed *Joseph P. Erwin.*

"Who left this?" he asked.

"I was not present at the time, sir, since the gentleman came late," said the manager. "But I understand it was General William A. White, sir."

"He asked for a reply?"

"He told the night clerk that if one were forthcoming it should be left at the desk."

Houston sat at a table and wrote swiftly:

Joseph Erwin, Sir: If it was reported to you that I stated on the floor of Congress that you were unfit for the position of Postmaster of Nashville, the report is correct. And I still am of the same opinion.

Yr. obd't serv't, Sam Houston.

He signed his name with a great flourish, sealed the note in an envelope addressed to Erwin, and handed it to the manager.

"Be so kind as to deliver this to whoever asks for it," he said.

The manager bowed and departed. Houston finished dressing, went down to the dining room and ate breakfast, and then walked into the taproom. It was midmorning but already the place had custom. A slender man in a plum-colored coat and a tall hat raised his glass. He was a friend, Colonel Jack McGregor.

"Toddy, General?" he asked.

"Too early, thanks," said Houston.

"I've had the word." McGregor glanced slyly at him. "It's to be governor, isn't it? Old Hickory's told a few of the inner circle. I drink to your success—of which I'm well assured."

Houston grinned his thanks. Then he said, "I'm glad to find you this morning, Jack. Before I think of politics, there's some other business intervening. Come over to a table where we can talk—and I think I'll have that toddy after all."

They found a table in the corner of the taproom, and he told McGregor of his correspondence with Erwin.

"I reckon that note I sent him will bring the bear out of the tree," he concluded.

"Yes, sir. I think it will." McGregor's manner was suddenly grave. "If Erwin challenges, I offer you my services, here and now."

"Thank you, Jack," said Houston. "This relieves my mind somewhat. Will you take care of any necessary preliminaries that may arise?"

Chapter Sixteen

*The saddle is on the other horse, General
White, and that's enough to be understood between gentlemen.*

SAM HOUSTON

1

The worst part of it was the uncertainty. Houston stayed in his
room, sometimes walking the floor with impatience. He did not know
what his enemy would do—nobody did. If Erwin challenged him he
would go through with the duel, but the eternal hours of waiting seemed
worse than the duel itself.

Houston took a drink from a whiskey bottle. Then another.

They did not help to calm him.

About noon McGregor at last came.

"How about it, Jack?" Houston asked.

"It's most extraordinary," said his friend. "Erwin's found it difficult to
get a second to deliver his challenge. It appears that you have a lot of
friends in Nashville, General."

Houston nodded.

"But he's found someone now," McGregor went on. "You'll scarcely
believe the kind of fellow."

"Who is he?"

"A stranger in this town. A man with—to say the least for it—an unusual name. He calls himself Colonel Smith T."

"T what?"

"That's it. T—or Smith T—is his last name. Dresses like a river gambler. Said to be a gunsmith by trade. Refers to himself as a 'professional
duelist,' and uses weapons of his own manufacture. Supposed to have
half a dozen killings to his credit, and habitually terrorizes his home
territory, which is Missouri."

"A hired bravo! To run Erwin's errands? Jack, I'll have nothing to do
with such trash."

"Very proper," McGregor nodded. "I thought that would be what
you'd say. Well, my instructions are plain. I'll go back down."

"Wait a minute. I'll go with you," said Houston.

His impatience was coupled now with curiosity. They descended and
Houston paused within the tavern, at a window, while McGregor
stepped out on the porch. It was evident that rumor of the impending

challenge had run through the town, for many men were in the square before the inn. At McGregor's appearance there was a stir in a group on the opposite side, and a tall man walked rapidly across.

Houston watched with intense interest.

McGregor stood at the top of the steps eyeing the stranger as he came to a halt on the ground below. He was a rakish, rawboned man, dressed very flashily in a high-collared salmon-colored coat, an extravagant waistcoat, and a ruffled shirt. His face was flushed, and Houston wondered whether the flush was from excitement, then decided it must be from drink. The fellow's tall hat was tilted at an aggressive angle.

"Are you Colonel McGregor?" he asked in a hoarse voice.

"I am."

"Colonel John Smith T, at your service."

McGregor nodded.

"I have, sir, a communication from Colonel Erwin to General Houston, which I now hand to you," said Smith T.

McGregor made no motion to accept the paper from the man, whom he regarded coldly. "General Houston can receive no communication from your hands, since you are not a citizen of this state," he said.

Smith T's face grew purple. For a moment he glared as if tempted to offer a challenge of his own. But then he turned on his heel and tramped away.

Houston was grinning when McGregor entered the tavern.

"I saw the whole thing," he said. "It isn't often that a prospective principal gets to witness the exchange between his representative and the other side. I must say that your behavior, Jack, was correct, most correct. If Erwin wants a duel, he'll have to find someone with standing to act as his second."

A man with graying hair, and a set of side whiskers almost white, approached them. He was dressed soberly in black.

"Dr. Shelby!" said Houston. "How's my old friend the surgeon, who patched me up after the Horseshoe Bend?"

"All right," said the physician nodding. He and Houston had been friends ever since the Creek War. "I saw your conversation on the porch, Colonel McGregor," he went on. "Colonel Smith T, isn't it? I happen to know of him, from a visit I recently paid to St. Louis. You may be interested."

"We are," said Houston.

"I've never met the man personally," said Dr. Shelby, "but I'm told he is a rapscallion who defaulted on a debt—gambling on a horse, it was—and when an effort was made to collect, killed his creditor and jumped the country, wherever he was living at the time—Kentucky I believe. He went to Missouri, which is the stamping ground of Senator Tom Benton."

"Yes?" prompted Houston.

"In that part of the world this man's regarded as a common killer—would have been hung long since, were it not for the rather sketchy criminal code and law enforcement of that state. On top of this he's a card sharper; and Missouri, whose folks are a sight more sensitive on the subject of cheating at cards than on homicide, has become too uncomfortable for him. That's why he's here—living in sharp circumstances, I understand."

"Hum," said Houston. "It's quite possible, then, that Erwin gave him a few dollars tip to bring that challenge."

"He may be a dangerous man," suggested McGregor.

"I can deal with dangerous men," said Houston.

2

Later in the afternoon Houston and McGregor, tiring of the game of Old Sledge they were playing in the taproom, stepped out on the porch for a breath of fresh air. Shelby was with them, and the talk was light in spite of the edge of tension beneath.

"By God—look!" the doctor suddenly cried.

Houston saw Smith T advancing, but accompanied this time by an elderly and portly gentleman, whom he recognized as General William A. White. He was a lawyer, well enough respected, who had served in the New Orleans campaign; but he was a Clay supporter and no friend of Jackson, or Houston.

McGregor, as accredited representative, stepped forward to meet the two. But to the surprise of everyone present, Smith T himself took a document from his inner pocket, and instead of handing it to McGregor, thrust it into the hands of Houston.

"There, Colonel McGregor!" exclaimed White triumphantly. "I reckon he'll not deny receiving it now!"

The action violated the code. McGregor should have been given the document, and since Smith T had been rejected, General White, if he was interesting himself in the matter, should have tendered it.

Houston shook his head and turned on his heel.

"I have not received it," he said. "I do not know its contents. I will not open it, but will refer its contents to Colonel McGregor." His anger was growing. "As for you, General White, since you see fit to busy yourself in this affair, I'll receive a challenge from you, with pleasure."

"I will receive one from you, General Houston."

"The saddle is on the other horse, General White, and that's enough to be understood between gentlemen."

"If I call on you, there'll be no shuffling, I suppose?"

"Try me!" said Houston.

Smith T thrust himself forward. "I want to be informed," he began truculently, "if your reason for not receiving the challenge from me is solely because I live in another state."

Sam Houston turned on him, his voice lowered to a menacing bass growl.

"No, sir!" he said. "I refuse because inquiry reveals that your standing and character in your own country debars you from the title of gentleman—*and you know this well!*"

Men held their breaths. It was a moment for the instant drawing of weapons, a street battle without formalities.

The two chief actors stared hard at each other. But it was in Houston's eyes that the devil of danger danced, not in Smith T's. The more powerful will won. The professional duelist took a backward step. A moment, and he turned and hurried away.

That evening Smith T, reputed slayer of six men, without giving any explanation, took a river boat, for—elsewhere, oblivion, to be forgotten, after his one moment of failure in the glaring limelight.

3

Andrew Jackson was astonished, not at the fact of the challenge, but at the strange manner of its delivery, and particularly at the curious twist whereby the adversaries were chosen.

Sam Houston himself recounted the story, and the General listened intently.

"Well conducted! Marvelously well conducted!" he exclaimed when he heard of Smith T's gasconade, and the manner in which he backed down. The General's eyes flashed, and Houston had the feeling that he would like to carry on the affair himself.

"And after that?" Jackson asked him. "What happened?"

"I received a challenge from General White, delivered promptly and in due form by a friend of his, a Dr. Anderson. General White declared that he had no personal animosity against me, but his honor demanded a meeting."

Jackson nodded. "Understandable. What about Erwin?"

"He appears to have lost his appetite for carrying the quarrel further."

"And left White holding the bag!"

"Yes."

"I said he was a puppy! Mark my words, Sam, Erwin will never recover from this! He'll never be able to hold up his head again!"

"I reckon not, sir."

"But what about the terms of your meeting with White? Pistols, of course. Twenty-four paces?"

"McGregor made that suggestion. But Dr. Anderson, while accepting the choice of weapons, felt the distance was too far. His principal, he said, is no very good shot——"

"So White wants to get closer to his work! You have to admire that. And what did you do?"

"When I thought on it, I realized that General White is probably the poorest shot of the three involved in this affair with me—Erwin, Smith T, and White himself. So I told them pistols—at *five* paces. Even White ought to be able to hit a mark as big as I am at that distance."

"Very generous of you, boy. I'm sure General White appreciates it."

"Dr. Anderson protested," said Houston. "He called the distance 'barbarous.' But General White approved. 'He knows my unsteady hand and gives me an advantage,' he told Jack McGregor."

Jackson drew a deep breath. "Before God, this General White is a very high-toned gentleman, and I regret he has been drawn into the thing through the cowardice of his associates."

He thought a moment. "But you, Sam, the quarrel was forced on you. As I've already told you, you shall use these grounds for pistol practice, and I will furnish my own pistols for the meeting, if they're acceptable. Further—in consideration for my deep feeling for you, boy—I'll stand up with you, as one of your seconds, if you'd like it."

Houston was touched by the offer. "I can't tell you, sir, how honored I feel at your suggestion," he said with emotion. "But I must refuse it with my deepest thanks. I couldn't think, sir, in view of the position you now occupy before the nation, of involving you in any part of a duel."

Jackson seemed almost regretful. "I suppose you are right," he said reluctantly. And after a moment: "Then remember this. When you draw, bite on a bullet. It will help steady your aim."

Thus they parted.

4

At twenty minutes before four o'clock, on the morning of September 22, Sam Houston was awakened by the barking of a dog.

In the darkness he stirred, and rose on his elbow, his eyes straining about him. Then he heard the heavy breathing of Jack McGregor in the next bed, and realized where he was.

The house in which they had slept that night belonged to Sanford Duncan, whose lands lay in Kentucky just north of the Tennessee line. Duncan was a member of the Kentucky legislature which vainly memorialized Henry Clay and the Congressional delegation of its state to vote for Jackson the previous year. When the situation was explained to him, he offered his grounds for the duel, since there was a law against such meetings in Tennessee and none in Kentucky, and even agreed to act as referee for the exchange of fire.

Noiselessly, in order not to awaken his companion, Houston rose from his bed and stole to the window. Though it was still night, the moon gave a silvery illumination to the landscape, promising a fair day. By the eerie light he saw the dog that had awakened him, a clumsy half-grown hound pup, which now sat on the grass, its tongue lolling out, gazing at the house expectantly.

Houston smiled. Sanford Duncan possessed two pups of the same litter. Because they fought frequently and with delight, he named them Andrew Jackson and Tom Benton, for those two battling statesmen. Houston, of course, cheered for the dog that bore the name of his friend, in those skirmishes; and he observed that Andrew Jackson almost always won them.

Now he recognized the dog sitting out there in the moonlight as his favorite, and to him it seemed a good omen that the pup named Andrew Jackson had awakened him. With the half-smile still on his face he went to the kitchen.

This was the morning of the duel. General White would meet him at dawn.

Houston disliked the institution of the duel from principle, considering the practice barbarous in spite of Jackson's disagreement with his views on the code of honor. But he found that he felt no particular excitement at the near prospect of the meeting, now that he faced it, even though this was his first.

In the kitchen fireplace embers still glowed from the previous evening. Stirring these, he placed on them a small iron crucible in which were some pieces of lead, to mold bullets.

Nobody in the house stirred. He watched the lead until it ran together in the crucible, became a silver liquid. Now he brought an iron instrument resembling a pair of pliers, except that its jaws when closed formed a perfectly round chamber—a bullet mold. Holding it above the crucible, with a pewter spoon for a ladle, he poured some of the molten lead through a small opening called the sprue until the chamber was filled, and let it harden. When he opened the jaws of the mold a lead ball fell out, perfectly round except for a small projecting piece left by the sprue, which he shaved off smoothly with a cutter.

It was a perfect casting. Just as he finished the ball and placed it on the kitchen table, he heard the shrill crow of a gamecock outside.

Another good omen. Houston admired a gamecock's courage. He picked up the new ball and marked it on one side for the rooster, on the other side for the dog. He resolved to use it for his first shot.

Then he cast a few more balls, and presently was joined by Duncan and McGregor in the kitchen.

"Up and busy already?" said Duncan.

"I like to make sure my bullet is perfect," Houston replied. He handed the marked ball to McGregor. "Use that particular one to load my pistol, Jack," he said, and he told them the story of the dog and the fighting cock.

A Negro woman servant appeared and silently made them batter cakes and coffee. By the time they finished this light breakfast Duncan said that it was time to go to the meeting place.

Together the three men walked down a dusky lane, saying little, feeling the strange reserve toward each other that almost equaled that which men feel when about to witness an execution. The eastern sky was bright, but the sun had not yet risen over the horizon when they arrived at the edge of the field that had been designated. The fence of this field ran directly along the state line, which was why it was chosen.

They found the other party already there, swathed in greatcoats because of the morning chill. There were formal greetings between the seconds. General White and Houston did not speak to each other.

Sanford Duncan walked out between the two groups.

"Gentlemen," he said in a grave and deep voice, "we are met here on an occasion both solemn and unhappy. May I ask if there is any possibility of reconciliation, before this meeting takes place which may be fatal to one or both of the principals, each of whom I hold in highest respect and esteem?"

A moment's silence. Then Dr. Anderson's voice:

"General White, the challenger, requests that we proceed, unless General Houston desires to withdraw."

McGregor answered quickly. "General Houston will not withdraw."

"Then, gentlemen," said Duncan, "it becomes the duty of the seconds to see to the loading of the weapons."

"Remember, Jack," said Houston. "Load my piece with the ball I marked this morning."

McGregor nodded and opened his hand. The marked ball already was in his palm.

A few minutes passed while the seconds, under the supervision of Duncan, were occupied in measuring the powder, ramming home the bullets in the two pistols, seeing to the flints, making sure that everything was in deadly readiness.

McGregor brought the pistol to Houston. "The ball you gave me is in there," he said.

"Thank you, Jack."

"God bless you, Sam."

Houston remembered Jackson's injunction, took a second lead ball from his pocket, and placed it between his teeth.

Over the woods to the east the first edge of the rising sun gleamed, suddenly brilliant.

"The time has come, gentlemen," said Duncan. "The principals will remove their heavy coats."

While they did so, giving the garments to the seconds, he solemnly

counted off five paces, digging a narrow scratch in the frosty grass with
his heel at each end of the measured distance.

"Five paces—fifteen feet," he said. "That, so I understand, is the
agreement?"

Both seconds nodded.

There was no advantage in positions, since Duncan had paced off his
line at exact right angles to the rising sun so that neither man would
have it in his eyes. Yet the seconds tossed a coin for the choice. Anderson won. After consultation with White, he indicated the north side.

"The principals will take their places," commanded Duncan.

Houston went to his mark and stood with his right side and pistol
arm toward his antagonist, his shadow gigantic as it stretched away toward the west. His teeth closed on the bullet in his mouth, biting hard,
and he tasted an acrid flavor of lead in his saliva.

General White's portly figure also had taken position.

"Gentlemen," said Duncan, "you may now cock your pistols, but you
will hold them muzzle down, pointed at the ground, until I give the
signal. The signal will be the word *Fire*, after which I will count slowly
to four, then give the word *Stop*. At any moment during that count,
but not before or after, you are at liberty to discharge your pieces. Is
that understood?"

"Yes," said Houston.

White gave a nod.

"Then, gentlemen, are you ready?" asked Duncan.

"Ready, sir," said Houston, through his teeth clenched on the pistol
ball.

"Ready, sir," White echoed.

So close were they standing that in that moment it seemed to Houston that when they raised their pistols the muzzles would almost touch.
He must fire quickly, if he fired at all.

Duncan's voice beginning the fateful count: "*Fire—one—two—
three——*"

He raised his pistol, pulled the trigger, felt the jolt of its recoil in his
palm.

If White fired he did not know it.

When the white smoke of the discharge cleared, he saw his antagonist
sinking slowly to the ground, his hand at his lower side. He had dropped
his pistol.

Instantly Dr. Anderson, McGregor, and Duncan were about the
stricken man. At once McGregor rose and came toward Houston.

"He's bad hit," he said. "We must get across the border into Tennessee
at once."

Houston handed him the pistol, which McGregor placed in the case
with its mate he had picked up from the ground. White's pistol also had
been discharged, Houston noted, but he had not heard the report or the

sound of the ball when it passed him. The shots must have been simultaneous, the smoke and report of his own weapon masking the other. He began to walk with McGregor south toward the fence that marked the state line.

A weak voice followed them. "General Houston——"

"I must go back," Houston said to McGregor.

He returned and knelt beside the prostrate man. General White's clothing had been unbuttoned by the doctor who was making an examination. His broad face was pallid, the brows drawn, the lips twisted with pain.

"Where is he hit?" Houston asked the physician.

"Shot through the groin," said Dr. Anderson.

Feebly White turned his eyes up to Houston. "General, you have killed me," he said in a faltering voice.

"I am sincerely and profoundly sorry," said Houston, and he meant it. "But you know it was forced on me."

"I know it . . . and I forgive you," said White. "We were both cat's-paws . . . for others. Now take my hand, and then go. I hold against you no ill will."

Houston squeezed the wounded man's hand. It was cold and clammy.

He rose. Greatly shaken he joined McGregor as they made their way across the line into Tennessee.

Chapter Seventeen

*The enemies of the General are dipping
their arrows in wormwood and gall and
speeding them at me.*

RACHEL JACKSON

1

In her young life Eliza Allen had hardly thought of the future, taking it for granted in a vague, untroubled, childish way.

The present was sufficient. She had always been pretty, passing through the "awkward age" with more grace than is given to most girls. Indeed, one could hardly have called her really awkward at any time. Perhaps there was a coltish period when she was a trifle long-legged and thin-bodied, but these matters adjusted themselves without being unduly noticeable to others, or unduly disturbing to herself.

Eliza knew that her father was a conspicuous man. Colonel John Allen had fought in the British war, took part in politics, owned a fine plantation and a famous thoroughbred breeding stable, and was sought after for his counsels. She was sure he was the most notable man in Tennessee, unless perhaps General Jackson—whom she remembered as very tall and very thin, and kindly in an austere way—rivaled her father in distinction.

Since she had the looks and blood of her family, her training from her earliest childhood had looked toward making her one of the great belles of the state. Each season, ever since she became aware of clothes, she was given an entire new wardrobe; and since her fourteenth year she had had the pleasure of choosing for herself what she wanted, what should be purchased, and what should be made by her mother's sewing women. In this her tastes ran to pale, pastel colors, and the mist of delicate fabrics, the light feeling of silk. Even her bed was made up with silken sheets of dovelike softness, pale green or pink in color.

By almost any standard Eliza could be called beautiful in a fragile way, with her wealth of soft blonde hair, a charming though somewhat adolescent figure, and long, slim hands.

Those hands usually were idle, except when they were engaged, a little reluctantly, in activities which were esteemed as accomplishments in women. Thus, she at first made samplers; and afterward learned to embroider bright designs in soft gossamer, the cloth stretched on a little hoop and the needle plying in and out. But this required perseverance, which she lacked. Once she started a piece she might not finish it, or if she did finish it, a very long time might be required for the languid operation—weeks, even months.

Books bored her, for she had never learned to read easily, and her parents did not allow her any of the light romances she might have found to her liking. When her father weightily discussed public affairs with friends in his home, she took little interest.

Idle though she was in mind, Eliza sometimes climbed the low hill behind the big house, on a summer day, to a little grove there; and all alone she would spread her skirts to sit on the grass. Nature gave her a dreamy enjoyment, though she had no intellectual curiosity concerning it. The appearance of a bird, flirting its wings in the branches overhead, pleased her in spite of the fact that she did not know what kind of a bird it was, and was too indolent to seek to find out. She liked the shimmer of light, the ripple of water in the little brook, the dappling of sun and shadow under the branches, the stirring of leaves in the breeze.

None of this aroused in her any consideration of what she, herself, was. Had the thought occurred to her that her feelings were symptoms of life budding within her, she would have been shocked and disturbed. Almost willfully Eliza banished from her mind any thoughts of the deeper meanings and responsibilities of life. She feared them.

She played the spinet indifferently well, and loved to dance; not to waltz, however, for her mother disapproved of "round dances," which were just coming into vogue and were considered by the old-fashioned very bold and even a little immoral. In the figure dancing, however, Eliza was graceful, and she discovered that she possessed the gift of awakening admiration in the eyes of men, which she found pleasing since it fed her little vanity.

Admiration was easy to discern when men looked at her, even older men. She became accomplished in receiving compliments, and rewarding them with smiles, thus gaining still more compliments.

Yet, though she used men as mirrors for her attractions, she was not interested in men and never seriously thought of them in any closer relation to herself. She had, in fact, only one deep interest: Eliza Allen. She loved herself, her own fair-skinned face, her rich blonde hair, her body which somehow in a few short months had developed into something very different from the thin, childish body that once was hers.

She made a confidante of her mirror, and would pose before it, enamored of the beauty she saw there. Often enough she had been told she was beautiful; it was a word she liked above any other to associate with herself. Her black nurse, doting old Aunt Dilsey, assured her of her beauty. Her father sometimes fondly did so also; although her mother with firmly pursed lips would say, "Pretty is as pretty does."

But her pride in this beauty was only a childish sort of vanity. She did not go far enough in her thinking to consider the purpose for which nature had endowed her with beauty. Eliza Allen shrank from pondering life from any realistic viewpoint.

To be sure, she took it for granted that one day she would be married. This was a matter of course; everyone got married. Marriage was expected of a girl. It gave her special social dignity, and a house of her own, and silver and furniture and servants, and a husband who would be very gallant to her, and whom she could display before other women.

But the deeper implications of marriage hardly clouded her mind. Of sex Eliza knew almost nothing. It was a subject never discussed; and when the first signs of her coming maturity made themselves evident she was given a cold, almost shamed, brief instruction by her mother, and then permitted to understand the mysteries by herself. Vaguely, she knew that married women had babies, but the exact process was never explained to her.

Colonel Allen bred horses, but she never went near the barns when this was in process, because she was told it wasn't "nice." Sometimes she heard the shrill, furious neighing of the stallion, presaging something violent and secret in the breeding paddock. But she ignored it as if she had not heard it, as indeed did her mother. Even to speculate on matters of this sort seemed shameful, and made her uncomfortable, and she really did not want to know.

So she lived on, childishly daydreaming, in affectionate possession of herself, creating about herself a sort of vacuum insofar as reality was concerned. And yet, unprepared and ignorant of life as she was, she was now accounted ready for marriage—and the Allen family was considered a most desirable connection everywhere in Tennessee. It followed that of late Eliza had been given more than casual attention by various young men, and had even received notes from a few of them, filled with stilted expressions of admiration. These pleased her vanity, but they seemed remote, as little a part of her as the paper on which they were written.

There came a night when young Rogers Denham, twenty years old and smelling strongly of pomatum, took her out into the garden and when they were alone together began to stammer, his Adam's apple working up and down rather ludicrously. She had known Rogers almost all her life, and had at times been rather scornful of him as a gawky, pimple-faced boy. But now somehow he seemed different, and when he managed to blurt out that he loved her, the tremor in his voice half-frightened her because of her strange inner warning of the emotion in him that caused that tremor.

But he hurried on, begging her to marry him; and without giving her a chance to reply, spoke of his family—which she knew quite well—and how there would be room for them, and a bright future in the Denham plantation, to which he would one day be heir.

She was tongue-tied by all this, unable to respond, and filled with conflicting emotions of wonder and alarm. He seized her hands and covered them with kisses, and would have turned his attention to her lips, had she not by the exertion of strength increased by panic, torn herself away from him and fled. Kisses she had known before, from her mother and father and brothers and feminine friends and relatives. But a kiss from a lover was something of which she had hardly conceived, much less the amorous embrace.

Afterward, with heart pounding, she burst into tears in her bedroom. Poor child, without benefit of counsel or experience, young Denham's proposal had only been frightening. Yet later, in the days that followed, she found herself able to think of Rogers with a kind of sorrowing tenderness, convinced that she had deprived him of some priceless boon.

It was this episode that caused her for the first time to face consciously the actuality that some day she must marry—an inevitability to which she surrendered without much question as she did to all the conventional things.

She decided that when she married—of course in the vague distant future—her husband must be nothing less than a demigod, a hero. Perhaps he might be a famous soldier, or a great poet, or a statesman. He must also be very handsome to be in some degree worthy of the beauty which was herself.

Rogers Denham she now looked upon as little more than a stripling. She felt sorry for him as one feels sorry for a person who has unwisely and vainly aspired to something far above his station and deserts; and she became a little annoyed with him because he persisted in making sheep's eyes at her whenever he was in her company.

Meantime she continued to live in the present, her world made up of trifles, dresses, styles, social affairs, ease, and irresponsibility.

2

In the weeks following her visit with her father to the Hermitage, Eliza heard much of Sam Houston. There was the story of the duel. She had seen old, fat General White, and felt sorry for him when it was said he might die of his wound. Later, of course, he recovered.

Meantime Houston was much on men's tongues. He was running for governor and, according to her father, very likely to be elected. Colonel Allen, in fact, seemed to be a great admirer of his.

Then one afternoon Sam Houston stopped at Allendale in his journeyings and was promptly urged to spend the night. Eliza shyly appraised him when she sat next to him at dinner that evening, and thought him very tall, somewhat overwhelming, rather overdressed, his gallantry almost exaggerated. He was, of course, outside her orbit, for he was past thirty, and she expected that he would hardly take notice of her, except perhaps for the perfunctory courtesies which older men display toward young girls who are the daughters of their friends.

But he showed her more real attention than this, and they talked for some time together after dinner. She was awed by his apparent great knowledge of the world; but he had a smiling way of speaking as if she fully understood what he was saying and he was therefore taking her into his confidence, when she really had no idea what he was talking about.

He was gone next morning when she arose for breakfast, but he left an impression on her that was very deep for her shallow nature. And he returned again—more than once during that political campaign—to spend a night at the Allendale plantation home.

Though Eliza remained almost a child in mind, a child could know very soon that Sam Houston's attentions to her were not perfunctory. And everyone else in her home sensed that when the stately candidate came to Allendale ostensibly to discuss politics with Colonel Allen, his real object was to see the colonel's pretty daughter. Even Eliza accepted this after a time, and its effect was vastly flattering to her.

Then came the election, with a torchlight parade in the neighboring town of Gallatin, and whiskey barrels broached in the streets. In a day or two it was known surely that Houston had won by a decisive majority over his Whig opponent, Newton Cannon.

Eliza for the first time felt a species of triumph; for she did not know Cannon at all, and Houston had many times bowed over her finger tips.

The state capital was now at Nashville, and the entire family attended the inaugural ball there, the colonel riding with his wife and Eliza in the coach, while Eliza's two younger brothers accompanied them on horseback. That night the girl was thrilled by the decorations of bunting and flowers and the many candles at the ball; and she spoke to General and Mrs. Jackson, and danced every dance, including two with the new governor himself.

She found herself trying to estimate Governor Houston, and it appeared to her, suddenly, that he came very near to fulfilling her secret ideal of the demigod—a hero, certainly, and a soldier. Also a statesman. And handsome. He was the tallest man she knew, and he seemed eager to please her slightest whim. Her vanity was immensely pleased to have people see that she, so diminutive and frail, could lead him about, the great giant, as if by an invisible leash of her beauty's hold on him.

Even after that, however, she was not prepared when the inevitable occurred. It was when he had been several months in the governor's office, and had affairs so well organized that he could leave them, that one day Houston came to Allendale. That evening he asked her to walk with him out under the stars. She consented, in a manner subdued and half-frightened. Suddenly he stopped and spoke to her as no man had ever spoken to her before, with a voice and look so stirring that she trembled.

"Eliza, my darling, will you make me the happiest man in the world, by consenting to be my bride?" he asked at the end.

She was unable to utter a word, standing still as if she were hypnotized. But he took her silence for emotion, and since she did not refuse, he believed she consented.

"Darling," he said, "come, let us go in and see your father, to ask his blessing."

Seeing her confusion and sensing her timidity, Houston did not offer to embrace her, only kissed her slender hand very softly and held it in his great paw, as he led her, hardly knowing what she was doing, to her father.

The interview that followed was as confusing to Eliza as the proposal under the stars.

"Colonel Allen, sir," began Houston. And he hesitated, for once abashed, looking from the colonel, standing very tall and stiff as if anticipating what was to come, to Mrs. Allen, a frail, delicate woman like her daughter, also stiffly standing, her hands folded.

He tried again. "Colonel Allen, I have the honor to request your permission to pay my addresses to Miss Eliza, sir. I mean, sir, I—very much desire to make her my wife. And I—we—have come to ask your blessing, sir, and yours, Mrs. Allen, ma'am."

Colonel Allen was hardly surprised, nor was his wife, although she began sniffing quietly into her handkerchief.

"Governor Houston," said the colonel, "I will say this to you, sir, I have regarded you with esteem, and I will not conceal from you that— er—noticing the way things were moving—it has been my hope—and I may add, Mrs. Allen's also—that you and my daughter might arrive at an understanding."

He paused, as if to swallow some emotion. "Now that you two have agreed," he went on, "it will be my dearest wish, and also Mrs. Allen's, that you will enjoy the richest happiness. I do give you my blessing— God bless you both."

Rather awkwardly, the colonel kissed Eliza and joined her hand with Houston's. Her mother came out from behind the handkerchief to smile, embrace the girl, and offer her cheek to Houston's kiss.

With these ceremonies over, Colonel Allen seemed much elated, as if he had done a great thing for his daughter; and for himself as well. The best brandy was brought out, and toasts were drunk.

Houston remained for the night, and at the end of the evening, which was gay, he and Eliza were left alone for a moment. His burning look aroused again the girl's terror, yet stirred her profoundly. Then, for the first time, she felt herself swept into his arms, and the burning, almost devouring pressure of male lips on hers.

It was her first kiss of passion from a man. She was astounded, almost repelled by it, and by the embrace that accompanied it. But she submitted to it. That night when she retired to her bed, she wept again, and lay awake for a long time, wondering childishly if that perhaps was the way babies were created to be born.

Next day, after Houston had departed for Nashville, she stammeringly put the question to Aunt Dilsey. Her plump black nurse shook with laughter.

"If kisses made babies, honey," said Aunt Dilsey, "they'd be a sight mo' people in the world than they is. An' Ah'll tell you' somep'n else— Ah nevah heard of a kiss leavin' a scar."

Relieved in that respect, but troubled in others, Eliza was kept busy in the months succeeding, with exciting preparations for the wedding, which her mother promised would be one of the grandest ever seen in Tennessee. Parties and teas and other social affairs, and matters concerning clothes, and silver, and linens, and various gewgaws, all of which seemed to go with being a bride, so took her mind off any introspections that she hardly gave thought any longer to her recurring fears, but instead began to believe that being the wife of the governor of the state was an eminence so lofty that she would sit higher among women than she had ever dreamed.

Her mother, during this period, gave her much counsel concerned with decorum, how to receive guests, how to visit in other homes, how to manage servants, how to attire herself suitably for occasions of different sorts, and matters of that nature. Counsel in what was far more important for a naïve and immature-minded girl, the actual physical meanings of marriage, Eliza did not receive. Mrs. Allen considered it indecent to discuss such things, even with her daughter.

So as her wedding approached, frail young Eliza Allen was prepared as well as her mother could prepare her, for everything she must know concerning her marriage, except the most important thing of all: how to act and what to expect from that mighty yet weak, indulgent yet selfish, adoring yet fearsome, mysterious, incomprehensible, alien creature—a man.

3

Having been promised his bride, Sam Houston found that he had few chances, in the next months, to see her. A long betrothal notoriously breeds misunderstandings, even when the couple is together frequently. When the prospective groom hardly ever visits his bride-to-be over long periods, she may be forgiven for feeling a sense of neglect which at its very least may cool her warmth toward him.

He had spoken of his love to Eliza, and received the blessings of her parents; and he hardly realized how he had swept the girl along by the irresistible wave of his dominating personality. Had he stopped to remember, he might have recalled that the pale, frail creature to whom he proposed that night did not utter one assenting word, either to him or to her father when the troth was pledged.

Eliza for much of this time was so occupied that she had little time for consideration; but the few occasions when she did look past the immediate future, far from bringing her joy, created in her a lack of anticipation that mounted almost to outright unhappiness. What would she do? She had permitted herself to be wooed and the pact sealed, but she knew none of the eagerness of a woman in love. Eliza, in fact, did not know that emotion as yet. She had given her unspoken consent because it seemed beyond her powers to refuse; but this she did not mention to her mother, who was in a whirl of activity, taking a vicarious maternal delight in the preparations for the grand affair which was to take place early the following year.

As for Houston, like many men who have become accustomed to the state of bachelorhood, he now found it difficult to surrender. He had made up his mind to marry, because marriage was a virtual necessity to a man in public life, and he loved his betrothed, or believed he did, though the advantageous nature of the match did not detract from it, from the standpoint of his natural ambitions. But now that he was committed he was almost fearful of the loss of his liberty. He therefore remained away from Allendale, when by making some effort he might have gone to Eliza and won at least a measure of her confidence by gentleness and understanding. As a result he remained practically a stranger to her.

He had, to be sure, the most valid excuses—if neglect of a bride-to-be can ever have a valid excuse. His duties as governor were heavy. More importantly, the Presidential campaign was thundering toward its close that fall of 1828, and it had become more bitter than any in the memory of America.

The Hermitage was near Nashville and he visited it whenever possible. More than once he found Andrew Jackson icy white with anger.

The old General was proving himself as fierce and potent a warrior in the field of politics as he had been in the field of battle. Once he set his mind to it, he marshaled his lieutenants across the nation exactly like a commander in a military campaign; and his foes, Henry Clay and John Quincy Adams, discovered to their consternation that his popular strength was mounting everywhere, however they struggled against it.

The party lines had formed. The President and his Secretary of State called themselves Whigs, and sought to align behind them all the old forces of power and prestige that once had ruled the country. Jackson's followers assumed the new name Democrats, and the ground swell grew as the common people rallied to this party standard.

In desperation Whig sources sought to discredit Jackson personally. It began with a whispering campaign. Then printed slurs appeared—chiefly based on the strange misfortune of his marriage to Rachel, when both of them believed she was divorced from Lewis Robards, though the divorce did not become final until later.

Houston had seen ugly samples. There was a handbill:

Andrew Jackson has spent the prime of his life in gambling, in cockfighting, in horse-racing, and to cap all tore from a husband the wife of his bosom. A vote for him will be a vote to sanction the code whereby if a man should fancy his neighbor's pretty wife, he has nothing to do but take a pistol in one hand and a horse whip in the other, and possess her.

Another, even worse attack, was published in the *National Journal*, a newspaper devoted to the Adams interests:

Gen. Jackson has admitted that he boarded at the house of old Mrs. Donelson, and that Roberts [sic] became jealous of him, but he omits the cause of that jealousy, namely that one day Roberts surprised General Jackson and his wife exchanging most delicious kisses. In this case Roberts acted a cowardly part in failing to shoot Jackson dead in his tracks. Later Mrs. Roberts made a voyage to Natchez in company of Jackson and Colonel Stark. The Gen. omitted to tell that they slept under the same blanket.

These charges and insinuations were brutal as well as cowardly: brutal because a timid and sensitive woman was the real victim, since though they were aimed at Jackson, it was Rachel who felt them most agonizingly; and cowardly because the perpetrators believed they were safe.

Each time he learned of one of these slimy canards, the old war horse of the Hermitage leaped in fury. It required the greatest and most continuous tact and diplomacy on the part of Houston, Carroll, and others, to prevent him from seeking out the traducers and exacting personal vengeance on them.

He expressed fully his own position on such despicable tactics when one of the newspapers supporting him, the *United States Telegraph*, came forth with an article imputing that John Quincy Adams had premarital sexual relations with Mrs. Adams before they were wed. To the editor of that newspaper, Jackson wrote a swift and final rebuke:

I never war against females and it is only the base and cowardly that do.
Andrew Jackson.

This was a lifetime tenet with Jackson. His natural chivalry and his idealism of women, which perhaps transcended realism, prompted it. But the injustices done to Rachel made it a crusade with him. His friends held their breath at each new incident and asked each other how much longer he would sustain such attacks without striking back.

The governor of Tennessee one day rode up to the Hermitage just after a new slander had been received there. In this Rachel actually appeared first, the prime focus of the canard which read:

Ought a convicted adulteress and her paramour husband to be placed in the highest offices in this free and Christian land?

Convicted adulteress . . . paramour husband! The white crest of the General was upraised and lightnings flared in his eyes as he showed it to Houston.

"I know who's behind this!" he exclaimed. "Henry Clay—the filthy blackguard! I've lately got intimation of some of Clay's secret movements, which if I can reach with positive and responsible proof I'll wield to his political and perhaps his *actual* destruction! He is certainly the basest, meanest scoundrel that ever disgraced the image of his God! But enough—*you know me!*"

Houston did know Jackson. He had trained for his own duel under the General's experienced eye. Inwardly he agreed as to the character of the man directing the slanderous attack. And he profoundly sympathized with the old warrior in his agony, his furious rebellion against the web of events that had so caught him up that he could not strike one blow for the woman he had always defended.

But it was imperative that the veteran be not goaded into some rash act.

"General, sir," he said, "this is hard, very hard. But again I beg of you and implore you, sir, to remember and keep foremost in your mind that the greatest possible stakes are involved here—your whole plan for this nation. Millions of people are affected. An aspirant for the Presidency must not fight a duel. It would ruin him. Have you considered that your enemies are perhaps trying to prod you into that very thing? It would be a triumph to them if you should play into their hands."

Jackson turned toward him a face white and lined with anguish and rage. Then he sat down abruptly and put his head in his hands.

"Oh, Sam, Sam," he said. "It is bitter, so bitter! But I know I must bow to circumstances. In my own heart I am forced to admit that what you say, what Carroll and Eaton and John Coffee all say, is true. But my wife! My poor, suffering wife! God, how can she bear it? How can I bear it?"

4

None was more emotionally sure that Jackson must not be dragged into a violent act than Rachel herself. Her tears held him back as much as the actual logic of the situation.

Houston left the General in his office, and went in to see her. He felt a deep affection for her, because he had always found her kind, and unselfish, and warmhearted.

Rachel bore her own pain silently. She feared to express it lest her husband break all bounds and do the very thing she was apprehensive he might do. But she could talk to Houston, who seemed one of the family, almost a son.

"Oh, Sam!" she said brokenly, when she saw him. And when he took her hand, she placed her head against him and the tears trickled down her cheeks.

"There, there, Aunt Rachel," he said, smoothing her hair.

"The enemies of the General are dipping their arrows in wormwood and gall and speeding them at me," she sobbed. "They have disquieted me with misery as they have no right to do, for I have never wronged any of them. And yet I pray for them. My Judge, above, will know how many prayers I have offered up."

All her life long she had fled from the scandal voices of her tormentors. All her life she had believed that obscurity was her only refuge. She had been glad in her heart when the vote of Congress defeated her husband, because she believed that now he and she would return home and live a quiet existence, free from all the pangs and aches which publicity had given her.

Yet obscurity was not possible. The General, in his determination to throw out of power men he considered dishonest, had plunged head-long into the new campaign. The results were worse than she feared. She felt stripped and exposed, naked and ashamed, under the vile glance and spiteful laughter of the world.

A more buoyant spirit, perhaps, might have thrown some of this sorrow off, but Rachel had lived with it too long. She embraced it rather than ridding herself of it; and it was eating at her vitals.

With concern Houston noticed a visible change in her appearance since the last time he had seen her. For years she had been fleshy, but now there seemed something flabby and unnatural about her corpulence. "Pursey" was the way he described it to himself.

He attempted his best little gallantries and quips, which always before had brought a smile from her, but her face remained unceasingly sad. For an hour he gently tried to cheer her up.

He was not successful.

5

Yet with all this pathetic tension at the Hermitage, the Jackson Presidential campaign was going incredibly well. Carroll, who well knew how to pull political strings, was alert and active all over the country. Eaton watched matters at Washington. Houston, in spite of the press of his statehouse duties, wrote many communications to newspapers, sometimes using two names for two different articles in the same journal. That fall, also, he was author of a book entitled *A Civil and Military History of Andrew Jackson, by an American Officer*, which became a national best seller.

Throughout the country, even in New England, "Jackson Clubs" sprang up. A broadside by the opposition decorated with the representations of eighteen coffins and purporting to show Jackson's "murders"—including his duel with Dickinson, and his military executions of mutineers and *agents provocateurs* among the Indians—failed to elicit as much public attention as did a slogan, paraded at militia rallies, mass meetings, and county fairs:

WASHINGTON AND JACKSON
YORKTOWN AND NEW ORLEANS

These matters in all truth left Houston little time to visit Allendale. Once or twice Colonel Allen brought Eliza and her mother to Nashville, but Houston found something odd in her behavior. Somehow he never was able to be alone with her. It was as if she purposely avoided such encounters, a behavior strangely coy. He was somewhat dashed, and should have taken warning. But he was so involved with the campaign now coming to its roaring conclusion that he did not dwell on her actions in his mind—as any man, expecting to marry a woman, should have done.

November—and Election Day. On a platform before the statehouse in Nashville stood a thirty-gallon barrel of whiskey, with the name ANDREW JACKSON upon it. Very soon afterward another barrel appeared on a similar platform with the name JOHN QUINCY ADAMS. Voters were invited to drink a dipperful, then cast their ballots; and that night Houston rode to the Hermitage with the gleeful report that the Adams barrel was "scarcely touched," while the Jackson barrel was "near dry."

Nashville and Tennessee were sure for Jackson. But the General's lieutenants, chief among them Governor Houston and ex-Governor Carroll, lived at the Hermitage the next few days, to be close to the focuspoint of news; for the returns from other states, in a day when a courier on horseback was the fastest means of communication, were necessarily slow in coming in.

Almost the first report to arrive at the Hermitage was the official count of Kentucky's vote—and Henry Clay had lost his own state to Jackson! Even the General smiled at that, for to whip the Cock of Kentucky on his own dunghill was no small triumph.

But there followed days of tension. The New England states were being swept by Adams. One after another Indiana, Ohio, and Illinois were counted in the Jackson column. The South was rallying: and then Pennsylvania and New York came in like twin typhoons of votes.

Jackson had won!

A most astounding victory, one that his most optimistic backers had hardly believed in, a tribute to one man's single-minded clarity of purpose against a party entrenched in power with its host of patronage beneficiaries, and what was thought to be the solidified habit of public thinking.

The final majority in the Electoral College was overwhelming—one hundred and seventy-eight for Jackson, to eighty-three for Adams.

Small wonder that the General's advisers at the Hermitage whooped with joy and elation.

"There'll be no rigging in Congress this time!" exclaimed Billy Carroll.

"Clay and Adams have received their punishment—a condign punishment!" exulted Houston.

But most strangely, the man who would seem to have most to savor in his epoch-making triumph, appeared to take little pleasure in it, now that it was won. The old General's face was unsmiling. After the labor of the campaign he was weary, but that hardly accounted for his mood. In the midst of the excitement and rejoicing, and with congratulations and good wishes pouring in from every hand, Andrew Jackson actually behaved as if winning the office of Chief Magistrate were almost an anticlimax.

"I am filled with gratitude," he said to his friends. "Still, my mind is depressed."

Houston knew he was thinking of Rachel.

When he visited her in her sitting room, and tried in his best manner to felicitate her on her husband's great victory, she murmured in reply:

"For the General's sake I am glad. For my own part I never wished it."

To her mind there loomed ahead only a long, long, dreadful ordeal. She had once more given up her pipe, in preparation for doing her best to live up to her husband. And her heart ached because she felt that however hard she tried, she could never be anything but herself: and she was sure that was not enough in the wife of the great man she knew he was.

Houston was perhaps as close to her as anyone in the world, save the General himself. He felt a great sympathy for her, and he sat by her and took her hand.

"Aunt Rachel," he said, "the General is a man the like of whom only once arises in perhaps a century. The people—all the people—need such a man as he is."

Tears welled in her eyes. "I know," she said, "I know I must not be selfish and try to keep him to myself. I've tried, and I can't do it—the world is always drawing him from me. But—but *they'll* never forgive me."

He knew what she meant: she dreaded encountering the fine ladies of the capital, and her husband's enemies, who already had tortured her.

"In all my life," he told her, "I've never known any other woman with your kindness and goodness and sincerity. Don't try to be anything but Rachel Jackson, truthful, warmhearted, a wonderful wife with simple tastes, who is not ashamed of them. You'll make their shams look tawdry by comparison. Be yourself. That's enough."

She thanked him. But she would not be comforted. She knew it was not enough.

6

As the weeks passed, Andrew Jackson worried more and more over his wife, whose depression seemed to be affecting her health. At the same time he found he already had to grapple with responsibilities that now confronted him. Yet he took time for other matters, too.

One day he and Houston were alone in the Hermitage office, and the General was toasting his backside at the open fire, while his guest helped himself at the whiskey decanter.

"Sam," said Jackson suddenly, "how well do you know Mrs. Margaret Timberlake?"

Houston was so startled that he almost dropped the glass of liquor in his hand. Why the question? Had not Jackson forgotten the episode at O'Neale's Inn those years before? He answered cautiously:

"Quite well, sir." And then he added, "Not *too* well."

"Why do you say that?" rapped Jackson.

Houston racked his mind for something that might have led to this inquisition. He had thought the matter cleared with the General, and he had never pursued the affair with Peggy . . . even though he had sometimes been tempted. That morning visit Jackson had paid him, even though no accusations were made or confessions given, had been a sufficient warning. Besides, John Henry Eaton, after all, seemed rather to pre-empt her. At this moment he was devoutly thankful for his discretion.

"Well, sir—" he began.

"Because you've heard things said of Peggy?" asked the General.

"Why—sir, I must be truthful with you—yes, sir, I have."

"You believed them?"

"Sir, I paid little attention to them."

"I'm relieved to hear you say this," said the General. "The girl has been the subject of malicious gossip—which, sir, is unfounded."

An affirmation without the slightest ambiguity. Then Jackson did not believe there had been a crossing of the lines of convention and morals with her by Houston. The governor experienced profound relief. He nodded, sipped from his glass, and waited to see where this led.

"Defamation of a female's character," went on Jackson, "is the most scoundrelly and despicable act of which a man may be guilty."

Now Houston began to understand the trend. The campaign of detraction against Rachel had made the old General a defender of any woman so assailed.

"I do most solemnly agree with you, sir," he said.

"Had you heard that Peggy's husband, Lieutenant Timberlake, is now dead?" asked Jackson.

"Why, yes."

"It was at sea. To show you the length to which gossipers will go, it is being rumored in Washington that he committed suicide. Furthermore the same spiteful gossip connects Peggy with John Eaton in a way to sicken an honest man's stomach."

Houston had heard this rumor also, to the effect that Timberlake cut his own throat because he heard his wife was "living in sin" with Senator Eaton. From his own experience with Peggy, he thought privately, there might be some ground for this gossip.

Jackson went on. "John Eaton is going to marry her."

At that Houston's eyes widened.

"While he was here during the campaign," said the General, "he spoke about it with me, saying that considerations of honor and justice inclined him to snatch her from the injustice done by a gossiping world, and at the proper time he would tender her an offer of marriage."

"And your reply to that, sir?"

"I said to him that if he loved the woman, he should go and marry her at once, and shut their mouths."

Houston was silent. He could foresee some embarrassments in store for Eaton in such a marriage. But Jackson's instinct to fight for a woman's reputation had become almost a mania.

"I've had a letter from Eaton since he returned to Washington," continued Jackson, "indicating that he should wait to marry Peggy until after my inauguration. Now, why should he think that?"

Houston shook his head.

"Sometimes I find it hard to understand men," the General went on. "Peggy is lovely and charming. If she's willing, and Eaton loves her— which he protests he does—why delay? It can only lead to more scurrilous talk. So I sent him a note by return post: 'Marry Mrs. Timberlake *forthwith*, or leave the O'Neale Tavern.'"

Houston listened with astonishment, thinking how that stern admonition must have shaken Eaton.

Jackson said, "I've just received Eaton's reply. I find it most satisfactory. Here, read it."

Houston took the letter. Eaton had written:

My sincere thanks for the kind suggestions made in reference to this delicate subject. Your admonition shall be regarded. In the first week in January an honorable discharge of my duty to myself and her will be met.

Certainly it was obedient and conciliatory, though the writer chose to regard the General's peremptory command as a "kind suggestion." But in all this, Houston noted, John Henry Eaton had not once spoken of love, but only of honor, justice, and duty. This omission appeared to have escaped the old General.

"It's a great relief to my mind," Jackson said. "I'm fond of little Peggy —she's been like a bright child to me. And I'm fond of Eaton, too. I know you also are his friend, which is why I have revealed these matters to you. I have important plans for John, as I have for you."

When Houston rode back to Nashville he reflected that the fate of Peggy O'Neale Timberlake was settled—for the time being at least. Andrew Jackson serenely believed she would now be safe and protected; but Houston thought of how gossip had pursued Jackson himself, and Rachel, and had never died.

Chapter Eighteen

*Those vile wretches who have slandered
her must look to God for mercy.*

ANDREW JACKSON

1

Another problem, far more deeply personal to the old General,
was not so easily resolved.

Andrew Jackson, newly elected seventh President of the United States,
must be in Washington before March 4, which was the day for his inauguration. Preparations already were under way for the journey to the
national capital.

But such a hegira would be long and full of discomforts and weariness,
and the General was more than concerned over Rachel. Since the election she had seemed less hopeful than before. Her physical energy sank,
and she brooded much. It was evident that with the excitement of the
campaign past, which to a degree had buoyed her up by its sheer drama,
her spirits were drooping lower, and her health deteriorating.

In these days the Hermitage was constantly filled with visitors, come
to express good wishes and congratulations, to offer services, sometimes
to seek tactfully for political favors for themselves or friends. Among
these it was the President-elect's duty to move, and be pleasant, and act
the gracious host. The long dining table was never set for fewer than
twenty persons, and new carriages and buggies were constantly arriving.

Rachel, however, rarely came down to the big reception room, preferring to remain in her own sitting room on the upper floor, sometimes
with a few friends whom she knew well, even asking to have her meals
sent up to her.

She seemed, indeed, so unwell that young Dr. Henry Lee Heiskell,
who was assistant to old Dr. Samuel Hogg, the Hermitage family physician, came regularly twice a week, to feel her pulse, look at her tongue,
and occasionally bleed her. Privately, the doctor shook his head over her
unhealthy puffy appearance. It had, to him, the appearance of dropsy,
which might be occasioned by a sluggish circulation due to some heart
condition, or by kidney trouble, or even by cancer. He did not venture
these thoughts to the General, not being sure himself what ailed his
patient, and being unwilling to add other cares to those already burden-
ing the white-haired veteran.

In spite of the young physician's ministrations and the efforts of her
friends to cheer her, Rachel continued to sink in spirits. She consented,

at the urging of some of her feminine visitors, to go to Nashville, there to select materials and be measured for "suitable dresses," including a gown of white satin designed expressly for the inaugural ball which she must attend. To all this she submitted wearily and without joy.

Once she said, to Mrs. Overton, wife of Jackson's friend the general, "I had rather be a doorkeeper in the house of God, than to live in that palace in Washington."

Then came a day, after one of those visits to Nashville, when her carriage was seen returning to the Hermitage, the black driver urging the horses at their fastest trot. Within it sat Rachel, alone, red-eyed from weeping, and almost hysterical.

"My God, what's happened?" cried Jackson when he assisted her out of the vehicle.

She only sobbed.

With the assistance of Aaron he took her to her room, almost lifting her weight up the steps.

"Lie down, my dear," he said. "Here, take a sip of this wine."

When they were alone, he closed the door and sat beside her high bed, affectionately stroking her arm.

"Now tell me what happened?" he asked after she had somewhat composed herself.

But it only set her off in a fresh storm of weeping. She would not, or perhaps could not, tell what had caused her intense emotional excitement.

She never told. Nobody ever learned what actually had occurred. One story was that she overheard two women, supposed to be her friends, discussing her cattily, and one of them had remarked, "What a spectacle will be presented by this illiterate country woman in the mansion of the President at Washington." Another was that she had seen at one of the newspaper offices in Nashville evidence that many of the slanders concerning her had been withheld from her, and they were worse even than she imagined.

Whatever the cause, she never revealed it, even to her husband; and she never rallied from it.

On December 17, Dr. Heiskell, hastily summoned, found Rachel writhing on her bed, with the General, nearly frantic with anxiety, hovering over her. She complained of severe pains in her left chest and shoulder, and the physician found her pulse weak and irregular.

The symptoms indicated to him a heart attack.

"I shall bleed her," he said. "It will relieve the back pressure into the pulmonary circulation."

The ghastly process began. Jackson himself believed in bleeding, a method in that day supposed to offer relief from almost any ailment. As he watched his wife's blood empty into a small bowl, he noticed that it seemed unnaturally thick and heavy, but he hoped that the operation would give her some comfort.

Dr. Heiskell, having taken what he considered sufficient blood, bound up the patient's arm.

"I think she'll feel better now," he told the General. "I will give her a sleeping potion. Rest is the best remedy for her at present. See that she remains in bed for two or three days."

"Yes, doctor. Thank you, sir," said Jackson with the pathetic gratitude and faith physicians usually manage to evoke from those ignorant of medicine, however unscientific they themselves may really be.

When Dr. Heiskell left that evening, Rachel was asleep in her high French bed, and the old General was sitting, white-faced, beside her.

Next day she seemed somewhat better, and was able to sit up in bed and eat something light, so that her husband was able to receive callers downstairs, and even take care of a little of his accumulating correspondence. He gave strictest instructions to Hannah, Rachel's personal Negress servant, to be with her every minute when he himself was not.

Among the visitors that day were both Dr. Hogg and Dr. Heiskell, who came out together to examine the patient.

Half-fearfully Jackson watched them go through the usual solemn mummery of pulse-feeling, tongue-looking, and heart-listening. At the end he asked hesitantly, "How do you think she is?"

"I believe, General," said Dr. Hogg, a kindly but somewhat pompous old gentleman, no more lacking in the true science of medicine than most of his fellow practitioners of the day, "that she will now continue to improve."

But she did not continue to improve.

Nashville had set aside December 23—the anniversary of the first desperate night action in the New Orleans campaign—for a great celebration and reception in honor of its most distinguished personage. A committee approached the General to inform him of the plans.

"There will be," said the spokesman of the committee, "a band concert, and speechifying—we have a list of eminent speakers, including Governor Houston, General Overton, Judge Trimble, and others. Afterwards there is to be a very elegant dinner and a grand ball, all in honor of you, sir. The town already is filled with people, some of whom have come from long distances to attend. Many of these are old veterans who served under you. Will you, General, consent to be there and ornament this occasion with your presence?"

"Yes, gentlemen, I feel that I ought to express my thanks for this kind of a testimonial," said Jackson. He thought a moment. "Unfortunately, Mrs. Jackson will be unable to do so. Yet I am glad to inform you that I'm assured by the doctors that there is nothing critical about her condition. So, though she, of course, will remain at home, I myself will be pleased and honored to attend."

The committee departed, and some of its members expressed the belief that the General looked more cheerful and spry than he had for some time. From this they argued that the General's wife must, indeed, be improving in an encouraging manner.

2

On Sunday morning, the day before the reception, Hannah came running to Jackson.

"Gin'ral!" she cried. "The missus is took with another spell!"

He rushed to Rachel's room. She lay on her back, breathing heavily, her eyes closed.

At his touch she opened her eyes and he saw fear in them.

"My side is hurting again, and I'm very dizzy and faint," she whispered.

Jackson shouted for Aaron. "Get the doctors! Tell them to get here as fast as they can gallop their horses! Take that chestnut colt, Damion, he's fast—and don't waste a minute of time!"

Aaron, the always faithful, was gone like a shot.

To Jackson it seemed an eternity before the doctors arrived, although they came immediately at his summons.

Once again they examined her and bled her. When they finished she appeared to be relieved, and less fearful.

"Could I sit up?" she asked rather pathetically. "I'd like to sit in my chair beside the fire. I'm so tired of this old bed."

Dr. Hogg looked at Dr. Heiskell. "If she moves with care, I see no objection to it," he said, and his colleague nodded.

"Let Hannah put me in my dressing gown," she said.

The men left the room while this was done. Then Hannah summoned them and both doctors helped Jackson lift the patient's heavy body out of the bed, and assist her to a rocking chair beside the fireplace in which the flames danced brightly.

She sat still for a minute, looking at the fire.

"This feels so pleasant," she said in her weak voice. Then she looked up at Jackson almost pleadingly. "Could I have my pipe?"

Not since before the election had she smoked, and it went to his heart that she looked at him so, for he had never asked her to cease the habit, or even mentioned it.

"Of course, dear," he said. "Have your pipe if you want it."

Rachel said something that later was recalled as cryptic: "I might as well."

Hannah, kind and devoted, smiled and made quite a little ceremony of filling the old corncob, and lighting it for her mistress with a burning splinter from the fireplace.

The doctors looked at Jackson.

"Come with us, General," said Dr. Hogg.

Together they stepped into the next room.

"What do you think?" he asked anxiously.

".This relapse—it's not encouraging," said Dr. Hogg, shaking his head.

"There appears to be a general debility," said Dr. Heiskell, "not only physical but perhaps mental——"

He was interrupted by a scream from Hannah in the bedroom.

Jackson was the first to rush through the door, the physicians at his heels.

Hannah, frightened and half-hysterical, was kneeling by the rocking chair, the body of her mistress partly supported in her arms.

Rachel's head had fallen to one side, her mouth sagged open, the pipe from which she had taken no more than a few puffs lay where it had dropped, on the hearth.

"She jes' say, 'Hannah, Ah'm faintin',' " sobbed the panic-stricken servant.

"Here—get her on the bed!" cried Jackson.

With the help of the two doctors he lifted the body of his wife, now somehow heavier, because completely limp, and carried it over to the high bed.

"Allow me, sir," said Dr. Heiskell. First he, then Dr. Hogg, leaned over and listened for the heartbeat and felt for the pulse. When they straightened and exchanged a look, Andrew Jackson saw their verdict: Rachel was gone.

But he desperately refused to accept it.

"Bleed her!" he cried in agony, able to think of no other expedient.

The effort was made. No blood flowed from her veins.

"The temple—try the temple!" he insisted.

From the temple Dr. Heiskell got two small drops of blackening blood, then no more.

Through the house began a wild wailing and chanting, the keening of the servants in their requiem for their mistress.

In a daze Jackson watched the doctors have a table brought on which to lay out the body.

"Spread four blankets on it!" he cried, still blindly refusing to accept the inevitable. "She may come to, even yet—and I don't want her to be lying on a hard table!"

But now at last the tears came to the iron soldier. And his grief was so terrible that they could not face it.

They left him alone, sobbing beside his dead.

3

For thirty-seven years Andrew Jackson had made of Rachel a cause. He had defended her, sometimes at the risk of his life and by the shedding of his blood; and he had sought to shield her from all things and all men.

Now she was gone, and it seemed his life was gone with her.

At times his long fingers would touch her cold forehead, as if to assure himself that the terrible thing that had befallen was really true. Again, those bony fingers would clutch his disordered white thatch of hair, and the sobs would shake his thin frame.

It was true. She was gone, and gone forever. Not even his unconquerable will, which had triumphed over every enemy and all his adversities, could bring her back from where the Dark Angel, Death, had taken her.

He wept beside her, and memories rushed wildly into his mind. There was something she once said to old General Overton:

"I have lived with Mr. Jackson for nearly forty years without an unkind word passing between us, and the only subject on which we ever differed was his acceptance of appointments. I was always unwilling for him to enter public life."

The only subject on which we ever differed . . . in his anguished mind it was like a tolling bell, a bell that accused him with every beat. He remembered how she had wept every time he left her to go on one of his far quests; and his heart smote him with a torturing sense of guilt when he recalled how often those tears of hers had annoyed him.

Annoyed him! He felt like a traitor to her. A lifelong traitor. If he had only been content to live with her quietly, as she wished, the wounds to her spirit that killed her might have healed.

But she was dead. Of a broken heart.

In his grief he blamed himself almost insanely as the tears ran unheeded down his sunken cheeks.

His ambition . . . *his* hunger for action . . . *his* pride . . . they, and his selfish insistence on following them, had killed Rachel, so he told himself.

The doctors came into the room, looked at him anxiously. His face was ravaged, he appeared wild, almost demented, in his agony.

At last they managed to get him away. He became calmer, and finally submitted to taking a sleeping potion.

That night, under the drug, he slept; but restlessly, tossing and muttering in his slumber.

4

The sad afternoon of December 24—the day before Christmas—the leafless interlacing limbs of the trees were stark against the leaden sky, and across the bare acres whistled a biting wind. They were in keeping, the bleakness of the day and the keening of the wind, with the sorrowing mood of the occasion.

On this day the Hermitage did not stand in isolation. Almost the entire white population of Nashville, all its visitors who had come to attend the Jackson testimonial reception so tragically canceled, all the dwellers of the countryside for miles about, were gathering in dense thousands around the house, dressed in the somber hues of mourning. They had come to witness the burial of Rachel Jackson, wife of Tennessee's greatest son.

Almost every one of those present had planned gala Christmas Eve celebrations for this day; but such affairs were discontinued or subdued. Since morning the roads leading to the Hermitage had been choked with buggies, carriages, and horseback riders, while countless pedestrians trudged across fields to be present at the rites, to pay tribute to the dead woman and the white-haired old man, now left alone.

To all the West, and particularly to the unlettered and obscure people of the West, it had seemed a triumph and vindication for themselves when one of their own, Andrew Jackson, was elected President, over the cold New Englander, John Quincy Adams, and the wealth and superior attitudes they believed he represented.

All men knew of the bitterness of the political campaign, and how the General's enemies had smirched his name and that of his poor wife. It was scoundrelly, Tennessee thought, to rake up old ashes, dead these thirty-seven years; especially when Rachel's bewildered pain and shame over something she really could not help, were considered.

In the crowds about the Hermitage, as in all crowds, certain morbid interests ran, and there were whispered speculations. How would a man of General Jackson's stamp behave under the grief of his bereavement? Would he perhaps weep like an ordinary man? Or would he be in iron, self-controlled possession of himself? Did he really suffer?

They massed about the Hermitage, trampling flower beds and breaking fences, many of them waiting, shivering and craning, in their rather ignoble curiosity, to see the old man in this supreme moment of his emotional testing.

At one o'clock the doors of the Hermitage opened, and four men came forth from the house, friends of Jackson, acting as ushers, to clear a lane through the mob to the freshly dug grave one hundred and fifty yards from the front door.

A few moments later the Reverend Dr. William Hume, minister of Rachel Jackson's church, stepped into view, holding in his hands an open Bible. There was a stir in the crowd, and more neck-craning, for the minister was followed by the casket, which was borne by six pall-bearers.

Many eyes were on the tall figure of the governor of Tennessee, who marched slowly at the front on the right. At the left in front was William Carroll, the former governor. The others all were men of importance in the community and the state.

But—Sam Houston, at the right hand, the leader, in the place of greatest honor—the chief pallbearer? It was the kind of sign for which many had been watching.

If Andrew Jackson assigned Houston to that place among those who carried his wife's body to her grave, did it not signify also that Houston was chief in the General's heart? It was whispered about, how the governor had arrived at the Hermitage as fast as a lathered horse could bear him when he heard the news of Rachel's death, and how he had not left the house or Jackson's side since that moment.

Then every eye saw the pathetic figure of the old man himself come from the door to follow the cortege. He was supported on either side by old friends—General Coffee on his right, Judge Trimble on his left, both unashamedly weeping. Andrew Jackson was dry-eyed, but obviously weak, almost tottering.

Hollow-cheeked, his pinched face even thinner than before, he kept his bare head bowed, its snowy white hair blowing in the wind, as he walked behind his wife's coffin, looking only at the ground.

But when the last solemn words of the burial service were said, and the coffin containing all that remained of Rachel Jackson was lowered into the grave, the old General at last gave way to tears, sobbing uncontrollably and leaning forward heavily, supported by his friends, crushed in body and spirit as he had never been crushed by any mortal adversary.

After a time, however, he straightened his figure, drew from his breast pocket a handkerchief, and dried his tears. Then he lifted his gaunt face skyward. Those assembled heard his voice, speaking slowly, as if it came from the tomb itself:

"I know it is unmanly, but these tears are due to her virtues . . . she has shed so many for me."

A pause, as if by an effort of will he was mastering a renewal of the grief which threatened to choke him. Then his voice strengthened:

"In the presence of this dear saint I can, and do, forgive all my enemies. But those vile wretches who have slandered *her* must look to God for mercy!"

He watched until the grave was filled before he turned back, still leaning on the arms of his friends, to his house.

The Pride and the Ashes,
*** 1834

*A*s the year 1829 dawned, the nation gazed toward the Hermitage in mingled speculation and concern. Reports from Nashville said that the President-elect was in failing health. It appeared that his age and the chronic ailments he suffered, combined with his depression caused by the death of his wife, had brought him very low—to the brink of the grave itself, according to some advices.

His followers and admirers across the whole breadth of the land told themselves that Andrew Jackson, what with bullet wounds, and severe sicknesses, and prodigious labors enough to break an ordinary mortal, had been down before, and his incredible will had always brought him back into action. They hoped anxiously that this might again be the outcome.

His enemies, and they were not lacking, said bitterly that they had no expectation that the country would be rid of the wild rabble-rouser from the West so easily; they rather believed the cantankerous old reprobate was immortal, and would plague America and the world long after honest men were dead and gone.

Both well-wishers and ill-wishers waited almost breathlessly for news of him, and meantime wondered what the new Chief Magistrate would do, to or for the country, when and if he did occupy the White House.

The Whigs, and the Conservative elements of both North and South, freely predicted the direst consequences with the government in the hands of a man so palpably inexperienced in diplomacy, national finance, public administration, and the whole complex realm of politics.

But in the nation at large a strange, almost incomprehensible thing had taken place. Not one in thousands of the ordinary people of America had ever seen Andrew Jackson, much less spoken to him or had any personal contact with him. Yet somehow, mysteriously, his extraordinary spirit and personality had permeated them. They believed in him as they had never believed in any other man before. He was attuned to them in a manner almost mystical; which no one, least of all himself in his honest humility, could explain.

Whatever the reason for it, in a brief time he had created loyalties and devotion as fanatical as were the hatreds he had earned. The common men had a kind of unreasoning faith that somehow things would be better when General Andy-by-God-Jackson took over.

Chapter Nineteen

We stand at one of those critical times in history when the destinies of men and nations are in the balance.

ANDREW JACKSON

1

He sat alone before the fireplace in his bedroom, staring into the blazing logs. Light and warmth are the twin gifts of fire, but there was neither light nor warmth in the deep-sunk eyes that seemed lost in the hypnotic effect of the upward-leaping flames.

In the days since he had buried his wife, Andrew Jackson had hardly spoken to a soul. The Hermitage was filled with guests: his adopted son, Andrew Jackson, Junior, now a student at college; his ward, Andrew Jackson Hutchings, young Andrew's closest chum; Rachel's nephew Jack Donelson, a fine intelligent young man who had been at New Orleans and for whom the General had a strong affection, and his pretty young wife Emily; other relatives of Rachel's. But he refused all well-meant offers to bear him company, saying he would rather be alone for the time.

So he sat in his bedroom for long hours in brooding melancholy, the people in the house hardly daring to disturb him. The servants who brought him food, faithful old Aaron or Rachel's kind black Hannah, came silently, almost furtively, and later took away the tray, noticing with misgivings that its contents had hardly been touched.

Jackson's gauntness had become almost skeletonic and his face wore that strange transparent look of one who is suffering from or has been through a long illness. His cough, from the old abscessed lung, which came periodically at periods sometimes months apart, but always racking him when it came, had returned. And he had a recurrence of his old bowel ailment to further weaken him. But it was illness of his soul, the unremitting grief that preyed upon his heart, that was more dangerous than illness of his body, frail as it was.

Again and again he moaned aloud as Rachel's torment came back to him, and with it his gnawing sense of guilt at having been the cause of it—indirect, but still the cause. Sometimes he tormented himself by asking the old question if it would not have been better had she never met him. But that was her unhappy fate—her fate and his. Andrew Jackson, newly elected President of the United States, that wintry day, felt defeated and solitary.

Bitterly he thought of the men who, in their spleen against himself, had tortured his wife. That smooth and graceless scoundrel, Henry Clay, he believed was at the bottom of the slanders. Once, before the election and Rachel's death, he had actually drawn up a summons to Clay, to face him with pistols on the dueling ground.

I could not at first believe that even you, sir, could descend so low. It did not seem possible to me that the Secretary of State, the second officer in the government of our Republic, would travel through the country for the cowardly purpose of slandering a virtuous female.

Thus the preamble of his defiance. But in the end he did not send it. Sam Houston spent a whole night with him on that occasion, using every resource of argument gradually to win him away from the idea of issuing the challenge.

Now, in his bitterness, he wished he had gone through with it. He would have shot down Henry Clay as he shot down Charles Dickinson.

Too late now. Rachel was gone and he had only his memories, sad and sweet, going back to her youth, their first days together. The long years between, sometimes gray and weary, he seemed to forget entirely, as if some mental scar had sealed them over.

Such was the intensity of his mourning, made more severe by self-blame, that some of his friends feared he might follow his wife to the grave; or else give up everything and become an invalid and a recluse.

But those who feared this did not know Andrew Jackson. Heart-torn as he was, and bedeviled by his old maladies of the body, the indomitable old soldier, who had never in his life turned his back on a battle, even now was rallying himself for a new battle, perhaps the greatest battle of his life.

The savage old man, leaning forward in his chair before the fire, understood two emotions passing well: loyalty and hate. Already these two had carried him past the crisis of his first sorrow and given him incentive to live on. Andrew Jackson had begun to think once more, and his thoughts, since his wife was gone where he could not help her, seized almost hungrily upon another cause to which he could devote himself without stint: his duty to his nation.

2

Downstairs he heard a rising of voices: some visitor, likely. He hoped they would leave him alone. But presently there was a timid knock on his door.

"Come in," he said with gruff resignation.

It was Emily Donelson, a sweet-faced, wide-eyed girl, Jack Donelson's wife, of whom the General was fond.

"It's—I thought you'd like to know—it's Governor Houston, General," she said.

Jackson straightened in his chair, the annoyance fading from his face. Houston was one person, perhaps the only one, he would have cared to see at that moment.

"Send him in, please," he said. "And Emily, my dear—have Aaron bring the old whiskey that Judge Trimble sent me."

She was gone. A moment later a towering figure entered the room.

"Pray remain seated, sir," said Sam Houston hastily as the old man made as if to rise. He came over, looking closely at Jackson's face, and their hands clasped warmly.

"I'm glad to see you, boy—most heartily glad," said the General. "Here's Aaron—I sent for my best whiskey when I was told you were here."

The servant placed a tray with a decanter and two glasses on the table by Jackson's chair, where lay his old, stained corncob pipe.

"Will you pour for yourself, boy?" asked the old man. There was something almost eager in his manner. Clearly Houston had come at just the right moment, when his company was most appreciated.

"Thank you." The tall man filled one of the glasses to the brim with the richly amber-hued liquid. "You, sir?"

Jackson shook his white head. "My doctor won't permit me."

"Then I drink to my strongest hope and expectation—a speedy improvement in your health, General." Houston tossed off the drink.

The white head inclined in acknowledgment. "Take that chair, won't you?" said the old man. Then he asked, "What are they saying now, Sam?"

Again Houston thought he could detect a new note of awakened interest and aliveness. He replied in a manner that he thought might stimulate his friend.

"There's been some talk—I might say a faint hope—among your enemies, sir—that you'll not feel up to assuming the heavy burden of the Presidency."

At once he knew he had touched the right chord. Fire flashed in the General's blue eyes. "They do so, eh? Well, damn their souls, I'll close that portal of hope for them! I shall go to the White House, Sam, and I shall conduct the duties of that office. I would not give the enemies of my dear wife the satisfaction of seeing me fail to do so." A spasm of anger passed over the pallid face. "May God forgive them, for I never can!"

"Nor I, sir."

"I believe that, boy. And I thank you for it," said Jackson, a warmth in his voice that had not been there for many days. After a moment's silence, he added, "I've been doing some thinking of late—my mind's not been idle, sir. It will do me good to air some of this with you."

Glad at this show of an awakened alertness, Houston poured another drink. But he did not raise the glass to his lips for a long time. Jackson's eyes gleamed pale and memorable as he began to speak, and when Jackson spoke thus, one listened. It was as if his thoughts, which had been dammed up, suddenly were released in spate.

"You say my enemies hope I'll not qualify for my office," he began. "Clay and Adams are the chief of those, I'll warrant. A putrescent pair of double-dealing Judases, who'd stoop to anything for their selfish ends. Why, I verily believe, sir, that those two would sell their own wives down the river into a whorehouse, if the price tempted them!"

In spite of himself, Houston grinned. This assuredly was the old Jackson speaking, and he felt profoundly grateful for it.

"But there are others," went on the old man. He mentioned Chief Justice John Marshall. "A bigoted hypocrite," he said, "with his doctrine of 'implied powers.' Implied by whom? By Marshall! And for whom? The monied powers. As, for example, the authorization of the Bank of the United States."

He stared broodingly into the fire. "And speaking of the Bank of the United States brings up the name of another in the category of Clay, Adams, and Marshall—that smug moneylender in the temple, Nicholas Biddle. The Bank and Biddle, who take orders from Clay and Adams, to create hard times or alleviate them for political effect, are the head and forefront of the money octopus that would throttle this nation. I'll meet them, sir—head to head! It may stun the monied powers, the plan that I'll submit. The government, sir, not private financiers, should control the finances of America. They'll howl, but that's what they'll have to swallow!"

He gave Houston a look that for a moment was almost whimsical. "I heard what John Marshall said: 'The wild asses from the West, led by Andy Jackson, will ruin the government.' John Marshall has devoted his life to giving over all possible power and privilege to the rich—a damned oligarchic heresy, sir, intervened on our democratic system of law. Well," he concluded grimly, "John Marshall will have to administer to me the oath of office, and it will give me a good deal of satisfaction, sir, for it will curdle in his stomach when he does so!"

Jackson took the corncob pipe from the table at his elbow and lit it. "I've had hundreds of pipes sent me, some of them very fancy," he said, his voice softening. "But I still smoke my old corncob. It's the sweetest of all . . . and she loved the cob, too."

In silence he puffed a few clouds of smoke, as his thoughts returned to her of whom he spoke. But presently he began again, looking into the fire, as if musing aloud.

"Something graver than the money problem must be faced. The question is whether this country will *even remain a nation*. Nullification— Secession! New England had the traitorous notion of seceding during the War of 1812. Now it's the South, worried over the slavery issue. Wherever it arises, that movement must be put down. And I'll do it, sir, if it's within my power. I'd cheerfully pay out what's left of my life and blood to preserve the Federal Union of the United States."

He turned his face to Houston, a hard bright gleam in his eye.

"There's still a further matter. I've been studying it, doing a vast deal of consideration these days. And I have hitherto revealed my thoughts to no man——"

"Perhaps not to me, either, sir."

"To you, yes, Sam. I've tested you, and you ring true." A pause. "After all, a man must have someone in whom he can confide."

Houston bowed his head, but did not speak.

"This one matter, then," said the old man, "I discuss with you under the seal—the seal of absolute confidence—the seal of your honor."

"I shall so hold it, sir."

"You must understand that this very thought itself is dangerous, so dangerous to utter abroad that it must not even be breathed."

"I understand you, sir, and give you my word of honor."

"We stand," the dry old voice went on, "at one of those critical times in history when the destinies of men and nations are in the balance. On the other side of the sea lies Europe—a festering sore, rotten to the core, subservient to its degenerate rulers, corrupt, heartless, willing at any moment in the future, as in the past, to sacrifice countless lives in wars of aggression to pander to the ambitions of some king or emperor or dictator with a crazed lust for conquest in his distempered head. On this side of the sea lies the United States, where alone in all the world dictators do not reign. What is the future of this land?"

"I do not follow your thinking as yet, General."

"Then I'll put it plainly. The United States is now, at this hour, no more than an Atlantic seaboard country. The greatest part of our population is east of the Allegheny Mountains. Yet to our west lies the major part of this continent. Who will have and hold that great area? The future of this nation and the entire concept of democracy lies in the answer to that question. For an enemy on our western border would be a never-dying menace and peril to everything America now stands for. I saw it—I saw it in Florida, which subservient Spain turned over to our enemy for a base of supplies and to stimulate inroads of hostile Indians. That particular threat is now eliminated. I saw it even more clearly when I beat back the British at New Orleans, and for the first time realized the growing cloud under which our land would cower if a hostile neighbor should occupy that vast western frontier."

"We have the Louisiana Purchase," suggested Houston.

"True. A beginning, a bare beginning, and it must be consolidated to do any good. But what of all the rest—the Oregon country, and California, and all the other great areas of empty lands lying between us and the Pacific?"

"What of the people who inhabit those areas now?"

"Inhabit?" The old man fairly spat the word. "You refer as inhabitants to a few thousand painted savages who wander over a million square miles of the fairest lands in the world, only to hunt or make war against each other? I tell you, sir, it is a sin against mankind to allow a handful of Indians to reserve as a hunting preserve the rich fields that would support millions of people in prosperity if tilled and developed— a manifest iniquity, sir, against all humanity!" He blew a cloud of smoke like a fire-breathing old dragon. "Besides, the savages can never hold that country against any civilized nation which covets it and moves to take it—and there are those ready to so move."

"Then Mexico——"

"Has the most shadowy of claims, based on the even more shadowy claims of Spain. The age has passed, sir, when some adventurer can wave a sword at the mouth of some unexplored river and proclaim that all the lands it drains belong to his master, the king of his country. Why, Sam, according to that false rule, the very soil on which this house stands belongs to France, whose explorers 'claimed' the Ohio drainage, including our Cumberland Valley. No, indeed, sir. The only rule by which territory can be claimed and held is the ancient Roman law of *occupatia*—occupation, tillage, population. An empty land is anyone's land."

"But Mexico can say that California and Texas are occupied."

"California already has thrown off the Mexican rule, which means that California will become a province of some more powerful nation. As for Texas—*it may be that a great destiny lies in Texas*. Keep your eye on Texas. Peopled? Yes, but largely by American colonists. When I am in the White House, I shall negotiate for the purchase of Texas— which I have always held belongs rightfully to us by the terms of the Louisiana Purchase, and which the Mexican government cannot even defend from the Indians. I shall fail in that negotiation. But an explosion is brewing there. Mark this well: Americans will not long abide the present system of Mexican dictatorship. Watch it narrowly."

"Texas . . ." murmured Houston to himself, and it was as if the name suddenly contained some mystical, unrealized, meaning for him.

"What of the rest of that country?" continued Jackson. "Britain now claims the Oregon Territory, and has a post of its far-spreading Hudson Bay Company—its precursor of empire—as far south, I am informed, as the Bay of San Francisco. Russia has eyes on California and has built fortifications on that coast. France is colony-minded and gazes greedily at Texas and California. Any of these would mean constant, unceasing tension on our undefended frontier. What if in France arises another Louis Fourteenth, or another Napoleon? Or Russia breeds another dictator as lawless as Tsar Peter? England is already the great world imperialist. The classic strategy of dictatorships—to lay a false claim to a piece of territory, move in troops, and present the aggrieved victim nation with a *fait accompli,* might in one gulp deprive us of everything west of the Mississippi—*including* the Louisiana Purchase. And we, a democracy, unprepared for war as always, must swallow the aggression, and wait for further and still further aggressions, until perhaps we are forced into a conflict in which our entire national identity may be lost. Will it be one of those inimical nations which is to possess the western half of this continent?"

Houston's absorption of an idea was always catastrophic in its force. He leaped to his feet and strode back and forth, head bent, brows knit in concentration.

"No! It must be us!" he exclaimed.

Jackson watched him with kindling eyes. "I'm glad you agree," he said. "For merest minimum safety this nation must place its borders on the two oceans. It must, please God, become a continental power, not a seaboard province. As you now recognize, extremest caution is necessary at this stage even to consider such a question. The nation is not prepared for so giant a step. And if Britain, or France, or even Russia had an inkling that such a thought was brewing, the decisive movement might be made by one of them."

Houston ceased pacing and stood by the fireplace, glaring into the flames as if Jackson's conception were blazing within him like the fire leaping up from those logs.

"What we are discussing," went on the old warrior, "if it were so much as suggested, would be killed at once by the Clays, the Adamses, the Websters, the Marshalls, the Calhouns. Part of America's so-called political leaders are wedded to the Atlantic seaboard; part are affected by the slavery question—a jealousy between North and South which grows more dangerous to the peace of this country every day; and all would flinch from the magnitude and the danger of such a proposal, however much a matter of life-and-death it might be."

Houston looked him directly in the eyes. "You have done me the greatest honor of my life, sir. Now tell me how I can help you."

"For the present nothing. Be ready when the time is ripe, and meantime ponder it. I do not myself know now the solution; but by keeping it constantly in our minds the key to the great scheme may unfold itself. Perhaps more important than anything just now is this: I am old, I do not know how many days I have left. I would bequeath to you the vision and the policy if I failed of it."

"You will never fail, sir!"

Jackson watched Houston standing with his eyes distant as if on some far vista. He was pleased, but he also knew very well how to change a subject and thus fix in mind the one abandoned. He now leaned back in his chair.

"I've watched you come up, boy," he said, "and it's been a mighty source of satisfaction to me. Barring mischance, I see a great future lying before you. A gentleman must know how to sit his horse, shoot his gun, keep his word, protect his honor, serve his country, and love his woman. In every respect you fit the picture—save perhaps the last. Yet it has been whispered to me there is a possibility—do I hear rightly?"

Houston colored. "Yes, sir. I hope to splice me a rib."

"And who is the lady?"

"Miss Eliza Allen, sir, daughter of Colonel Allen of Allendale. I met her for the first time right here at the Hermitage."

The white head nodded. "That was the report that came to me. I've known the family a long time—the Allens are high-toned, surely."

Houston hesitated. "She's young, sir. Not yet twenty. And I'm thirty-four. Is she too young for me, do you think?"

"Thirty-four? The threshold—the very threshold of a man's greatest period of vitality and achievement. As for the girl, a woman is ready for marriage as soon as she becomes a woman. I'd have no fears on that score—if she loves you."

"I at least love her. And I believe she returns my feeling, though I've neglected her shamefully during this political campaign."

Jackson gave a slow grin. "I can see how a woman might be most enraptured with you, boy. Indeed, perhaps there have already been a few . . . ?"

Houston stirred uneasily and looked at the floor.

"I do not pry," said Jackson. "A man's gallantries are his own business—so long as he's free. I'll confess to you that I may have had my own little period of wildness, before I married." He broke off. Then: "If you've had some few experiences with the fair, sir, forget them now. A wife is an anchor needed by any man, and to follow the conventions is extremely needful, especially for one in public life."

"Yes, sir," said Houston.

"By the way," the General said, "I had a visitor yesterday—an emissary from Billy Carroll. Billy, who has had his two years of sabbatical leave, has his eyes on the governorship again, which surprises nobody.

His friend asked if I'd be good enough to indicate the course I'd pursue if he was opposed by you."

"What did you say, sir?"

"I told him the contingency had not yet arisen, and I therefore could make no statement."

For a moment Houston was silent. Then he said, "With your permission, sir, I intend to stand for a second term."

"Permission I have not the right to give or deny."

"But your blessing, sir—that's what I wish for."

Andrew Jackson puffed on his pipe for a few moments before answering. He knew Billy Carroll as a remarkable man. He had fought well under the General in the Creek War and at New Orleans. Since that time he had shown something approaching outright genius in his political operations. Always fastidiously groomed, with those steely eyes and impassive countenance, he spent much time traveling through the country, and was almost as well known personally to as many persons as Jackson himself, though hardly with the same warmth and enthusiasm.

But the General knew, too, that Carroll, very rich, was also very ruthless. On one basic matter they differed: to Jackson friendship was everything; to Carroll politics came first, and there were those who doubted if he knew the real meaning of friendship. Now that he was openly a gubernatorial candidate the question of what Houston, who naturally might expect a second term, would do in the face of this determination, was a subject of wide speculation, with the lines already being drawn in Tennessee, though the election was not until the following spring.

At length Jackson made his reply:

"You have my blessing, boy. You'll always have it. Yet you must understand that at this time I should not extend my open endorsement either to you or Billy. Billy has the bit in his teeth, and he's as strongheaded as an iron-mouthed mule. There's no heading him off. And a good friend Billy Carroll has been to me. Yet when it comes to making a choice between him and you, there can be only one answer. I have plans for you, Sam, as I've told you before—mighty plans. I've touched briefly on some of my beliefs and hopes. Only you share them with me fully. I will say this to you: go ahead and enter the race for governor. When the proper time comes, if it is in my power, I will do something that may be of assistance to you. At the present it would be unseemly for me to do so."

"That's all I could ask, sir."

"When will you announce?"

"After my wedding."

"The date has been set?"

"January 22."

"Ah. I'd hoped to be able to kiss the bride, but I must be gone East before then. Well—at least my wedding gift will be there for Eliza. I

She had consented, in the first place, to be a bride because it was the thing to do; because of the wishes of her parents, who considered the match a brilliant one for their daughter; and because it was the only sensible solution for any girl's life. At the time she had been carried along by Houston's impetuosity, too unformed in her mind to know how to resist. Nevertheless, in the past weeks she had discovered in herself a deep-seated rebellion, which someone wiser than herself might have recognized as a disturbing possibility in the future of her marriage.

Eliza had told everyone that she loved Houston—she repeated it often, as if it would make it true. But did she? She may have been in love with a dream she had imagined from childhood, and which she now tried to crystallize as a substitution for the very human, flesh-and-blood man she was to take for better or worse.

A more sophisticated age might find it difficult to understand another factor contributing to her confusion. Only comparatively recently had the naïve girl really come to consider seriously—at first through hints, not from her mother, but from kindly old black Aunt Dilsey—that something mysterious and somehow terrible was connected with marriage, which her childlike mind actually had hardly imagined.

The climax to this came only a few days before the wedding, when Aunt Dilsey, out of sheer compassion, sat down with her and talked in a way Eliza's own mother should have talked years ago. As delicately as possible Aunt Dilsey explained to her what a man desired of a woman: something very private, and very personal, and to Eliza's mind at the time even shameful. Had this information been imparted to her properly at a much earlier period, she would probably have grown accustomed to it, finally accepted it, in the end perhaps even looked forward to it. But brought thus suddenly to a focus, she was terribly shocked by it. Her prudish mother had never permitted her to witness the natural reproductive processes of the animals of the plantation, and all talk, ideas, and books which bore even lightly on the subject were carefully screened from her.

Eliza, in her ignorance, on her wedding day was unprepared, confused, divided against herself, half rebellious, half triumphant, afraid yet courageous, shrinking from what seemed an abyss, yet fascinated at being the central figure on the stage. Pride forbade her being an "old maid," and now she was on the brink of becoming a bride, the heroine of this climactic occasion, a girl about to be transmuted into a woman of consequence.

All of this at once wonderfully attracted her; yet caused her also to recoil in unutterable and undefined dismay.

2

Early evening came, and the candles made a soft shimmering light, and Governor Houston arrived at Allendale, to be greeted by Colonel and Mrs. Allen and the guests, although Eliza, of course, remained in seclusion.

Presently the Reverend Dr. Hume, who had conducted the funeral service for Rachel Jackson, took his place in the ballroom where waited the bridegroom, towering over all the guests. An orchestra of colored musicians began to play the wedding march, and Colonel Allen conducted his daughter, clad all in white and wearing her mother's white veil, down the winding stair.

When she saw Houston, waiting there for her, Eliza felt panic and faintness. But her hand was on her father's arm, and he conducted her on, not dreaming of what was taking place in her emotions.

Then she was standing beside Houston, listening almost without hearing to the voice of the minister, answering when prompted almost without knowing what she said, and in the end limply accepting a kiss from her newly pronounced husband.

With that the fateful ceremony was over, and Eliza, borne away by laughing and chattering members of her own sex, was relieved and almost gay; while Houston joked and laughed with the men who crowded about to congratulate him.

Dinner followed, stately and lengthy. At one end of the long table, rich with linen, silver, and crystal, and brilliantly lit by candles, Eliza sat beside Houston, facing her father and mother at the other end, with a great array of guests lining each side. It was a banquet typical of the time, an array of rich foods, capped by the wedding cake. Eliza, seeming prettily confused, gave the ceremonial first cut to the cake, then surrendered the office to the servants, who brought to each guest a piece of the confection. Thereafter toasts were offered, an endless number it seemed to her, one of them by Sam Houston to his bride. But though the other listeners applauded his offering as eloquent, even poetic, Eliza sat with a bent head as if she hardly heard it.

Dinner ended, and there was great mirth and jollity, including witticisms, some of them almost broad, and teasing by the younger ladies, directed in part at the bride, but especially at that wonderfully handsome groom. On every side young people—and some not so young—engaged in flirtations. And when the orchestra struck up again, and Colonel and Mrs. Allen led the grand march, there was loud applause, and cries for Eliza.

But Eliza was nowhere to be seen. Houston, dragged out on the floor by a laughing bevy of girls, took his place with one of them. There were knowing looks and smiles at the apparent flight of the new little bride, especially among the feminine guests, to whom the symptom seemed familiar.

They did not know, nor did Houston, that Eliza had fled from the ballroom to the only trusted friend she knew: not her mother, or her father, but old Aunt Dilsey.

At first she sobbed on the kind old woman's shoulder. Aunt Dilsey sought to comfort her, and brought Cologne water to eradicate the stains of weeping.

Then for a long time Eliza sat silent, with Aunt Dilsey's arms about her, while the old woman crooned to her, talked gently to her, soothed and calmed her as she would a baby. The girl could not, however, be induced to go downstairs.

Midnight came. Many of the guests were departing, and both the old Negress and her charge knew it was time for the bride to join her bridegroom. Aunt Dilsey could not permit any such scandal to occur as would happen should an Allen woman flee from her nuptial chamber on her wedding night.

At last she stood up, put the last touches to Eliza's eyes and hair, and removed most of the ravages of her weeping.

"Now, honey," she said firmly, "yo' go on up to yo' husban'. An' don't git skeered. Everybody gits married, an' yo' kin see fo' yo'self that they seems happy with it. It's jest a li'l matter of gittin' used to things. Try an' please that man of yours, an' eve'thing will be all right. Now go, chile."

3

Houston, who had remained with Colonel and Mrs. Allen to see the last guests off, was unable to retire to the bedroom assigned to him and his bride until far after midnight. He mounted the stairs with the kind of excited anticipation which might be expected in a bridegroom hastening to his first intimate tryst with his bride. He thought perhaps she would be in bed, and he should make his apologies and explain why he was so late before he embraced her. Perhaps she would even be asleep, and he wondered if it would be too inconsiderate of him to awaken her if she was.

When he opened the door of his room, the lamp was lit. The girl, instead of being in the big double bed, was still attired in the pink silk peignoir with which Aunt Dilsey had clothed her, and huddled, wide awake, in a chair with a blanket about her. He closed the door, and smiled at her. Then, at the pitch of desire, he rushed over to her—far too impetuously, it seemed—seized her in his arms, and kissed her with the kind of fervor he imagined she would expect.

But he did not know the virginal mind. Instead of responding, she went pale and shrinking, and struggled to break away from him, a look of combined terror and desperation in her face.

Astonished and uncomprehending, he released her and stood back. "What's the matter, darling?" he asked.

"Don't touch me—keep your hands off me!" she cried.

"But—what do you mean? You're my wife——"

"I don't want to be! I *never* wanted to be!" she half-whimpered.

He was stunned. But after he stared at her a moment, he thought he understood. Poor thing—so young and inexperienced—she was hysterical and frightened. She really did not mean what she said. She *could* not mean it.

He must be wise with her, give her time to grow accustomed to him, to learn that his only desire was to make her happy. He would be very gentle, try to anticipate her slightest wishes, woo her by kindness. He could not believe that she did not love him. In her fear, he thought, she said the first thing that came to her tongue, to keep him at a distance.

That night Sam Houston rolled up in a coverlet on the floor. Eliza lay in bed, sleepless and terrified. He was sleepless also, but from a different reason. He had been eager, had dreamed that she would be wonderful in the way women sometimes were—with soft fury, soft whimpering moans, soft instinctive responses.

In all this she had disappointed him, but her denial of him only made his desire for her greater. All through the dark hours he lay awake in his frustration, his ears strained for the slightest sound from her who lay so near to him, belonging to him by the laws of God and man, yet for the present unattainable.

Thus, their wedding night.

4

It was snowing next morning, the earth softly white, with large white flakes drifting thickly down.

At breakfast, which Houston had with Colonel Allen alone, he said he was anxious to get back to Nashville. Only a few days before the *Banner and Whig*, Erwin's newspaper which had an open quarrel with Houston, had announced with considerable flourish that General William Carroll, Tennessee's military hero and capable former governor, would be a candidate for re-election. Houston had expected it, but he could not avoid the feeling that Carroll was selfish in the matter, since by long custom a man who has served one term in office was considered entitled to a second term, all things being equal. He wished to return to the capital so that he could confer with some of his friends and prepare to meet this challenge.

Colonel Allen gravely agreed, and inquired if his son-in-law had spent a comfortable night. Houston assured him, quite untruthfully, that he had done so.

An hour or so later the coach was brought around, and Eliza, having breakfasted, appeared all bundled up against the cold, with her mother, Aunt Dilsey, and many bundles and trunks. When the departure took place, to Houston's relief Eliza played up quite well, though she wept a little in her mother's arms. This seemed natural in a girl leaving her home for the first time, and when they drove away in the falling snow, showered with rice and good wishes, Houston began to hope that his bride might now warm to him.

But sitting upright in the coach, Eliza hardly spoke. Once when he reached out to wrap her more warmly, she drew as far away as she could to the other side of the seat, and stared straight ahead, not even looking at him. He was more puzzled than ever, though not angry. On the contrary, he began to wonder if in some manner he had offended her.

He hoped to reach Nashville that evening, but the snow thickened and the cold increased. In the middle of the afternoon he told his Negro driver to turn off up a lane which led to Locust Grove, the plantation home of a friend, Robert Martin.

The Martins were delighted to shelter them, and pleasant Martha Martin made much over Eliza. She and her husband observed with approval that Sam Houston was most attentive to his new wife; but the girl excused herself and went up to her room early, while the governor remained below, talking on politics and other affairs with Bob Martin. When at last he also went upstairs he appeared to be in the best of spirits and the Martins were happy for him.

What they did not know was that Houston for the second night slept apart from his wife.

Next morning, when he came down, Eliza kept to her room. He breakfasted with the Martins and their two little daughters, while a tray was sent up to her.

The snow had ceased, but the lawn before the house was beautifully white, and the two small girls clamored to play in it. Houston was so delighted with them that when Martha Martin bundled them up, he put on his greatcoat and went out with them.

Watching them through the window of her sitting room, Martha saw the tall man romping with the children. Then a snowball battle ensued, the laughing rosy little girls pelting the governor, while he also laughed as if he himself were a child.

As she smiled at this scene, Martha heard a step behind her. Eliza had come down. Laughing, Martha turned to her guest.

"It seems as if General Houston is getting the worst of the snow-balling," she said. "You'd better go out and help him."

Eliza's face was like stone. "I wish they'd kill him," she said.

Astonished at such a remark from a bride of less than two days, Martha glanced at her. She knew bitterness when she saw it, and surprise changed to shock.

Martha Martin was Sam Houston's friend. She was suddenly deeply concerned, but she was too tactful to inquire further or attempt to advise. Instead she took Eliza to the fireplace for coffee, and talked of other things, seeking to charm her out of her mood. She did not succeed. When Eliza later entered the coach with Houston to finish the trip to Nashville, she was still cold and unsmiling. Martha was troubled, but she said nothing of this at the time, not even to her husband.

There had been enough travel on the road that morning so that the drifts were broken, and the ride was short. But as before it was silent, Eliza drawn far away from her husband. Houston, increasingly puzzled and hurt, now began to experience a little indignation.

But he suppressed the feeling and summoned his patience again. A surprising barrier existed between them; he must overcome it. The process, he feared, might be slow and difficult, but he believed that by unremitting care and understanding he could in the end succeed.

He therefore did not take his wife directly to his apartments in the Nashville Inn, but instead begged a few days' hospitality at the home of a cousin, Robert McEwen, whose wife Eliza knew. In that stay he sought to be more attentive, more complimentary, more eager to please her than ever during the days of his courtship. And the girl, who seemed now to wish to make a good impression, smiled and was pleasant in company, so that Mrs. McEwen declared to friends that she had "never seen a more affectionate couple."

She had not an inkling of Houston's sore heart; or of Eliza's strange iciness that was like hatred when the two were alone together. Or that they continued to sleep apart.

5

It was fortunate for Sam Houston that the sudden furious contest which had arisen in politics gave him something to occupy his mind and energies, even though it could not make him forget the maddeningly unfair, not to say unnatural, impasse in his own household.

The day after his return to Nashville, the *Banner and Whig*, which had devoted a full column to the candidacy of Billy Carroll, contained a three-line squib:

We are requested to announce the present governor of Tennessee, Honorable Samuel Houston, is a candidate for re-election.

A most temperate announcement, to say the best for it; and certainly not the way Houston sent in the item. His name was Sam, not Samuel;

he once had corrected Andrew Jackson himself on that point. But so, as if to nag him, the newspaper put his candidacy before the people.

Now that the battle was joined, men began to ask again what the old General would do. Some speculated that the mere fact that Houston entered the race at all after Carroll was an avowed candidate, must mean he had Old Hickory's private endorsement, perhaps to be made public later.

Now they studied the young governor in a different light. Was he a Man of Destiny, who might some day succeed Jackson in the White House? What, after all, could be more logical? Points were marshaled to buttress this line of conjecture.

Point one: Houston was a war hero, who had suffered battle wounds for his country.

Point two: He was born in Virginia, the "Mother of Presidents," and was by upbringing a Tennesseean, in the fast-growing West.

Point three: He was a born orator, who could stir the hearts of his audiences as few men could.

Point four: He had made a fine record, both as a congressman and as a governor.

Point five (and greatest point of all): He was known to be dear to the heart of the man who was the new President of the United States, Andrew Jackson.

Should Houston win over Carroll, who controlled so many political strings, he would prove himself a candidate who could run like a race horse. But Carroll was a dangerous political opponent who would test Houston to the final precinct and the final vote. Cautious men did not take sides openly, waiting to see what would happen before declaring themselves.

Meantime, Houston thanked the McEwens, and took his wife to the Nashville Inn, to a suite which would be his permanent residence until he could find a house suitable for her. The necessities of politics forced him to be away much of the time, and perhaps this was not entirely unwelcome to him, for when he was at home the situation continued in a way that became almost unsupportable.

However he tried to win her, Eliza refused him. Though she showed a smiling face in public, he had not so much as been allowed a kiss by her since the first night of their marriage.

He did not reveal this unhappiness. It was too humiliating. In this respect Eliza held an advantage over him, which she began very quickly to realize. For political as well as personal reasons, he wished above everything to avoid any situation that might cause scandalous gossip. He therefore did his best not to offend her, and because she insisted on it, his wife, still a virgin after all these days, had a room separate from his in the suite at the Inn.

Yet her behavior was so frustrating, so incomprehensible, so maddening, that in spite of himself resentment grew in him. She was cheating him, torturing him, living up to none of her vows or obligations. Never in his experience with women had he known any like her, and it was his misfortune that he chose out of all women this one: although he did not yet regard it as a misfortune, and still hoped against hope to win her out of herself.

The thing was explosive. It could not last forever.

Chapter Twenty-One

Whatever the price of silence, I will pay it.

SAM HOUSTON

1

That which finally happened could not have happened, at least in the manner it did, had it not been for the exhilaration of a triumph.

Houston threw himself into his campaign, occupied himself with it, worked at it almost desperately, as a relief for his sore spirits. Up and down the state he traveled, speaking and shaking hands; and his methods had so much of a whirlwind quality to them that men began to say he was a political figure such as Tennessee had never seen. He had learned the value of dressing to catch the public eye, and he rode fine blooded horses, beautifully equipped. Whether at log rollings, barn raisings, barbecues, or more formal occasions, he was nearly sure to be present; and when present he was the unfailing center of attraction.

Sometimes he would, in the backwoods districts, challenge the village champion to a friendly wrestling match—all vicious and foul tactics barred—and afterward speak to the crowd that came to see. His two hundred and forty pounds of superb muscular physique, on a six-foot six-inch frame, made him invincible. He never lost any of those impromptu matches; and it was said he never lost a precinct in which he spoke to the crowd afterward.

At home the situation remained maddeningly unsatisfactory. But abroad he gained confidence daily; at times he could almost forget Eliza. There came a day, as the election neared, when he issued a public challenge to Carroll, for a debate on the issues. Carroll did not relish such an encounter, but he felt forced to accept. It was a novelty so great that on the day chosen, thousands gathered at Cockrell's Springs to witness the forensic battle between the two rivals.

Whiskey flowed freely. Whole steers were barbecued. The morning was devoted to an impromptu horse race in which a gray gelding owned by Colonel Willoughby Williams, sheriff of Nashville, won over a brown horse carrying the colors of Horace Potter, of Clarksville. Since Williams was a close friend of Houston's, and Potter a supporter of Carroll, it seemed a favorable augury for the incumbent governor.

Long before three o'clock, the hour announced, a throng of several thousands was jammed about the temporary platform erected in the open air in a pasture. Promptly at the scheduled time the speakers and their escorting committee made their way through the press to the rostrum. There were seven in the group: the two principals; Colonel Allen of Allendale and Judge Jacob Isaks of Winchester, for Houston; Judge John C. Guild of Gallatin and Colonel Joseph P. Erwin of Nashville, for Carroll; and Congressman Pryor Lea, of Knoxville, as moderator.

The toss of a coin decided that Carroll should first address the assemblage; and the crowd craned its necks as the former governor, sleekly attired as usual in gray, stepped forward. Carroll, however, was not the man to capture this audience. His manner, as always, was cold; and his pedestrian speaking style evoked little enthusiasm—some yawns, in fact, before he was through with his hour's address. He did not even rise to the level of a harangue, and the crowd, which anticipated forensic fireworks, felt defrauded.

But when Sam Houston was introduced, interest immediately quickened. He caught their attention even before he spoke, with his mighty figure and great head, his plum-colored claw-hammer coat and white satin waistcoat. Then his voice rose like a trumpet, a virile, far-carrying baritone. He had been trained in a native school of oratory, the councils of Indians, and with his words of fire and power he mingled vivid imagery to illustrate his periods. To his audience he seemed to dwarf his opponent, not only physically, but in eloquence and sincerity. And when he concluded his speech, the vast roar of applause lasted for ten minutes or more.

Houston was quite flushed with elation at such an ovation. For more than an hour he stood, receiving congratulations and enthusiastic promises of support from citizens who crowded forward to shake his hand. Long before he finished greeting his well-wishers, William Carroll and his immediate party, almost unnoticed, had left the scene.

Colonel Williams made him an enthusiastic report:

"I mingled with the crowd during and after your great speech, Governor. I've never seen such a response! It's all Houston—they're solidly behind you, sir! You can whip Billy Carroll at every turn, and this has proved it, and he knows it!"

Another friend, John Boyd, had a happy suggestion:

"You'll be riding past my place on your way home. I've invited some people there for a cup of comfort. Will you honor us, Governor?"

"Why, yes, thank you kindly, John," said Houston. "For a brief time only, however. I'm a married man, you know."

Boyd laughed.

"Understood," he said. "We'll let you get away. I know you're eager to see your little lady. And if you need any witnesses to tell her how well you did today, you can call on any of us!"

He did not know how Houston winced at this good-humored assumption that all was cordially well in his home.

There was a good-sized crowd at Boyd's plantation, and Houston passed through it, making himself pleasant. Then his host spoke:

"Your friends wish to drink some toasts to your success, Governor," he said. "Not only in today's debate, which was a smashing victory, sir, but in the election, of which we all feel confident."

"Why," said Houston, "I'll drink to that myself, John!"

For weeks he had hardly tasted liquor, fearing it might offend Eliza. Now he felt a sudden desire to let go, to enjoy himself, to forget for a moment at least the disappointments and frustrations of the incentives of his heart and flesh.

The glass was brought, and he drank. His whole system seemed to welcome the fiery taste in his mouth, the warmth in his belly. The whiskey was excellent, and he had carried a thirst too long. He drank again, and again, and it seemed even finer. It was late at night and most of the guests were gone when at last he called for his horse, mounted somewhat unsteadily, and rode toward Nashville.

As he traveled through the darkness, thoughts began to drum in his tipsy brain; thoughts surrounding the woman in his suite in the Nashville Inn. The thoughts formed themselves out of his frustration, his longing for the woman, his growing resentment at the way he had been tricked and misused by her.

His thoughts said to him: You've had a wife for weeks, now, Houston, and in those weeks you've never once had the pleasure of her. What about her, Houston? Is she so different from other women . . . other women you've had? Were they too good for you? She's a woman like the others, Houston, and when it comes down to facts, she's not one bit better than the others. Yet *she* thinks she's too good for you.

The swirling thoughts took another direction: She's your wife, Houston. What's a wife for—a decoration? No, Houston, she's for something more important than that. Among other things, she's for a man to enjoy in bed, for bearing his children. But do you really have a wife, Houston? Isn't she something else—a doll maybe, a selfish, foolish, empty-headed doll? Are you going to go on letting the doll you married make a fool of you? Go on treating you like a foolish schoolboy? You're supposed to be a grown man, Houston. Are you going to keep acting as if you have no rights or natural human feelings? Oh, no, Houston! If you have any manhood left, you're going to show her what a man really is. You're going to make a woman out of that doll you're keeping in your home, *and you're damned well going to do it tonight!*

2

Long after midnight he mounted the stairs to his rooms. The door was locked, but he opened it with his key.

Entering quietly, he looked toward the room where Eliza slept. Even in the gloom he could make out that the door was ajar, to allow air to circulate. So confident was she of her ascendancy over him that she did not even bother to close her door!

He went to the door and peered in. There she lay in her bed, the golden girl, beautiful in slumber. Moonlight from the window just touched her face and the lovely hair outspread on her pillow. Since their marriage he had dutifully occupied another room and another bed. But now his anger and his desire, stimulated by the liquor in his brain, were like a flame in him. He intended at last to occupy that same bed with her.

Clumsily he stripped off his clothes, leaving them in disarray on the floor. Eliza did not wake until he pulled back the covers and got into bed with her; and even then, her mind still clouded by sleep, she did not quite realize what was happening.

But when she felt his hands on her, she knew and was instantly fully awake. All her life long she had accepted her femininity, enjoying without costs the pleasures and triumphs it provided her. Now, a terrified instinct told her, she was about to give payment for it.

She tried to fling herself out of the bed, her eyes starting with fear. But he had her, she was powerless against his bull strength, he drew her to him, against his naked body. His mouth covered hers, pressing against hers as if it would exhale from her her very life.

A sense of disgust filled her as his tongue probed between her lips. The raw smell of whiskey on his breath completed her repugnance. Not only was she frightened now, she was terribly repelled.

Always she had loved soft things, soft materials, soft colors, soft air. Now she encountered harshness and maleness. The covers of the bed were disordered, thrown off in their struggle together, and for the first time, by the moon's light, she saw and felt what the male body is, and she was not prepared for that reality. What she perceived in his nakedness, in his expression, was to her a dreadful evidence of his intention, of something terrible he would do to her, something she associated in her mind with the indecent, the surgical, the horrible.

She tried to cry out, but her mouth was closed by his. Her slender body was now beneath him, and her own weakness sickened her. Now, some ancient runic instinct of her sex told her pitifully, now it was coming, now she was going to have it whether she desired or not. Still unable to speak because of his brutal mouth, she felt him seeking the entry, finding it . . . she was sure he would tear her apart.

Despair added to her terror at this violence. One of her hands, outflung, encountered something on the table beside the bed. Her fingers clutched it and she struck at him, as hard as her frail arm could swing it.

The weapon could hardly be called that: a brass candlestick, no more. And her puny blow on his head did not seriously hurt him.

Yet he did not give the thrust she dreaded. Instead, he half released her, as if to look at her, a changing expression on his face. With a violent effort she pulled herself free and sprang to the floor.

Now at last she could speak. "Get away from me, you stinking, filthy beast!" she screamed.

"Eliza——"

He, too, rose from the bed, and his magnificent torso, with its superb proportions and muscularity, might well have thrilled a warm-blooded woman, an experienced woman. In her it aroused only greater fear and repugnance.

He took a step toward her and she shrank in fright, desperately brandishing the candlestick.

"Don't you dare come near me, you—you—dreadful animal—or I'll kill you with this!"

Houston halted. The candlestick was nothing to fear in her hands, but he had suddenly become sober. Innate decency was a part of him, and he now realized that he had gone to the extreme of attempting to rape her. If that was the only way to possess her, it demeaned her—and him. He would never again attempt that way.

Suddenly he was shamed by consciousness of his nakedness. He seized a blanket from the bed and wrapped it about him.

Then he faced her, like some great Roman in a toga, and regarded her for a long time in silence, while she trembled in a corner, holding her nightgown clutched to her body, the candlestick in her hand.

"Eliza," he said at last, "you're my wife. I've been kind to you, and patient with you. All I want is what a husband has the right to expect——"

"I don't want to, I won't let you!" she cried.

"But you're my wife——"

"I never wanted to be!"

"Then why did you marry me?"

"Because I—because I *had* to!"

"You married me with no intention ever of being a wife to me?" he asked incredulously.

She did not reply.

A thought came to him, and with it a new anger, a different anger. "Then there's someone else—another man—isn't there?" he asked slowly.

"No!" she exclaimed. "No—there isn't!"

"But I say there is—there must be," he said with dangerous calm. "Yes, I see it now. You have another man—a lover. You've had him all the time. It explains the whole business—your coldness to me, your cheating, dishonest way with me. Who is this lover for whom you keep your favors? Tell me his name!" A sudden scowling suspicion was in his eyes. "Has he been here—with you—*while I've been gone?*"

She went pale at the injustice of the accusation, for she had never been faithless in that manner. She did not, indeed, have the warmth of heart and blood to be faithless.

Suddenly she began to sob, wildly. And he, realizing he had gone too far, became anxious to calm her. But she would not be appeased.

"Leave me alone!" she wailed. And then, rage mounting: "Nobody but a filthy-minded, whiskey-soaked brute would say a—a thing like that to—to me! I'm g-going home! I'm going home right now—and don't you try to stop me! I wouldn't stay another minute with a—a beast—who would *think*, let alone *say*, a thing like that! If—if my f-father knew —he'd shoot you for it!"

She was hysterical, yet her determination was evident.

"Eliza," he began, "think before you do something rash——"

"Get away from me! And if you don't order a coach for me, I'll have the night clerk order one! I'm g-going home!"

She began to sob again.

In that moment Houston saw with immense clarity, but too late, what he had done. He had given her a pretext, perhaps one for which she had been waiting. Frustration and anger were swept from his mind by fear—fear of scandal. It was he who now became the pleader, the penitent. With every possible promise he tried to soothe her, to change her purpose. But the girl was beyond all control, weeping, threatening to scream for help, and to accuse him of brutalities and monstrous acts if he attempted to detain her.

There was nothing he could do. He tried to help her pack her things, but she wanted none of his help, snatching the garments out of his hands when he clumsily brought them to her, tears blurring her eyes and staining her face.

Toward morning he sent for his coach, placed her in it, then watched her ride away without once looking back.

For years Sam Houston would regret that moment. But Eliza would regret it for the rest of her life.

3

In his room the haggard giant sat, shaken as in his whole existence he had never been shaken before. More than once in the recent hours he had considered taking his own life; but his strong sanity prevented that. He had thought of writing to his greatest friend and patron, Andrew Jackson, but he gave it up because he did not think he could explain even to the old General the true, intimate, disgraceful cause of his sudden separation from the girl he married.

He sought to remain in seclusion, but the news was out and all Nashville was talking. At last he admitted two friends: Colonel Williams, the sheriff; and Dr. John Shelby, the man who had treated his wounds at the Battle of Horseshoe Bend.

Vainly these two begged him to tell them what happened.

"Eliza and I have separated," he said in a weary voice, "but I cannot tell you the reason for it. The cause is something I will never disclose to a living person."

He refused food.

"But you must eat," said Dr. Shelby. "You can't live on whiskey."

"Doctor," said Houston, "I'm in the torture chamber of hell."

"We've got to think of the public," pleaded Williams. "What explanation will be given them?"

"No explanation is possible."

"This is serious. You're in a political campaign——"

Houston shook his head. "The people will have to give themselves any explanation they wish."

"I've been in the street," said the doctor. "Excitement is growing. If no particulars are furnished, gossipers will put the worst possible interpretation on things. Even though they know not a single detail, they're already saying that you've 'wronged' your bride."

Houston rocked his head slowly back and forth, like a man in great pain, his eyes gazing down at the floor beneath his feet.

"If you don't make some explanation," begged Williams, "you'll sacrifice not only yourself, but your friends also. Billy Carroll will have no mercy on us."

"I can't help it. I'm a ruined man. I will exile myself," said Houston.

After a moment he reached over to the table and took from it a written paper, which he handed to Williams.

"Read it," he said.

It was a formal resignation of his office as governor, addressed to General William Hall, Speaker of the senate of the Tennessee legislature.

Shocked to the core, Colonel Williams read it. Though it was fairly long, one paragraph in particular caught his eye:

. . . Although shielded by a perfect consciousness of undiminished claim to the confidence & support of my fellow citizens, yet delicately circumstanced as I am, & by my own misfortunes more than by the fault or contrivance of anyone, overwhelmed by sudden calamities, it is certainly due to myself & more respectful to the world, that I should retire from a position, which, in the public judgment, I might seem to occupy by questionable authority. . . .

"'Delicately circumstanced . . . questionable authority,'" repeated Williams. "You make it sound almost as if you accuse yourself. Are you sure you want to send this?"

"Yes."

"But it conceals more than it discloses. Carroll will make a perfect mountain of this. I beg you, give us one word or sign wherewith to defend you."

"It is a private matter," said Houston drearily. "Whatever the price of silence, I will pay it."

"This is quixotic!" protested Dr. Shelby. "Have you thought that this might injure Andrew Jackson himself? If you'll only speak out, stating merely that your wife left you out of pique, without laying any blame on the lady—though surely she must be blameworthy to some degree— we can still save your political life."

Houston answered dully, "My old friend, the President, would be incapable of placing blame on a lady. Nor would he respect one who did."

It thus became clear to his friends that he was in a mood almost irrational, too crushed by sorrow and some sort of self-blame to understand or be concerned about the calamities brooding over him and everyone concerned with him.

4

The sudden and unexplained resignation of Houston created a sensation all over Tennessee, and the scandal tongues grew busy. A woman had been wronged: this was evident to those who knew nothing at all about it. And those same mongers, with nothing more than their own salacious imaginations to go on, whispered of bedroom practices which were alleged to have driven Eliza Houston from her home.

Eliza herself, when she came home pale and weeping, told her parents only that her husband had accused her of infidelity, omitting every other detail in the separation, especially her refusal of herself to him.

White anger burned in the girl's family, and in the family's friends. At Gallatin, near Allendale, an angry mob burned Houston in effigy.

Eliza sat alone in her room and wanted none to come near her. Belatedly she had begun to contemplate her actions; and their results, in retrospect, now seemed more cataclysmic than she had dreamed they would be, or than they had any right to be.

She learned of Houston's resignation from his high office, the burning in effigy by the mob, the manner in which his name was being blackened.

She was revenged: a terrible revenge . . . but for what?

Eliza found it impossible to truly decide what reason she had for revenge. Her husband wanted her. She knew that. And now for the first time an inarticulate wish formed in her, as if in answer to a strange mystery connected and entwined with instincts and feelings new to her, which she could not define.

If only . . . but it was too late. Too long she had played at life, and fled from reality like a child from imagined terrors. She had been unequal to the role of being a woman. A storm engulfed the man whom, she knew at this late date, she had wronged. In the presence of the typhoon of public hate she had unloosed, she felt small and weak. So she hid herself, and wept much; and her people, mistaking the reason for her tears, grew even more wrathful toward Houston.

A letter came, addressed to Colonel Allen, Eliza's father:

Whatever had been my feelings in relation to Eliza at one period, I have been satisfied and believe her virtuous, as I have assured her. If mortal man had dared to charge my wife, or say ought against her virtue, I would have slain him. That I have and do love Eliza none can doubt, and that I have ever treated her with affection, she will admit. That she is the only earthly object dear to me God will bear me witness. Eliza stands acquitted by me. She was cold to me, and I thought she did not love me; but she knows that such was one cause of my unhappiness. You can think how unhappy I was to think I was united to a woman who did not love me. That time is now past, and my future happiness can only exist in the assurance that Eliza and myself can once more be happy, and that your wife and yourself will forget the past.

Your obedient servant, Sam Houston

She was cold to me . . . the only faint reference Sam Houston made to the underlying cause of the rupture. What might have happened had Colonel Allen allowed Eliza to see this longing letter? She did not read it. Her father pocketed it, believing she had no interest in it, or in the man who wrote it.

5

And still the storm grew. At Nashville crowds filled the square and there were shouts for Houston to show himself. That particular taste for the stinking carrion of scandal which some persons seem to possess, brought more and more each day to take part in demonstrations.

Houston, in seclusion, waited for an answer to his letter. No answer ever came.

In an agony of spirit he sent a message to the Reverend Dr. William Hume, who had married him and Eliza, asking the minister to come to the Inn. When the reverend gentleman arrived, he was surprised to find a humble Sam Houston, who asked for the rites of baptism.

But personal pressures appear even in matters of religion. Dr. Hume, because "the respectable connections of the lady [Eliza] are much offended," declined to perform the baptism.

Houston was hurt, but did not debate the question of whether or not it was a minister's duty to baptize anyone, however great a sinner, if the ordinance was sincerely asked.

A day or two later Williams and Dr. Shelby found him in his rooms, burning his correspondence. His portmanteau was packed for travel.

"Governor," said the physician, "they're saying outside that you're afraid to show yourself."

"It matters not what they say," replied Houston.

"I hesitate to tell you this—" began Williams.

"Say it."

"You have been posted as a coward."

Houston's great form reared itself from the chair. "Who did that?"

"I don't know—it wasn't signed."

Without a word Houston drew on his coat, clapped his hat on his head, took a stout cane in his hand, and went down the stairs from his room, followed by his two friends.

The jackdaw mob stood before the Inn—some there from malice, some from curiosity, not a few carrying out urgings by secret agents of Billy Carroll.

Sudden silence fell as Houston stepped to the edge of the porch. He looked the crowd over sardonically.

"I am given to understand," he said at last, "that someone has taken it upon himself to placard me."

He paused, as if listening for a reply. The mob remained awed and mute.

Houston spoke again, his voice hard as iron. "I invite him—or they— who are responsible for this denunciation to come forward to me now and make it good."

Dead silence.

Long minutes ticked by as he stood there, his eyes going over the crowd, face by face. Wherever his eyes rested, men stirred uneasily, as if they feared that they might be remembered, and wished now that they were somewhere else.

Once more Houston spoke. "I give notice, to each and every one of you, that though I am leaving this city, if any wretch utters so much as a whisper against Mrs. Houston, I will return and write the libel in his heart's blood!"

He let that sink in. Then he turned back into the Inn.

A little later, carrying his portmanteau and accompanied by his two friends, he appeared once more, descended the steps from the porch, and walked toward the steamboat landing.

Not a word was uttered by anyone in the mob. No move was made to deter him; men stepped hurriedly out of his way. When he was gone the placard was torn down. People now knew who the real cowards were.

Chapter Twenty-Two

There is a vulgar saying of some vulgar
man, I believe Swift on such unions—
about using a certain household . . . and
then putting it on one's head.

C. C. CAMBRELING

1

Dim burned the solitary lamp that lit the vestibule of the White House. By the pallid illumination of a single candle Andrew Jackson, seeming more than ever weary and worn, sat in his study, working late in the night at the papers heaped on his table, the rest of the household long asleep.

The long, long shadow of the years! More than ever in her life Rachel now seemed to be with him. The band of crape on his sleeve would be there to the end of his days; and about his neck he wore on a black cord the miniature that was his favorite portrait of her.

Since her passing he had undergone a slow metamorphosis. Living, he had identified her with himself, unconsciously as an extension of himself; perhaps as a cause for which to battle. Dead, he enshrined her as flawless and other-worldly, and too soon withdrawn.

Too soon withdrawn! Therein, to him, lay the tragedy of divine wastage, the law of loss, which he knew was unending on earth, but whose right he could not bring his soul to acknowledge.

Never given to introspection, the white-haired widower was not really aware how since her death he had taken to idealizing Rachel, forgetting her every weakness or shortcoming, and creating of her in his heart an image different and more lovely than she really was.

Whoever acted as hostess for the old President—it was Emily, Jack Donelson's wife at the moment—the silent, unseen spirit of Rachel Jackson was, and would be, the true mistress of the White House.

He was the President of the United States, duly inaugurated and vested with the vast powers of that office. But he felt in it no especial pride, only a heavy duty. He had accepted another responsibility, the greatest in his life; and the old man's preoccupation with that duty was intense, his feeling for the nation that he must lead almost mystical.

One reason for his present weariness was that from the beginning, though he was ill at the time, he had refused to isolate himself from the people who had elected him. On his journey to Washington they crowded about him, elbowed him, cheered him, sometimes questioned him in the crudest manner.

When his steamboat stopped at the dock at Cincinnati on the journey up the Ohio River, a greasy, slouchy fellow accosted him in the crowd.

"General Jackson, I guess?" said the fellow.

Jackson bowed assent.

"Why, they told me ye was dead," was the next sally.

"No, Providence has hitherto preserved my life."

"An' is yer wife alive, too?"

The wound was still fresh and agonizing. Jackson could only shake his head.

"Aye," said the man, with a bumpkin's smugness, "I thought it was one or t'other of ye."

Some of those near him saw Jackson wince at the mention of his wife's death. What they did not see or understand was that he would not have dreamed of avoiding, or resenting, such questioning. He considered that he now belonged to the public.

When he reached Pittsburgh, to begin the overland journey to the capital, he refused a private equipage and took the public stagecoach. Wherever a halt was made people clamored to see him. At length, to avoid the labor of climbing in and out of the coach, he took to riding on the high front seat with the driver. There he would stand patiently with his hat off, in sun or rain, to acknowledge the cheers of the village crowds.

The day came when he mounted a temporary platform on the Capitol steps at Washington and gazed down at a sea of faces. It was noticed that the outgoing President was not there. John Quincy Adams, in his bitterness over his defeat, thought to snub the inauguration by absenting himself, and took instead a solitary horseback ride in the suburbs.

It was an ungracious act; a childishly petty act. And it was a futile act, for the inauguration forgot all about Adams. The thin, tall, white-haired figure on the platform was greeted by a roar of applause so vast that

Daniel Webster, who was present, sourly remarked, "Those fools really seem to think the country is rescued from some dreadful danger."

Some, of Webster's political persuasion, believed rather that the country was being plunged into danger. A tall man with iron-gray hair and jet-black eyes, looking like a shrewd country lawyer save for his black robe, stood before Jackson. Chief Justice John Marshall, the arch-Federalist, had not shunned the inauguration as Adams had done; and now he administered the oath of office, though he believed by doing so he was exposing to imminent peril his entire life's work on the bench.

When Andrew Jackson raised the Bible to his lips and kissed the book, another tremendous roar broke from the crowd. At last he was officially the President, and they believed they had a champion in the White House.

They came in mobs to the reception at the White House that evening, and well-garbed Federalist and Whig leaders could hardly control their disgust at seeing hunters from Kentucky and Indian fighters from Tennessee, with farmers and herdsmen and small shopkeepers and all their women, crowd into the august dwelling of the President, the first time so plebeian an assemblage had ever been admitted. It must be confessed that the manners of these people were as bad as their enthusiasm was great. Men with boots covered with the red muck of the streets stood on chairs covered with damask satin, to see the new Chief Magistrate. They clamored for refreshments and drained whole barrels of punch to his health; and in the process broke much china and glassware.

Good-natured though it was, the mob became almost dangerous as it crushed about the new President. Jackson, near to prostration before the evening was over as he tried to speak kindly to all who approached him, at last was forced into a corner of the big East Room, where a cordon of his friends formed a living barrier about him to protect his frail figure.

That night, when at last he was permitted to retire in complete exhaustion to his bed, he reflected that he had very heavy burdens to bear. But he still refused to deny himself to the public.

2

A month had passed since that day, and he was learning other things: the intransigence of politicians, the glacial slowness of Congress, the ceaseless treachery of intrigues beneath the surface.

Old and ailing though he was, the President was yet a man in whom existed pent energies, summoned by a will power unmeasured even by his friends, which he turned against whatever problem, human or abstract, confronted him. Late on this night he was laboring alone with profound concentration upon the multiplying matters which required his attention.

There were foreign affairs: France evaded payment of promised reparations for damage to American shipping during the Napoleonic wars; Britain barred the West Indies to American trade; the Maine boundary was in dispute; insistent demands from Southern and Western states called for annexation of the Mexican province called Texas, on the ground that it was now chiefly populated by Americans.

There were domestic affairs: the tariff, and South Carolina's growing threat to nullify that law; the national debt; the problems of Indian removal to open more lands for settlement; requests from logrolling congressmen for various internal improvements to satisfy their constituents; the budget and tax structure; and the Bank of the United States, whereby private interests, iniquitously as he believed, controlled the money power of the nation.

There were also personal affairs. Wearily the white-haired President considered a letter from Billy Carroll of Tennessee:

That fate of Houston must have surprised you. His conduct, to say the least, was very strange, and charity requires us to place it to the account of insanity. I have always looked upon him as a man of weak and unsettled mind, incapable of manfully meeting a reverse of fortune.

To Carroll, whose ambitions looked upward as high as the White House itself, Houston's downfall was like a sending of the gods; and he was doing all in his power to make that downfall final and ruinous. His messengers hurried in every direction bearing the story of Houston's family tragedy and strange exile; and also artfully suggesting theories of their cause. Houston was described as a drunkard. Episodes in his wild youth were dredged up to show him as a libertine. He was depicted as shallow and unstable, and any fault or indulgence in him was magnified into something like a crime.

This particular letter, however, to the old soldier in the White House was ill-aimed and ill-timed. Jackson snorted. Weak and unsettled? He knew Sam Houston too well for that.

When the news first reached him it bewildered and stunned him. How strange and unhappy! And involving one whom he regarded as a son, about whom he had built some of his greatest secret hopes!

But as he read Carroll's letter he smiled grimly. This very letter must have crossed in the mails another letter, written to Carroll by Jackson before he learned of Houston's downfall. It would, he reflected, be a sufficient answer to this missive.

In it the President offered General William Carroll the post of Minister to Brazil. To the man who received it the meaning would be clear: it was intended as a means for him to save his face by retiring from the race for governor of Tennessee; and it was a revelation that Jackson intended to back Houston, which would have made certain the latter's election.

Long, long would cold-faced Billy Carroll consider that letter; and the consideration would be bitter. He knew now how he stood with Andrew Jackson, on a basic difference in viewpoint. To Carroll friendship meant nothing compared with power; to Jackson friendship came first of all, and he did not trust a man who would sacrifice a friend. Billy Carroll would be governor of Tennessee, since he now had no opponent, but he must swallow, and then digest, the realization that his ambitions and hopes ended there.

3

A second personal problem arose while Jackson was eating his meager breakfast of oatmeal and milk next morning. He had summoned John Henry Eaton, whom he had appointed Secretary of War.

That very appointment, announced before the inauguration, created a problem in itself. Eaton had made good his promise and married Peggy Timberlake. But gossip already had done its work with her reputation, and Congressman C. C. Cambreling expressed the opinion of many in Washington when he wrote to Martin Van Buren, governor of New York:

Poor Eaton is to be married tonight to Mrs. T . . . ! There is a vulgar saying of some vulgar man, I believe Swift on such unions—about using a certain household . . . and then putting it on one's head.

And a certain dowager, more notable for her weight than for her wit, had said: "Public opinion will not allow Senator Eaton to bring his wife into society."

These people did not know that Rachel Jackson's death brought Andrew Jackson to Washington with an irreconcilable, almost irrational, fury against persons who traduced a woman's reputation.

When he proposed Eaton as Secretary of War, the entire Congressional delegation from Eaton's and his own state, Tennessee, called on him to suggest that Eaton ought not be included in the Cabinet.

"And why not?" he asked. "Is Senator Eaton unworthy?"

Colonel Towson, tall, imposing, and gray-haired, answered:

"Certainly no one would say that Eaton himself is unworthy of trust. But there is an encumbrance——"

"What is it?" demanded Jackson, knowing already.

"Eaton's wife. She bore a bad reputation before her marriage——"

"Eaton married her," interrupted Jackson, "and a worthy man could hardly have an unworthy woman for his wife."

He could feel his temper rising, getting out of hand. But the delegation failed to see the danger signs.

"But, sir, you dare not give Eaton so high an office," Towson insisted. "Washington society will never receive Mrs. Eaton——"

It was rash to suggest that Jackson would not dare do anything.

"Who," he asked icily, "composes Washington society?"

"Why—the ladies."

"The ladies? Do the ladies suppose I have come to Washington to make a Cabinet for their social pleasure, or for the country? Do the ladies think themselves superior to the woman who bears John Eaton's name? Are they prettier, smarter, more pleasant company?"

"That's not the point, sir," said the spokesman. "She will not be countenanced by respectable females."

Jackson's hand felt for the miniature of Rachel he now wore always on his breast.

"Females? Respectable?" he exploded. "I'll tell you what they are— they're dirty detractors! And I'll show them what I think of their filthy slurs against one of their own sex! Go back and tell the ladies of Washington that I'll name whom I will!"

The delegation departed in more haste and confusion than it came.

Yet the matter did pose a problem, annoying and trivial, but one he did not feel he could ignore. The problem had become somewhat more complicated very recently.

4

Eaton arrived promptly. He was not ill-looking except for an increasing baldness which he sought to conceal by combing his hair down over his forehead. But this morning his face was grave with concern, and the concern was occasioned by his wife.

Peggy, he was discovering, possessed more than her share of feminine vanity and feminine ambition; and having by some miracle risen from tavern girl to a lady of the Cabinet, she intended to reap the social rewards of this prodigious ascent. He knew the dangers of such ambition on her part, and he knew also her headstrong willfulness, a stubbornness increased by overheard gossip.

There had been a prophecy by spiteful Margaret Bayard Smith, one of the capital's feminine censors, having to do with "a wedding extorted by exigency, and sanctified by a shotgun."

"I'll never leave here," Peggy exclaimed when she heard that, "until nine months have passed in the presence of my enemies, and open proof is given of the lies they have told."

She was as acid-tongued as any of her sex. "Who are those who snub me, anyway?" she had declared with a biting laugh. "For one, the great-granddaughter of a Puritan brewer, whose affectation of morals is as stiff as her stays. For another, the niece four degrees removed of a Cavalier cutthroat who was sold as a convict to the James River Colony."

The ladies thus devastatingly described did not love her for it.

Eaton feared the situation was growing impossible, and he dreaded to hear what the President, who with all his complex and important problems must be asked to deal with something as trivial as it was impossible of solution—the bringing about of understanding, good feeling, and good sense among women—might have to say about it.

It was a relief, therefore, when he heard Jackson's first words.

"John, you've heard about Sam Houston?"

Eaton nodded.

"I don't understand it," said the old General. "But this I know: Sam Houston has not told his side of the matter. Nor would I ask it of him. I cannot believe he has done anything truly dishonorable, despite all they say."

This was conceded by Eaton.

"He left Nashville without explanation," went on the President. "I have word that he has gone west—I suspect to his old friends the Cherokee Indians, now living in the trans-Mississippi."

"We have a garrison at Fort Gibson, in the Cherokee country," Eaton suggested.

"Instruct the commander to keep an eye on Houston's doings and report them." Jackson paused, then spoke weightily. "This is a man, John, with almost limitless possibilities—for good, or if misdirected, for ill. I know him; I trained him myself. It would be most unhappy if this recent strange event should so embitter him that he took the wrong path."

"The order shall go at once, sir."

The President took from his desk a long-stemmed clay pipe, filled it from a pottery tobacco canister, lit it, and puffed it for several minutes. Eaton fidgeted in his seat.

"I have received a letter that I wish to discuss with you," the old man said at length. "It is of a painfully personal nature, but you ought to know about it. Before I give it to you to read, I wish to assure you that I do not believe a word of it."

Mechanically Eaton took the letter and read:

Honored and Respected Sir: I feel it my duty to address you in connection with something of importance which may prove an embarrassment to you unless forewarned. I refer to the situation with regard to Mrs. John Eaton.

Painful as is the subject, it must be discussed, and you are entitled to a full account. From girlhood, sir, this woman has borne a bad reputation. You must be aware that the ladies of Washington will not speak to her, and have not for some time past. I must tell you that a gentleman, the morning after the British Minister's ball, said at his tavern breakfast table that "Mrs. Eaton brushed by him last night pretending not to know him; she had forgotten the time when she slept with him." I am informed that her servants are told to call her children Eaton, not Timberlake, for Eaton was their right name. Furthermore, a clergyman of Washington has lately told me that Mrs. Timberlake had a miscarriage when her husband had been absent for a year. As to Mr. Eaton, his own friends, seeking to save him from this woman, persuaded him to board elsewhere than at the tavern she frequented. I should also remind you, sir, that your late and lamented wife, Mrs. Jackson, had a bad opinion of this woman. And it is stated by numerous witnesses that Mrs. Timberlake and Eaton took trips together, and traveled as man and wife, recording it in hotel registers in New York and elsewhere.

For your own sake, for your dead wife's sake, for your Administration, for the credit of the Government and the Country, you should not countenance a woman like this. Unpleasant as it has been, I feel that I have done my duty in apprising you of these circumstances, and I trust you will accept it in that spirit, and that you will believe in my sincere devotion.

Your friend and obedient serv't, Ezra Styles Ely, D.D.

Jackson's eyes never left Eaton's face while he read the letter. Eaton was his friend. Furthermore, he himself had peremptorily ordered Eaton to marry Peggy Timberlake "forthwith" when she became a widow, "to restore her good name"—and this when Eaton seemed undecided what course to take. The President felt deep responsibility in this matter.

He remembered the Reverend Dr. Ezra Styles Ely as a tall, austere, politico-preacher of Philadelphia, who had been active in behalf of Jackson's candidacy in the recent election. But mention of Rachel in the letter had an effect opposite from that intended by the epistoler. Coupling Peggy's name with that of Rachel caused the old widower unconsciously to bracket them together, and the cause of the "traduced woman" rose again.

"I myself can give the lie to one statement in that letter," he said before Eaton spoke. "Far from having a bad opinion of Mrs. Eaton, my beloved wife had the warmest affection for her."

"Sir, this is a *tissue* of lies," declared Eaton. "I don't know the man who was at the British Minister's ball, but I'd like to trace him down and make him eat those words! As to the trips I'm alleged to have taken with Peggy, I never traveled in her company but once, and then her husband was along."

"The statement about the miscarriage?"

"There was an accident. She was injured in a runaway." Eaton did not add that he was with her when the runaway occurred.

Nor did he add that there actually had been a miscarriage, sometime in the weeks or months after Timberlake was at sea. He himself was in

Tennessee at the time it occurred, and he could, if necessary, plead ignorance of it.

But he was fully aware of it, for a good reason: Peggy had told him. He was not, in point of fact, sure whether the child was Timberlake's or his; and neither, said Peggy, was she, which is why she confessed it to him.

A vagrant thought: could it have been that neither he nor Timberlake fathered that child . . . ?

He did not voice that thought. Instead, he sought to put it out of his mind.

Chapter Twenty-Three

What object do you have, sir, in filching from me my good name?

PEGGY O'NEALE EATON

1

It was a ridiculous mess for the Chief Magistrate of a nation to be involved in; but the President allowed no false considerations of his dignity to sway him. If he felt a thing was right, he put his whole soul behind it; if wrong, an equal force against it.

In the kind simplicity of his mind, he believed that Peggy Eaton was in the right; and perhaps he might even have succeeded in quelling the scandalous gossip concerning her, had it not been for Peggy herself.

Taking Dr. Ely's letter, clause by clause, he set about to learn the truth, in so far as he was able. And in due time he wrote a letter to that reverend gentleman, which fairly bristled. In it he made the following points:

One: He offered affidavits from a dozen of O'Neale's former boarders, stating that they knew of "no bad name" Peggy carried.

Two: The gentleman alleged to have spoken of "sleeping" with Peggy was found—a Mr. Hyde—and he denied the statement, saying that he could not have been more astonished "at a charge of high treason" than at being accused of it.

Three: Investigators, who at the Presidential order went to lodgings where Peggy, with her husband and Eaton had stopped, reported the landladies unanimous in saying that all had been right and proper.

Four: The President offered the opinion that the refusal of "certain so-called ladies" to speak to Peggy signified nothing more than feminine spite, not worthy of attention.

Five: He suggested that in his humble opinion a minister of the gospel would be better employed conducting his sacred offices than in purveying idle gossip of this nature.

When Dr. Ely, in Philadelphia, received this letter, he became most sorry that he had ever become involved in the matter, and sent a note to the President admitting he might have been mistaken.

Jackson turned to his more important tasks, believing he had vindicated his friend's wife; and Jack Donelson, Rachel's nephew, whom he had brought to Washington as his private secretary, wrote a friend:

The petticoat war has ended, no lives lost. The General, in the goodness of his heart, thinks that Mrs. E. has attained a triumph.

And thus it might indeed have ended, with even the ladies of Washington acceding—however reluctantly—to the will of the fierce old man in the White House, had it not been for one item that Jackson himself had regarded as too delicate and private to investigate: the question of the miscarriage. After all, the old General said to himself, miscarriages were regrettable but not infrequent; and with small actual knowledge of women and their ways, he innocently assumed that if one had occurred it must have been in the natural, if unhappy, course of events due to misfortune of which one did not speak.

It was Peggy, when she learned that it had come to the President's attention, who would not let the matter die. A genuinely complex woman, there was beneath the aura of frivolity that floated about her a passionate determination to have things her own way.

All her adult life she had been a man's woman, and she did not pretend otherwise. A woman who bewitches men must respond to them, holding out to them a shimmering evocation of the mystery of sex, with a play of little acts and glances and words by which she returns their interest in her. At this game she was expert, and at any social gathering she always had men flocking about her. Other women bored her, and she showed it. They hated her, but for their hate she did not care a snap of her tapered fingers.

From the time she was no more than thirteen, men had been more than attracted to her, and in the free atmosphere of her father's inn she had far from discouraged their warm and secret attentions. Her body was sinuous, her mind sensuous . . . only she could have told to how many of her wooers she succumbed. But in this she was as enigmatical as any of her sex, and nobody ever knew.

Once, however—only once—an indiscretion of hers bore fruit in an embarrassing consequence. The miscarriage *had* occurred. But who, she asked herself, told of it? Not John Eaton—he was too deeply involved personally. Her mother? No. The question preyed on her mind day and night, until at last her self-possession snapped.

And suddenly, on a reckless emotional impulse, she fanned the smoldering gossip, which the President of the United States had tried to quench, into a full blaze of scandal.

2

Dr. Ezra Styles Ely, dry, gaunt, and precise, was sitting in his study preparing the next Sunday's sermon, when a servant announced that a gentleman and a lady were in his parlor to see him.

The minister laid aside his notes and went. In the parlor he found a woman—undeniably attractive, but evidently nervous and distraught— and a man named Bradford, a publisher of books and tracts in Philadelphia, whom he knew slightly.

"I am Dr. Ely," he said. "You wished to see me?"

He spoke to the man, but it was the woman who answered him.

"I am Mrs. John Henry Eaton," she said. "Mr. Bradford, who publishes some of my husband's writings, accompanied me here at my request."

Mrs. Eaton! The minister looked at her uneasily because of her voice and manner, which betrayed excitement.

"I demand the source of the information you gave to the President, concerning an occurrence by which you implied I was guilty of adultery!" she blazed.

Dr. Ely blinked and took a backward step.

"My dear woman—I can't give my source," he protested.

"I'll not leave your presence until I have your author!" Her voice was strained, trembling with her emotion.

"But—it was given me in confidence—" began the preacher. Then he stopped.

Signs of approaching hysteria were becoming all too evident in the woman. To have a person such as this go to pieces in his parlor, screaming and sobbing, saying nobody knew what, was too alarming. He capitulated.

"My informant, if you must know, is the Reverend J. N. Campbell of Washington," he said.

Now it was Peggy who took a backward step, or rather a lurch, so that Bradford put out a quick hand to support her.

"Reverend Campbell—of the Presbyterian church in Washington?" she almost faltered.

"The same."

For a moment Peggy did not speak. Dr. Ely had named the pastor of the very church which Andrew Jackson attended.

"Let us go," she said to Bradford after a moment.

Without another look or a word of farewell she left Dr. Ely standing in his parlor, something very like consternation on his lean-jawed face.

3

Riding back alone in her carriage to Washington, Peggy Eaton reflected almost morbidly on her situation.

That she had a miscarriage, evidently, now had become public knowledge. Would it also become public knowledge that it was worse—a deliberate abortion?

With a sense of nausea she remembered the whole messy, agonizing, humiliating episode. It had happened, true enough, while John Timberlake, her husband, was at sea. But it was only a few weeks after his departure, and had the circumstances been normal she might have borne the child with full faith that its paternity would be recognized as Timberlake's.

But the circumstances were not normal. For months before he left on his cruise, she and Timberlake had been estranged: to a degree that in that time he did not share her bed, sometimes not even her apartment, and never once had the intimacy of sex with her.

In those months other men had looked at her with desire in their eyes . . . and she was vibrant, sometimes irresponsible . . . and with a sense of pique against her husband such as more than once in history has impelled women to behave recklessly.

She knew that Timberlake had suspected her. Once he gloomily told Dr. Craven, the O'Neale family physician, that he "was sick of the sight of land and must go off to sea," adding, "My wife is now indifferent to me, and there are plenty of men at the tavern to keep her interested."

When he did go, however, Timberlake did not know she was pregnant. Only she knew how far along she was in her pregnancy, but she also knew this: when the child was born he would be able to compute the time when it was conceived, and that could only be disastrous, for he would know it was not his.

She did not *dare* have the child. At length she consulted her mother. Good Mrs. O'Neale was horrified at the thought of abortion, which not only was illegal but dangerous. Yet she was loyal, and when Peggy confessed to her the true inner circumstances, with a mother's affection for her daughter she agreed to help.

Unhappily, the matter could not be kept an entire secret. Mrs. O'Neale felt bound to inform a few of her closest friends, under pledges of greatest secrecy—which, in matters of this intimate nature among women, are not always to be relied upon. There also was the hideous old crone, a disreputable midwife, who was brought in and paid to do the ghoulishly needful things to bring on premature birth.

So Peggy underwent the sickness and the anguish and the risk of her life. She survived; and in the days while she was recovering, she schemed up a story to explain matters. To those who were in possession of the secret she said that she "felt it would be kinder to spare a child the hazards of a home depending on a seafaring, drunken father."

A thin excuse, and she knew it. Later it became even thinner when Timberlake returned from his cruise and in due time she bore another child, a little girl, to the same seafaring father with all his weaknesses.

All this, Peggy believed, was her private affair and she tried to live it down. But now, she discovered, it was not private; others were making it their business. Nor had she succeeded in living it down.

4

She resolved that she must, in some way, scotch this report.

John Henry Eaton was a pleasant and sociable man, and able enough, in his way. But in his short marriage with Peggy he had already discovered it was far easier to accede to her than oppose her. Good sense told him that she would be far better off if she allowed the whole matter to rest, and wait for the President's open friendship to have its effect.

But Peggy was passionately determined, and so, with resignation, he accompanied her next day when she called on the Reverend Mr. Campbell, the pastor of Jackson's church.

As soon as he saw her, the minister knew that he was in for a painful scene, and he sadly reflected that a frantic woman is in some degrees worse to face than an angry tiger. But there was no escaping it, and Peggy came directly to her point.

"I have been in Philadelphia," she said, and her voice showed the emotional pitch to which she had been wrought. "There I interviewed Dr. Ely. He gave *you* as the source for a *lying letter* he wrote to the President. What object do you have, sir, in *filching from me my good name?*"

The minister was understandably cautious. "If you're going to put me through an inquisition, madam," he said, "there must be a witness to the conversation. Fortunately, Colonel Towson is in the house. I shall summon him."

"Colonel Towson! Great God I *am* undone!" exclaimed Peggy.

It was this very man who led the delegation that protested to Jackson against her husband's appointment to the Cabinet—because of her.

But she regained command of herself when the gray-haired, pompous colonel entered the room. It was to Reverend Campbell she turned.

"Now, sir," she demanded, at once putting him on the defensive, "when did this alleged occurrence take place, and who informed you of it?"

"Why—as I recollect—the summer of 1821," he said, hesitantly.

"No," Towson interrupted, "it was 1822."

"Sir, we do not ask your interference or suggestions!" exclaimed Eaton.

"I but offered a correction——"

Eaton rose, his face flushed, and stepped angrily toward Towson. "You'll answer for this!" he said furiously.

It was a tense moment, but Peggy was adept in changing the complexion of such moments. As her husband made a threatening gesture, she grasped his arm.

An instant later she was down. Whether it was play-acting or an actual fall, she had collapsed backward, striking her head on the sofa, and forming a pitiable heap on the floor, in an apparent faint.

"Bring water!" cried Reverend Campbell in real consternation.

"No! Smelling salts! Have you any smelling salts?" exclaimed Eaton, kneeling and supporting Peggy's head.

The fainting device worked. All the men had forgotten the immediate quarrel.

"Would to God I'd never had anything to do with this!" the minister said in shocked tones.

And Peggy appeared to recover sufficiently to hear him say, "The story was told to me by Dr. Craven."

At that she again relapsed, and though smelling salts by this time arrived, she was brought to herself with seeming difficulty. In truth she came perilously near to fainting in actuality this time.

The reason? She suddenly remembered Dr. Craven came to her *at the time of her premature accouchement.* She was very sick, and one of her mother's well-meaning friends took it upon herself to summon the physician.

Dr. Craven arrived, but the old hag who had attended to the disgusting and evil rites cackled at him.

"The whole thing's over, and you've lost a job," she said, with the malice of age—and of the illegal practitioner.

So Dr. Craven had told Reverend Campbell!

At the moment it seemed a deadly blow; but later, when Eaton took her home, Peggy rallied. Dr. Craven, she now remembered, was dead these several years. At least he could not testify *directly.* But would Andrew Jackson believe his own pastor was a liar?

Her next act was pure effrontery, but dictated by desperation. She carried her case and her woes to the President himself.

5

The old General was occupied with the most exasperating of duties: appointments of persons to various public offices, and the hearing of pleas and complaints.

For years—since Jefferson's administration—the governmental bureaus had been undisturbed, and in those years it appeared that inefficiency, indifference, and corruption had crept in. Amos Kendall, the undersized Kentucky editor, auditing the Post Office Department records, found substantial defalcations, and a widespread abuse by government employees and elective officers of franking privileges which was costing the treasury thousands of dollars each year.

War and Navy department records revealed "charges against the government" which could not be explained. Many civil servants cynically refused to pay personal debts, some taking bankruptcy as often as twelve times a year. No less than eighty-seven "trusted" employees, some in the higher echelons, had prison records.

To this scandalous situation Jackson turned his attention.

"Lengthy tenure of office without adequate supervision, and with assurance that by political connections men are safe from dismissal, however inefficient or even corrupt they are, is at the bottom of this shameful situation," he diagnosed, and ordered a cleanup.

At first the notoriously dishonest, untrustworthy, and neglectful were dismissed. A few were sent to prison deservedly.

Yet already the cry was being raised that the "Spoils System" was in operation: men were being dismissed merely because they were political opponents of the Administration.

When Martin Van Buren, the new Secretary of State, and his chief aide Silas Wright of New York, offered a long list of changes merely to strengthen the new political machine, the outcry of the enemies of the Administration redoubled. The President had a simple rule of thumb. He believed in rotation in office, and he would ask:

"How long has this man been feeding at the public trough?"

"Twenty years," might be the answer.

"That's long enough to live at the expense of the taxpayer. I'll appoint your nominee in his stead."

But sometimes he refused.

On this very morning, when Peggy and John Eaton arrived at the White House, he was seeing a General Van Rensselaer, who was a Federalist and an enemy of everything Jackson stood for. The general was eighty years old, and he came to plead that he might not be removed from his quite lucrative position as postmaster at Albany.

In the midst of his plea, he rose, and in an agitated manner began to take off his coat.

"What are you doing, sir?" asked Jackson, in surprise.

The old man began to unbutton his shirt to strip it off also.

"Sir, what in Heaven's name are you doing?" Jackson repeated.

"I'm going to show you my wounds, which I received in fighting for my country against the English!" quavered Van Rensselaer.

Jackson was shocked. "Put your coat back on at once! I'm surprised that a man of your age should make such an exhibition of himself!" And when this was done: "Go back to your office in Albany. You are not being removed."

A few minutes after Van Rensselaer left, Van Buren and Wright found the President nervously walking back and forth in his office, smoking a long-stemmed clay pipe.

"That old man, sir," said Wright, "is a veritable asp in your bosom. He's forfeited every claim to your kindness—he worked night and day for Adams. If he's not removed, the party and Administration will be seriously injured!"

Jackson flung his pipe into the fire, smashing it.

"I take the consequences, sir!" he exclaimed. "By the Eternal, I'll not remove the old man—I *can't* remove him, sir! Why, Mr. Wright, do you know that he carries more than a pound of British lead in his body? As long as I'm President he shall not be removed from office!"

It was immediately after that that two new callers were announced: the Secretary of War and his wife.

"Ask them to come in," he said to Jack Donelson.

As soon as they entered, he perceived with some alarm that Mrs. Eaton had been weeping. Andrew Jackson did not fear bullets, cannon balls, or hell and all its fiends. But he had never learned to face a woman's tears without something closely akin to panic. Now he feared that Peggy Eaton's weeping, which obviously had only just been soothed by her husband, might break out afresh at any moment.

"What is it? What's the matter?" he asked with concern.

"Mrs. Eaton—Peggy—" began the Secretary of War. But his wife immediately interrupted him.

"Oh, General—" she wailed. "I've bub-bub-been so falsely mum-maligned—and by ministers of the gug-gospel, too——"

Jackson's worst fears were realized. She burst into a cascade of tears, choosing his, rather than her husband's, bosom to sob against.

To the old General tears were evidence of the deepest of emotions, profound sadness. He had shed them at his wife's grave, but hardly ever anywhere else since childhood. In his simplicity it did not occur to him that tears came easily to women, especially to a woman who was a consummate actress, and that they might arise from anger, petty malice, disappointment, even be willfully produced to impress a man—as in the present instance.

He wished very much to comfort her, and produced a handkerchief from his pocket, meantime looking rather helplessly across at Eaton, who stood by.

"What has happened?" he asked.

"I'm very sorry, sir," said Eaton. "She went to those two preachers—Ely and Campbell—and they were unjust and cruel. She even had a fainting spell at Campbell's house——"

A renewed wail from the vicinity of the President's chest.

"Now, Peggy my child—you must straighten up," said Jackson, putting her from him by a slight exertion of force. "I must have your full account of this regrettable occurrence."

At this, by a seemingly miraculous effort at self-control, Peggy told her sad story of the interviews with the two ministers, their coldness and prejudice. After which she returned to her weeping, with, however, one glance from behind the handkerchief in which might have been detected a gleam that could only have meant triumph. She had expected the old man would succumb to her emotional display—it was a usual reaction—but Jackson's agitation and concern showed that he was even more susceptible to these feminine tactics than most men. Peggy Eaton felt she had won a decisive advantage, and was planning already, though the handkerchief at her face was tear-stained, the next moves in her campaign.

"I'll look into it, my dear," said the President. "Now go home and dry those tears, and you and John must come to supper tonight."

At this she was able to give him a bright-eyed look of thanks as she and her husband departed.

The General liked Peggy, who had always been cheerful and pleasant toward him and his late wife, so that they developed a fondness for her. He also felt a responsibility toward John Henry Eaton. And there was his instinct to defend a "traduced woman," an outgrowth of his own agony with Rachel.

But he hardly understood the force against him, the obduracy of women en masse, once they make up their minds, particularly when they feel righteous in so doing.

Thereafter the strangest thing took place, a thing difficult to believe if one knew Andrew Jackson of the stormy but clear-hewn career. He could see keenly through the shams and weaknesses of men; but he was totally unable to see through the shams and pretensions of a woman.

Peggy Eaton, as bold and unscrupulous as she was clever, believed she could manage the old General. In her feminine rancor she wished to sink her claws into the women who had snubbed her. Her audacity caused her to move toward the White House, to use the President himself as her cat's-paw; with no thought or care as to how her frivolous vanity and malice might complicate his labors and problems.

6

Jackson's first act was characteristically direct and blunt.

When he heard that even members of the Cabinet had spoken unfavorably of Mrs. Eaton, he summoned them to the White House, together with Dr. Ely and Reverend Campbell.

They gathered in the conference room: Martin Van Buren, Secretary of State; William T. Barry, Postmaster General; John Branch, Secretary of Navy; John McPh. Berrien, Attorney General; Samuel D. Ingham, Secretary of the Treasury; and John C. Calhoun, Vice-President. All of these were important men, men of wide influence. With them sat the two divines. Only John Eaton, the Secretary of War, was not present, "for delicate personal reasons"; but he was represented at the meeting by Major W. B. Lewis, his friend, brother of his first wife, and now head of the White House staff.

Upon this group the white-haired President gazed searchingly.

"Gentlemen," he said, "I have called you here because of a contemptible calumny against the character of Mrs. John Henry Eaton. I have asked these two gentlemen, ministers of the gospel, to attend, trusting that they will set this straight."

With surprising naïveté the old man actually hoped that this might be the outcome of the meeting. But though he could command armies, face armed enemies, and overcome great political combinations, he was to discover that he could not cope with something as insubstantial as slanderous gossip.

Both clergymen rose at once at the conference table.

"Sir," said Dr. Ely, "with all respect to you, I decline to exonerate Mrs. Eaton."

Reverend Campbell, by this time goaded to stubbornness, said, "Mr. President and gentlemen, if necessary I stand ready to prove, in a court of justice, *more* than I have said."

Jackson gazed at them with an expression mingled of incredulity, dismay, and wrath. But the two reverend gentlemen bowed and quickly withdrew. A little later the Cabinet was dismissed also.

By that meeting, official in nature, the sexual guilt or innocence of Peggy Eaton became a public, almost a national issue.

What complicated the situation was the effrontery of the woman herself. Without hesitation she took advantage of the President's championship of her. His invitations to her husband and her to the White

House she accepted as if she coolly assumed this was the wise and natural course, which it was not.

Very quickly Jackson discovered rebellion in his own household. When he took residence in the White House, he asked two of his favorites, his nephew Jack Donelson, now a major, and Jack's pretty, slim young wife, Emily, to live with him. Jack Donelson, devoted to his uncle, became the President's private secretary. Emily took over the management of the twenty-seven White House servants, and acted as official hostess at the executive mansion, with grace and credit.

Now, between Emily and Peggy Eaton, antagonism at once reared itself. Young Mrs. Donelson had heard enough about the other woman to consider her bold, ill-bred, and brazen. And the President found his niece up in arms after the first visit of the Eatons.

"That creature!" she exclaimed. "Can't you see it, General? She's shallow and selfish and pushing——"

"Emily," he said quietly, "we will not discuss Mrs. Eaton."

She flushed and was silent. Later she wept in humiliation when she was alone with her husband. With difficulty Jack Donelson managed to calm her—for the time being—and convince her that she should play the social game as the President wished it.

This might have sufficed had Peggy herself been less arrogant. She sensed Emily's enmity, and returned it; and it gave her a feline pleasure to make the President's hostess writhe. Her visits became purposely frequent and Emily's chill was met by Peggy's lofty amusement, a situation impossible to be long continued.

Andrew Jackson himself, for all his enormous personal dignity, began to be criticized as making himself "ridiculous." Some of the opposition politicians even went so far as to attempt to suggest that the old widower had more than a fatherly interest in the dashing young woman. One anti-Administration newspaper actually voiced the thought:

Is a Madame Pompadour or a Countess Du Barry now in control of the Government of the United States?

But this was too ridiculous even for the General's bitterest enemies. So the tune was changed, and instead of Madame Pompadour a new name was invented: "Bellona, Goddess of War." A rather neat conceit, Henry Clay said, for not only was she the wife of the Secretary of War, but she was stirring a profound conflict not only in social but political circles.

In those months the Eaton affair became such a topic of discussion, speculation, and resentful gossip that the capital almost lost sight of the gigantic labors the old man in the White House was performing. Some members of the Cabinet he had chosen were proving disappointing in both energy and ability. But Jackson hardly needed a Cabinet.

He was, in actuality, his own Secretary of War, and he oversaw a great reorganization of the military forces of the nation, promoting men who merited promotion, retiring various figurehead officers, beginning the introduction of the rifle to replace the musket, in general tightening and making more efficient the whole army.

He was his own Secretary of State, dealing personally with the tense foreign relations with Britain and France; and almost singlehanded he struggled with other heavy problems, such as the Bank of the United States, the vexed question of the tariff, the dangerous movement toward Secession on the part of some states; and did all these things capably, showing a power of accomplishment that was amazing.

In sheer admiration one member of the Supreme Court said of him:

"The qualities that make Andrew Jackson great are a natural gift for leadership and the paralyzing swiftness with which he translates thoughts into actions. If he fell from the clouds into a city on fire he would be at the head of the extinguishing hosts in an hour. He would blow up a palace to stop the fire with as little misgiving as another would tear down a board shed. In a moment he would will it proper and in ten minutes the thing would be done. He cares not a rush for anything behind: he looks ahead."

And yet, while he was plunged into these difficulties, there was beneath the surface of his Administration a struggle for preferment of which he was hardly aware, in which Peggy Eaton, flaunting her success, yet not wholly triumphant as she wished to be, became a pawn of political strategy.

7

Two men, each intensely ambitious, each close to Jackson, played a ruthless game to eliminate each other from the line of succession to the old hero when he left the White House.

A third, by no means close to the President, also had ambitions. Henry Clay still hoped that the lightning might strike, and he might achieve his mightiest ambition in the next election if he played his cards right; but of this the General was fully aware, and fully determined to prevent it.

Of the two in his "official family" he was less cognizant. One of them, John Caldwell Calhoun, as Vice-President stood in direct line. At times, when the old President's health seemed to fail, the South Carolinian even had moments of hope that the succession might come soon, by the President's death.

But as the rawhide constitution and inflexible will of the old General brought him again and again back, to continue his labors, Calhoun took to brooding at nights, when he was not entertaining guests, as he often did quite elaborately from policy. Men marked his intense preoccupation when he sat as presiding officer of the Senate: an impressive, some-how forbidding figure, with his harsh, hollow-cheeked face, stiff iron-gray hair, and eyes so black and piercing that they seemed almost to reflect light in the darkness. Calhoun had little love for Jackson; but with a practiced schemer's skill he concealed his envy and played out his political game.

His rival in this hidden duel of ambitions and wits was Martin Van Buren, Secretary of State. Van Buren was a short, pompous little man with gray hair curling about his head, who believed his position was as strong as that of Calhoun. He dressed always with extreme care, but soberly, his waistcoats, cravats, even his hats, in subtle harmony with whatever suit of clothes he chanced to wear that day. It was whispered that he spent so much time before the big mirror in his apartment that a large worn spot had been made where he stood. Yet the man was no fop, nor particularly vain of his appearance. He dressed to make a good impression, considering it important to do so. And whatever his failings he was what Calhoun was not: a forthright believer in and supporter of Andrew Jackson.

Between these two the status of Peggy Eaton, by a sort of inevitability, became a theater of war, and each of them approached the delicate question with his own peculiar tactics.

The fall social season in Washington, by long-established custom, opened with the dinner given by the President to the members and ladies of his Cabinet. To this affair went the Eatons as a matter of course; yet from the first moment, Peggy was hardly noticed by the other Cabinet wives, nor by Emily Donelson, the hostess. They lavished their attentions and conversations elsewhere, and Mrs. Eaton must have had an unpleasantly lonely evening of it, had not Mr. Van Buren made a special effort to entertain her.

Calhoun slyly observed the united coldness of the women toward Mrs. Eaton; and also the somewhat evident efforts of his rival to compensate to her for that coolness on the part of her sex.

He considered: Was Martin Van Buren hoping by supporting Peggy Eaton to ride into Andrew Jackson's favor? Then if Peggy Eaton were discredited, her fall would take her champion with her. Looking over the assemblage, he believed that the odds were all against her. The ladies present represented the important feminine opinion of all Washington. And thus the battle lines were drawn, Van Buren and Calhoun on op-posite sides as usual.

Jackson himself, a stranger to feminine subtleties, hardly understood what went on that evening. But thereafter began a strange, hidden war, such as women sometimes conduct. No overt aggressive acts took place, but the knife was always present for any with the discernment to see.

It began with the Calhoun dinner. All members of the Cabinet and their ladies were invited, save only the Eatons. So evident was that omission that it created talk all over the city next day.

Mrs. Eaton did not lack resolution. Having received her slap in the face, she set out with determination to find out who were her friends, who her active enemies. One after another, she called upon the wives of the Cabinet members. The answer always was the same—the hostess was "out." At each home she left her card, which by polite custom should have brought a return call. None of the ladies returned her calls.

Next, Martin Van Buren gave a dinner at the Brown Hotel, since he was a widower and lived in bachelor apartments. When it became known that the Eatons were on the invitation list, so many regrets were sent that though all the members of the Cabinet sat down to the really beautiful repast the Secretary of State provided, the only Cabinet wife present was Peggy Eaton herself.

She carried her head high that night; but next day she and her husband paid another visit to the President. Again feminine tears flowed—more terrifying to the old General than a battery of enemy artillery—and through Peggy's sobs he was made aware that there was a campaign being conducted to ostracize and humiliate her.

The old soldier acted at once; though hardly advisedly, in a matter so perplexing as women's relations to each other. He called his Cabinet to a special meeting, and when the gentlemen were seated, he read a brief statement from a written sheet of paper:

I do not claim the right to interfere in the domestic relations or personal intercourse of any member of my Cabinet. But from information and from my own observation I am fully impressed with the belief that you and your families have, in addition to the exercise of your and their undoubted rights, taken measures to induce others to avoid Mrs. Eaton, and thereby to exclude her from society and degrade her. If her character is such as to justify measures on the part of my Cabinet, it is I who am responsible for this alleged indignity to public morals. I will not part with Major Eaton, and those of my Cabinet who cannot harmonize with him had better withdraw, for harmony I must and will have.

He finished reading and removed his spectacles. "Well, gentlemen, what have you to say?"

The gentlemen turned toward him bland faces. They had not knowingly been guilty of the offense which the President described, they explained. They were sure, they said, that the dinners and parties given by their wives concerning which Mrs. Eaton protested, had no such purpose in view. Naturally, however, they added, no man can always be responsible for what his wife thinks or does in matters of this strictly feminine sphere.

Jackson, sitting with his written statement on his knee, stared at them, as much as to say: What damnable liars you all are. But he did not voice this opinion, and dismissed them to go about their business.

When Eaton, that night, recounted the episode to his wife, Peggy exulted. She believed she had won an important battle. But winning a battle does not necessarily mean winning a war. The next battle, which on the surface was to appear a decisive triumph, would be, though she would not realize it at the time, a stunning defeat.

But still, for a time, Washington was to see the fine white-haired old General put through paces that demeaned him, by a selfish, vain, even guilty woman.

Chapter Twenty-Four

> *Our Union:* It must and shall be pre-
> served!
>
> ANDREW JACKSON

1

Now, in the midst of this vexing travesty of feminine envy and spite which went on about him, Andrew Jackson sat down in his littered study to compose his first Message to Congress.

At first he labored on it alone, outlining the points to be discussed in it, then writing; casting and recasting sentences laboriously, covering whole pages with his firm, even penmanship, only, perhaps to cross the whole thing out and consign the pages that cost so much toil to the wastebasket, as he took fresh paper for a new effort.

After two days and late nights of this, he one morning went to breakfast, which he always ate early, to find Jack Donelson there before him.

"Why, Jack, my boy," he said, "you're up early."

"I found it hard to sleep, sir," said Donelson. "I knew you were working most of the night. And here you're about to start at it again, at six o'clock. At this rate, I'm afraid for your health, sir. If I could only do something to help—after all, I *am* your secretary, sir."

Jackson gave him a warm little smile. This was his favorite nephew, almost his favorite relative, and he, and his wife, and their two small children had done much to ease his loneliness in the solitary task of being President of the United States.

Jack Donelson had been with the General or near him almost all his life. Jackson remembered the eager boy, who had his first taste of battle in the New Orleans campaign, and how well he had acquitted himself. Even before that, from the time he was a small child, he had been much about the Hermitage, a bright lad who often brought a smile to Rachel's sad face. Since his uncle had gone into politics, Jack Donelson had thrown himself with his whole soul into the cause.

Now in his thirties, he possessed the Donelson good looks, although he had put on a trifle of weight and his hair was receding slightly on his forehead. For all that, he had something of the alertness of a terrier in his snapping Donelson eyes, and his manner toward the President was a mixture of reverence and devotion hard to express. Jackson loved this young man.

"I'll confess to you, Jack," he said, "that the hard thing in the writing of such a document as this Message, is a simple matter of muscular mechanics, due, I believe to age. I suffer at times from what is called, I believe, 'writer's cramp.'"

"Yes, sir," said the younger man. "I wonder you've never mentioned it before. I could serve you at least in the actual penning of your thoughts, and save your strength."

"You can do better than that," said the President. "You can help me with the thoughts themselves."

Thereafter it was Donelson who wielded the pen, and the General, sitting back in his chair, usually smoking a corncob or clay pipe, dictated slowly and with the surety of a keen and well-ordered mind. It was the beginning of a much closer relationship, and Donelson, who hitherto had cared for accounts and correspondence, from that day also was an intimate counselor in state matters.

It was the beginning also of another departure. The President, having sounded his Cabinet on the Eaton matter, perceived that he could not fully depend on all its members, for if they were not loyal in an unimportant affair, they might be vastly disloyal on some great one. He began to draw unofficial advisers into his office.

This crew was oddly assorted in appearance. In addition to Donelson, there were Amos Kendall, with his prematurely white hair, his sardonic eyes, and his bowed back, terribly crippled by arthritis; undersized Francis Preston Blair, who weighed less than one hundred pounds, and always looked as if he was wearing a suit from a rummage sale, but a brilliant editor of the Washington *Globe*; Isaac Hill, a New England newspaper owner who strongly supported Jackson; and sometimes Duff Green of the *United States Telegraph*—although the participation of this last was soon terminated. To these were added on occasion Martin Van Buren, John Henry Eaton, Thomas Hart Benton, the bull-like Missouri senator, and James Knox Polk, the congressman from Jackson's own district in Tennessee. Opposition newspapers derisively dubbed them the "Kitchen Cabinet," but in the next months they gave the President less selfish and more loyal service than his actual Cabinet had ever offered him.

Meantime, the Message to Congress, when it was completed and sent, was statesmanlike, it was agreed even by the President's opponents. It took a firm, yet reasoned tone toward matters in dispute with foreign governments; suggested compromise on the tariff law so objectionable to South Carolina; gave ways and means to open more Indian lands for settlement; stated that the national debt should be paid, and that Jackson intended to pay it.

One paragraph in the Message created a stir. The President pointed out that the charter of the Bank of the United States would expire in 1836, and suggested that it was time to consider another agency to replace the Bank, since it had "failed in the great end of establishing a uniform and sound currency."

One who long studied that final clause was a suave gentleman in Philadelphia: Nicholas Biddle, president of the Bank of the United States, considered by some—and with reason—the most powerful man in America, because of his enormous financial control as virtual dictator of the nation's fiscal affairs. The longer Biddle studied the Message, the less he liked it; and yet he considered that there was no present cause for concern.

That wild jack from Tennessee expressing an opinion on financial affairs? Assuredly he was out of his depth.

It was a small cloud in the sky, yes, but Biddle doubted it would brew up much of a storm. He put the Message aside and returned to his truly great affairs, the operation of his mammoth Bank with its many branches and its almost governmental powers. Nevertheless, like the man of high capacity that he was, he kept in a corner of his brain that clause of the President's, for future consideration; and possibly for future manipulation, in which he was as skillful as he was secret.

2

A greater question than the Bank suddenly confronted the nation.

Behind it was an arch-schemer without an equal in his day, John C. Calhoun. The lean and dark Vice-President had watched with growing misgivings the progress of the Peggy Eaton affair; and observing the President's inflexible loyalty, he had already experienced a presentiment that he had chosen a wrong side in that petticoat controversy which he, as much as anyone, had inflated to far beyond its actual importance. It might now mean even his political ruin.

But Calhoun was enormously resourceful, and his ambition knew no barriers or bounds. Like Milton's lost archangel—to whom, in fact, his enemies had not infrequently compared him—he believed it "Better to reign in hell than serve in heaven."

How to achieve this? His subtle intellect conceived a scheme through which, if he could not be President of all the nation, he proposed to be President of at least a part. John C. Calhoun's devious plan contemplated nothing less than the final and decisive splitting of the United States into two nations, the North and the South, with the great end in view that he, John Caldwell Calhoun, should rule the Southern independent government thus created.

It was a scheme as ingenious as it was bold and unscrupulous; and no other mind knew the final objective in Calhoun's mind. He plotted to work for the weakening, perhaps the destruction of his nation through the very democratic legal processes of that nation: as dangerous and clever conspirators had worked from the time of Catiline on, and would continue to work in the future.

More than once in the past the vexed question of the sovereignty of individual states as against the overriding authority of the Union had been debated. Thomas Jefferson, author of the Declaration of Independence and greatest of liberal thinkers, had at least implied that the Union was "a federation by the consent of the states." Upon this Calhoun now placed the interpretation that consent, once given, could also be withdrawn as an inherent right.

Throughout the nation his political agents began a quiet campaign to enlist behind this idea the liberal constructionists of the Constitution. It found backing among many impractical theorists, and among many practical men in the Cotton States, where Calhoun's idea gained wide acceptance because the planter economy already feared the antagonism in the North against slavery.

But Calhoun was too cunning to base his scheme on slavery; which he knew was an issue far too vulnerable. Instead he chose for his weapon the tariff, considered discriminatory in both the South and the West, as an invention for the exclusive benefit of the industrial North to the cost of the agricultural areas.

It was now of utmost importance to learn how Andrew Jackson would react. Calhoun, considering the man and the situation, read over the section in the Message to Congress in which the President recommended a compromise on that very tariff law; and he concluded that the old General, a slaveowner and cotton grower himself, and elected largely by the votes of the South and West, would hardly intervene personally in such a matter, even if he dared. It might mean his political death if he did so.

Though Jackson was like a sphinx when sounded on the question, Calhoun took notice that among his closest friends was Senator Robert Y. Hayne, of South Carolina, one of Calhoun's own strongest adherents. The tall, blond Hayne, with his handsome face and graceful manners, was a man of extraordinary charm. He was at all times a welcome guest at the White House, and his portrait hung in the President's study, a mark of esteem, surely.

Hayne also was a superb public speaker; and because of Jackson's known kindness toward him, Calhoun chose the senator as his instrument for the opening salvo in behalf of State Sovereignty, by which the right of Nullification would be established, and from that the right of Secession.

The occasion was selected with subtlety: a day early in January 1830, the springboard an obscure resolution from which Hayne could branch forth in his great effort, catching the speakers of the North, as it were, unprepared for an immediate reply.

It worked admirably. On that day Robert Hayne, an orator hardly to be matched in all the South which was notable for its orators, speaking on the resolution, began suddenly an excoriation of the whole theory of the Federal Union as holding precedence over the sovereignty of individual states. It was a brilliant speech. The senators listening, even those who disagreed with its premise, sat through that speech mentally admiring its eloquence, its polish, the keenness of its satire at times, its wonderful warmth and sincerity at other times. It created no little consternation, for few of its opponents that day could see how anyone on short notice could adequately answer it.

But in the Senate, listening, sat a short, solid man with powerful shoulders, a massive forehead, hair and skin so dark that they seemed foreign, a mastiff mouth, and eyes black and brilliant under cavernous brows. Daniel Webster was not particularly important in the Senate, because he was indolent, liked his brandy too well, and was more interested in the legal fees he received for practice in the Supreme Court, than in the deliberations of the body to which he was elected. Yet he was known as a powerful speaker, and when at the close of the session he announced that he would answer Hayne, the whole capital was stirred.

3

Word reached the White House, and that morning Andrew Jackson called his nephew into his study.

"Jack," he said, "I understand that Webster is going to speak today in answer to Bob Hayne. I'd like to have you attend the session, and give me a report on it. Will you?"

"Certainly, sir."

Donelson departed for the Senate chamber. It was fortunate that he had precedence as the President's secretary, for when he arrived there the chamber already was crowded to capacity. Even the anterooms and halls outside were packed with persons straining to hear.

A Senate usher conducted Donelson through one of the cloakrooms, and found him a seat close to the front.

When Daniel Webster stepped to the rostrum, Donelson thought that his face was grave, even portentous. Then his voice, magnificent and far-carrying, rose, to be heard even out in the corridors. The man knew the destinies of the moment and also its grave dangers; and the very greatness of the hazard uplifted him.

"Mr. President," he began, addressing Calhoun in the chair, "when the mariner has been tossed, for many days, in thick weather, and on an unknown sea, he naturally avails himself of the first pause in the storm, the earliest glance of the sun, to take his latitude, and ascertain how far the elements have driven him from his true course. Let us imitate this prudence; and before we float farther on the waves of this debate, refer to the point from which we departed. I ask for a reading of the resolution."

That is neat; most neat! Jack Donelson said to himself.

Not only did the reading of the unimportant resolution call attention to Hayne's artifice in using it as an excuse for his speech, but it riveted the entire attention of the assemblage on the orator's next words.

At the conclusion of the reading, Webster began his peroration, and Donelson noted how calm, resolute, and impressive was his manner. In a few brief periods he first defended his state of Massachusetts; which Senator Hayne had derided for a lack of patriotism, going back to the War of 1812 for his arraignment.

"There she is," said Webster, after briefly sketching the record of Massachusetts in the Revolution. "Behold her and judge for yourselves. There is her history; the world knows it by heart. The past, at least is secure."

And then, in tones of deepest feeling, "Sir, where American liberty raised its first voice, and where its youth was nurtured and sustained, there it still lives, in the strength of its manhood and full of its original spirit!"

Any doubt Jack Donelson had of Webster's ability to cope with his opponent at this sudden notice, was gone. Already his interest had taken another turn. He realized that he, and those with him, were in the midst of an incredible experience, an epoch-making masterpiece of forensic genius.

He saw how the wonderful voice and personality of the orator so captivated the packed auditorium that men sat almost breathless, as if hypnotized.

Webster continued his great, resounding, Miltonian phrases, and now his hearers, even those who opposed his doctrines, were caught up in sheer wonder and admiration. Donelson listened, rapt, as the orator's powerful periods towered in cumulative grandeur, sentence above sentence, as if he strove like the Titans to reach the very skies.

Men asked themselves: Can he continue this incredible flight? Will not the resources of imagination, learning, even genius, reach a limit from which only the fall, the anticlimax can be expected?

But Daniel Webster, in that almost godlike hour of his great inspiration, never faltered. His listeners were too far carried away by the spell of his unexampled eloquence to think of anything but the tremendous, almost awesome, thunder of his words.

To Jack Donelson, the swell of that voice and its solemn roll seemed to lift him spellbound on its deep and thrilling cadences, like waves on the shore of some far-resounding sea; the grandeur of those phrases were fit for the mighty theme they were pleading.

At the end came Webster's wondrous conclusion, uttered with such solemn significance that no man who heard it could ever forget it:

"When my eyes shall be turned to behold, for the last time, the sun in heaven, may I not see him shining on the broken and dishonored fragments of a once glorious Union; on states dissevered, discordant, belligerent; on a land rent with civil feuds, or drenched, it may be, in fraternal blood!

"Let my last feeble and lingering glance rather behold the gorgeous ensign of the republic, now known and honored throughout the earth, still in full high advance, its arms and trophies streaming in their original luster, not a stripe erased, nor polluted, not a single star obscured, bearing for its motto no such miserable interrogatory as 'What is all this worth?'—nor those other words of delusion and folly, 'Liberty first and Union afterwards.'

"But everywhere, spread all over in characters of living light, blazing in all its ample folds as they float over the sea and over the land, and in every wind under the whole heavens, that other sentiment, dear to every American heart: *Liberty and Union, now and forever, one and inseparable!*"

He was finished. At first not a sound came from the audience. Men, as if unconscious of the close, and seeming still to hear the all-pervading voice of the orator, retained their positions, heads inclined toward him, faces awed, in profound, undisguised, devoted attention.

Then the trance was broken in a universal, long-drawn, deep sigh. And after that the tremendous outburst of the ovation.

Donelson found himself, like the others, on his feet cheering as if he were mad, almost blistering his palms as he clapped them together. About him all were equally frenzied in their tributes.

For minutes it continued, one great swelling roar of heartfelt applause from men who knew they had witnessed and heard one of the mighty masterpieces of its kind in all the world's history. Not even the gavel in the hands of bitter-faced John Calhoun could restore order while senators and high officers of the government as well as many others stood on their seats to give voice and expression to their transports of enthusiasm.

When at last quiet came, the Senate simply broke up and departed. Nothing possible could transpire in the remainder of that day that could compare with the miraculous thing which had happened there.

4

Jack Donelson rode his horse back to the White House at a gallop, and went at once up the stairs to the President's study.

"How did Hayne fare at Webster's hands?" was Andrew Jackson's first question.

"Badly," said his nephew.

"I thought as much," said the President. "Webster is a lazy and greedy man, for whom it is hard to have much respect. But once he begins to soar in a speech, the very angels stop to listen."

"It was magnificent!" burst out Donelson. "You have no conception of it, sir, without having been there! I'm still almost dazed at this minute, under the spell of that incredible eloquence!"

Jackson smiled. "So I can see," he said.

His nephew, who in that hour had become a fervent Union man, was no wiser than before as to how the General would act on the question which suddenly had been erected into a nationwide issue, when he left the old man's presence.

It was an issue on which sides were taken hotly, especially in the Senate, where the Webster and Hayne adherents now formed an almost visible separation. Daniel Webster, flushed with his monumental triumph, and feeling that he had uttered the ultimate word on the question of Union versus State Sovereignty, had his speech printed in thousands of copies, to be broadcast over the land.

But the White House remained silent; and meanwhile there were certain straws which encouraged the Calhoun-Hayne faction to believe the wind might actually be blowing in their direction.

First, Thomas Hart Benton arose on the floor of the Senate, roaring, and flayed Webster for suggesting that State Sovereignty might lead to civil war. Benton, although once Jackson's mortal enemy, had become a stalwart supporter of the President, and his speech, therefore, seemed significant as possibly having the nod of the Chief Magistrate.

This was followed by editorials leaning toward the Hayne position published in the *United States Telegraph*, whose editor, Duff Green, was supposed to be close to the ear of the President.

At length Calhoun called together his inner circle of friends.

"The birthday of Thomas Jefferson, now dead these four years, has its anniversary April 13," he told them. "The occasion should receive a proper observance, should it not?"

He paused and they listened for what the dark South Carolinian would next say.

"I propose," he went on, "that we organize a dinner to which all who honor the memory of the greatest exponent of liberal thought in our history may subscribe and attend. It will be a brilliant occasion. There will be toasts by some of the most gifted among us—you, Senator Hayne, of course. I have in mind a series of toasts which would build to a climax in a manner showing the inevitable logic of our cause. Three will be devoted to Jefferson, his ideals, his achievements for the nation. To these no exception can be taken. Next will follow other toasts, building toward one to the Virginia and Kentucky Resolutions, written by Jefferson and Madison in protest against the tyrannical Alien and Sedition Acts, whereby a law-abiding citizen could be fined and sent to jail merely for uttering an opinion adverse to the constituted authorities. In those resolutions, gentlemen, the father of the Democratic Party first used, himself, the word 'Nullification.'"

He gazed about at them with his luminous eyes.

"The final set toast, I think should be by our friend and peerless orator, Bob Hayne. It is logical to draw an analogy between the Virginia and Kentucky protests against illegal usurpations of powers by the Federal government, and South Carolina's protest against the iniquitous tariff laws which that same government would cram down her throat."

Hayne bowed in assent.

"The program, you see, gentlemen," continued Calhoun, "is symmetrical, well-balanced, and at the same time brilliantly clear. From Jefferson, the great liberal, to the present question, on which we will show that we take our stand on the solid ground of his teaching, we will present a powerful and complete statement against the arrogation of tyrannical powers over the protests of the Sovereign States."

The men applauded.

"The President, of course, will be invited," said Calhoun.

"Will he come?" asked Hayne.

"How can he refuse to attend a dinner of tribute to Thomas Jefferson?" returned Calhoun. "He will come, gentlemen. And by courtesy his will be the first of the volunteer toasts, after the set program. In the face of that eloquence and those arguments, and that array of intellect and political power, knowing that his chief supporters are on the side of States' Rights, I think we will smoke the old fox out. He must declare himself in favor of his own party, his own people, and the principles of democratic justice!"

5

The great dining room of the Indian Queen Hotel began to fill early. Every place at the two long tables had been subscribed; and men, attired in formal black, began to stroll about, finding their place cards. But an atmosphere of excitement was evident.

Calhoun, watching from near the door, saw a group of gentlemen gathered, with heads together, talking earnestly. He recognized them as part of the Pennsylvania Democratic delegation in Congress. They were discussing the printed program of toasts, left beside each plate.

Suddenly, in a body, they tramped toward the door.

"You're not leaving, gentlemen?" asked Calhoun.

"We are, sir," said one of them. "Your program is an affront to every lover of his country, if the titles of your toasts and the character of the speakers is a true indication."

"Then a very good evening to you." Calhoun bowed coldly.

They trooped out.

It was dampening to his spirits; but a moment later he forgot about the Pennsylvania delegation. The President was entering.

In the months since he had arrived in Washington, ill, tired, grief-stricken, and uncertain where he could turn for loyalty, Andrew Jackson had proved to his enemies and friends alike that he had a volcanic inward force which made light of difficulties.

Something else about him was equally apparent: men who came into his presence, however powerful or famous, seemed dwarfed by that strange, stern, white-faced personality.

It was so now. As the General entered, he seemed instantly to take possession of the scene, dominating the room and everyone in it.

To Calhoun he bowed courteously; and the latter, with something of a flourish, escorted the President in person to the place of honor at the head of the first table. He himself took a chair at the far end.

Thomas Hart Benton sat at the President's right. Calhoun was flanked by Robert Y. Hayne and Hugh Lawson White, senator from Tennessee. Up and down the two tables could be seen most of the important political leaders in both the South and West; a very notable company.

Throughout the banquet Jackson hardly spoke. But he was closely observed by everyone present. As President of the United States, it was known that he would be called upon to give the first of the voluntary toasts of the evening, after the formal program.

Once he picked up and studied the list of toasts. What would he say or do? He laid the list down unruffled and serene. Calhoun and his close coterie argued from this that he had no hostility to the purpose of the affair. Calhoun himself even was encouraged to hope that there might be an expression of support which would have momentous effects upon his own great secret plan.

A tall, very polished, gentleman arose: Congressman William H. Roane of Virginia, the announced toastmaster, a well-tested Jeffersonian, with the elegant manners of an aristocrat.

"Mr. President," he said, "distinguished guests, I will not stand for more than a moment between you and the treat which lies before us. Our speakers are known to you all, and their qualities and eminence make this an occasion that will long be memorable. Gentlemen, it is my great pleasure, as well as my honor, to introduce to you the Vice-President of the United States, Honorable John Caldwell Calhoun."

Calhoun was to set the atmosphere of the evening. He gave a quite beautiful eulogy of Thomas Jefferson, referring to him as "that great promulgator of liberal political thought," and took occasion to pay a flattering little tribute to "our distinguished and beloved President, here present, a true exponent of the principles which he so splendidly shares with the late Sage of Monticello."

Amid applause he sat down, and the evening was launched. In all there were twenty-four regular toasts, as advertised by the card. One by one they built up the case for State Sovereignty, ending with a brilliant oratorical flourish from Senator Hayne, on the lines laid down by Calhoun, and ending with a proud allusion to "South Carolina, the Palmetto State, first of all the colonies to adopt an independent constitution during the War for Independence, ever a leader in the struggle for liberty in this nation and the world."

The program was, all in all, a superb piece of architecture, the various toasts presenting the arguments and philosophy of Calhoun so that they seemed unanswerable. But the time had come for the volunteer toasts, the moment for which everyone really had waited. Throughout the speeches Jackson had sat expressionless, listening without any evidence of assent or dissent.

"Now, gentlemen," said the toastmaster, "I give you a great soldier, a great citizen, a great administrator, a great patriot, a man beloved of us all—the President of the United States."

As the white-haired General arose, the entire assemblage, in tribute, rose with him. He stood, perfectly impassive, waiting for the applause to die down and the banqueters to resume their seats. When at last quiet fell, he fixed his blue eyes on John C. Calhoun. In the tense stillness his voice came clear to all:

"Our Union: *It must and shall be preserved!*"

A gasp went over the room. Calhoun looked suddenly as if he had been struck a staggering physical blow.

But the old soldier still grimly stood, his glass raised in his hand. It was a signal that the toast should be drunk standing, and there were men at those tables who would almost have drunk poison first. But he remained, glass uplifted, compelling them by the sheer power of his will.

They began to get to their feet, some promptly, others reluctantly. Calhoun rose, but his hand trembled so that a trickle of yellow wine ran down the edge of his glass and dripped on the white tablecloth.

Then Andrew Jackson raised his glass to his lips. Every man there obeyed his unspoken command; and though some of them barely tasted the wine, others drank with earnest approval.

Jackson placed his glass on the table, and inclined his head.

"Gentlemen," he said, "I thank you all, and I pray that you will now excuse me. There is much work awaiting me in my office."

As he walked toward the door, two men hurried to intercept him. One was Hayne, his face quite pale.

"Mr. President," he said anxiously, "will you consent to the insertion of one word in your toast before it is given to the newspapers for publication?"

"What word?" asked Jackson.

"The word 'Federal,' making it 'Our Federal Union——' "

For some reason Hayne thought this might take some of the hard steel impact out of the statement. But to Jackson the meaning was just opposite, strengthening rather than weakening his words.

"Do so, with my consent," he said.

The second man to reach him before he left was Thomas Hart Benton.

"Sir," said the big Missourian, "in one sentence you have done more than Daniel Webster did in three hours of oratory. You have convinced Tom Benton."

Jackson took his hand. "If I only did that, it would be worth everything," he said.

When he was gone the banqueters hurried to follow him. What had begun as a brilliant fanfare for State Sovereignty was ended by one brief, trenchant sentence: the stern declaration by Andrew Jackson that the united nation was superior to any individual state, or to any individual person, however ambitious.

Chapter Twenty-Five

She will agree.

JOHN HENRY EATON

1

He could conquer men, but he could not conquer women.

The Eaton situation continued to nag; and now Peggy became overconfident, feeling that her hold on the old man could not be shaken. She chose a moment when he was most beset by his worries to send a stiff and cold note in response to an invitation to supper at the White House:

It would only be another feast for part of your family to make me the object of their censures and reproaches.

Emily Donelson, whose duty it was to receive and respond to social correspondence at the White House, read it, of course—as it was intended that she should. The crisis followed at once.

Emily showed the spiteful note to her husband. She had reached the complete end of her patience. The two of them confronted their uncle with the message.

"Why," said Jackson, blinking through his glasses, "what can she mean?"

"She means me!" said Emily, wondering—and not for the first time— at the obtuseness of men.

"But you never——"

"Of course I never have! I've been polite to her. I've submitted to that creature's impudence. But I'll suffer no more of it! This is the final straw——"

And Emily resorted to that unfailing feminine weapon, tears.

"Now, now, my dear child!" exclaimed Jackson, in consternation.

He was bewildered, and he loved this girl like his own daughter. She had been sweet and gracious as his hostess and dutiful and conscientious as manager of his household, and he was grateful to her. But he did not know what to say to her in this mood.

Jack Donelson had his arm around his wife, and he spoke.

"With every regard, sir, for you, Emily has determined to leave the White House for our home in Tennessee, rather than submit to any further encroachments Mrs. Eaton continues to make. I, of course, must accompany her."

"But Jack, my boy, think of what you're asking! How can I deny the hospitality of my house to my Secretary of War and his wife——"

The General found that his niece had made up her mind.

"I will n-never speak to that w-woman again—" she sobbed.

He watched them go out of his office, the young man and the girl about whom he had wrapped his heart, and the weight of his cares suddenly seemed more oppressive than ever before.

2

It was far past midnight when he pushed aside the papers on which he had been trying to work.

The thoughts would not come, they were disordered, thrown out of balance and logic by other thoughts and feelings.

For the first time he felt old. He had been wounded, and sick before, many times, and he had known weakness so that he could hardly raise a hand. But those were the weaknesses and indispositions that came to a body perhaps unfortunate, but in its full tide of life.

Now it seemed that the spring of his vitality had dried up; he was a solitary old man, without love. In all his years he had never felt such a weight of loneliness.

He rose and went to his bedroom, neglecting even to drink the hot milk prescribed for him before he slept. He would not sleep this night, and he knew it.

He piled the pillows under his white head, and lay on his right side, because when he lay on his left he invariably began coughing, and the old wound in his shoulder ached.

After a time he turned over on his back.

But no rest there, either.

His Bible lay on the bedside table, and since Rachel's death he had taken to reading a chapter of it each night. This night he seemed to remember something in the second book of Chronicles: the death of an evil king, Jehoram. Yes, there it was, the Twenty-first Chapter.

And he departed without being desired. . . .

An old man whom nobody wanted, even to speak to. Could any more terrible epitaph be written of anyone?

And yet what had brought this about? Andrew Jackson, tossing in his bed, sorrowed but could not say to himself that he had done a wrong to the couple. At least he could not perceive the evil.

He could not, out of principle, go to the length of telling the Eatons not to call.

Dislike between women—he had witnessed it before, and sometimes for the most obscure reasons or with no reasons at all that he could discern.

Feeling probably, instinct, distrust and rivalry perhaps in feminine interests no man could understand: at least not he.

Emily was leaving him, and taking her husband and the little ones with her. Strangely, he found that he was not angry with her or Jack. Perhaps it was his fondness for them which made him accept their desertion without any feeling but grief.

He groaned to himself. Why had the Eaton matter arisen? Why had he involved himself so deeply in it? It was like a burden on top of all his burdens, and he sickened of it. Was the world right and he wrong?

He began to wonder if he was merely stubborn. But no, in a matter of principle there could be no compromise. It was no mere stubbornness he believed. And yet . . . Emily was kind and unselfish, and she must feel very deeply to behave in this way. He longed for Emily to stay with him; Emily, and Jack, and the children.

Toward morning he rose from his bed, wrapped a robe about him, and sat down to write a letter. He took a long time in the composition of it, and felt tears in his eyes: a sensation so unusual that he blew his nose vigorously, almost startled.

The following morning a servant delivered the pathetic little note to Donelson, who was helping his wife in their rooms, packing their belongings preparatory to their departure. It read:

Dear Jack: If you should not think it too great a sacrifice, which I ask of none, I will be glad that you remain until after the meeting of Congress. For upwards of a year you have appeared to be estranged from me, which under my bereavement made my tears flow. When you leave, whatever cause I have to regret or complain, you will carry my friendship with you, and my prayers for your happiness and that of your amiable family I can never cease to love. Very affectionately, your uncle and sincere friend,

Andrew Jackson

"Do you see?" said Jack Donelson, when he and Emily read the letter together. "I *can't* leave him—not just now. I can't bear to hurt him so. You take the babies and go home. I'll join you after the adjournment."

Emily's eyes filled, for the almost timid and wistful letter touched her, too. She nodded in agreement.

When later she, her two children, their Negro nurse, and their belongings left the White House for Tennessee, her husband remained with the President. But the understanding was definite that his stay was on a temporary basis.

3

To Peggy Eaton it appeared to be her most complete triumph. When she heard of it she made no attempt to hide her elation.

Had she not made the General's very family see that she stood first with him? Emily—that little snip—was banished. Who else now would dare cross swords with Mrs. John Henry Eaton?

An even bolder thought: the White House now had no official hostess. Why not Mrs. John Henry Eaton as hostess of the Executive Mansion? This was ambition, perhaps—but why not ambition? Was it so out of the question, now that the family objections had been swept aside?

A heady thought: the one-time tavern girl, Peggy O'Neale, presiding at the receptions and state dinners of the first home in the nation!

She believed—she was sure it could be done. A little further ingratiation with the President, a little further prodding of her husband, and she could manage an invitation from the lonely old man for John Eaton and herself to take up residence at the White House. There she would gather into her capable hands the management of the social calendar, the planning of brilliant affairs, the complete control of the invitation list.

Then let the haughty women of Washington think back on and rue what their behavior toward her had been! She could fancy herself making some of them fairly crawl, and the thought of it made her eyes gleam, her nostrils flare, with a foretaste of a humiliated woman's revenge.

It did not concern her that the old General in the White House had been deeply wounded by the storm she had created in his family. It showed in him. He seemed whiter, thinner, less erect.

At last—though Peggy Eaton did not know this—he wrote to Emily, in Tennessee, a pleading little note:

The House appears lonesome. I miss you and the sweet little ones. First and last the separation has almost destroyed me. As to the affair concerning Margaret Eaton, it is no longer a personal one. It has become a political affair whereby John C. Calhoun hopes to weaken me and open his way to preferment and my ruin.

When she received that letter, Emily wept again. She was stricken at heart because she had deserted the fine old gentleman who had been so unvaryingly kind to her and hers: the more so, since she had begun to realize that she had abandoned him to the merciless designs of the woman who clearly believed she had raised her banner over the General's tent.

Thinking with a woman's mind, Emily Donelson suddenly divined at least a part of what Peggy Eaton might be planning. That would be worse than anything that yet had happened. Her common sense returned to her, and she made her first tentative move to forestall the Eaton woman. By return post she wrote to her husband:

In spite of everything I love Uncle Jackson, and have loved him since my childhood. I would rather support my loneliness than have you leave his side. More than that, if it will help matters, I will swallow my pride, return to Washington, and to please dear old Uncle, visit Mrs. E. sometimes officially.

But just at that time a minor miracle took place.

4

At least it always appears as a somewhat miraculous happening when weakness and subservience become strength and decision; especially when it is unexpected as to the time and the person when this startling change is wrought.

Martin Van Buren could not be called entirely unselfish. He saw that his chief rival had deeply injured his political prospects by running afoul of Andrew Jackson on the State Sovereignty issue. But though Calhoun had lost ground, he did not perceive that he himself had appreciably gained ground.

It is very likely, therefore, that the action he took had in a measure behind it the hope to further strengthen Jackson's friendship for him. Nevertheless, it must also be surmised that he felt genuine sympathy for the old warrior and fully understood the incompetence of the Cabinet which was the cause of most of his woes.

Martin Van Buren unexpectedly one day offered his resignation as Secretary of State.

"Why?" demanded Jackson quickly.

"To smooth over many vexations," said Van Buren.

The President grew cold. "Mr. Van Buren, I have made it a rule through life never to throw obstacles in the way of a man who wishes to leave me."

"But, sir," said Van Buren, "I made the offer solely out of my loyalty to you, because it might enable you better to deal with various of the enemies of your Administration."

At once the General was penitent and seized his friend's hand.

"Forgive me!" he said. "I've been too hasty."

The following day, at a called meeting of the Cabinet, the resignation of the Secretary of State was announced to a somewhat stunned gathering. Of them all, Van Buren seemed the most cheerful, and as the Cabinet members left the White House, he said, "Gentlemen, I've ordered a little spread at my home. Will you join me?"

At Van Buren's table John Henry Eaton was strangely silent. The resignation of the Secretary of State, and the probable reasons behind it, were causing him to do some profound thinking. In that hour of personal inventory, he whom his wife had all this time led around and bent to her will, saw with blinding clarity what evil she was doing to the man who had always befriended him and her.

"This is all wrong," he said suddenly. "I am the man who ought to resign!"

Van Buren gazed at him strangely. "What would Mrs. Eaton say to this?"

"She will agree," said Eaton, white and grim.

History recorded that she did agree. But what was the nature of the scene when her husband informed her, whether bitter, stormy, or tearful, neither of them ever revealed.

Some indication of her feeling over her crushing defeat just when she anticipated the fullness of triumph was indicated when the President and Mr. Van Buren went to call on her and her husband, who had been appointed governor of Florida after his resignation was accepted.

And how did Margaret Eaton behave toward the old gentleman who had put himself to so much inconvenience, brought upon himself so much criticism, caused himself so much trouble over her?

She received him as if he were an utter stranger. Formally she addressed him, coldly she replied to his remarks. When he departed with Van Buren, he shrugged his thin shoulders.

"Very strange," he said.

It was his only comment on a demonstration of ingratitude and a display of spleen by a woman who no longer could use him.

But the relief at the White House was immediately evident.

When John Henry Eaton departed for Florida with his unwilling wife, the other members of the Cabinet, with the exception of the Postmaster General, resigned also at the President's pointed suggestion, creating a nine days' wonder in Washington.

The new Cabinet he appointed, it was immediately evident, was of a far higher quality than the old. Having had a chance to observe and become acquainted, the General drew some capable men into his government. Ponderous, bald-headed, capable General Lewis Cass replaced Eaton as Secretary of War. Jackson's old New Orleans friend, Edward Livingston, became Secretary of State succeeding Van Buren, who went to England as Ambassador. Others also were of more than average ability: Lewis McLane for the Treasury, and Levi Woodbury for the Navy, were able men. The new Attorney General was almost unknown, stooped, carelessly dressed, tall and lean, with a narrow countenance, squinting eyes due to bad sight, and tobacco-stained teeth—Roger B.

Taney, who was to prove himself one of the greatest lawyers in America.

One bright morning a coach swung up the White House drive, and Andrew Jackson, appearing even more overjoyed than Jack Donelson himself, assisted Emily from the vehicle, placed a fond avuncular kiss on her smooth cheek, then hugged her two children.

For the first time since he had occupied it, the White House became a pleasant place in which to live. The President enjoyed young people, and the Donelsons attracted many as guests, some of them relatives of their own and their uncle's. With harmony restored in both his household and his Administration, Andrew Jackson seemed visibly younger and stronger: he could now turn undistractedly to his next major problems.

The Way of a Wanderer,
*** 1832

The Reverend Dr. William Hume wrote to a friend, the day after Sam Houston disappeared from Nashville:

Sic transit gloria mundi. Oh, what a fall for a major general, a member of Congress, and a Governor of so respectable a state as Tennessee!

In that paragraph the reverend gentleman revealed not only a little parade of classical learning, but a curious smugness. He had presided at three occasions fraught with consequence to Houston: he conducted the sacrament of burial for Rachel Jackson, where Houston, next to General Jackson himself, was perhaps the deepest mourner; he pronounced the sacrament of marriage for Houston and Eliza Allen; lastly, he refused the sacrament of baptism, even when the ruined Houston pleaded for it. Perhaps the Reverend Dr. Hume may be forgiven a trifle of smugness. It is not every small man who plays so decisive a role in the life of so great a personage.

In any case, his general sentiments were echoed all over Tennessee. What a fall! Like the archangel hurled down from heaven!

Friends of Houston sorrowed, and if politically minded, wondered gloomily about their own futures. Enemies gloated. Mean-minded men licked their chops over such a disaster to a person so notable. But nobody knew where Houston was, or what was his far bourn.

Nor did Houston know his destination, or care.

Chapter Twenty-Six

History sometimes makes strange shifts
in the destinies of nations—and men.

SAM HOUSTON

1

Helena: apex of the Arkansas Territory.

Before it the Mississippi River ran, at once a muddy tyrant and a servant, bearing on its swelling bosom a various water traffic: flatboats, broadhorns, rafts, and their awkward kindred, carrying toward the Gulf the produce of the interior. Rivermen usually halted at Helena, if only to pay tribute to the dramshops and gambling places, or to frolic with the girls in the bawdyhouses by the river front.

Everywhere, beyond the town, lay virgin wilderness. But up the slope of a hill from the river straggled a collection of houses, many of logs, with a few unimposing warehouses, stores, and low taverns near the wharf.

Late one afternoon a flatboat floated down from the north toward the town pier. At the steering sweep stood a lank riverman in linsey; in the bow a young Negro held by their leashes two barking dogs; and on the low cabin two men sat, slovenly, dirty, and unshaved.

One of the men got down from the cabin top and went forward as the Negro boy dextrously threw a rope about a post on the pier to bring the craft to a stop. Filthy and disheveled, only his mighty stature would have identified him to one who once had known the recent governor of Tennessee.

Sam Houston had spent weeks floating down the Cumberland to the Ohio, the Ohio to the Mississippi, and the Mississippi to this place. He had journeyed slowly, stopping now and then to gun for wildfowl, or to fish; but occupying his time chiefly by drinking, for the sake of drinking alone.

Emotional, as his tutor Andrew Jackson never was, and lacking the

General's iron control, he was in a state of mind so abject that his pride and his care in appearance were gone with all his hopes, creating a profound change in the man.

Several loafers sat on a pile of lumber, spitting and whittling, without offering to assist the flatboat in its mooring. But one of a different type walked along the wharf with a kind of careless grace, neatly dressed, at his belt a long and heavy knife in a leather scabbard.

Even half-drunk Houston could judge a man. In this stranger he saw physical competence, and an alert, level look of the eyes uncommon in the shiftless population of the river front.

"Tie up your damn noisy dogs, Natty," Houston said over his shoulder to the flatboat man, "and come up to the tavern." He glanced at the stranger. "I suppose there *is* a tavern," he growled.

"Of a sort, sir," said the other.

Houston's bearded face swung around on him. The stranger observed that all the lines in it were loose and deep as from a long debauch, the eyes bloodshot, the skin under them pouched. Yet the face, somehow, was unforgettable.

"Perhaps, sir," rumbled Houston, "you'd be good enough to indicate its direction."

"My pleasure, sir."

Houston stepped from the boat to the wharf, and the stranger, tall himself and not accustomed to looking up at anyone, found that he had to raise his eyes to meet the gaze of this giant with the great bear-like body.

"You appear, sir, to be a gentleman," said Houston. "May I take the liberty of inquiring whom I'm addressing?"

"The name," said the other, "is James Bowie."

"Bowie? James Bowie? Sir, is it possible that this is the celebrated——"

One of the wharf loafers snickered. "That's who you're lookin' at, mister."

Bowie! The master of the famous knife! Handsome, by no means truculent in appearance, a gentleman and well-dressed—yet by all accounts a figure in a dozen duels almost too bizarre for belief!

"I count it an honor, sir, to meet you. Your name is a household word, sir." Houston extended his great paw of a hand. "Permit me to introduce myself—Sam Houston, of Tennessee."

Bowie took the hand and felt its grip. It was his turn to stare. Could this sodden wreck, unshaved and filthy, be the famous Sam Houston? It seemed impossible. Yet belief was compelled.

What had brought him to this state? Visage flushed and puffy, beard shot with gray, hair unkempt and long, breath heavy and sour with liquor—dissipation had worked devastation here. Yet even dissipation had not diminished the jut of the great, hawk-like nose, or softened the hard-lipped mouth. Sodden with liquor, fumbling, wretched, Sam Houston was an epic figure still.

Bowie said, "It's your own fame which extends to every part of the land, Governor——"

Houston lifted a hand. "By your good leave, sir—plain Sam Houston, adventurer."

On the dock the loafers nudged and whispered. Upon them Houston bent a silencing glare.

"Please come aboard, Mr. Bowie," he said.

Bowie followed as the fantastic figure in skins, with hair falling about the massive neck, and moccasined feet huge as those of a grizzly bear, led the way down into the darkness of the small, crowded cabin, and there felt about.

"It was here," Houston grumbled. "Right here on the floor." He paused. "It must be Haralson, the dog! Mr. Bowie, you have no conception of how the fellow drinks—and when the liquor's in him, truth and honesty are out." He raised a bull-like bellow. "Haralson! Haralson!"

A rakish, grinning face appeared at the door.

"Where did you put the brandy?" Houston roared.

Haralson grinned more broadly. "In the chest, General——"

"Stop calling me General! And get it for me!"

Haralson, an obvious ne'er-do-well, who seemed to have attached himself to the flatboat and its odd crew, threw open the chest and brought from it a glass jug in wicker, holding about a gallon. Houston seized it, squinted appraisingly through the wicker, and said, "Haralson, you're not worth the inroads you've made on this brandy!"

Still grinning, Haralson withdrew to the deck.

"You first, sir," said Houston, offering the jug to his guest.

Bowie drank, finding the brandy inferior, and returned the jug.

Now the unkempt giant took a long, gulping swig.

"Bowie," he said, wiping his bearded lips, "do you know that you're a legend—a full-blown legend—and in your own lifetime? Mighty few have known that experience. The bowie knife—is that the famous blade? I'd like to examine it."

Bowie drew the weapon and tendered it, hilt first.

In his two palms Houston held it, examining it intently. It had a curious balance, he noted, probably an aid in throwing. The cross hilt was of brass with balled ends. The blade itself was fifteen inches in length, as thick at the spine as if two or three knives had been welded together, but with a sinister curve toward the point and an edge as deadly keen as a razor.

"Is this the original?" he asked.

"Yes, sir."

"Half the men in Tennessee are carrying bowie knives these days. They're on sale everywhere. But not blades like this."

Bowie sheathed it with a nod. "If you'll honor me," he said, "I'd like to play host to you at supper in the tavern." He hesitated. "What of your—er—friends?"

"We part company here," said Houston. "Natty Skaggs—who owns this boat, the Negro boy, the dogs, and the cargo—heads for Natchez. Haralson—who owns nothing except unlimited time and a prodigious thirst for liquor—goes with him. I myself travel west—toward the Rocky Mountains where, I hear, gold is to be got."

"I know nothing about the Rockies," replied Bowie. "But I have in mind a country big enough even for a man as big as you. Texas."

"You're going to Texas?"

"I live there. San Antonio de Bexar. Here only on business."

Houston nodded his huge, shaggy head. "There's a destiny in Texas. Texas may well be a star some day, a guiding star, sir, in the history of this republic."

"Texas," said Bowie politely, "is a province of Mexico."

"True. But history sometimes makes strange shifts in the destinies of nations—and men." The last words seemed to change the trend of his thoughts. "Yes, men also. You lead a wondrous life, Mr. Bowie. You do as you wish, go where you list. Responsibility and disappointment do not destroy your mind or soul. But Sam Houston—Sam Houston is a ruined man."

Bowie was struck by the intense melancholy of the voice.

"Houston once had high hopes and ambitions," the giant continued. "Now he is a vagrant and outcast, scorned by the lowliest."

Bowie felt pity and great friendship for the huge bear of a man, sitting there in the ill-smelling cabin, with his head bowed.

"Let's go and find something to eat," he said.

That night they dined together, and together drank. It was a notable occasion, a friendship that ripened fast. And when they said farewell, Bowie squeezed Houston's hand.

"Come with me to Texas," he urged.

"No, my feet are turned toward the mountains. But though we scarcely know each other, I have found a great fondness for you, Jim."

"And I for you, Sam."

"Yet our paths already must separate."

"In Texas," said Bowie, "I will remember Sam Houston in the mountains."

"And in the mountains I will remember Jim Bowie in Texas."

2

Indian country again. Houston realized it days after he left Helena, very suddenly by certain signs. He had purchased a horse, and the trail he rode led up the valley of the Arkansas River toward Fort Gibson, a military post and an agency for the Cherokees.

He felt a sudden quickening of interest. This was the land to which the Indians he had known as a boy were sent when their hunting grounds were taken by land-hungry settlers in Tennessee.

A little later he saw his first two Indians. They were spearing fish by a little stream, and at the sight of him one snatched up a fish spear as if to fling it. But a moment later he lowered it, though his face still was unfriendly.

They were Cherokees—well-grown youths, strong, limber, and active. He recognized their way of dress, brightly colored calico shirts hanging over leather breeches, plain moccasins, deerhide strips tying back their hair from their foreheads. They stared at him with eyes black as flies, the lids slightly squinted as if shunning the light into which they always gazed. A few fish lay on the grass, one still thumping its tail.

Houston spoke to them, in the Cherokee tongue. They were surprised, but he could see that they were at pains not to show it. Their faces, the foreheads puckered by nature, remained expressionless. In silence they stood, but the taller one rested the butt of his spear on the ground, as an indication to the stranger that his first defensive attitude was not needful and they knew he was no enemy.

"I am called Co-lon-neh," said Houston, still in their language. "Do my friends know of Oo-loo-te-ka, the chief?"

At this they could no longer hide their astonishment, and they spoke to him respectfully but eagerly. They were themselves of Oo-loo-te-ka's village, and they told him it was only an hour's travel from this place.

Now they gazed at him with open curiosity. Perhaps they had heard of him by his Indian name, Co-lon-neh, the Cherokee word for Raven. But it was years since he was among the Cherokees and these must have been small children in those days.

After a moment the younger Indian went off and returned with two ponies which had been tethered in a grove of hackberry. At this the elder looked at Houston, and wet his lips with his tongue, though he did not commit himself to speak. It was plain that he offered to take the white man to his people, but felt it was the visitor's part, not his, to make known his intention.

Houston understood all this quite well; and made the request. At that, they assented politely.

But first, before they started, the elder youth took a deerskin sack which was tied to his saddle, and placed it on the ground. When he opened it, Houston saw that it contained some pieces of dried meat, and a small corn-meal loaf, baked without eggs or milk or salt, and shaped with the hands, called journey cake because it was used for provision in travel, and corrupted by some whites into johnny cake.

The young Indian offered it silently, as if to say that a person who perhaps came from afar might enjoy a bite before continuing on his journey; but he did it all with a most perfectly casual air, because he did not want to lay any stress on so trifling a service.

Houston knew Indian politeness. He dismounted and took a bit of the dried meat. It tasted of smoke, and perhaps of sweat, and perhaps of the kind of healthy dirt that gathers around the camp of a primitive people.

After years of the soft luxuries of civilization he suddenly discovered in himself a hunger for this crude food. He chewed its tough, leathery strength with pleasure; and afterward broke off a small piece of the journey cake and ate that also. The taste of these simple viands aroused in him a feeling akin to homesickness.

The two young Indians also helped themselves when their guest had what he wanted, eating quietly with faces averted, since he was their senior and it was not seemly for them to gobble openly in his presence.

With a gourd they dipped water from the creek to wash down the food, but Houston took a pewter cup from his saddlebags. He observed that the two young Indians were fascinated by the cup, their eyes clinging to it, though they tried to make their faces look hard and indifferent, so as not to fall into temptation.

When he had drunk, he smiled and handed them the cup. "It is yours," he said. "You are brothers? You must share it between you."

They stood blank-faced, trying not to show their cupidity, but then of a sudden they grinned with gratitude. Then he and they mounted and the youths conducted him to their village.

He understood that the food they had eaten together was more than mere refreshment. It admitted the visitor to their people's protection and hospitality as long as he proved worthy.

3

A scattering of rough log cabins roofed with bark, many dogs snarling and yelping, and children scampering into their homes, to turn and peer wide-eyed out of doorways: and Sam Houston came riding back to the Cherokees.

From one of the cabins stepped a portly old man with a blanket about his waist and a red handkerchief binding his braided gray hair. Houston dismounted and advanced toward him.

"Oo-loo-te-ka," he said.

On the chief's broad visage came an expression of joy. He placed both hands on Houston's shoulders and gazed deep into his eyes.

"Now has the One Above answered our prayers," he said. "My son, Co-lon-neh, has come home again."

"It has been long."

"Too long."

As they spoke, looking into each other's eyes, the people began coming from every direction, wishing to see the visitor whom the chief greeted so warmly. Many remembered him from the happier days when they dwelt at Hiwassee in Tennessee. The old men greeted him gravely, and some of the men in their prime knew him and were remembered by him.

There also were tall, erect young fellows, like the two he first met, warriors by nature, eager hunters and not to be despised in any contest of speed or strength. These stood back politely, but looked at Houston with appraising eyes. They had heard tales of him as the greatest athlete the Cherokees had ever known. A giant he was, surely. Some of them mentally measured themselves against him; and they agreed to themselves that in any trial of strength the newcomer would prevail. But he had grown heavy, and they did not feel that he possessed any longer the speed and agility that went with the game of Indian ballplay.

Behind the circle of men, the women and children peered and stared, smiling at each other and laughing in low voices. To Houston the Cherokee daughters seemed comely, as they had always seemed. One caught his eye especially: tall, not overplump like some Indian women, perhaps in her late twenties. Her face was more delicate than most of the others, her eyes large, black, and brilliant.

A dawning recollection: could that one be Tiana, the girl he had known in his youth? He became sure it was she; but he was careful to show no recognition. It would be contrary to good manners to do so. Assuredly she must be married, and one of these men would be her husband. Etiquette forbade paying attention to the wife of another man, unless one were related to her by blood.

Oo-loo-te-ka gazed about him with a broad, almost religious joy, and lifted his voice.

"This is my son, the Raven," he announced to all. "He has come to live with us. Tonight we will feast, for this is a great happening. My son is a chief among the white people, filled with wisdom, and he has come to help us."

This assumption was no part of Houston's plan. Yet the old man believed with such childish faith that he had come to aid the Cherokees that he did not have the heart to utter a denial. Besides, he had no special destination at present.

He had spoken to Jim Bowie of the mountains and a search for gold. But the mountains were far, gold-seeking a vague pursuit.

Furthermore, ever since the moment he met the two young Indians beside the creek and tasted food with them, he found himself slipping back, easily and pleasantly, into the ways and thinking of the Cherokees. His tongue had not forgotten the language, and he had no difficulty remembering the customs and courtesies of the people.

Almost with the relief of one weary and finding rest, he took up his residence, at least for the present, in Oo-loo-te-ka's house, the largest cabin in the village, which was cared for by the chief's old wife, Sarah, his other wife having died since the tribe moved out into this wilderness.

4

Spring had passed and summer begun. In the Indian village Houston found himself living anew. He began to notice and take pleasure in things of which he had been unconscious for years in his hurried life: the frog chorus down by the river, the warbling of a mocking bird, the keen scent of wood smoke, the laughter and playing of children.

Sometimes in this western country the sun beat down fiercely. At other times storms would erupt unexpectedly in the midst of what had been sunny calm, with earth-quivering thunders and rains swept across the land by winds of wild, untempered fury. Once again he knew the feeling of enormous forces, the overwhelming pressures and energies behind those widely moving masses of cloud and air. Storms in the midst of peace seemed symbolic of what fate had dealt him; and yet contact with pure nature strengthened him and armed him to sustain the disaster that had crushed him.

He found an old friend in the village: John Rogers, with whom he had sported and hunted as a boy, and who scouted for General Jackson during the Creek War. John's brother James was absent on an errand for Oo-loo-te-ka to the eastern Cherokees, but there was another member of the family about whom Houston inquired warily.

Tiana? Yes, said John, Tiana was here in the village, Houston remarked that he thought he noticed her in the crowd the first day he arrived. Married, he assumed casually.

As a matter of fact, no, John said. She had been married, to a Cherokee named David Gentry, a good man and a blacksmith. Gentry was, however, dead—killed two summers before by the Osages. The wild and bloody-minded Osages were fierce enemies of the Cherokees, he added.

Houston received this information with gravity. One did not probe into the doings of a man's womankind, although Tiana was not John's full sister. She was his half-sister, her mother being the younger of the two wives of John Rogers, the elder, a subchief now dead. Nevertheless, though the tenets of good taste forbade further inquiry, the news in many respects altered Tiana's status in Houston's mind. He had seen her: she was handsome. About her began to creep the wraith of earlier desires. Then he put this thought away. There were matters to consider more immediate and less personal than an Indian woman.

In those early days he slept much, and revived his body. The mornings were cool, and at dawn he would arise to look across the valley which sometimes was sheeted in white mist, and through the cottony fog hear the lowing of cattle moving to their grazing. In the heat of the day he retreated to some shady place, indolent and measurably content. Nobody chided him for this. He was a guest and his wishes were respected.

Yet he did not withhold himself from the life of the village. At times he talked gravely and thoughtfully with the elders, and particularly with his foster-father, the chief.

Oo-loo-te-ka, in these days, was gravely troubled. His people, he said with sorrow, were in bad straits. They had been forced to go out into these wilds because white men wanted their lands in the east, and they had been promised a down payment of money for relinquishing their ancient holdings, besides annuities.

The money had not been paid, nor were the annuities forthcoming. Meantime, white agents robbed and corrupted the Cherokees; and evil white traders defrauded them, making drunkards of the men, and seducing their women so that the number of half-breed children who could not name their fathers multiplied, an offense to every honorable Cherokee.

Worse: there was unceasing war with the Osages, a wild and savage tribe to the west, who would not permit the Cherokees to go to the fall hunt in the buffalo country, though the government had promised safe passage thither. The chief enumerated the Cherokees who had been slain in fights with the barbarians, one of them being that David Gentry whose death made Tiana a widow.

And here existed a grave inherent difficulty. For every Cherokee life taken by an Osage, his warriors wanted an Osage life. Thus a blood-feud grew. Oo-loo-te-ka, wiser than his people, saw to what this would lead, and greatly desired peace, but did not know how to go about achieving it.

Yet he did have a plan, and he confided it to his adopted son. If he could unite the so-called "Civilized Tribes" in the Territory—the Cherokees, Creeks, Choctaws, and Chickasaws—into one single nation, they not only might force peace on the Osages, but they would form a barrier to prevent the white tide ever from overwhelming them again.

As a preliminary toward this end he had already called a council of the important men in all the Cherokee bands to meet in his village.

To all this Houston listened with closest attention. An idea stirred vaguely in him, something that might be important in the affairs of all men.

5

On the day of the council many Cherokees came to Oo-loo-te-ka's village, the men decked in their best, their women vivid in colored costumes and ornaments. Beside the river, where a grove of fine trees cast a pleasant shade, they sat in groups, or walked back and forth, or reclined, waiting for the feast being prepared—five entire steers, barbecued over deep pits filled with glowing coals, and attended by a small army of Negro cooks, slaves of Oo-loo-te-ka.

Among these stalked a lofty figure in white buckskin, a scarlet cloth wound turban-like about his head, a scarlet blanket draped from his shoulders. Houston had shaved clean his face, braided his long hair, and adopted the costume of the so-called "blanket-and-rifle" party: the conservative Cherokees, who preferred the old ways to the new. This won him favor, especially from the veterans. He was an object of intense scrutiny, every move, word, and gesture closely noted, weighed, and commented upon.

Presently the voice of Oo-loo-te-ka was heard asking for quiet, and the Cherokees gathered about the revered old chief, who stood with an arm about the shoulders of Houston.

"Now, let all people hear me!" he said. "This is Co-lon-neh, my son, who lived in my lodge on the Hiwassee many years ago. He is a great man, and the white people call him General and Governor. Now he has come back to us, his people. He has thrown away his white name, and wishes to be known only by his Cherokee name, Co-lon-neh, the Raven. When he was in the seats of power among the white people, my son was always a friend of the Indians and protected them. By his own act he has forsaken the white men and their ways, and desires now to be a warrior and counselor of the Cherokee Nation. Let us all, therefore, sit here under the trees, and let the food be brought, and let us eat with joy that a mighty one who was lost to us has come back to us."

There was clapping of hands and the sound of applause. Now the Negroes came bringing the meat, already cut into pieces, on wide trays of woven withes. Each Indian took a dish of baked clay or wood which was given to him, and helped himself to as much as he wanted, and there was enough and to spare for all.

While the people ate, Oo-loo-te-ka conducted his son about among the seated groups, making him acquainted with them. It was seen that

the Raven remembered his Cherokee years, speaking with grave deference to the elders, with dignity and warmth to men of his own age, and
kindly to women, being especially careful to praise the good looks and
brightness of their children.

Beside one woman, sitting on the ground, he paused.

"Tiana," he said, "it makes warm the heart of this one to see you
again."

She lifted her head and gave him a quick, timid look, then bowed
her head again.

He passed on.

Suddenly the hum of pleasant talk was cut by the shrill peal of a war
whoop. Dead silence fell over the assemblage.

They all saw him: an Osage warrior.

He had ridden, a stark and savage figure, into their very midst. In
contrast to the finery of the Cherokees, he was naked to the waist, his
bronzed body innocent of any ornament, even paint. His bullet head
was shaved, except for a bristling ridge of hair from his brow back to the
crown of his skull; his pony's bridle was of untanned rawhide, a quiver
of arrows and a bow hung at his back, his breechclout was of deerskin,
his legs bare and wiry, his moccasins worn with weather and use.

Yet he looked about him with haughty contempt.

The war whoop was followed by no hostile action, for the Cherokees
were too stunned by this bold intrusion to act. Besides it was quickly
seen that the Osage wore no war paint. He therefore came in peace.

From his leather girdle the barbarian took a folded paper, which he
handed to Oo-loo-te-ka. The chief, in turn, gave it to Houston to read.

The note was brief. Houston glanced up. "I must go with this man,"
he said.

Before the crowd had time to inquire, he mounted a horse and rode
away with the spectacular savage.

Then Oo-loo-te-ka lifted his voice and said that the Osage was a
courier from Auguste Pierre Chouteau, a famous trader on the Six Bull
River, who had called the Raven to talk with him on important affairs.
The council, he added, must proceed without its guest of honor.

6

A white-painted two-story log house, with a broad veranda, surrounded by a stake-and-rider fence and shaded by some fine trees, over-
looked the Six Bull River. When Houston and his guide rode up, groups
of Indians—Osages—were lounging in the shade of the trees, eating
meat provided by their host, their horses tethered to the fence and
switching their tails against the flies.

At the gate they were greeted by Monsieur Chouteau himself, a short, slender man, with a mustache, dark eyes, and expressive hands: a typical Creole, but with the authentic blood of adventure. His father was credited, among other things, with founding the city of St. Louis, and no less than four members of his family had ranged widely through the West, building trading posts and extending the frontier.

Chouteau was attired in white linen, a broad planter's hat, and polished boots, but he seemed not to notice his guest's barbaric garb.

"General Houston?" he asked. "My poor house is greatly honored."

Houston dismounted and shook hands with him.

"I came at once when your messenger brought your invitation."

"My thanks for this promptness. There are matters on which we two can 'put together our foreheads,' as the Indians say."

He conducted Houston to the house. A dozen Indians occupied the first room they entered, all sitting on the floor, smoking their pipes.

"A hunting council," explained Chouteau. Not one of the Osages looked up as he led the way to the room beyond.

Here a table was spread at which the host and his guest took seats. Two Indian women, in shapeless calico dresses, entered silently, bearing platters of food, and Houston remembered that he had been told Chouteau had three wives—these two Osage women, with whom he lived and reared half-breed children, and a white wife in St. Louis whom he never visited.

The supper was substantial: roast beef, fried venison, corn bread, and excellent wine. Neither Indian wife shared it, but they stood leaning against the wall, solemnly watching the two men eat.

"I called on you when I learned you were in the country," said Chouteau presently, "because there is a danger brooding of which few are sensible." He spoke excellent English, but with the slight accent of an educated French Creole. "I fear the outbreak of a gigantic Indian war, which not only would decimate the tribes, but would bring death and desolation to all the white outposts and settlements on the western frontier."

"Why this danger?" Houston asked.

"Mismanagement and corruption by the whites. For example, my Osages have not received their annuities of food and clothing from their agent, John F. Hamtramck. They believe he spends the money on his squaw—incidentally an Osage woman whom he purchased from a prominent chief. He always displays her loaded with beads, trinkets, and fine garments, including a green mantle set off with silver lace. Out of sheer hunger, some of the young Osages have driven off cattle belonging to white men."

Chouteau paused and gazed earnestly at Houston.

"Can you blame them, sir?" he continued. "And this is only one symptom of unrest which is general. Colonel Brearly, agent of the Creeks, speculates in their allotments. Major E. W. Du Val, of the Cherokees, is no better. The discontent of the tribes makes them grow ugly. A single spark might ignite an explosion, and unless the Indian service can be straightened out and peace cemented here in the Territory, war might burst from Canada to the Gulf!"

Houston nodded. "The old story. I'll give you what help I can. Meantime, we have one opportunity. Between us, I believe we can bring about peace sorely needed, between the Osages and the Cherokees."

They sat up late with plans for this project. Houston felt that he was in the midst of affairs once more. It was activity, and it was definite in its aim, and he slept well that night, as if his racked brain had found relief in having something to work upon.

Chapter Twenty-Seven

I belong to myself.

TIANA

1

In the next weeks Houston was gone much of the time from Oo-loo-te-ka's lodge, visiting agencies, speaking to other Indian councils, writing letters addressed to officials in Washington.

This was all very well for the time being. With Chouteau's help he actually succeeded in bringing about an understanding between the Osages and Cherokees, preventing further war between them and easing the tension on the frontiers. Among corrupt agents and cheating white traders he created no little alarm, and some few reforms even occurred. But in the end nothing very important happened as a result of all his activity; and none knew its futility better than Houston himself, with his experience in governmental ways.

Inevitably his depression returned, if possible more deeply than before. He sat much alone, brooding on the prodigious fall he had taken, the shattering catastrophe of his life. At times he wondered about Eliza, her perverse behavior, and the incalculable power women possess. Small, weak, not even given to thinking or feeling deeply, she had yet destroyed him as completely and irrevocably as if she had been a giant in physical strength and mental power.

For the first time he, who had blamed himself for everything, began to consider that she, too, was blameworthy. She cheated him, drove him almost out of his mind to an action of which he was ashamed, and then used it as the excuse to create a situation that made him appear a scoundrel before the world, while she escaped censure by the unassailable fact that she was a woman, protected by conventions which disposed the opinions of men in her favor.

Even he, the injured one, was instinctively bound by those conventions: to the point that his thinking of Eliza did not take the form of resentment. He simply turned his whole mind away from her. In that period he took again to drinking heavily.

As fall came on, the days grew chill and the nights were crisp in the starlight. This was the season of spirit-soaring sunrises and sunsets; and in the daytime a diaphanous bluish haze hung over the far hills and valleys—Indian summer, the white men called it.

It was a time of visiting and feasting. Some annuities, through Houston's activity, had been paid; and the crops had not been bad. Dread of the Osage war was lifted by the peace treaty, and the Cherokees could feast, dance, and sing. At times in the evenings the voices of the Indians, slurred by distance, sounded lazy and musical.

Children were everywhere. Children and dogs. The Indian men had little patience with the children, ordering them away when they interfered with work or talk. But the mothers spoiled them, and when a little one fell down and hurt itself, the Indian women would make a great to-do, beating the earth with sticks, pretending to punish the place where the child was bumped by the ground, thus bringing back laughter to the small face.

The dogs fought over bones or pieces of meat at times, and at other times lay together sleepily with one eye open, enjoying the warmth of the autumn sun. Children and dogs got along well. They slept together, and both dogs and children scratched for fleas. The littlest tots went toddling about with puppies in their arms.

Sitting alone, Houston watched these things. He also observed something else.

Sometimes at night, young couples would steal off from the fire about which people were gathered to eat and talk, and disappear in the darkness. They might be gone for a time, and then perhaps come back into the light of the fire from different directions, their faces elaborately innocent as if they had been on some matter-of-fact errand. Their elders appeared not to notice this transparent trickery, deeming it the affair of young men and maidens, a preliminary to eventual marriage and a new crop of Indian babies.

But the sight of the furtive couples, disappearing and returning in the night, brought naggingly to the mind of the silent watching man a need of his own. Months had now passed since Eliza and he parted, but the frustrations she had built in him, even before the final quarrel, grew and festered in him.

At best Sam Houston was a man of superb virility, curbed and controlled by training and will. At worst he was a creature of lawless passions, with a stallion hunger for a woman's body.

He sought to put this out of his mind and preserve his continence simply by not thinking about it. But not thinking about it was the most difficult thing he had ever undertaken. He could not keep from following with his eyes and his thoughts any lissome young woman who crossed his line of vision. Sex became to him an almost constant tantalizing obsession.

One, especially, had the power to disturb him. She was tall, with singular grace of carriage, slender in a womanly manner, showing pride and taste in her appearance, for her thick hair was sleekly braided and bound about her head, her small moccasins beaded in flower designs, and her white doeskin dress close-fitted at hips and waist. He knew her: Tiana, John Rogers' sister, handsomest of the Cherokee women. At times he would have spoken to her, but he could think of no proper way to approach her, or any topic of mutual conversation. On her part, she never appeared to look at him but went her way in the village, sometimes even passing quite close to him as if he did not exist.

Nevertheless, with all her indifference, she stimulated in his mind such thoughts that he felt in them a danger. Should he so far forget himself as to make a gross suggestion to any of the Cherokee daughters, but more especially Tiana, it might lead to a train of consequences unforeseen and perhaps most unhappy.

If he seduced a woman for mere sex relief, with no intention of anything else, he might one day feel a knife slipped into his back between the ribs by one of her male relatives, should she reveal that he had not done the right thing by her. On the other hand, he was not prepared to consider marrying an Indian woman, even under the rather informal ways of tribal custom; for it would make him a "squaw man," which was a designation of contempt he had no wish to accept.

2

Whiskey was the best antidote for such thinking. He could buy liquor in driblets, for he had funds he brought from Tennessee. But with his usual large notions he conceived the idea of becoming a trader. A trader, he reasoned, could order as much liquor as he desired.

In this illogical frame of mind he wrote to a liquor dealer in Memphis for a shipment of five barrels of whiskey, and a barrel each of brandy, rum, gin, and wine.

Late in the year he received a summons to appear at Fort Gibson and show cause why he should not be prosecuted for bringing liquor into the Indian country without license and contrary to law. His shipment, he was notified, was impounded at the cantonment.

Houston rode at once to the frontier post: a log stockade with a row of log buildings inside, and a flag drooping from a peeled sapling pole. A sergeant, who obviously did not approve of a white man in Indian garb, passed him at the gate; and on his way across to the headquarters building he observed a squad of soldiers drilling on the parade ground, and a prisoner gazing disconsolately through the bars of the guardhouse, probably for being drunk at formation.

A smart young subaltern escorted him to the inner office of Colonel Matthew Arbuckle, a large person with a bald head and a kindly manner, whose blue uniform coat wrinkled across his round belly. He was an old army man, and he had seen a deal of human wreckage in his time. It was, however, difficult for him to consider the spectacular giant in buckskins who entered his office as human wreckage, in spite of what he had heard about him.

"General Houston, sir," announced the subaltern, saluting, and retired from the room.

Arbuckle rose and shook hands. "I know of you, sir, by reputation," he said. "Sit down, please."

They gazed across the desk at each other, and in spite of himself the colonel was impressed. This man was a heavy drinker, perhaps—but then, Arbuckle liked a dram himself. An idea occurred.

"Cut the dust in your throat, sir?" he asked.

From his desk drawer he produced a bottle and poured a drink—then another for himself. Houston thanked him, sipped, and observed with approval that the colonel had a sound taste in whiskey: what he took on his tongue was no ordinary rotgut.

He rather liked Arbuckle. What he did not know was that his host carried on a quite regular correspondence with no less a person than the Secretary of War, on the subject of the doings of a certain exile who once had been governor of Tennessee.

"Now as to this business," said the colonel, "you appear to have shipped nine barrels of liquor into this Territory, and without a license."

"I intend, sir, to set up as a trader," said Houston.

"Even in that case you must have a license."

"Not so, sir," said Houston. "You are a representative of the government, but I'm not under your jurisdiction. I am a citizen, not of the United States, but of the Cherokee Nation. I must therefore decline to apply for a trader's license and pay the required fee, for the reason that it would compromise the sovereignty of the Cherokee Nation."

In some perplexity Colonel Arbuckle passed a plump hand over his bald head. This man had a lofty way of speaking, certainly, and a sonorous voice that made his words sound somehow more impressive. Furthermore, the citizenship question was one that had never been raised to him before. He wondered if it was legal for a citizen of the United States to become a citizen of the Cherokee Nation, and he found himself mightily discomposed. But then he remembered that he had his orders.

"Selling liquor to the Indians is strictly illegal under any circumstances," he said.

Now it was Houston, confronted by this flat statement, who discovered he must change his base.

"As to that," he remarked easily, "I have no intention of selling liquor to the Indians."

The colonel stared.

"For your own use, then?" he inquired politely.

"Well, yes," said Houston.

Nine barrels of liquor appeared, to Colonel Arbuckle, to be a large amount for the personal consumption even of this man. But from the amount of interest Washington had displayed in him, he must be important. The colonel felt bound to accept the statement.

"In that case, sir," he said, "the liquor should be stored here. Except, of course, such as you from time to time require for your own needs. I suggest the store of John Nicks, our licensed post sutler."

"No objection, sir," said Houston.

His plan of being a trader had suddenly come to nothing, but at least he had saved his liquor from confiscation.

In the end he came to a friendly agreement with Sutler Nicks, whereby the consignment was taken off his hands at the going price; except for one barrel of whiskey, to be tapped whenever he desired strong waters.

He tapped that barrel far too often. Even when winter came on, with snow on the ground, Co-lon-neh rode frequently to Fort Gibson. Lonely officers' wives at the fort, whom he charmed with his gallantry when sober, learned to avoid him when drunk. The Cherokees became accustomed to the sight of him riding home, reeling in his saddle. Sometimes he hardly ate for days, remaining continuously intoxicated, a demijohn his only companion.

Worse: he became careless of his appearance, allowed his garments to become dirty and wrinkled, seldom shaved. At times he hardly knew what he was doing, and on occasion was ugly and dangerous.

In a morose mood one day he encountered at Fort Gibson a quarrelsome trader named Hendricks, with a grudge against a missionary, the Reverend Loring S. Williams, who had reported his dishonesty among the Choctaws to the authorities. The man was somewhat drunk, and so was Houston, and Hendricks was uttering threats against the inoffensive little minister.

"You're looking for Williams?" said Houston, barring the path. "I am the Reverend Williams."

Hendricks regarded him with amazement. "You can't be!" he said. "Why, Williams ain't no more'n half your size, an' weakly to boot."

"That's the same as calling me a liar," said Houston, suddenly menacing. "When you call me a liar, you'd better be prepared to back your words, or eat them!" From his belt he whipped two bowie knives. "Here —take your choice!"

Hendricks made his choice: he ate his words, apologizing most contritely. And he found that he had urgent business elsewhere, as fast as his somewhat unsteady legs could carry him. The wholesome result was that the Reverend Mr. Williams henceforth had nothing to fear from him.

But some of Houston's quarrelsome periods had results far less beneficial. The unhappy climax came when one day his kindly old foster-father tried to take from him a jug which in his condition he assuredly did not need. With a snarl of anger, Houston swung his huge fist and smashed the old man to the ground.

Other Cherokees came in numbers sufficient to subdue him. Next day, when he sobered up, Oo-loo-te-ka, with fatherly affection, forgave him. But Houston did not forgive himself. He asked a meeting of the village council, to hear from him a public apology.

The Indians gathered in the council house, the men seated in a circle, the women standing behind them. One face at the back seemed to draw his eyes from all the others. When he spoke, it was as if he addressed himself to her, Tiana.

"I stand before you as one guilty of the worst of offenses: ingratitude, and raising my hand against our chief and my father, Oo-loo-te-ka," he said. "I was crazy with liquor, but this is no excuse. A man who does not reverence his father is worse than a wild animal. Co-lon-neh speaks with shame of himself. He asks the pardon of his people."

Brief it was, but a complete humbling. As he spoke, Tiana listened with the others, but he marked no change of expression in her face. He wondered if she pitied him or despised him, and he hardly knew which was the worse. After that day he did not again see her for some time; yet he could not entirely get her out of his mind.

He tried to cease drinking but found that he lacked the will power to do so; and never in his life before had his will failed him. In this period of his disgrace the older Indians of the village were in the main tolerant. But the children at times watched with glee his awkward, fumbling antics, and they invented a name for him: Oo-tse-tee Ar-de-tah-skee—Big Drunk. In his sober moments of self-loathing Houston knew he well deserved that disgraceful title.

Yet even in these depths, he was not entirely forgotten by the outside world. Men remembered the Houston of the commanding presence and the daring will; and strange letters came to him from individuals who hoped for fortunes in land-grabbing if Texas should free herself from Mexico. A filibustering expedition, no less, was the theme on which they played, with himself as the leader.

His whiskey-whirling brain turned to extravagant imaginings. Texas . . . the very name had a fascination for him. And there was Oo-loo-te-ka's proposal to unite the Civilized Tribes. A barbaric army . . . to conquer a new empire?

He answered those letters in a manner too fantastic for any but a mind clouded by the twisting fumes of alcohol. To one man, whom he knew only by name, he wrote:

I intend to conquer Mexico or Texas, and I will be worth two millions in two years.

To do him justice, after he had written such a letter he usually forgot within an hour that he had written it, or to whom it was sent. But in the distant White House a white-haired man, who had his own ways of discovering matters of importance, became concerned. One day Houston received from Andrew Jackson a personal communication:

When I parted from you I then viewed you as on the brink of happiness and rejoiced. About to be united in marriage to a beautiful young lady, of accomplished manners, and respectable connections, & of your own selection—you the Governor of the State and holding the affections of the people —these were your prospects when I took you by the hand and bade you farewell. You may well judge my astonishment and grief at the sad intelligence that you were an exile from your country.

Warmth and affection and concern in that. *Astonishment and grief* . . . the very words comforted the exile, since they conveyed to him the knowledge that in spite of all the stories which must have been told the President by enemies who wished to discredit him, his old friend stood stanch.

The letter went on to take notice of a report of an "illegal enterprise" of conquering Texas. It ended:

I must really have thought you deranged to have believed you had so wild a scheme in contemplation, and particularly when it was communicated that the physical force to be employed was the Cherokee Indians. Indeed, my dear Sir, I cannot believe you have any such chimerical visionary scheme in view. Your pledge of honor to the contrary is sufficient guarantee that you will never engage in any enterprise injurious to your country that would tarnish your fame.

Houston's reply was immediate: it gave the pledge of honor required, and his honor was a thing he never in his life took lightly.

But again, after this, he reverted to his long-continued whiskey swilling. The winter passed and he hardly knew the days one from the next. The Cherokees thought it was sad to see the befuddled giant to whom men once looked with respect, now become a boozy brute worthy only of contempt.

At last spring came. As the days warmed and the trees budded, then leafed out, Houston sometimes, in his drunken confusion, wandered far out into the forest, to fall flat on the ground, lying there until he slept off his debauch and woke again, his head pounding and his stomach loathly sick.

3

One such morning, late in the spring, he opened his eyes and found himself gazing up into the interlacing green of the leafy branches above. He put his hand to his face: it bristled with a tangled beard of weeks' growth, and it was wet. He was, in fact, wet all over from a heavy dew which had settled while he slept swinishly there.

At once he became violently nauseated as usual; but after a time he managed to raise himself to a sitting posture, with his back against a tree. There he sat for some time, his head bowed miserably on his chest, fighting against a desire to retch.

Gradually he gained control over his stomach, and his mind began to clear away the fog that blurred his thinking. But his thoughts were unwelcome and bitter: his life, its brilliant promise, the way he had thrown it all away. For him, he considered in his despair, remained now only a sordid existence as a besotted, adopted member of the Cherokee Nation; living on the charity of Oo-loo-te-ka; a disgrace to himself and to anyone who ever had befriended him; derided even by children.

Such thinking usually drove him again to drinking; but looking about him dully he could see no demijohn. Evidently he had not brought one with him when he came out into these woods.

It was at this moment that he heard, as if with half an ear, a sound that caught his attention. It was a woman's voice, singing softly. He leaned back against the tree, putting his hand to his aching forehead. She seemed quite near, but when he looked about the little glen among the trees where he sat, he saw no one.

Presently he realized that she who was singing did not know he was there. He began to wonder who she was. Curiosity at last overcame other feelings, and he scrambled awkwardly to his feet. For a moment he held to a tree, regaining equilibrium, then turned his unsteady steps toward the sound of the singing.

She was kneeling beside the stream, washing some clothes. As he looked at her kneeling there, her form so slender and lovely, the curve of her hips so gracious, a kind of rapture came over him.

A moment later she turned, and he saw her eyes widen with surprise, perhaps alarm. As he supposed, until that moment she was entirely ignorant of his near presence, the sound of the splashing of her work and her own voice hiding his steps as he approached her.

He stood still, and she remained on her knees, her face now averted, washing the cloth in her hands on some smooth stones beside the running water, into which over and over she dipped the fabric. It seemed to him that she did this as if her mind was not on it; as if she wondered what he intended to do; as if she thought that by keeping busy she might avert some half-dreaded happening.

She was Tiana. A memory came to him of the Cherokee town on Hiwassee Island; a memory of another day when she knelt as she did now, beside a basket of washing on the bank of a river. On that day the two of them, there under the bushes beside the rushing stream, discovered together the deepest inner secret of nature. He was her first man; she his first woman.

At the bank this morning Tiana was no longer a girl. She was a woman fully formed, and fully aware of him. She was also beautiful: because of her clean good looks the white people who knew her had paraphrased her name from the Indian, Tiana, to Diana, the name of the Greek goddess of the moon and the hunt. And she was a widow, living alone, having suitors but accepting none of them.

All at once he felt shame in her presence. Most unpleasantly he must reveal that he was just recovering from a debauch, his clothes wrinkled and foul, his face unshaved and dirty. Compared with her smoothness and neatness, her glossy braids bound about her graceful head, he felt bestial.

Without a word he turned and walked down the stream bank to a place where he could wash his face. But this was not enough. He was filthy all over: suddenly he wished to be clean.

Still not speaking to the woman, he hurried off through the woods to the village. At a pool in a creek, some distance farther along and well concealed, he bathed quickly and thoroughly, using sand from the bottom to scrub himself in the chill water.

Dressed once more, he continued at a rapid pace to his Indian father's home. Oo-loo-te-ka was not there. The old squaw, Sarah, was, but she did not speak to him, nor he to her.

He went to his bundle and changed to a clean deerskin hunting shirt and new leather breeches and moccasins. Then he shaved his face, combed the snarls out of his long hair, and braided it. All this took him thirty minutes or so; but he nevertheless started back to the place where he left Tiana, wondering rather forlornly if she had finished her task and gone.

She was still there, kneeling at the water's edge, wringing out her cloths. A dappling of sunlight created highlights on her glossy black hair.

When he came she looked up at him. Her lips, fuller and riper than those of most Indian women, were slightly parted, her eyes dark and lustrous, with wonderful lashes of jet.

She did not smile or speak. Instead she gathered the garments, which she had finished wringing out, into a bundle wrapped in a dry cloth. Then she rose, a single effortless movement from the ground, and without a word started away, her bundle in her arms.

His eyes followed her . . . supple and slender as a white birch . . . dress fitting tight about her form to reveal the graceful movement of her back and hips as she walked . . . arms, slim yet strong, upholding their burden. . . .

He swallowed and moistened his lips. Then he spoke, and his voice was almost harsh with appeal.

"Tiana . . ."

Just the one word, but she stopped. It was as if she had listened for him to call her name, expected him to call it. Her back was still toward him, her body slim and lithe, her little feet close beside each other.

Blood pounded in Houston's temples. "Tiana, look at me."

She obeyed, slowly turning about, arms still holding her bundle.

He took two steps toward her. "Do you belong to anybody, Tiana?"

"My husband died," she said in a voice subdued. "I belong to myself."

The Indian way of looking at matters. An unmarried girl belonged to her father, to give her away or sell her to a husband for a marriage price. When she married she became the property of her husband. But if the husband died she was her own property, her body to dispose of as she pleased. She could choose any man she desired, and if she married again her status was altered because she did not come to him by barter. Having once owned herself she retained some of the property rights in herself. Tiana had been a widow for two years; and a widow, if attractive, possessed important advantages. Yet she had not taken a man.

There was reason for this. She had seen no man she wanted . . . until Houston appeared in the village. At this minute it seemed to Tiana that the answer was given for her long rejection of those who sought her.

She saw that he had hastened to cleanse himself, put on new garments, make himself neat and good to look upon. Also, she remembered vividly that first experience with him on the river bank at Hiwassee. Perhaps since that far day she had never been able truly to place another man in the same niche in her heart that this man occupied.

All of this added up to important totals in her thinking. But for the present she stood perfectly still and silent. She felt that she should not move, could not move until he told her to do so. She felt as if she were under a spell of some kind, and she waited, her head now lowered, her eyes on the ground, conscious only of his near presence, and his gaze upon her.

"Tiana," he said again, and stopped.

She knew . . . precisely she knew what he wanted of her. If she would escape it, this was the time for her to protest, or pretend not to understand, or flee. She could do none of these things.

She did not speak. Her breasts rose and fell with her rapid breathing. She knew that when he told her what she must do—here, now, in the woods beside the river—she would do that thing. She waited for what he would command her to do, and she could not disobey him now if she wished. Until he told her to move, she would remain standing there facing him, if it were for the rest of her life.

His voice again: "Where is your house, Tiana?"

Her eyes flew wide open and she looked up at him. His throat was swelling and throbbing, and she could not misread that look in his face.

Yet—he had asked the proper question!

Her house. He had not asked her to give herself to him here among the bushes; although she would have done that thing for him without resisting or complaint.

Instead, he asked for her house: and this to her Indian mind conveyed a meaning important and very different from a mere furtive lechery out in the woods.

She could find no voice to answer him. But holding her bundle against her body she turned and began to walk through the trees. She heard him following, could almost feel his eyes on her, observing each subtle movement of her form.

Her house was quite near. It was somewhat isolated from the other Indian cabins, but of logs like the others: a single room. She entered quickly and laid down her bundle. A moment later his figure darkened the door.

Tiana looked up at him. His face was almost grim, a passionate gravity, purposive and relentless.

One step she took backward . . . the instinct of her female self; the evasive, alluring suggestion of flight, wholly unconscious yet exactly the thing to inflame him; an act old as nature.

When he seized her by the shoulders, she felt it almost with relief, as if at the ending of some unbearable suspense. In her breast beat a wild pulsing of excitement, responding to his overwhelming excitement.

No suggestion of escape now. She felt his first fierce kiss.

Unresisting, she raised her slender arms to allow him to slip off her doeskin dress, and stood before him for a moment, wonderful in her nymph-like beauty.

He lifted her and laid her on her pallet. His hungry body surged over her. Only consummation now was important to her, to him. She was eager, hot, ecstatic, her body in its desire flinging upward against his.

In her he assuaged all the frustrations, longings, and desires that had built up in him during the long unhappy months that had passed.

4

Having possessed Tiana, there were matters for Houston to consider. She was a self-respecting Cherokee woman. Knowing this he took her to her own house, which to her had definite importance.

Under Indian custom marriage was easy. It required no more than that a couple start housekeeping together, and state publicly that they were man and wife. Usually when a young girl married there was feasting and a ceremonial of giving by her father and receiving by her husband. But a woman who already had been married, had become a widow, and thereafter took a new man, did not wish or ask for such a ceremony.

Houston simply moved his belongings from Oo-loo-te-ka's cabin to Tiana's. She cooked for him and shared her bed with him. Thus they were wedded in the eyes of the tribe.

Womanlike, she believed that she had surrendered to him: in actuality, he had surrendered to her, and to circumstances and necessities. If men wanted now to call him a "squaw man," the privilege was theirs. He had taken the step which he long had rejected. Tiana had brought about this, and he did not regret it.

In his relationship with her there was at first a thought of complication: he already had a wife, Eliza, back in Tennessee. But he reasoned the matter closely and arrived at the following conclusions:

He had determined to sever all connections with white people, become an Indian, and so remain throughout his life. In so doing he accepted citizenship in the Cherokee Nation and was governed by its customs and laws, not those of the whites which he had rejected.

To take an Indian wife thus became natural, not lawless. Even if it were granted that he was still married to Eliza, while living with Tiana in wedlock, the Cherokee custom ordained that a man could have more than one wife, and many of the important men did so.

Furthermore, Houston no longer considered himself truly married to Eliza. She had never been a wife to him. They were wedded in name only, and she had returned to her father untouched, as she had come to him.

He was thus able to turn to his Indian woman with warmth and affection, casting the white woman not only out of his life but out of his mind . . . almost.

In the months after he began living with Tiana, the older Indians gravely agreed he improved in life and habit. Though he still drank, he no longer embarked on such lengthy bouts of drunkenness. He became interested in affairs, acquired some land, bought a few horses and cattle, and purchased two young Negroes from Oo-loo-te-ka, as servants and field hands. After a time he built for Tiana a larger house than her one-room cabin, and named it the "Wigwam Neosho."

For the tribe he undertook matters of importance. He furnished a list of corrupt agents to Washington, and followed this with a personal letter to Andrew Jackson, President of the United States. When Oo-loo-te-ka, out of unhappy experience, suggested that this letter might never be delivered, he smiled grimly and wondered aloud who would dare withhold or even delay a message sent with the superscription of Sam Houston and addressed to the old man in the White House.

Once or twice in those months he was absent from the Cherokee country for periods quite extended—on business for the tribe it was said, although the nature of this business was not disclosed. Yet it was known that he had suggested a new ration policy for the Indians, even offering to contract to supply rations himself at prices below those currently charged to the government by contractors.

But this bit deep into the interests of powerful politicians and the moneyed men who controlled them, for Indian contracts were profitable. Nothing came of this offer.

5

In the new dawn, toward the end of the year, Houston came from the log house and stood blinking in the clear white light. Behind him Tiana appeared in the doorway, sleep still fleeing from her eyes, and watched him.

He was dressed for travel, in hunting shirt and breeches, the moccasins she had beaded, a silk turban about his head, his saddlebags already packed.

Though her face showed none of her inner thinking, she knew what fate was doing to her. She was losing him; and she had been a good woman to him. Since the first day she had him she had expected this final hour, yet she had dreaded it. To keep him forever was like trying to stop the rushing waters of a river from flowing in their natural course. For weeks she had marked the signs: his ponderings as he thought over some plan, sometimes drinking, but more often sitting silent, his brow furrowed.

A few days before the chiefs had given him a paper. It was Houston's idea and he wrote the instrument itself. To it the three principal chiefs, Oo-loo-te-ka, Walter Webber, and Aron Price, had each affixed his mark, making it official. The paper read:

Whereas Sam Houston, late of the State of Tennessee, has been residing in the Cherokee Nation for some time past, and,

Whereas, in consideration of his former acquaintance with; and services rendered to the Indians, he has been granted forever all the rights, privileges, and immunities of a citizen of the Cherokee Nation, as though he was a native born Cherokee,

Now, therefore, be it known, that in full confidence of his integrity, wisdom, and talents, the said Sam Houston is hereby commissioned, and with this instrument is authorized to act, with all the powers and responsibilities of

AMBASSADOR OF THE CHEROKEE NATION,

to represent the interests of this Nation, and to speak for this Nation as its chosen, legal, and authorized representative.

Ambassador of the Cherokee Nation. This morning he was going; and Tiana, with the fatalism of her race and sex, knew that even if he ever returned, it would be only as the bumblebee which poises momentarily to take honey from a bloom, then soars away. Indian in thought and training, she neither questioned nor complained.

It was now November, the leaves already turned and mostly fallen, with the frosts. Houston looked at the sky, clear and blue, as if looking at this wilderness freedom for the last time. Then he turned to the woman in the doorway.

"I must say farewell now, Tiana," he said.

"Yes," she said simply.

"I have made out a paper, signed before Oo-loo-te-ka, which is here in my hand, and I give it to you. By it, this house and its fields, the two Negro slaves, the twelve cattle, the chickens and the two pigs, all the horses except the one I will ride, and everything else, except my clothes I wear or carry in my saddlebags, and the little money in my wallet, belong to you."

She bowed her head, but was silent.

"You have been good for me," he went on. "You lifted up my heart when it was flat on the ground."

He paused, and looked at her with an expression of genuine sadness, of genuine regret.

"I may not return," he continued. "If the things that I have in my mind to do are to be accomplished, I cannot return . . . except perhaps for a few days. You are free to take another man if you wish."

"I do not want another man," she said in a low voice.

He took her face between his hands. "I will never forget you, Tiana."

She did not reply, but she went to the corral and caught for him the horse he wanted. When he saddled the animal, mounted it, and rode away, Tiana watched him as long as he was in view: first a powerful man on a little, springy horse; then a smaller, scurrying figure; at last a dot disappearing on the road in the distance.

After that she turned back slowly into her house. She was sad. And yet, she thought to herself, it was something to have had a man like that, if only for the brief time she had him. . . .

Chapter Twenty-Eight

Money is inhuman. It has no blood, no nerves, no morality, only selfishness. Consider the thirty pieces of silver for which the Iscariot committed the greatest of all betrayals.

ANDREW JACKSON

1

The Ambassador of the Cherokee Nation, in buckskins, wearing a scarlet blanket over his shoulder as a robe, and a silk handkerchief as headgear, appeared like an apparition in the lobby of the Indian Queen Hotel in Washington. As the picturesque giant set down a pair of saddlebags and came over, the clerk at the desk, new to his job, gaped.

"A room, sir," said the apparition.

"Name, sir?" asked the clerk.

"General Sam Houston, Ambassador of the Cherokee Nation."

The name had somehow a familiar ring, and the manner of the visitor was too impressive to permit discourtesy.

"Ambassador, sir?" said the clerk. "A room, certainly. Please register here." He stared at the bold signature. Then he had a satiric thought. "This may be of interest to you—I understand there is a reception for the Ambassadors and envoys of foreign nations at the White House this very evening."

"Indeed?"

"I merely offer the information with the thought that you might care to attend, since it is, I assume, for the entire diplomatic corps." The clerk, with a straight face, accented the last two words slightly.

Houston looked at him somberly. "Perhaps I may," he rumbled.

"Your key, sir. Shall I have the boy convey your baggage to your room?"

"Thank you, I have but my saddlebags. I will attend myself to the room."

The clerk said, with a hint of irony, "I hope you will find everything satisfactory, sir."

Houston bent on him a look half humorous, half grim.

"Young man," he said, "you're new to this town, aren't you? Let me just say that Houston was accustomed to the facilities of this place while James Monroe was still President of this republic."

He picked up the saddlebags and mounted the stairs to the second floor.

The clerk looked after him with a quizzical expression.

"Ambassador of the Cherokee Nation," he murmured to himself. "Blankets and beads at a diplomatic reception? I wonder. . . . 'Perhaps I may,' he says. Perhaps he will!"

Houston, alone in his upstairs room, did some thinking.

A reception for the diplomatic corps . . . why, he was a diplomat himself. He had not, to be sure, received an invitation, but then the White House would not know of his presence in the capital.

This long journey had been made by him to obtain better treatment for his adopted people, and he had hoped for a friendly reception by the President, based on a kindly letter or two he had received through the Fort Gibson post.

But in his travel across the country, he had begun to wonder. In Tennessee he had an enemy with blood as cold as a serpent's. Governor William Carroll had erected the circumstances and conjectures concerning Houston's break with Eliza into a mountain of slander, disparagement, and imputation that seemed to bury his rival in ruin. Furthermore, he intended to keep that ruin absolute. Save for Carroll the talk about Eliza and Houston might long since have been forgotten.

But it was not allowed to fade away. Houston was told by friends whom he saw on the steamboat journey up the Ohio River that Billy Carroll had obtained and given circulation to an "open letter" addressed to the Raven, and printed in the *Arkansas Gazette*. The letter was written by a crooked Indian agent, and was a vicious attack on the man who was ferreting out corruption in the Indian department. As far as Carroll was concerned, the pertinent points were contained in the concluding paragraph:

Without wishing, sir, to triumph over *fallen greatness*, I will now bid your turbaned honor adieu, leaving you in the enjoyment you may find *in your new matrimonial alliance*, hoping your fair bride may induce you to make a prudent husbandry of whatever resources you may have left, and awaken to you a sense of your degradation.

Sam Houston a "squaw man!" Carroll made sure the word reached the Allen family, and hence Eliza.

He saw to it also that the item reached Andrew Jackson—and the world knew how touchy the old man was about any irregularity with women.

Houston knew that last fact as well as anyone. Perhaps by this time, he considered, the friendship of the President might have changed to coldness, even strong disapproval and dislike.

Perhaps . . . Houston grinned. At least he knew how he could find out just how he stood.

2

Snow covered the ground as he rode up to the Executive Mansion. That a social event of importance was going forward was evident, for the windows of the White House were ablaze with lights.

A Negro groom who took his horse stared at him with his eyes almost popping from their sockets. The Raven, far from attempting to garb himself in the clothing of civilization, had come, as Ambassador of the Cherokee Nation, in the attire of the people he represented. He had, perhaps, made his appearance even more bizarre.

As he ascended the steps to the door, a flustered official made an effort to detain him.

"Who let you in? What are you doing here?" he demanded.

With a single motion of his arm, Houston thrust the man aside.

"Major Lewis, have you forgotten an old acquaintance?"

"It can't be—why, it is—General Houston——" Lewis almost gasped. "But what are you doing in that getup?"

"I understand that it is customary for diplomats to wear the ceremonial dress of their respective countries at an affair of this kind. Houston is the Ambassador of the Cherokee Nation, and this is ceremonial attire among the people he represents."

Major Lewis took a step backward.

"Does the President know you're here?" he asked.

"No, sir."

The major-domo was plainly at a loss. Yet he could hardly refuse admittance to this man. He capitulated.

"Very well, General Houston, I'll announce you."

"Don't bother. Houston will introduce himself."

The East Room was a kaleidoscope of contrasting colors. Gentlemen in formal black mingled with gentlemen in brilliant military dress uniforms. Ladies wore every hue, with décolletage notable. A turban here— the envoy of the Serene Porte. Gold braid on green and red yonder —the Ambassador of Mexico. Scarlet, gold, and white there—a military attaché to Her Britannic Majesty's Embassy. Medals, ribbons, decorations everywhere. Gallantry and coquetry, all in the most sophisticated manner. A typical gathering of the foreign diplomats, conversing in a dozen languages, but taking care to preserve the sleek decorum, the niceties, the gilded smiles, the suave manners of their ultra-polite profession. At the moment the President had not yet appeared, being detained on some affair of government business in his office, but Emily Donelson and her husband were doing their best to attend to the hospitalities.

All at once, into this assemblage strode a barbaric figure, gigantic and theatrical. Thrown about his shoulders, a scarlet blanket made a splendid flare of color. The fringes of his leather breeches tinkled with metal ornaments. Beaded designs decorated his moccasins and hunting shirt. About his bare head, the long hair of which was braided in two thick plaits, was a beaded band, from which at the back of his head, a single war eagle's plume, vivid in its black and white, stood upright.

He stopped at the entrance. Every person in the large chamber turned to stare at the wild and savage intruder, conversations halted in mid-sentence, surprise appeared on faces trained to show no surprise.

"My word, a red Indian, isn't it?" said an English voice.

"Will it raise the war whoop?" a woman inquired.

"Scalp us all?" another said, feigning alarm.

It caused a titter, giving way to general amusement, finally to laughter.

Sternly dark, without moving a muscle of his face, Houston stood looking at the Ambassadors and their ladies. He, too, was awaiting the appearance of the President.

A murmur in the assemblage.

"The President is about to appear."

A moment later a door opened, and the tall, spare figure of Andrew Jackson, dressed in severely plain black, with the usual crape on his sleeve, came forth.

In the East Room every one of the notables present waited almost breathlessly to see what he would do about the strange apparition from the wilderness.

The white-haired President advanced among his guests, displaying the beautiful charm, tact, and graciousness which continually surprised those who encountered him for the first time. To this one he gave a pleasant smile, to that a nod, to the other a word or two.

Then he halted. For the first time he saw the red-robed figure standing alone by the door. With that sight he seemed to forget everyone else in the room.

An expression of incredulity crossed his face, followed instantly by one of joy.

"Houston!" he said, as if to himself. "Sam Houston, by all that is holy!"

All at once he hurried forward.

"Sam Houston! Sam, my boy!" he cried.

A moment later every dignitary present saw what seemed an incredible thing. The dignified, austere President of the United States and the great barbarian threw their arms about each other in a wild bear hug.

Then they stood back, laughing with delight, to look well at one another.

"Boy, you're a welcome sight to these old eyes!" said the President.

And, "General, I've been dreaming of this for it seems ages," said the savage.

"What brings you—in this style?" asked Jackson, with a smile of warm affection.

"I was told there was a reception for the diplomatic corps. I come as Ambassador of the Cherokee Nation."

In sheer happiness the old man laughed. Then he took the barbarian by the arm. "Come, you must meet your fellow diplomats—and their ladies," he said.

No question now of the standing of the blanketed newcomer. The envoys present and their feminine companions made haste to approach and be introduced. And it was notable that they now appeared to be delighted to make the acquaintance of a man so colorful; and whose manners, on nearer contact, were so charming and impressive; and whose story, being whispered about now that his identity was known, was so romantic.

3

Long after the reception ended and the last guest departed, Jackson and Houston sat together in the President's smoking room.

There was much personal history to be caught up. Houston related his adventures, saying nothing of his Indian wife. Jackson did not bring forward the subject.

The visitor's problems were laid before the President.

"Every one of the Indian agents against whom charges are laid by the Ambassador of the Cherokee Nation will be investigated, and if the charges are discovered to be true, will be dismissed or prosecuted," said Old Hickory formally, as if addressing an envoy of a foreign power. But the twinkle in his blue eyes belied the formality.

There were other, more personal matters. John Henry Eaton was gone from Washington, and with him the volatile Peggy.

"I confess it was a relief when John Eaton resigned from the Cabinet, much as I treasure him and am fond of Margaret," said Jackson. "The situation was almost amusing, except that it was so exasperating. Did you ever try, Sam, to make headway against massed female prejudice? It's like attempting to run knee-deep in sticky molasses. You put out a lot of effort, but get nowhere."

He paused, ruminating. "I did my best: it was not enough. But I fear

Margaret was disappointed with my poor efforts in her behalf. She seemed quite distant the last time I saw her."

Houston remarked that women, as a class, were kittle cattle.

"At least things are more pleasant in this house," said Jackson. "My nephew, Jack Donelson, is back as my private secretary, and with him his wife Emily, and their children, and a number of the other young people of my family. I could never understand my little Emily. She's the personification of sweetness and generosity. Yet she seemed to take a sudden dislike for Peggy Eaton, for which I could see no logical reason, but which became so impelling that at last she returned home, leaving me without a hostess at the White House. I must say that the ladies, even the finest and best of them, sometimes baffle me completely."

To this Houston answered with an Oh, and an Ah. He understood far better than the old man why women took up arms against Peggy Eaton, but he forbore attempting to explain.

"The affair had this result, however," commented the President. "It revealed to me my real enemies. Clay, of course. Calhoun, after I threw the principle of the Federal Union in his very teeth, at his own banquet, has since resigned the Vice-Presidency, and is rusticating in his native South Carolina—preparing, so I understand, to run for the Senate."

"I have known—and told you—for years, that he is a blackguard," growled Houston.

Jackson was silent, studying him. It came over the President that time and vicissitudes had vastly changed this man. His very appearance was altered.

His great head had become leonine, with its broad long nose, monolithic chin, and wide, grim mouth. But the most arresting thing about him was his eyes. Always Sam Houston's eyes had been remarkable, but maturity and trouble had strangely altered their expression. Shaded by heavy, bristling brows and half-slitted, the opaline light-gray of them, intensely watchful, almost threatening, reminded Jackson of some great predatory cat.

This was Sam Houston still, but a more savage, older, perhaps wiser Sam Houston. The President observed him with affection, but also as a superb judge of men. He saw in his friend disillusion, but also competence; a hardy strength born out of bitterness, like an instrument forged and tempered by adversity.

Another oddity: Houston frequently referred to himself in the third person, like Caesar in his *Commentaries*. An affectation? Jackson decided not. It was an Indian habit ingrown through long discourse in the native tongue and probably as unconscious as it was ingrained.

4

But now the President continued, and politics was in his very breath.

"Henry Clay, that political gamester, will try again for the office I now hold," and his eyes gleamed like blue steel. "I hear that another bargain is in the making. Clay's jackal, John C. Breckinridge, will resign his Senate seat, so that Clay himself can be elevated to that position. With the Senate rostrum as a sounding board, Clay will then redouble his attacks on my Administration. Adams will support him. So will Calhoun—who also goes to the Senate upon the resignation, for his convenience, of a man I once called friend, Robert Y. Hayne. So will all of the Whig Party, which now numbers in its ranks all the old Federalists. Together they believe they have an issue which will defeat me."

"And you, sir?"

"I'll tell you this, boy, with all sincerity. I'm a tired old man, and not well. That lung trouble—I believe Dickinson's old pistol ball is in there somewhere—keeps coming back on me. I've had swellings in my legs lately. Dropsy, the doctor says, but it's gone for the time being. And though I eat little, sticking mostly to the old army diet of rice, and drink no spirits at all, I'm still troubled periodically with the flux. These things I cite to you, not because I seek your sympathy, or because I'm a chronic complainer, but to explain why I sometimes feel discouragement. There are days," the President stared gloomily into the fireplace, "when I think the only consolation this side of the grave would be to retire to the Hermitage, spend my latter days beside *her* tomb, and at last lay my bones beside her."

This mood of melancholy was so unusual that it struck Houston with grave force. He was looking into the heart of a lonely man, a man whose only solace was in the past, whose inflexible will kept him without relaxation at a task he sometimes found distasteful, but the responsibility of which he would not shun: the guiding of the nation.

"You say, sir," Houston said, seeking to bring the conversation back to its former line, "that Clay and Adams and the others have an issue?"

Jackson straightened, his moment of discouragement ended.

"The Bank of the United States!" he said. "Clay will ram a bill to recharter the Bank—four years ahead of time, mind you—through Congress at this session. I will veto that bill. The Whigs expect to use the Bank in their campaign. Hard times are always political ammunition for the party out of power, because they bring discontented and unhappy people into opposition to the Administration that is in."

The old man paused to relight his pipe.

"The Bank of the United States can create a panic—an artificial panic

—whenever it wills. I verily believe such a panic will be set in motion if I veto the recharter, in hope of defeating me."

"But this is inhuman!" exclaimed Houston. "To bring hardship on innocent families for the sake of political advantage——"

"Money is inhuman," Jackson said. "It has no blood, no nerves, no morality, only selfishness. For money some men will do anything. Consider the thirty pieces of silver for which the Iscariot committed the greatest of all betrayals. Do you know, sir, that the ancient Greeks symbolized all human qualities with natural objects?"

"Yes, sir, I do remember that."

"What was their symbol for courage?"

"The lion."

"For freedom?"

"The eagle."

"Good. For wisdom?"

"The owl."

"Now," said Jackson, "what was the symbol for what some men consider the most important of all instincts—acquisitiveness, or in plain words, greed for money?"

"The hog."

Jackson smiled. "I observe that you're well grounded in the classics. Also that you see my point."

Houston nodded.

"The Bank of the United States," said the President, "is an enemy of the people because of that very power to create artificial panics at will —as well as for other reasons. It is a product of the brain of Alexander Hamilton. It does not belong in a democratic nation. Consider these things."

He paused and then began to enumerate his points one by one upon his fingers.

"Of its capital of thirty-five millions, the government has subscribed one-fifth. It is the repository of the public funds, which it uses for its own banking purposes without payment of interest. It can issue bank notes up to any amount it desires, without anyone to say no. It is not taxed by the states, and no rival institution can be chartered by Congress. It has twenty-five directors, but of these the government can appoint only five. In return for all these privileges it pays a bonus of one and a half million dollars—a bagatelle—and performs the trifling service of transferring public funds and making public payments out of government funds, without a charge. And for this it considers it has performed a great favor!"

Jackson leaned over and tapped the younger man on the knee to emphasize his next words.

"Sir, the Bank is a great private monopoly upheld by the government, but independent of the government. Its power over the currency is almost limitless. It is a hydra designed for an evil purpose, to enable men of wealth and power to bend the government to their purposes. I will scotch that hydra!"

Fascinated, Houston listened as the white-haired warrior outlined the reasons why he would, in spite of age and illness and weariness, face to a finish the great national banking institution, with its branches all over the country, and the countless men under obligation to it, as well as the political party that would espouse it.

Unquestionably, he thought to himself, Andrew Jackson had grown vastly greater in stature since he had assumed the responsibilities of Chief Magistrate.

"I can only hope, sir, that the people will see this thing your way," he said.

"I have confidence in the people," said Jackson. "I'll take this issue directly to them. The people will be for me, if every other force and power is ranged against me."

The old man's eye chanced to light upon a folded newspaper which lay on the table. He reached over and picked it up.

"The *United States Telegraph*," he said. "Duff Green edits this travesty on journalism. He formerly was one of my loudest supporters, but I found him untrustworthy. Actually, he was a Calhoun man all the time, and when Calhoun broke with me, Green went also. At least he's in the open now, and I'm well rid of his false asservations of loyalty. He loses no opportunity to take pot shots at me, and this is particularly interesting. It's a report of a speech in Congress, which, by the way, affects yourself."

Houston took the paper. A certain William Stanbery, a representative from Ohio, was quoted as saying, in the course of a virulent criticism of the Administration:

"Was not the last Secretary of War, Major John Henry Eaton, removed because of his attempt fraudulently to give Governor Houston the contract for Indian rations?"

Houston almost gasped. It was, he believed, the first time his name had been mentioned in a public discussion for a long time; and now it was used in an effort to discredit his greatest friend.

"This is a damned lie, and an insult!" he exclaimed. "Houston did make a bid on the contract—an honest bid—but nothing came of it. It's a blow beneath the belt, sir! Who is this Stanbery?"

"A man who was elected to Congress, so it happens, because he proclaimed that he was a supporter of mine."

"And then turned against you!" Houston crumpled the paper in his fist. "This fellow will hear from me!"

Jackson gave his odd half-smile. "I've learned—or hope I've learned

—one lesson in this strange situation of mine, Sam. You've at times in the past been under the impression that I have a temper?"

"Well, sir, I'll not deny that I've seen you fly off the handle—always for good reason, of course——"

"The temper is still there, Sam. But I keep it under better control. Don't let this sort of thing ruffle you—it doesn't ruffle me. After you've been in Washington awhile, you'll learn to consider the source, and discount what is said."

But when Houston left the White House late that night, the offending newspaper was still clutched in his hand.

Chapter Twenty-Nine

Texas might trigger these United States into an explosion across this continent!

ANDREW JACKSON

1

An unpretentious little man, almost boyish-looking for all his forty-six years, sat at his desk in the House of Representatives, listening to a lengthy roll call on some order of business, when he heard a disturbance at the rear of the hall. James Knox Polk glanced back—and recognized the cause of the disturbance.

Sam Houston, appearing strangely out of place in his buckskin hunting clothes, was disputing with the sergeant-at-arms.

Polk rose and hastened toward the scene of the argument. He well knew Sam Houston—he it was in fact who succeeded Houston in Congress, when the giant became governor of Tennessee. He was mild-mannered, was Jimmie Polk, with wide gray eyes, a rather small head, and brown hair worn quite long and brushed back behind his ears; but for all his quiet ways he had become a power in Congress. This spring of 1831 he was the Administration floor-leader, an expert on parliamentary rules, a deft political tactician, and a man of honest beliefs for which many who did not agree with him admired him.

As he neared Houston he saw that the big man was a little tipsy. Polk did not drink himself—this same Sam Houston in fact had once pronounced him "a victim of the use of water as a beverage." Nevertheless the two men were friends, and if Sam Houston meant to get himself into trouble, Jimmie Polk meant to prevent it if possible.

"What is it, General Houston?" he asked. "You know it's against the rules to come on the floor of the House without special permission."

"Where's this fellow Stanbery?" demanded Houston. "Show me Stanbery."

"Mr. Stanbery?" said Polk. "I'll show him to you, sir, but you'll have to wait until the session is over to speak to him, unless he consents to wait upon you outside. There he is—the large man in the brown suit—in the fourth row next to the right-hand aisle."

"He's pretty near as big as I am," said Houston speculatively.

It began to dawn on Mr. Polk what Houston desired of Stanbery.

"General," he said, "you must not make a scene in Congress. It would not only ruin you, but it would gravely damage our friend."

The reference to the President did not escape the giant.

"Houston recognizes that it is improper for him to enter the floor," he said with almost exaggerated dignity. "Do this for me, Jimmie—hand Stanbery this note."

"No, not here," protested Polk. "A note such as I suspect you have ought not be delivered on the floor of Congress."

A gleam of humor came into Houston's eyes. "Always the stickler, aren't you, Jimmie?" he said.

But he turned and left the Capitol.

Later that day, however, Representative Cave Johnson of Tennessee, no such stickler as Polk, approached Stanbery with a written challenge from Houston.

The Ohio congressman rejected it. "I will not receive a note signed by Sam Houston," he said. "I do not have the pleasure of Mr. Houston's acquaintance, nor do I desire that honor—if it is an honor."

Johnson reported the conversation and Houston's face darkened. "In that case," he growled, "Houston will introduce himself to the damned rascal."

A day or two passed and gossip said that Mr. Stanbery had taken to carrying a brace of pocket pistols. If this report reached Houston's ears it did not visibly affect him.

Late on the night of April 14, Senator Alexander Buckner of Missouri, and Representative Blair of Tennessee, were walking with Houston toward his hotel, when they saw a man cross the street ahead of them. Pennsylvania Avenue was only dimly lit by its occasional street lamps, but Blair uttered an exclamation.

"Why—there's your friend Stanbery," he said.

Houston at once quickened his pace. Blair turned and hurried rapidly in the opposite direction, as if to avoid being involved, but Senator Buckner followed Houston.

The man ahead heard rapid steps following him and turned.

"Are you Mr. Stanbery?" inquired Houston.

"Yes, sir, I am," replied the other.

"Then you're a damned rascal!" cried Houston.

Buckner saw him raise the walking stick he carried and strike Stanbery on the head, knocking off his hat.

Stanbery was a big, burly man, but he showed immediate terror.

"Oh, don't, don't!" he cried, lifting an arm to shield himself.

As Houston struck at him again, he turned to run. Like an Indian, Houston leaped on his back and hurled him to the sidewalk, where they rolled over and over, Stanbery screaming loudly for help.

All at once Buckner saw the congressman draw a pistol from his coat pocket and thrust the muzzle against Houston's breast. The senator halted, breathless and horrified at the prospect of sudden tragedy. Houston, expecting death, did not quiver.

Stanbery pulled the trigger. A snap of the gunlock, the flint struck fire—but the charge failed to explode.

Houston tore the weapon out of his hand, lifted him by the slack of his coat to his feet, and sent him stumbling down the street with a kick.

2

Undeniably, the incident was brutal and savage.

When a note from Stanbery, who went to bed to nurse his bruises, was delivered to the Speaker to be read to the House, in which it was stated that he had been "waylaid on the street, knocked down by a bludgeon, and severely bruised and wounded, for words spoken in his place in the House of Representatives," that body, over the opposition of Jimmie Polk, voted overwhelmingly ordering the arrest of Sam Houston.

Duff Green had the entire fight—Stanbery's version—on the front page of his newspaper under a headline: *Most Daring Outrage and Assault*. The article, written with venom, described the attack as "brutal," "cowardly," "an act of savagery"; but it was in the concluding paragraph that Green vented his real spleen:

What gives more importance to this transaction is the known relation that Houston bears to the President of the United States. He was the individual who placed in the hands of General Jackson Mr. Monroe's letter to Mr. Calhoun that made so important a part of the "correspondence" between the President and Vice President. Although he left Tennessee under circumstances that produced the greatest excitement, took up his residence with the Indians, and adopted their costume and habits; and although the proof that he contemplated a fraud upon the government is conclusive, yet he is still received at the Executive Mansion and treated with the kindness and hospitality of an old favorite. We have long seen, that the tactics of the Nashville school were to be transferred to Washington and that the voice of truth was to be silenced by the dread of the assassin. But we have not yet taken fear as our counsellor.

The law of Congressional immunity had been invoked. Houston submitted to arrest by the sergeant-at-arms with an impassive face.

He came before the House, wearing his buckskin clothes and scarlet blanket, and bowed to the Speaker on his dais.

Andrew Stevenson of Virginia, the Speaker of the House, read aloud to him the formal arraignment.

"Mr. Speaker," said Houston, "I request time to prepare my defense."

Stevenson looked at him. "The defendant will be granted forty-eight hours," he said.

3

Andrew Jackson was profoundly concerned. In spite of his warnings Sam Houston evidently had allowed his temper to get the better of him and involved himself in a serious predicament. He summoned Houston to the White House.

"You've got yourself into a fix," was his opening sentence.

"I reckon, General, you can say that," said Houston.

"This is a grave matter, sir. I can hardly blame you for chastising the scoundrel, but he was speaking under the privilege of Congressional immunity, one of the body's most cherished privileges. If you're found guilty you can be fined heavily, even imprisoned. What defense do you propose?"

"I have not yet fully considered it."

The President thought a moment. "Who will conduct your case?"

"I suppose I'll have to conduct it myself."

"You should have an attorney, if only to give the matter an air of importance. I suggest that you retain Francis Scott Key. He's a friend of ours, and he has a certain prestige because of that song he wrote, 'The Star-Spangled Banner.' "

"Houston can't pay him."

"His fee will be taken care of." Jackson considered his friend for a moment, taking in the beaded buckskin coat and blanket with disfavor.

"Haven't you any other clothes?" he asked.

"No, sir. These are all Houston has."

The President drew open a drawer of his desk and took out a black silk purse which clinked as he tossed it across.

"Dress like a gentleman," he said. "It will buck up your defense."

"Thank you sir," said Houston as he picked up the purse. This kind of solicitude went deep to his heart.

After a few more words he left the White House.

But though he was fitted by a tailor with a suit of excellent material and sober hue, with a white satin waistcoat to set it off, and had his hair shorn to a civilized length by a barber, his case did not prosper before Congress.

Day after day it continued. Francis Scott Key, the attorney, a small man with an anxious look on his face, seemed unable to present his client's case in a forceful manner; and it was not long before Houston practically conducted his defense for himself.

From the first, public interest was intense, and each day that the trial continued the galleries of the House chamber were crowded with spectators. Newspapers devoted their most important columns to the proceedings, tinging their accounts with their sentiments, whether for or against Jackson and the Administration. Throughout those proceedings Jimmie Polk, getting his orders daily from the White House, sought to marshal his friends and those of the President in behalf of the accused.

Stanbery, who had spent some days in bed, one morning took the stand for the prosecution, gave his account of the encounter, and displayed his bruises, upon which he still wore bandages.

"Mr. Stanbery, weren't you armed at the time of this episode?" asked Houston on cross-examination.

"Well—yes."

"With what?"

"A pistol."

"As a matter of fact did you not have on your person two pistols?" After some hesitation, Stanbery at last admitted this was true.

"And attempted to fire one of them into my body?" asked Houston.

"Sir, I was acting in self-defense!"

"In self-defense, Mr. Stanbery? Now tell us what lethal weapon I was carrying."

"A club. You bludgeoned me with a club."

"A club?" Houston paused and took from the desk before him a light walking stick. "This is the so-called club, gentlemen," he said to Congress. "It is simply a hickory shoot I cut myself. Can it be called a club or bludgeon? You can judge for yourselves how light it is and that it was never intended for a weapon, for I shall pass it about, and the members may examine it, feel it, and heft it."

The stick was handed down the line of desks, and Houston returned to the cross-examination.

"Now, Mr. Stanbery," he said, "in your accusation, you stated that I waylaid you. Is it not true, on the contrary, that our meeting was entirely accidental?"

Stanbery was forced to admit that it was.

"One more thing, Mr. Stanbery," said Houston. "You made an accusation of fraud against me here in Congress. Had you then, or have you now, any evidence of the correctness of such an imputation?"

"Objection!" cried several of the members. And one of them, a leader of the anti-Jackson faction, said, "Mr. Stanbery need not answer that question. It is a matter of privilege."

But James K. Polk was on his feet. "Mr. Speaker," he said, "I demand that the gentleman be required to give an answer."

The Speaker of the House ruled that the matter should go to a vote. In the roll call Polk's motion was carried by a vote of one hundred and one to eighty-two.

Reluctantly, Stanbery answered. "It was no part of my intention," he said slowly, "to impute fraud to General Houston."

"Thank you. I have no further questions," said Houston.

Stanbery, who had appeared to far from good advantage under Houston's relentless cross-examination, left the stand with visible relief.

The trial dragged on. Senator Buckner, who saw the encounter, was called as a witness for the prosecution. He gave a straightforward account, but sent a titter through the chamber when he said, "Houston then stood up, landed a few more licks with his cane, and as a finishing touch, lifted the congressman's feet in the air and *struck him elsewhere*."

The Speaker rapped for order, and Stanbery created a momentary sensation by rising in his seat and exclaiming, "That is destitute of truth, and infamous!"

Later, however, he withdrew the statement and apologized to Senator Buckner.

It was April 26 before Mr. Key made the opening plea for the defense. He seemed unsure of himself, and spoke in a monotonous manner as if his heart was hardly in his cause. The defendant, he said, did not strike Stanbery for words he spoke in Congress, but for words attributed to him that were printed in a newspaper.

Even Houston's friends considered this argument very thin, inasmuch as the words printed in the *United States Telegraph* were verbatim from the stenographic report of the speech which was published in the *Congressional Record*.

"If that's the best they can do, Houston's finished," remarked Jimmie Polk after that day's adjournment.

Delays, other witnesses, copies of the *United States Telegraph* and the *Congressional Record* put in evidence to show that Stanbery's remarks in session were quoted exactly. On the afternoon of May 6 Houston went to his hotel room with a notification that he must conclude his defense on the following day.

4

Before noon next day, the chamber of the House of Representatives was filled to its utmost capacity. Every seat in the gallery was taken, and chairs were placed in the aisle and at the rear to accommodate the overflow. Cabinet members, senators, high officers of the army and navy, members of the diplomatic corps, justices of the Supreme Court, and others of eminence were in the crowd to see the climax of a trial that had caught the nation's attention.

At noon Speaker Stevenson called the House to order. As quiet fell, the tall figure of the man who was the center of all interest appeared, strode down the center aisle, and bowed before the draped dais.

Then Houston began to speak, and his rich voice was heard without effort in the farthest corners of the great vaulted chamber, catching his auditors in the spell of one trained in the school of native oratory at the red man's council fires.

"Mr. Speaker," he began, "arraigned for the first time of my life on a charge of violating the laws of my country, I feel all the embarrassment which my peculiar situation is calculated to inspire."

A graceful opening, the voice attuned to courteous introduction. But the next statement was made with passionate earnestness.

"I disclaim, utterly, every motive unworthy of an honorable man. If, when deeply wronged, I have on impulse violated one of the laws of my country or trespassed the prerogatives of the House, I am willing to be held to my responsibility. All I demand is that my actions may be pursued to the motives that gave them birth."

His voice lowered to a note of genuine pathos.

"I stand before this House, branded as a man of broken fortune and blasted reputation. Never can I forget that reputation, however limited, is the high boon of heaven. Though the plowshare of ruin has been driven over me and laid waste my brightest hopes, I have only to say, with the poet Byron:

"*I seek no sympathies, nor need;*
The thorns which I have reaped are of the tree
I planted; they have torn me and I bleed."

A departure, this, from his old favorite, Alexander Pope, but the quotation served him well. Everyone in the hall understood that he asked not mercy, but justice.

Applause broke from the galleries. Houston was forced to pause for a moment, before he could resume.

As he did so, a bouquet of roses fell from the gallery at his feet, and above the hum of voices a woman was heard exclaiming, "I had rather be Sam Houston in a dungeon than Stanbery on a throne!"

Perfectly well he knew how to use this to his advantage. He stooped, picked up the flowers, and bowed over them; but he did not raise his eyes, as if he felt that his position was such that he should not accept the tribute other than humbly.

For a few sentences he spoke of his devotion to his country, his desire to serve it, his record as a soldier and public servant, the misfortune— delicately alluded to—which destroyed him at the high tide of his success, "through no one's fault but through the extreme of misfortune."

Then, as a perfect stillness fell, his voice rose again in its wonderful musical virility:

> *"There is a proud undying thought in man*
> *That bids his soul still upward look*
> *To fame's proud cliff! And longing*
> *Look in hope to grace his name*
> *For after ages to admire, and wonder*
> *How he reached that dizzy, dangerous*
> *Height, or where he stood, or how;*
> *Or if admiring his proud station fell*
> *And left a name alone!"*

It was beautifully done. Those who heard him were struck by the immense poetic earnestness with which he spoke the lines; and that those lines expressed the inward soul of the man himself, no one doubted. But none knew that the lines were his own, composed three years before, during his exile and at the depth of his despair; and therefore poignant to him in a way to which his voice and look gave witness. He had them with him now as he resumed his plea, dwelling on the perils of legislative tyranny, mentioning the despots of history.

"Had I been guilty, as accused, of lying in wait to attack Mr. Stanbery," he continued, "I would have been armed with something more dangerous than a light cane. But that meeting, as shown by Stanbery's own testimony, was entirely accidental; and it was he, not I, who was armed with deadly weapons."

He went on to insist passionately that he had committed no offense for which he should be punished by Congress.

"If I have violated any privilege, that privilege must somewhere be declared," he said. "If it exists at all, it lies as a little spark, deeply covered; not even the smoke of it has appeared."

There spoke the Indian orator, with forest imagery. And suddenly he turned to the attack:

"When a member of this House, entrenched in his privilege, brands a private citizen, in the face of the whole nation, as fraudulent," he trumpeted, "he forgets the dignity of his station, and renders himself answerable to the party aggrieved! If gentlemen disregard the ordinary rules of decorum, and use in their place language injurious to individuals, can they expect to be protected by privileges they have forfeited?"

His voice lowered to a tone of solemn warning:

"Men can never be conquered so long as the spirit of liberty breathes in their bosoms; but let their legislatures once become corrupt and servile, then the freedom of the people becomes an easy prey."

He paused a masterly moment, in a silence that was breathless, while his audience leaned forward to catch his next words. They saw him lift his eyes to the flag draped behind the Speaker's dais, and then:

"So long as that proud emblem shall wave in the Hall of American Legislators, so long shall it cast its sacred protection over the personal rights of every American citizen! Sir, when you shall have destroyed the pride of American character, you will have destroyed the brightest jewel that heaven ever made!"

Another pause, and then, in a voice which shook with the depths of his emotion:

"But, Sir, so long as that flag shall bear aloft its glittering stars, so long, I trust, shall the rights of American citizens be preserved safe and unimpaired—till discord shall wreck the spheres—the grand march of time shall cease—and not one fragment of all creation be left to chafe the bosom of eternity's waves!"

So he finished, superbly. And with his bow to the Chair, the chamber rocked with the vast sound of cheers and applause. Despite the beating of the Speaker's gavel, Houston's friends gathered about him to shower their congratulations on him. And Junius Brutus Booth, that king among Shakespearian tragedians, came plowing through the crowd, embraced him, and cried:

"Houston, take my laurels!"

5

So dramatic was the speech, and so moving, that many of the very foes who had clamored for Houston's punishment now no longer desired it. Yet the resolution had to be voted, of course, in spite of Jimmie Polk's fight against it, because the privilege of the Congress must be upheld.

But the sentence? That Houston should be "reprimanded by the Speaker."

Once more Houston advanced down the aisle and stood before the dais. Andrew Stevenson, the Speaker, grave, dignified, and just, addressed not only him, but the assemblage present:

"I have a duty to perform, but I cannot do so without alluding to the character and intelligence of the accused, who has himself been honored by a seat in this House. We all know, every one of us, of the high achievements of General Houston, and his great contributions to this nation. As a soldier, he served with intrepid heroism in battle against the enemies of his country, and received wounds and poured forth his blood like water for his nation and its flag. As a citizen he has held numerous high offices of trust, including those of representative in Congress and governor of his state; and never has he betrayed that trust, or performed his duties without distinction and great honor."

Having in a few words taken every bit of the sting out of what necessarily must follow, the Speaker gazed upon the accused.

"I forbear to say more, General Houston," he resumed, "than to pronounce the judgment of this House, which is that you be reprimanded by the Speaker—and I do reprimand you accordingly."

That, and nothing more. A tap on the wrist, rather than a bludgeoning of justice. Actually, even better: rather than a tap on the wrist it was more like an accolade on the shoulder, delivered for all the world to hear.

Prodigal use did the newspapers make of that point in their accounts of the dramatic conclusion of the historic trial. Overnight Sam Houston was returned to full stature as a national figure. And when, a little later, a Congressional investigation asked by him found that both Sam Houston and John H. Eaton were acquitted from any imputation of fraud in the Indian-rations affair, the triumph was complete.

6

Most delighted of all was the old General in the White House.

Houston happily accepted an invitation to a private dinner with the President. There, in the old intimacy, they talked of many things, and Andrew Jackson said it added ten years to his life to see matters thus happily resolved.

When coffee and wine were brought after dinner, the talk became even more confidential.

"Some time ago," said the President, "I learned that a certain personage—well known to us both—had communicated with certain other persons with regard to the organization of an expedition against the Mexican province of Texas, for the conquest and possession of that province."

Houston turned a slow, foxy smile on his chief, like a child caught in mischief.

"Yes, sir. I agree that we both do know the personage of whom you speak."

"Such an enterprise was illegal, sir."

"You forbade it."

"I did."

"When you did so, the whole thing ended, as I wrote you. Houston was an outcast, disowned by his own state, and he believed also by his friends. A naturally reckless mood, sir. Perhaps, also, he sought the bottle too frequently as a staff for his limping spirits. Overtures were made to him . . . a man might be excused under such circumstances, I hope you will agree, sir."

"Yes, I understand your depression," said Jackson.

"But you disapproved—and I, with a saner viewpoint, agreed with you—the whole thing became chimerical. Houston is finished with it."

"You have lost all interest in Texas?"

"At your command, yes, sir," said Houston.

"But I have not!"

Houston stared at the thin, sword-blade of a face. The enigmatical old man seemed in one breath to make an assertion, in the next to contradict it.

"On the contrary," said the President, "I am deeply interested in Texas. Do you remember a conversation you and I had years ago—a *confidential* conversation, concerning the critical situation confronting this nation with regard to the lands lying west of our borders?"

"I do, sir."

"There have been times—in view of certain reports I received—when I wondered if you had forgotten its confidential nature."

Houston leaned forward, color coming into his face. "Never, sir, on my honor," he said earnestly. "In connection with this, your name has never passed my lips, nor has the government ever been connected with it by me in the slightest degree. Texas—you did powerfully emblazon it on my mind—so powerfully, sir, that perhaps in my delusions and despair my imagination did turn at times in that direction for want of some more fruitful field of thought. I will confess to you that a certain gentleman communicated with me, offering considerable finances to forward a project of conquest. They thought that with Houston's influence among the Indians a sufficient body of armed warriors might make a quick invasion. But even I could see how fatal that might be, since it would fall on the very American settlers who are esteemed as the best of the population of Texas. They are, incidentally, the hardest fighters, too."

"Hum. Your influence with the Indians. We'll return to that. But now let's go into my smoking room."

Jackson rose and led the way. When they were seated in the smaller chamber, pipes alight, the President once more took up the line of conversation.

"Texas," he said, "is a problem—and a challenge."

"Yes, sir." Houston devoted himself to listening.

"By rights, I have always contended, it should belong to the United States, since the original boundaries of the Louisiana Purchase can be shown, by the records of the French themselves, to have extended at that time to the Rio Grande River."

Houston merely nodded.

"When I invaded Florida—very necessarily and properly, to chastise the Seminole Indians—Monroe weakly disavowed our right to Texas, to soothe the feelings of Spain. That right nevertheless continues to exist, and the more so since Mexico has thrown off the Spanish yoke, so that Spanish claims, weak and flimsy as they are, become even less valid."

Houston again nodded.

"Even John Quincy Adams recognized these facts," Jackson went on. "He made an attempt to purchase the province. Failure. Since I assumed this office I've made the attempt twice, offering as high as five millions. Failure each time—due not so much to the fact that the people of Mexico desire this far province which they cannot even defend, but to the shifty and venal character of their series of dictators, who desire bribes. With corruption I'll have no dealings."

Puffs of smoke like jets of steam went up from the President's pipe.

"The Texas situation, since that day you and I discussed it at the Hermitage, has become explosive," he said. "Americans—and there are twenty thousand of them, so I understand—are restive over being bullied and mistreated. There have already been incidents. There's no telling —no way of telling, Sam—what might be the outgrowth of some future incident that could be magnified into a revolt. An appeal for recognition and intervention? Should Britain, for example, choose to intervene, perhaps furnish arms, money, or even a naval demonstration, she'd have her foot in the door toward which she's looked longingly for two centuries."

"What about the United States?"

Jackson snorted. "With our political situation as it is—North, South, East, West—Nullifiers and Unionists—pro-Bank and anti-Bank—Slave and Abolitionist—Democrats, Federalists, Whigs, Locofocos, Radicals? It would take something drastic to make our politicians forget their feuds and envies to work together for once as a single and united nation. And yet—and yet——"

He paused again, puffing at his pipe more slowly, his eyes distant as if seeing some far vision.

"And yet," he continued after a moment, "if the cards fell just right —*Texas might trigger these United States into an explosion across this continent!*"

Houston was caught by the words, tremendously impressed and excited, almost seeing Andrew Jackson's vision himself.

"Let me help, General—" he said.

The old President returned to his former manner, dry, matter-of-fact, the white fire that had revealed itself for a moment now concealed.

"I'll say this to you, Sam," he said. "I'd be most heartily glad for true information from Texas, from someone in whom I have perfect trust——"

"I would give my life to preserve your faith in me, sir."

"Of course," said Jackson, "I could never acknowledge that such a person represented me or my views. Information would have to be couched in such terms that the President of the United States could, and would, disclaim it if it happened to go astray."

"That is understood."

"There is a Biblical injunction: *Let not thy right hand know what thy left hand doeth.*"

"The left hand would keep in mind that injunction."

The President knocked the ashes from his pipe.

"Sam," he said, as if completely changing the subject, "there are certain tribes of Indians on our western borders—Comanches, Lipans, Kiowas, and others—who've caused trouble repeatedly. When they decide to go after scalps, which is often, there's hell to pay. You have a gift with Indians. How would you like to undertake to act as a sort of envoy and peacemaker among them?"

Houston looked him directly in the eyes, and for a moment their glances locked and held in complete understanding.

"General, I'll undertake your commission," he said.

The next day he was gone and not for years did Washington see him again.

Chapter Thirty

If we're going down, let's take an eye or an ear of the enemy with us, so he'll not soon forget us!

ANDREW JACKSON

1

The President's health was the severest handicap to him. It was at times so bad, including his periodic cough and swellings of his feet and ankles, that he moved about with difficulty.

Yet his outlook was more cheerful, now that his household was happy again; and there was a regular hour each evening when he went to the nursery and laughed as he watched the Donelson children romp and play. There were two of them, Andrew Jackson, a lusty small boy, and Mary Rachel, the toddling baby girl. The little people knew their privileged position, and imposed continuously on the General, which delighted him.

When measles came that winter, he was more concerned even than their mother; and the sight of the old man in his nightgown and robe, with carpet slippers on his feet, limping down the dimly lit White House hall toward the nursery at night when he thought he heard a cry or a new sniffle or sneeze, became familiar to the household.

Measles passed, the children were again in good health, and young people came to visit the Donelsons—and more formally the General—and enliven the house with their laughter and sometimes their flirtations. In those days Andrew Jackson was happier than he had been at any time since Rachel's death.

With warmer weather his health improved so much that he was able to ride again, his favorite exercise. Above most things he loved fine horses; and he knew as much about conformation and bloodlines and training methods as any man. He had a few animals—a saddle horse or two and some racing stock—shipped to Washington from his Hermitage stable for his relaxation.

Unlike Jackson, Martin Van Buren did not like riding. His legs were short, his body stout, and he was conscious that he did not cut a good figure in the saddle; whereas the General always was impressive. Nevertheless, knowing that the President liked a canter when he could spare the time, Van Buren bought himself a gelding of sober age and habits, and offered himself as a companion.

Jackson was glad to have his company. Van Buren had resigned as Secretary of State to ease the Cabinet tension, and Jackson named him Ambassador to England. But with almost his last act before resigning as Vice-President, John C. Calhoun blocked his confirmation: a shabby performance which Jackson hotly resented.

"It will kill him, sir, kill him dead," Calhoun had exulted to Thomas Hart Benton, speaking of Van Buren.

But the Missouri senator retorted, "You've broken a Minister, but elected a Vice-President—and perhaps a future President of the United States."

It was now clear even to the dullest-minded that Jackson was building up Van Buren to succeed him when he left the White House. Calhoun knew it, and kept an icy silence. No silence, however, did his acid enemy, John Randolph of Roanoke, keep.

"Calhoun must be in hell," said he. "He is self-mutilated like the Fanatic who emasculated himself."

Jackson said nothing, but enjoyed his rides with Van Buren.

On a certain morning the two of them, accompanied by Jack Donelson and Congressman Balie Peyton of Tennessee, rode out to the National Jockey Club to look at a pair of promising fillies the President was training there for a coming race meeting.

At the track they found a number of persons already gathered and showing excitement.

"What's going on?" asked Jackson.

"A horse is acting up, sir," someone said.

From the barn came the enraged squeals and snorts of a furious stallion.

"Which horse?" asked the General.

"Busirus, sir. They're trying to get him out into the paddock."

"Ha! Busirus! Irvine's horse. A bad actor, but a splendid animal. I'd like to have him in my own stables."

At the moment a plunging stallion, massively muscled, eyes glaring red with rage, wicked ears laid back, broke from around the corner of the stable, with two grooms frantically hanging to his bridle bits. The animal was saddled for a trial run, but it was difficult to see how his little Negro jockey could mount him.

"Why don't you break him of those tricks?" Jackson shouted. "I could do it in an hour!"

He rode over to the rearing brute, his eyes blazing.

"Here, sir! Down! Damn it all, *down!*" he cried in his shrill voice.

Amazingly, Busirus quieted at the commands of the thin-faced man with the fiery eyes, and the jockey took advantage of the opportunity to climb into the saddle.

Almost at once the stallion began to rear and snort wildly again. Van Buren had ridden up to watch, and the General turned impatiently.

"Get behind me, Mr. Van Buren! He'll run over you, sir!" he ordered. "Take your position by the judge's stand, Mr. Peyton! You ought to know where the timer should stand!"

Both men hurriedly obeyed his commands.

"Now, get him out on the track!" Jackson directed the jockey and grooms.

As they tried to bring the furious beast to the starting line on the oval, Jackson's two fillies were brought out, their jockeys already up. Now the great stallion seemed aroused to even greater excitement.

"Hold him!" shouted Jackson to the jockey. "Don't let him break down that fence! Now bring 'em all three up and give 'em a fair start!"

Almost nobody else could have brought order out of that mad confusion. But in a few moments the three horses were away. Busirus, acting badly again, was at first left behind. But as the two fillies swept around the turn he set out furiously to overtake them. He actually did succeed in making up a considerable part of the distance, but his early disadvantage was too great. Bolivia, one of the Jackson fillies, flashed past the finish post first.

The race had taken the edge off Busirus and he was quite tractable as the horses were returned to the stables. Peyton, who held the watch, announced the times. It had been a most satisfying trial, and after the excitement he had participated in the old General was in unusually high spirits as he rode back to the White House.

"I admire your command over horses, sir," said Peyton, a fine horseman himself.

Jackson laughed. "Maybe, as one of my Negroes once said, it's only a matter of being able to *think* like a horse. You know, some of my enemies accuse me of doing that all the time."

In the exhilaration of the open air, the action, the atmosphere of the paddock, which he loved, he seemed for the moment to have forgotten his heavy tasks and concerns.

"I remember a night when a friend of mine, Patton Anderson, got into a little argument with a crowd of men at Clover Bottom, the Nashville course," he said, his eye lighting with recollection. "It was after dark, and they meant to handle him roughly. He came toward my fence and they followed. I met them at the stile. As soon as he was over I tried to argue with them that they weren't acting the part of gentlemen in mobbing a man like that. But they were furious and said they were going to get him. I saw the only chance was to bluff them off. So I put my hand in my coat pocket. There was a tin tobacco box there—the nearest thing to a weapon I had—although for some reason everyone in those days seemed to think I always went around with a pistol."

He paused to grin at his listeners.

"I opened the lid of the tobacco box, and said, 'I'll shoot dead the first man who tries to cross that fence!' Their leader put his foot on the first step of the stile. I brought out the tobacco box—it was too dark for them to see what I had—and held it out toward them. Then I gave the lid a click. Upon my soul, gentlemen, it sounded just like the cocking of a pistol. And do you know, they scampered like a flock of rabbits!"

His laugh rang out quite merrily, and his companions joined him.

It had been a good morning, a refreshing morning. He looked forward to noonday dinner. The White House was filled with young people and a pleasant array would sit down. Emily Donelson—sweet Emily—would be there; and Mary Eastin, a niece of Rachel's; and Mary Ann Lewis, daughter of Major Lewis; and Cora Livingston, daughter of the Secretary of State; and Mary McLemore, another Tennessee cousin. All of these were pretty, lively, charming girls.

As for young men, there would be Jack Donelson; Andrew Jackson, Junior, and his crony Andrew Jackson Hutchings, these two on vacation from college; and for older men Martin Van Buren, Major Lewis, and the General himself. It could not help being a gay occasion, and he felt that after it he could go to his desk fit and ready for anything that might confront him. He hardly dreamed that what confronted him might be the hardest fight of his political life.

2

On the very day, almost at the same hour, that Jackson was allowing himself the bit of high-spirited action at the National Jockey Club, a gentleman whom he knew slightly from a single personal meeting, but very much better through reputation, was considering him and his policies in a mood far from pleasant.

The gentleman sat in a high-ceilinged, richly paneled office, in a solid building with Grecian columns on its front, at one of the principal street intersections of Philadelphia. That building was the central edifice of the Bank of the United States, from which a continuous stream of orders, written instruments, checks, accounts, credit ratings, and other financial exchange went to its various branches over the country, and hence to the people of the United States. The man who sat in his magnificent office in that building was Nicholas Biddle, president of the Bank of the United States.

An extraordinary personage was Nicholas Biddle. He was handsome, suave, always fashionably attired, with soft hands and irreproachable manners. He was also talented, for he had made a literary mark as a poet and historian, spoke and wrote several languages, was a connoisseur in art and wines, and collected fine books. Furthermore, he had created of his Bank an institution so powerful that now, in his middle forties, many men considered him the most important figure in America, perhaps greater than the President of the United States himself.

In short, Mr. Biddle had the tastes of an aesthete. But he also had the reckless daring—and some said the lack of scruples—of one of Henry Morgan's old marauding buccaneers.

Of late he had become perhaps somewhat swelled with his own importance, regarding his Bank and its field—which was the nation—as a personal empire. In his view the Bank was on a level with the state, and not responsible to it except under the narrowest interpretations of its charter. He actually had written to Thomas Swann, president of the Washington branch of the Bank, this bold declaration of his stand:

No officer of the Government, from the President downwards, has the least right, the least authority, the least pretence, for interference in the concerns of the Bank. The officers of the Bank should regard only the rights of the Bank and the instructions of those who govern it, and should be at all times prepared to execute the orders of the board, in direct opposition, if need be, to the personal interests and wishes of the President and every officer of the Government.

But on this day the author of that pronouncement, sitting in his office with its paintings by Gainsborough, West, and Stuart, was doing some deep and not altogether pleasant pondering.

The subject of his concern was the charter of the Bank, which must be renewed in 1836. That was, to be sure, four years away. But if Andrew Jackson was still in the White House then, Biddle foresaw danger to his institution.

He had, some time previously, made a point of visiting Washington, and calling at the White House for the specific purpose of meeting and estimating the character and abilities of the President. Having been led to believe he would encounter a "wild frontiersman," he was on that occasion not a little surprised to discover in Andrew Jackson a man as cordial and polite as himself—and as inflexible. Their talk was inconclusive, but Biddle returned to his office in Philadelphia quite sobered.

The banker had full confidence in his own extraordinary capabilities, but he also was an exceptionally shrewd judge of human character. In the white-haired President he had encountered something almost unprecedented in his life's experience—an inward steel, a clear vision which saw through every artifice no matter how skillfully presented, a complete incorruptibility. Nicholas Biddle knew he had been in the presence of a truly *great* man.

But, great or no, Jackson was only a man; and the Bank, to Biddle, transcended any individual. He had heard a report that because of ill health the President might not seek a second term. If not, the charter would be renewed in 1836 without much question.

But what, he asked himself, if Jackson *did* run for a second term? He must be defeated!

The banker habitually made his larger plans in terms of years. And finance—in which he was expert—was by no means the only field of endeavor by which he had reached and maintained his present preeminent position. Biddle was also a deep student and practitioner of political manipulations.

He now considered possible strategies. If Jackson should run again, the first and great necessity was to find a candidate to oppose him, one who might beat him—and who was not deaf to the wishes of the Bank. He began appraising potential figures.

John Quincy Adams, the former President, of course. But no, Adams had not even been able to be re-elected. His personality was wrong. Biddle considered him through, finished as White House material.

There was Daniel Webster, the nation's foremost orator. Webster was at that very time an attorney for the Bank, receiving a handsome retainer merely to exercise his great speaking talents now and then in the Bank's behalf. But Webster was indolent, liked his brandy too well, and was greedy for money. He could sway audiences for a cause with his elo-

Magnificent Destiny

quence. But could he arouse affection and loyalty for himself? Biddle decided not.

Now, Henry Clay—*there* was a better prospect. Biddle was well acquainted with Clay. He was charming, witty, a sparkling conversationalist. And he was an orator who stood second only to Webster himself.

But Clay was reckless and sometimes careless; a man of broad visions but few settled principles. John Quincy Adams had once ticked him off: "His school has been the world, and in that he is proficient. His morals, public and private, are loose, but he has all the virtues indispensable to a popular man."

With his weaknesses and strengths this was a man who, unlike Webster, might win the love of the people. Those same weaknesses and strengths might also, Biddle considered, make him most valuable to the Bank of the United States.

A few days later Henry Clay received an invitation to visit Biddle's Philadelphia home. He was prompt to accept. There was a superb dinner —a private affair—and he was shrewd enough to guess what was in the air. He did not mention politics during the dinner; but when Mrs. Clay and Mrs. Biddle excused themselves, and the senator and the banker sat to wine and cigars, the subject arose inevitably.

"Let us speak frankly," said Biddle. "I understand you'll be a candidate for the Whig nomination for President in the coming election."

"I will be," said Clay. "And within the walls of this room, I'm certain that I can win the nomination. Enough delegates in fact are already unofficially pledged to carry the convention."

"Aha! And may I ask, Senator, what you think of the chances of the Whigs—and yourself?"

"Sir, I would not go into this thing if I did not think I would win. Andrew Jackson has alienated the South by his stand against States' Rights; the North by his opposition to the tariff; the West by his refusal to support public works—it's his dream, you know, to pay off the public debt and he hoards every penny to that end. He's alienated thousands all over the country by his arbitrary, tough, drill-sergeant ways toward all who oppose him. And last, but not least"—Clay glanced keenly at the man across the table—"he has alienated the entire business community of the nation by his attacks on the Bank of the United States, which is, in my humble opinion, the foundation of our financial stability."

Through the cigar smoke, Biddle nodded. "An excellent summation, Senator. But though you make it sound as if a yellow dog could be elected against Jackson, he'll be harder to beat than you think. He has the knack of appealing to popular prejudices. His war record impresses the unthinking 'patriots.' And I fear he's made many fanatical friends, as well as hot enemies, by what you call his 'drill-sergeant' manner of dealing with men and affairs."

He paused to sip from his wine glass.

"Nevertheless," he continued, "Jackson must be defeated. As you've remarked, the business community is concerned over his radical position toward the Bank, which has maintained and increased the growth and prosperity of the nation through sound fiscal policies."

Clay nodded, waiting.

"You know as well as I, Senator," went on Biddle, "that any open avowal of support for a candidate by my institution might work adversely for him. But if the institution were made an issue—let us say as an innocent victim of malice—or stubborn short-sightedness——"

"I have it!" exclaimed Clay, bringing his fist down on the table. "Make it an issue—by proposing that the charter be granted *now!* Excellent arguments could be adduced for such action—the faithful and wise stewardship of the Bank ought to be rewarded—it's time to extend the charter to permit making of long-distance fiscal plans—manufacturers and merchants want to know how they stand—any number of cogent reasons." He gave a half-humorous gleam. "And not least important is the fact that in *this session*—we have the votes to do it!"

Biddle smiled in his peculiarly charming but recessive way. "I believe, Senator, that we're on an excellent understanding." He raised his glass. "To your complete success, sir, in your plans for the coming election; and also to the American people, who will, I am persuaded, be the greatest beneficiaries of your happy attainment of the Chief Magistracy of the nation."

"And to you, sir, and the Bank of the United States," Clay responded. "May you both continue long to render the always efficient and wise service of guiding the fiscal policies of this nation."

3

"Fight it!" said Andrew Jackson.

He had called a meeting in his office at the White House of his closest advisers, to consider the resolutions just introduced, suddenly, in both houses of Congress, to extend the charter of the Bank of the United States another twenty years—a full four years ahead of the expiration of the present charter.

Seated about him were Thomas Hart Benton and James Knox Polk, leaders of the Administration forces in the Senate and House respectively; Van Buren and Donelson; and two men of odd appearance but unusual talents, Amos Kendall and Francis Preston Blair. Kendall, sly and silent, was the White House correspondent for many journals throughout the country. Blair edited the Washington *Post*, the chief Administration newspaper. Both men wielded pens that were at times vitriolic, at times brilliant, at times soberly and solidly persuasive.

"Mr. President," said Polk in his calm, even voice, "are you sure that you want to risk everything—your whole edifice of plans, your Administration's prestige, your own place in history—on this fight? I have to tell you that an unofficial counting of noses in the House indicates that we'll lose if we oppose the resolution."

"What do you say, Tom?" asked the President.

Benton nodded gloomily. "The proponents of the Bank have cunningly chosen their own ground and their own moment for the battle. Their supporters are in the majority. I do not think it is possible to defeat them."

Jackson seemed to consider. "I didn't think Henry Clay would dare try this on me," he said at length.

He was fully aware that his back was to the wall in a suddenly precipitated death fight not only for his own future, but for his superb vision for America. But his eyes gleamed with a fighting light.

"You little know me, gentlemen, if you think considerations of my personal interests or fate would influence me against fighting with everything at my command what I think is an evil for our country."

He paused, gazing at them, one by one.

"We're dealing," he went on, "with power based on money, and therefore without conscience—an infamous alliance between Clay, the Whigs, and the Bank. The very fact that the Bank permits itself to be made an issue, thus putting forth its power which usually is exercised secretly though continuously felt, is a signal of danger so serious to the nation that we must be willing to make any sacrifice to avert it."

Tom Benton sat back like a stern Roman centurion. "You, sir, are the commander," he said. "I for one will follow orders to the limit of my ability."

"I, too," said Polk, with simple sincerity.

"Thank you, gentlemen." He held them all with his keen glance. "Now, you agree that we'll be defeated in Congress. I want you to make that battle as long-drawn-out as possible. Permit no quick vote. See that every defect in the Bank and its system is aired. Let the people have a look at the institution itself—and at the men who are intent on saddling it on the nation for another score of years. A quick decision would be complete victory for Biddle, Clay and company. But a long-contested battle, even if it consists of a series of stubborn rear-guard actions, may have results those high moguls don't anticipate. Whatever the cost, fight it! With everything in you, *fight it!*"

He paused. Then he rose and bade them good night. But as they departed he gave them a hard-lipped smile and a final word.

"They have us on the hip at present, gentlemen, and the first fall may be theirs. But back on the frontier of my home state of Tennessee they fight what is called rough-and-tumble. No holds barred. Kicking and gouging and biting. We can't afford polite manners here. We are for the moment outmanned, but if we're going down, let's take an eye or an ear of the enemy with us, so he'll not soon forget us!"

Chapter Thirty-One

That statement has all the fury of a chained panther, biting at the bars of his cage!

NICHOLAS BIDDLE

1

At times in his preoccupation with national events, and particularly as the debate over the Bank charter began in Congress, the old General seemed to lose all touch with his personal world. Yet the business of life went on about him.

Young women lightened the atmosphere of the White House, brought there by the congenial Donelsons. Where young women are, young men flock. The President was treated to a constant kaleidoscopic spectacle of new dresses, bright faces, and as a counter to these, youths in wasp-waisted coats, tight trousers, and cravats that seemed to choke them.

He viewed this with some astonishment, but when, one after another, Mary Eastin, a Tennessee cousin of the Donelsons, announced her engagement to young Lucius Polk, brother of the congressman; Mary Lewis, the major's daughter, was won by Alphonse Pageot of the French Legation; and Cora Livingston, daughter of the Secretary of State, pledged herself to Thomas P. Barton, a young man with a future in the diplomatic service; the old man in each case gave a dinner, drank a sparing toast, and engaged in quips with the couples involved. Wedding presents became a search for Emily Donelson, who was commissioned by Jackson for this service.

In the midst of this, something even more intensely personal brought the General out of his preoccupation. Andrew, Junior, his adopted son, had now grown to be a handsome young man with a taste for dashing clothes and a more than usual susceptibility to charming young women. His love affairs had been numerous, and rather ill-starred: not that he was unattractive, but that he was unfortunate in his choices. Once he believed himself madly in love with a little coquette, who played with him, and then quite heartlessly turned to another man who pleased her whim, leaving him with a broken heart. The heart speedily mended when he became acquainted with another young lady. This, however, was even worse. The young lady's father was a Whig, who so disliked Andrew Jackson that he ordered Andrew Jackson's son off the premises and forbade his daughter ever to see him again.

Then, surprisingly, young Andrew was married.

He brought his bride from her home in Philadelphia, where the wedding took place, and introduced her to the White House family, and especially his father. Her name had been Sarah Yorke, before she became Mrs. Jackson; she was an orphan of Quaker descent living with relatives when young Andrew found her, a small, dark, quiet girl. So obviously awed was she by the enormous dignity and prestige of the General that she crept around like a timid, retiring small mouse among the belles who were guests at the White House.

The President sensed her timidity, and sought to show her especial friendliness.

"I receive you as a daughter," he told her, "and I trust my son will make you as happy as I am certain you have made him."

The astonishing thing was that she made the General himself happy, creeping into his affections by her sincere and humble, almost childlike adoration of him. She called him "Father," which not even her husband had ever done, and warmed his heart by so doing. The index of his esteem for her was that he allowed her each evening when he went to bed, to take the sacred Bible that had been Rachel's, and read to him his nightly chapter from the Book.

She was not happy in Washington society, and one day he called her and young Andrew before him.

"I have a task for you two," he said. "I want you to go to Tennessee and take charge of the Hermitage for me. Will you?"

Young Andrew nodded, pleased; and Sarah had never looked prettier as her eyes lit up at this request which went straight to her heart.

"The Hermitage," the President went on, "has been a constant worry to me of late. It suffers from lack of personal management. I mean to throw the care of the plantation on you, my son and daughter, so that I need never more pester myself with this world's wealth. My only ambition is to go to the Hermitage so soon as the interests of my country will permit me, and there put my spiritual house in order and go to sleep alongside my dear departed wife."

The young couple departed for the West as soon as arrangements could be made, and the General honestly felt that he could devote an even fuller attention to the crisis now confronting him on the national scene.

2

In the Congress his lieutenants were fighting what he himself had described as a "rear-guard action" against the Bank, and to the President his own enforced inactivity was maddening. So passionately sure was he that it was both evil and dangerous for a private monopoly to have its grip on the monetary lifeblood of the American people, that sitting by and depending on others to carry on his battle seemed the hardest thing he had ever been called upon to do.

Particularly so was this when it developed that Nicholas Biddle had reason to congratulate himself on the team he had brought together in Congress: John Quincy Adams, out of retirement; Daniel Webster with his thunderous periods; Edward Everett, a new oratorical prodigy; Senator George McDuffie, a Calhoun disciple, carrying the South Carolinian's orders and prestige. At the head of them Henry Clay leading the fight in behalf of the Bank.

In those days even to his opponents Clay seemed to assume new stature. Never had he been so persuasive, never so winning, never so able. At times he was imperious, as when he denounced the foes of the charter resolution as "ignorant, ill-informed, or evil." At other times he was kindly, captivating, with a sunny smile and a humorous quip.

But the Jackson forces fought tirelessly also. Clay's chief opponent, Thomas Hart Benton, bellowed his denunciations in the Senate of "an unconstitutional monopoly, which defies the legislative acts of sovereign states, and uses every means that wealth, political chicanery, and legal cunning can devise to perpetuate its own existence." In the House of Representatives, Jimmie Polk was proving wonderfully adroit in using every legal expedient to drag out the proceedings—endless committee hearings, roll calls, amendments, motions to table, and debates.

Yet under Clay's whip adverse resolutions were tabled, amendments killed, the Bank forces made repeated efforts for a showdown vote, and though their opponents still managed to hold off that conclusion it became apparent that eventually the vote must come.

In the White House the strenuous old President discovered a way to use his time to advantage. Day after day he conferred in his office with two particular men: Francis Preston Blair and Amos Kendall.

A pair of more singular-appearing individuals would have been hard to discover. Blair, editor of the Washington *Globe*, was undersized and unpretentious. Always his attire looked seedy and ill-cared for, his hair disarrayed, his carriage careless. He weighed hardly more than one hundred pounds, but he had a piercing eye, and his newspaper fiercely and unhesitatingly defended every act of Andrew Jackson.

Between Kendall and the President existed a bond of which neither ever spoke—both men suffered from ill health. Kendall, his hair prematurely white, was bent half-double with torturing arthritis; and he was so nearsighted that even with his thick-lensed glasses he must bring a document close to his nose to read it. Yet he wrote with a vivid, sometimes biting style, that made his contributions acceptable to journals all over the country.

"We've got to acquaint the public with what's going on in Congress," Jackson said to these two. "The only way I know is through the newspapers, and since we can't be of much use in the parliamentary battle, let's devote ourselves to disseminating the news."

In the succeeding weeks while Blair's newspaper with each issue published the latest developments in the Bank fight, Kendall and the President often worked late in the night together, Jackson lying on a sofa; Kendall, with his bent back, crouched over sheets of paper on which he scribbled while the President suggested or discussed points with him. Between them the general public was made acquainted with instances of violations of the Bank's charter, abuses of the same, and other questionable points of the Bank's conduct, brought out in hearings in Congress, through journals which could never have obtained the information in any other way.

3

The strain told on the General. His brief period of relative good health was succeeded by illness, some of it occasioned by his extreme nervous tension.

He was no docile invalid. At times he seemed to be wrathful at his own body, because it served him so ill. He frequently rebelled against orders by the White House physician, a personable young man, Dr. Robert Paget, who would have sent him to bed.

Emily Donelson could do more with him than anyone. She was not only a clear-eyed young woman, very good to look upon, but in her quiet way a natural executive and organizer. To keep the great household of the Executive Mansion, with its corps of servants, running smoothly, provisioned, cleaned, made pleasant and cheerful always, at the same time caring for a husband and two lively children—while preparing for the arrival of a third expected in a few months—and to do all this apparently incidentally, with a hundred other activities filling her mind, required a very high level of ability.

The old General valued her and was fond of her: but she knew the surest way to reach him was through her children. Little Andrew by now was five, an eager boy already begging for his own pony. Mary Rachel, a small two-year-old sprite, knew how to tyrannize over the white-haired old soldier as no one else had ever been able to tyrannize over him.

Considering the President's condition, Emily, who worried over him, believed that he needed a change in surroundings and the tonic of fresh air. He had been for weeks confined to the rooms he chiefly occupied, his bedroom and study. Since horseback riding was out of the question for him in his ailing condition, she suggested, and sometimes induced him, to go with her and the two children on short journeys in the White House coach—sometimes to Georgetown, sometimes to the Capitol square, sometimes down to the Potomac River.

Usually on these rides he amused himself with the children, delighting in their sayings and antics. But on one day in May the old man sat with little Mary Rachel on his knee, silent and apparently distraught.

The day was beautiful with soft spring warmth, and as they took the road down toward the Potomac bridge, in some of the meadows red clover was blossoming. Cattle contentedly grazed, bobolinks sang and hovered in marshy spots, the sun reflected on the placid surface of the broad river as if from a silver shield.

"It's a glorious day," Emily finally ventured, to break in on his abstraction.

He seemed to rouse himself. "Why, yes, so it is," he said. And he gave her a fond smile. "Strange how a man can ride along, not even noticing until someone with a poet's eye for beauty exclaims 'It's glorious,' and the man suddenly looks up and sees that it is so."

She colored prettily at his compliment. "You seemed so remote, Uncle Jackson—I'm afraid you're sacrificing yourself too greatly to your duties —worrying about the Bank question, and all——"

He gazed at her directly, and for a moment his naked soul seemed to shine in his eyes.

"What do you think about a man's duty to his country, Emily?" he asked.

And as she was silent, he answered his own question. "It is so much greater than any man that sacrifice cannot even be mentioned in connection with it. I am nothing. This country is everything."

She thought at that moment that she knew him better than she had ever dreamed of knowing him before, his great and selfless heart. But he went on.

"I wasn't at the moment worrying about the Bank—or Congress. Would you like to know what I *was* thinking?"

"Why, yes—of course."

"Emily, my mind was on Sam Houston. For months I've not heard from him direct. I've learned that he spent some time in Tennessee, and a period in Natchez, and visited the Cherokee country again. The last word of him was from Fort Towson, in the Indian country, direct across the Red River from Texas. After that he seemed to disappear—at least insofar as my knowledge of him is concerned."

"You think a great deal of General Houston, don't you?"

"A strange and turbulent man, Emily—but, yes, I hold him in deep affection, for he has always shown perfect friendship for me. Sam Houston has one clear characteristic of genius—he dares, and he has supreme confidence in himself. Most men, when they spread their wings into the blue empyrean, more than half expect to fall. And if they do fall, they never rise again. But Sam Houston has fallen—once, prodigiously—yet he soars again and never casts his eyes downward nor doubts the strength of his wings."

"He will write soon, I'm sure," she said comfortingly.

He nodded, but did not reply. His mind again was on Houston. He had given him instructions . . . he hoped Houston understood what was implicit in them as well as what was directly spoken. But the Texas question was too delicate and vital to discuss.

Emily misinterpreted his silence as a sign that he was ailing again. At the White House that evening, she spoke to Dr. Paget with a troubled face.

"The President grows thinner each day," she said. "I don't see how he continues. Surely *something* can be done for him."

Dr. Paget, in his early thirties, was a keen young physician, but he felt in this matter the need for aid from a more experienced mind. That very evening he encountered a professional friend, Dr. Purvis Brown, a celebrated Philadelphia surgeon, who happened to be visiting in Washington, and solicited a consultation with him.

Dr. Brown was a large man, several years older than Dr. Paget, with a serious countenance and a carefully trimmed gray beard. He considered Dr. Paget's request, and asked:

"What do you think ails the President?"

"Frankly, he complains of so many things that one would be tempted to consider him a hypochondriac——"

"Ha!"

"Except for the fact that every one of his disabilities is a *fact.*"

"Hum. You've checked them yourself?"

"I have, sir," said Dr. Paget. "Repeatedly. The coughing, the fever, the dysentery, the pain in his arm, the swellings of his lower extremities —I've verified them, every one. On my professional reputation, they would have retired any other man but Andrew Jackson not only from public life, but perhaps to his deathbed. He has will power, sir, of which you can have no conception until you know him. It is that, and that alone, that keeps his really frail and ailing body to its tasks."

"I see," said Dr. Brown judgmatically. "An interesting and unusual combination of symptoms. I will be honored to examine the President, if he will consent."

Emily obtained the consent, and next day the two physicians called upon Jackson, finding him as usual seated at his desk, hard at work. He greeted them courteously, and answered without hesitation all of Dr. Brown's keen questions. At the end he regarded the two physicians with grim interest.

"What is your conclusion, gentlemen?" he asked.

Dr. Brown's broad countenance bore a frown of deliberation, and Dr. Paget looked anxiously at his older colleague.

"Let us begin with the cough," said Dr. Brown at length. "It is pulmonary trouble, of course. I would diagnose consumption were it not for the fact that it has afflicted you so many years. A true consumptive, Mr. President, would have been dead long before this."

Jackson nodded.

"The dysentery," continued the physician, "also appears to be of long standing. Chronic. I've seen such stubborn cases before. You may have been poisoned by drinking miasmic swamp water on some campaign. As to relief, the prescriptions Dr. Paget has given you are the best I could suggest. The swellings of your feet are perhaps due to stagnation of the circulation, caused by much sitting and little exercise. You should lie at times with your feet elevated to let the blood get back into the circulation."

The President listened with close attention.

"One thing, however," said the doctor. "That bullet in your left arm. It may be causing lead poisoning, which in turn sometimes creates symptoms such as anemia, severe colicky pains, and disturbed nutrition. I would strongly suggest that one of these days the bullet be removed."

"Well," said Jackson, "I've carried that ball for almost a score of years —since the old Benton encounter. But if you say have it out, let's have it out."

"When you feel a little better, sir, I'd like to have you in my hospital——"

"Why not now—and *here?*"

Dr. Brown stared. "You mean in this room—and with no preparation?"

"Exactly. Take it out in the old field-hospital style."

Jackson rose to his feet, removed his coat, and rolled up his shirt sleeve on the thin arm.

"I'd like to have you lie down, sir—" began Dr. Brown.

Jackson took a firm grip on his walking stick. "I'm ready now," he said.

Dr. Brown was shocked. "You don't mean you propose to undergo the operation *standing?*"

The General grinned. "I prefer it that way. Go ahead and cut."

On Dr. Brown's face was an almost helpless look. But then he shrugged as if this was beyond his power, and sent for a bowl and bandaging.

No anesthetics here. The keen scalpel in Dr. Brown's hand made its incision.

Not a wince or a sign of pain on the President's face, which Dr. Paget watched anxiously.

Another cut. The blood flowed down Jackson's arm in a stream which was caught below his finger tips by Dr. Paget's container.

"Ah—there!" exclaimed Dr. Brown. "Here's your little souvenir!" He held up the bloody lead slug.

Jackson watched his arm being bandaged and glanced at the bowl where his blood had been caught.

"At least that saves bleeding me—for the present," he said.

Later, after he left the White House with Dr. Paget, Dr. Brown said, "You spoke of his will power. The man must be made of steel!"

When the ordeal was over, Andrew Jackson declared that he felt better, and that evening ate what was for him a hearty supper.

4

The very morning following, those who came to the Senate gallery, merely to look at the famous men there, witnessed a dramatic incident which was a direct result of the "rough-and-tumble" tactics of Jackson's forces and the growing acrimony resulting.

Thomas Hart Benton, powerful in figure and voice, was thundering once more against the Bank of the United States.

"A kingly autocracy!" he declaimed. "With perilous power over the welfare of the people, and the servants of their republic! I am willing to see the charter of the Bank expire—to see the currency of the Federal government return to hard money as intended by the Constitution, rather than the rag-paper money the Bank issues and spreads abroad over the land!"

Henry Clay was on his feet. "Will the gentleman yield?"

Senatorial courtesy ordained that a speaker holding the floor should yield on request, for a brief interpolation by a colleague, and Benton bowed.

"This attack on the Bank of the United States," said Clay in bitter humor, "is ill-timed and ill-directed. I know its origin. It is the gentleman in the White House—with whom, I should like to remind this body, the senator from Missouri once had a bloody personal rencontre, and has said that should General Jackson be elected President, Congress must guard itself with pistols and dirks!"

Benton swelled with rage. "That, sir, is an atrocious calumny!"

"What?" retorted Clay. "Can you look me in the face, sir, and say that you never used that language?"

"I look," exclaimed Benton, "and I repeat that it is an atrocious calumny, and I will pin it on him who repeats it here!"

Clay flushed with anger. "Then I declare before the Senate that you said those very words!"

"False! False! False!" bellowed Benton, moving furiously toward the Kentuckian.

The Senate was in an uproar, the moment perilous, for both men were known duelists. Several members rushed to keep the angry disputants apart. Senator Tazewell, who was in the chair, hammered on his desk with his gavel and shouted for order.

Quiet presently was restored, and after Tazewell spoke somewhat severely of such conduct by the members, Senator Benton said:

"I apologize to the Senate for the manner in which I have spoken—but not to the senator from Kentucky!"

Quickly Clay responded:

"To the Senate I also offer an apology—but to the senator from Missouri, none!"

Men breathed more freely when Benton and Clay later were induced to shake hands.

That evening Francis Preston Blair gave a quite amusing account of the incident to Jackson.

"Good for Tom Benton," chuckled the President. "By the way, I have a token I'd like you to give him."

He penned a short note:

Dear Senator: I congratulate you on your able and valorous fight in the current Bank controversy. As a memento of my admiration and high regard for you—and as a relic of a time when you and I did not agree so well—I herewith return to you an article that I believe is rightfully the property of the Benton family. Assuring you of my deep friendship, and hoping soon to see your personally, I am, Yr. Obdt. Srvt., Andrew Jackson.

It was Benton's turn to chuckle when Blair next day presented the odd gift of the pistol ball with its twinkling little note.

"No," he said, "I can't accept it. Please take it back to the President and say to him for me that he has acquired clear title to it in common law by twenty years' peaceable possession."

"Only nineteen years," Blair reminded him.

Benton gave his great guffaw. "Oh, well," he said, "in consideration of the extra care he's taken of it—keeping it constantly about his person, and so on—I'll waive the odd year."

Jackson also laughed when Blair reported the conversation to him. And thereafter the friendship between Benton and himself deepened, and the breach which should never have occurred at all was completely healed at last.

5

Summer came on, hot and muggy, and Henry Clay was now the duly chosen nominee of the Whig Party, with Biddle and the Bank bolstering his forces in various smooth ways.

The eventual showdown vote in Congress could no longer be delayed in spite of the battle by Jackson's lieutenants.

The first ballot was in the Senate. It went as predicted by Tom Benton: twenty-eight votes for renewing the charter; twenty votes against it.

Three weeks later it came before the House. The result was one hundred and seven votes to recharter, only eighty-five against.

Nicholas Biddle, assured of victory, was in the House gallery to witness the roll call. Afterward he was congratulated by crowds of congressmen, and in the evening gave a reception at the Indian Queen Hotel, where the champagne flowed so freely that some of the gentlemen, late at night, had to be helped into their carriages.

Henry Clay was jubilant. "We've knocked the crown off the head of King Andrew the First!" he exulted.

"What if he vetoes the bill?" asked Biddle.

"If Jackson vetoes that bill," said Clay, "I'll veto him!"

At the White House the President for the first time found his close circle of advisers against him. Van Buren, first to call on him, found him in bed with one of his periodic ailments aggravated by overwork.

"Mr. Van Buren, I'm glad to see you," said the thin old man.

Van Buren gripped his hand. "You've heard about the charter resolution?"

"Yes . . . we lost. Both Houses have passed it."

A spell of coughing shook the gaunt figure on the bed. When it passed, he gazed at Van Buren and passed the bony fingers of his left hand through his disordered white thatch. He was worn and weak, but undaunted.

"The Bank, Mr. Van Buren," he said feebly, "is trying to kill me, but *I will kill it!*"

"You intend to veto the bill?"

"Yes, sir."

"I beg you," said Van Buren, "don't risk the danger. The matter is a *fait accompli*. It would be wiser to submit gracefully and sign the bill."

"I never back up from a fight, sir," said the sick old man.

But even Donelson, Blair, and Kendall urged that he sign the bill.

"Gentlemen," he said, "I'm going to veto that bill, and in such terms that nobody can think I will countenance its revival at a later date!"

He let that sink in and added:

"Nicholas Biddle and Henry Clay together caused me to change my plans, and I don't often change plans I've made after full deliberation. It was my intention—and I may say my strong desire—to retire after the finish of this term. Being President of the United States, gentlemen, is the hardest kind of labor, and you know I've not been well." A pause. "But the move to recharter the Bank four years ahead of time forced me to reconsider. That's why I asked that the fight be prolonged. I'm going to make the Bank the central issue in this next campaign!"

Jackson's veto message, when delivered to Congress, contained some passages that were memorable:

Distinctions in society will always exist under every just Government. Equality of talents, of education, of wealth, cannot be produced by human institutions. In the full enjoyment of the gifts of heaven and the fruits of superior industry, economy, and virtue, every man is equally entitled to protection by law. But when the laws undertake to add to those natural and just advantages, artificial distinctions, to make the rich richer and the potent more powerful, the humble members of society, the farmers, mechanics, and laborers, who have neither the time nor the means of securing like favors to themselves, have a right to complain of the injustices of their Government. Its evils exist only in its abuses. If it would confine itself to equal protection, and, as heaven does its rains, shower its favors alike on the high and the low, the rich and the poor, it would be an unqualified blessing. In the act before me, there seems to be a wide and unnecessary departure from these just principles.

It struck the Bank and the Whig faction with the force of a bolt of lightning. Henry Clay's long face lost its proud look of triumph in one of consternation.

Nicholas Biddle shouted at him, "That statement has all the fury of a chained panther, biting at the bars of his cage!"

Daniel Webster, arising in the Senate, boomed:

"The message of the President manifestly seeks to influence the poor against the rich. It wantonly attacks whole classes of people, for the purpose of turning against them the prejudices and resentments of other classes."

These men spoke with the heat of nervousness and fear. The Alexander Hamilton–John Marshall–Federalist postulate that property should control government and with it the lives and fortunes of the people, had run headlong into the new Andrew Jackson doctrine that property had no superior claim to privileges and benefits under government and law.

To Biddle this was "anarchy." To millions it was hope.

At a single stroke Andrew Jackson had answered Clay's stratagem of bringing the Bank into the political arena, voiced his own matured governmental philosophy, and drawn with drastic clarity the lines of the coming battle.

When Clay could not muster in Congress the votes to override the

President's veto, the campaign had an issue as fundamental as it was bitterly personal.

Chapter Thirty-Two

When Andrew Jackson starts talking about hanging, men start looking for ropes!

THOMAS HART BENTON

1

Jackson for President!

With Martin Van Buren as his running-mate, for Vice-President.

Henry Clay and Nicholas Biddle recognized the formidable nature of their foe, and marshaled every force to overthrow the man they stigmatized as "radical" and "dangerous." Those resources were impressive. The Bank of the United States alarmed depositors and borrowers alike with stories of financial catastrophe if Jackson was elected. Two-thirds of the nation's newspapers bitterly opposed the General, for they were beholden to the Bank also. A meat wholesaler in Cincinnati announced that prices he would pay to farmers for pork would be cut in half should Jackson be re-elected—which God forbid. One Pennsylvania industrialist dismissed all his employees, "because of unsettled conditions," with a strong implication that he would not re-employ them should the General win. Many shops and factories notified their workers to "vote their bread and butter"—in other words, cast their ballots for Clay and the Whigs—with a broad hint that disobedience in this respect was tantamount to disloyalty, which meant discharge.

In this wild national excitement Andrew Jackson, the man most discussed, remained imperturbably calm. He even smiled when Martin Van Buren, in considerable alarm, came to him one day.

"Do you realize, sir," said Van Buren, "that arrayed against us are the nation's greatest financial institution—the nation's foremost orators—the nation's Supreme Court—the nation's transportation systems—the nation's newspapers—the nation's manufacturing and mercantile companies—the nation's States' Rights advocates—the nation's Federalist doctrinaires—the nation's best-equipped and financed political party—every single major and important force and power that can be brought to bear?"

"True, Mr. Van Buren," said Jackson. "Everything seems to be against us—except one."

"What is that, sir?"

"The American people."

Better than any man of his day he knew his people.

Everywhere the hickory poles began to appear again. Spontaneously-gathered crowds listened to spontaneous speeches by plain men. Torch-light parades formed without any particular organization or direction, stirred only by the common folks' admiration for Andrew Jackson.

The President remained busy most of the fall at his desk, but Thomas Hart Benton, Martin Van Buren, Jack Donelson, General Lewis Cass, and others stumped the country for him, while Amos Kendall and Francis Preston Blair bombarded the small section of the press that was loyal to him with campaign releases.

2

On a certain day in the heat of the campaign all business at the White House was suspended. The President received no callers, but sat nervously in his study, or paced the upper hall of the mansion.

In one of the rooms of the Donelson apartment there was excitement and bustle, with Dr. Paget presiding.

Emily Donelson was having her baby.

All that day and most of the night Jackson sat in fevered suspense and fears. At times he heard faintly a woman's cries—the birth pains.

He was familiar enough with the process of bringing into the world a new life, but he wondered, as he had wondered before, at the anguish, hardship, and terror of it. It was this fact of giving birth, as much as the strangely romantic chivalry in his nature, that gave him, whenever he was in the presence of a woman, the curious sense of being with someone a little higher or better than he was, to whom he should bow, and show respect as if she were somehow other-worldly.

He loved Emily, and every distant sound of her voice pierced his heart with a sympathetic pain.

At last there was a new ado. Presently Jack Donelson, accompanied by one of the women who had been in the bedroom, came out into the hall, carrying in his arms a small bundle.

Jackson hurried toward him.

"Is it all over?" he asked anxiously.

"Yes," said Donelson. "It's a boy."

"But what about *Emily*?" The old man had never been able to make the transition from the mother to the child quickly in his concern.

"The doctor says she is fine," said Donelson. "You can go in and see her, if you like."

The General bent over the bed. Emily seemed very white and hollow-eyed, her hair in braids on the pillow.

"Emily—my dear—" he almost faltered.

She gave him a dazzling smile!

"Did you see my baby?" she said. "Isn't he wonderful?"

Once more he was amazed at the almost instant recovery, the forgetfulness already of the birth pains, in the mother's joy at the birth of a child.

He kissed her forehead, and went away, strangely awed, strangely reassured, not only concerning Emily, but concerning all mankind.

3

In November the President journeyed to Nashville to vote. Jack Donelson went with him, but Emily and the children remained in the White House.

Jackson was confident, almost gay, at the Hermitage on election day.

"It will be a walk," he told Donelson.

There was another reason for his new, almost jubilant, spirits.

He found that the affairs at the Hermitage had not progressed as well as they might, under the handling of young Andrew, who appeared to need counsel in aggressive management. But this hardly seemed important compared to another discovery.

Sarah was pregnant: Andrew Jackson was to be a grandfather!

He was all concern and delight, and assured himself that everything possible would be done for her when time for her confinement came. She seemed pleased, though she was secretly slightly amused at his making so much of what she, like all women, considered one of the natural processes of life.

He voted and it was almost perfunctory in view of his interest in Sarah and the coming event. But after all, he could not long continue to enjoy matters of such purely personal interest. He must prepare to return at once to the capital, where Congress would be meeting after the election recess.

He had predicted a "walk" in the election, but its magnitude was hardly expected, even by himself. When the ballots were counted Andrew Jackson had in the Electoral College two hundred and seventeen votes, against Henry Clay's forty-nine, and seven for William Wirt, a Baltimore lawyer who ran on a platform of opposition to the Masonic Lodge.

"A third term!" his supporters cried in the flush of the great triumph.

"No," said Jackson positively.

He wearied himself on the slow return journey with necessary appearances and receptions.

"The vote," he said to Donelson, "not only gives the Bank its answer from the people, but strengthens my hand against what I foresee as the next great problem—which will be dealing with the Nullification movement."

One night in Pittsburgh, on the way back to Washington, he coughed up a quantity of blood. Those about him were greatly alarmed.

But it had happened before—the old lung abscess—and when the hemorrhage was over the General lay back in his bed and showed them a clipping from a newspaper, which expressed the final bitterness of the men he had defeated in the election:

There is one comfort left: God has promised us that the days of the wicked shall be short; the wicked is old and feeble. It is the duty of every good Christian to pray to our Maker to have pity on us.

Jackson grinned while they read it.

"I have no intention of dying for the gratification of my enemies," he said.

Next day he was up, and shortly afterward was able to resume his journey.

But still there was no word from Sam Houston.

4

Up from South Carolina had come Jackson's old enemy John C. Calhoun, to take the seat in the Senate vacated by Robert Y. Hayne. As Congress reconvened, the President received a report on him from Donelson.

"He's a thinner and more sallow Calhoun, sir, and his hair, which you know is lank and was once coal black, is now heavily sprinkled with gray. He seems to be grimmer and more dangerous than he was before. His lips have acquired the habit of pressing thinly together, giving the appearance—with those almost luminous black eyes of his—of holding deep within him a great passion."

"I know that passion!" exclaimed the General. "Call it ambition— lawless ambition!"

"He disregards the unwritten rule of the Senate which calls for sober dress clothes," continued Donelson, "and appears instead in suits made of white cotton nankeen."

"Flaunting his arrogance as self-appointed spokesman of what he calls the 'Cotton Kingdom'—and would make it a veritable kingdom, if he could, with himself as its monarch!"

"He's extremely polite to everyone—almost overly polite. But he takes no part in the social life in which he once was so active——"

"Too preoccupied with the ambition that devours him!" But Jackson was more concerned than even Jack Donelson knew. Calhoun had an important following.

To Thomas Hart Benton, next day, the President said, "You know that John Calhoun is the head and forefront of the Nullification movement, which indeed he fathered. He's a brilliant man, and therefore dangerous. In his bitter period of exile he's devoted his destructive talents to scheming that's both bold and perilous. Mark me, Tom, if John Calhoun sees the opportunity he'll split this Union for his own selfish advantage without a qualm of conscience—and his doctrine of Nullification will be the cleaving wedge he'll use!"

Scarcely a week later the prediction was justified. South Carolina, controlled by Calhoun and Hayne forces, had adopted an Ordinance of Nullification, declaring the Federal tariff laws unconstitutional and oppressive, and not binding upon the people of the state.

The General had just finished writing a letter to his son, asking about the condition of Sarah, whose expected time for confinement was near, when the news was brought to him by Livingston, the Secretary of State.

"So it's come," said the President. "Mr. Livingston, we are here dealing with Nullification, which can only mean Secession, and that is Rebellion. If it continues it will be my bounden duty, sir, to call out the army of the United States, place myself at its head, and put down that traitorous movement—with blood if necessary, sir! *My own blood* if it is called for, to preserve this Union!"

Thereafter the swiftness of the President's actions left men almost gasping.

First he ordered a proclamation: "A solemn warning, Mr. Livingston. I was born in South Carolina, sir; she is mistaken, bemused, but not traitorous. She must be shown the perilous path on which the arch conspirators are leading her."

When reports of wild excitement came from South Carolina as a result of the proclamation stating that the Federal authority would be enforced, and fiery young men were said to be drilling as militia companies to resist "invasion," Jackson called on Congress to authorize him to employ military forces, if necessary, to collect government revenues.

"What if Congress refuses?" asked Van Buren.

"The preservation of the Union is the supreme law," said the grim old warrior. "If Congress fails to act, I will use my power as Commander-in-Chief of the armed forces. The Constitution forms a government, not a league. To say that any state may at pleasure secede from the Union is to say the United States is not a nation!"

Van Buren had timid misgivings, but Jackson had none.

Down in South Carolina, Governor Hayne, hearing of what was called the "Force Bill," also had misgivings, and temporized by suspending the Ordinance of Nullification until the outcome of the debate on the President's bill in Congress.

It was the first backward step for the Nullifiers. But in the Senate the Force Bill, also dubbed the "Bloody Bill," loosed an almost unprecedented flood of oratory.

"Charleston, the flower of the South, is a beleaguered city!" thundered Senator John Tyler of Virginia. "I can see in my mind's eye South Carolina's towns leveled, her daughters in mourning, her men driven into morasses where Marion found refuge! But I cannot see her conquered!"

Calhoun himself, gloomy, strange, and biting, climaxed the roar of opposition by declaring, "Should this Bloody Bill pass it will be resisted at every hazard—even death!"

The old man in the White House remained grimly silent.

But Thomas Hart Benton, conversing late at night with Congressman Robert P. Letcher of Kentucky, a close friend of Calhoun's, dropped a significant remark.

"I talked to the President today," he said. "He demands that the Force Bill go through *as is*, without the blunting of a single barb."

"He may find demanding—and receiving—a bit different," replied Letcher sarcastically.

"Think so?" said Benton. "Let me tell you what he said to me. He said that if he discovered the instigators of the South Carolina Nullification movement, he'd bring them before a court—prosecute them for treason—and hang them—even if they are members of Congress!"

"Oh, surely not!" cried Letcher in horror. "He wouldn't hang a member of Congress!"

"My friend," said Benton, "when Andrew Jackson starts talking about hanging, *men start looking for ropes!*"

Within the hour, though it was after midnight, Calhoun was listening to that remark from Letcher's own lips. Early the next day, at Calhoun's request, the Kentuckian called on the President.

Andrew Jackson, in his study, looked over his steel-bowed spectacles at his visitor. "What can I do for you this morning?" he asked.

"Why, sir," said Letcher, "I wish to clear up a rumor, which I do not believe for one moment, but which I thought ought to be reported to you." He repeated his conversation with Benton.

The President removed his glasses, and his blue eyes seemed to blaze.

"Mr. Letcher," he said, "Senator Benton did not misquote me. I know, sir, what's been going on. And I'm determined that the law shall be put into execution—not against the misguided fellows who are only dupes, but against John C. Calhoun, sir, the chief conspirator! And if another step is taken, sir, to defy the government, by the Eternal, I'll try John Calhoun for treason and hang him on a gallows higher than Haman!"

Nobody could ever accuse John Calhoun of cowardice. But he knew his own guilt, and he knew the inflexible determination of Andrew Jackson. When Letcher reported the President's words to him, his sallow face went deathly pale.

There were others involved, and consequences greater than himself, to the brink of which he had pushed them. It was noted that when the Force Bill came up, Calhoun did not vote against it, being conveniently absent from roll call. The bill passed and Andrew Jackson had his authority. Almost immediately word came that South Carolina had rescinded her Ordinance of Nullification.

For a time the crisis was settled, but it was a victory, as none knew better than Jackson, won at a cost: the cost of widening the breach between the North and the South. To his old friend John Coffee, he wrote in a spirit of prophetic pessimism:

The Nullifiers in the South intend to blow up a storm on the slave question. This ought to be met, for be assured these men will do any act to destroy this Union and form a Southern Confederacy bounded, north, by the Potomac River.

Far to the west, in the frontier village of New Salem, Illinois, a long-legged young man who, as his father said, "always looked as if he was hewn out with an ax," read Andrew Jackson's proclamation against Nullification and Secession, with its deep credo that the United States was not a league but a nation, and Secession was Rebellion. Abraham Lincoln would read it again before composing his inaugural address in 1861.

5

At this very time, belatedly, news of a different kind came—from the Hermitage—to the worried old President.

Sarah's child was born. Her confinement had been difficult, and she was in labor for three days, but now she was safely past her ordeal. The baby, a tiny girl, was named—and it rang all the bells in the General's heart—Rachel Jackson!

Andrew Jackson had never been more pleased; and he thought that Emily Donelson was even more excited and happy than he at the news.

Now, if he could only finish his labors, and return to his home to enjoy his family and his grandfatherhood!

He was finding the ceaseless labor and sedentary inaction harder with each month. The papers, the endless papers coming to his desk, to read, sign, reject, answer, the minutiae as well as the important details of government which only the President could take care of, oppressed him.

He felt his age, and he remembered once when Sam Houston quoted to him something which he said was from the *Iliad*, having to do, as he recalled it, with old men, sitting above a gate, talking together in thin sweet voices, like grasshoppers clustering and squeaking on a stalk of wheat in the sun on a frosty morning.

His own voice had become thinner, and he was very weary, and the four walls of his office became irksome to a man who all his life had lived strenuously. But duty was duty, and there was no rest from responsibility, and he could only think back with longing on his days of great strivings and risks and adventures.

6

The assassin's name was Richard Lawrence.

He was thirty-five, small in stature, with a strangely pale face which accentuated his black hair and almost startlingly black eyes.

For eight months he had done no work, though as a house painter many jobs were available. In those months he grew so strange and moody, even quarrelsome, that his own family hardly knew him. A curious touchiness possessed him. If anyone laughed, he flew into a rage, thinking the laughter was directed at him. Once he threatened to kill a Negro servant girl for laughter which she did not utter, and in fear she begged to be sent away.

He was unmarried, but lived with a sister and her husband, in a flat in Washington, within walking distance of the Capitol. Much of his time was spent reading, particularly newspapers, and he frequently sat in the gallery of the House or Senate listening to the sometimes intemperate debates that went on there.

The real world hardly existed for him, but he vacillated between two worlds of fantasy. One of these worlds was very satisfying to him, and in that world he pictured himself as about to step on the national stage as a hero, to receive shouts of welcome and adulation from the crowds for some deed of greatness and heroism. In the other world, to which he often relapsed, he saw himself as poor, unrecognized, socially ostracized, maliciously discriminated against.

The danger in his distempered mind was that gradually it fastened upon a conclusion, the result of the inflammatory journals he read and the inflammatory speeches to which he listened. Andrew Jackson, the President of the United States, was his great enemy. The newspapers said that Jackson's opposition to the Bank of the United States would paralyze the country's industries. Lawrence considered how he himself suffered, was short of pocket money, and his imaginings took a new turn: Andrew Jackson was responsible for his personal monetary condition; therefore Andrew Jackson owed him a living.

Nobody inquired into this strange preoccupation of his: nobody considered him important enough to be concerned over. Yet Richard Lawrence, in the twisted vagaries of his mind, built up his fancied grievances

and resentments until he became what the world fears, an irresponsible
mad-dog killer. He continued to read the papers, and one day came
across an item concerned with the death of a congressman, Warren R.
Davis of South Carolina, who was to be given a funeral in the House
chamber. In an obscure last sentence the item stated that the President
of the United States was to attend the funeral.

Andrew Jackson had been advised against making personal appearances without strong escort. Since the election he had received anony-
mous letters threatening his life. But he paid no attention to them, other
than to endorse them to Blair to print, with appropriate remarks, in the
Washington *Globe*.

"If a man hasn't courage to sign his name to a letter," he said, "he'd
not have the courage to carry out his threats."

That day he drove to the Capitol, and sat in the gathering of congressmen and senators at the Davis funeral. The chaplain preached in
the manner of his time, his discourse being filled with references to the
futility of life, the near presence of death, the need for preparation at
all times to meet the awful majesty of God. All in all, it was reckoned a
good sermon of its kind, sufficiently depressing to send the audience
away in a successfully solemn mood.

Jackson passed through the crowd in the rotunda, nodding and
speaking to acquaintances and friends, on his way to the east entrance,
where his carriage waited at the foot of the stairs.

With dramatic suddenness the thing happened. From behind one of
the great pillars of the portico stepped a smallish man with a face of
surprising pallor. His hand beneath his coat drew forth a pistol and
extended it almost to the breast of the President, who halted not more
than two yards away from him.

No man who witnessed it ever forgot that moment. Jackson's face
grew taut and stern. Before anyone else he realized the intention of the
assailant.

Then Richard Lawrence pulled the trigger.

There was a loud report, and immediate tremendous confusion. Men
looked at the President, expecting to see him stagger and fall. He did
neither.

Instead he cried, "What! What is this, sir?"

In that moment those who saw him recognized his terrible capacity,
his ability to deal with a supreme situation. With his cane in his hand
he rushed forward to strike the man who had fired at him.

Instantly the assassin dropped his pistol, drew a second from his
pocket and fired it also, the report sounding like a rifle shot.

Still the old General did not flinch or step back.

Before he could reach the assailant, however, his naval attaché, young
Lieutenant Gedney, hurled himself on Lawrence and brought him
crashing to the stone floor just at the head of the steps.

By this time others had moved forward, seizing the President, expecting him to sink down, since assuredly he had two bullets in his body—nobody could have missed at that close range.

Clearly Jackson's voice was heard over the tumult. "Let me go, gentlemen! I am not afraid! They can't kill me! I can protect myself!"

The disheveled prisoner was pulled to his feet, his arms pinioned behind him, a dozen men holding him, his face like a snarling cat's.

Men turned with horror and alarm toward the President.

"What about you, sir? Are you hit?" asked Levi Woodbury, Secretary of the Treasury.

"No, sir. He missed me both times," answered the General.

"Thank God!" cried several voices.

Anger now turned on the prisoner. Walking sticks were lifted, they would have clubbed him, perhaps lynched him on the spot.

But the President was in command now.

"Do not harm him! See that he is confined and given a fair trial!"

He pulled his hat down over his brow and, apparently unruffled, prepared to resume his way to his carriage.

Now someone raised a cry of astonishment. The two pistols of the assassin had been picked up and examined, and the mystery of Jackson's escape was solved. Both were of the percussion type, and both percussion caps had exploded—*but neither of the pistols had been discharged!*

The exploding caps had sounded so loud in the rotunda that everyone believed the pistols were fired full into the President's breast.

7

How little the incident impressed Jackson, where it so deeply shocked and impressed everyone else, was seen by Jack Donelson when later he came to the White House after an investigation. His uncle was playing with the children in his study, laughing at little Andrew's antics, finding a peppermint in his pocket for little Mary Rachel, and holding the bubbling and squirming baby on his lap.

"Well?" he said to Donelson.

"I can only say, sir, that your escape was miraculous," his nephew replied. "The two pistols are an elegant matched pair, and in most excellent order. I closely examined them with General Hunter, who is an expert in small arms. We drew the ball out of one with a screw. The barrel is about six inches long, and was packed almost to the muzzle with a charge of fine glazed dueling powder, on which the bullet was well seated.

"I myself took the second pistol, which was loaded exactly like its mate, and having taken a fresh percussion cap from a box of them found in the man's pocket, I fired it. The ball passed entirely through an inch plank at a distance of five or six yards, and lodged, nearly buried, in a thick beam on the wall six or seven yards farther distant. If it had struck you, sir, it would certainly have been fatal."

"Why didn't it fire?" asked the President.

"Nobody can explain it, sir. We reloaded those pistols several times, with the same powder and the same caps, and they discharged without failure each time. General Hunter estimates that the chances of those two successive misfires were less than one, in one hundred and twenty-five thousand."

"The Almighty must have spared me," said Jackson soberly.

Then suddenly a different expression came into his face, and he grinned at the squirming child on his knee.

"I think—yes I know—the baby needs to be changed."

He rose and carried the child to the door, calling the nurse.

"I'm sorry, sir—" began Donelson when he came back.

"Why?" asked Jackson. He gave another grin at a small damp spot on his knee. "Never be sorry over anything natural. That little process of life was more important to the tiny one than a Presidential election or the winning of a war."

He became serious. "I noticed that man's manner, from the moment my eye caught him. It was firm and resolved until the failure of his last pistol, when he seemed to shrink, rather than resist." And he added, "Get to the bottom of this, Jack. I want to know who put the fellow up to it."

But the investigation showed only that Richard Lawrence was a madman—hopelessly insane. He babbled that "General Jackson killed my father at New Orleans"—and it was known that his father, an Englishman, had died only a few years before in Washington of natural causes. Then the assassin changed his story. Jackson had ruined the country. Jackson owed him money, reason unspecified. Jackson knew that Richard Lawrence was in reality the king of England, and would not help him gain the crown that rightfully belonged to him. Jackson even was aware of his intention to kill him, and that he had a right to do so.

The poor fellow became inarticulate, his insanity so apparent that he was not prosecuted but sent instead to an asylum as a dangerous lunatic.

Jackson seemed almost disappointed that nobody had "put the fellow up to it," as he expressed it. Then he said, "On the other hand, I'm glad of it. I'd hate to think that any man, even one of my most inveterate enemies, would stoop to anything so despicable."

Then the grin came again. "So the whole thing turns out to be an anticlimax. A madman tries to kill the President and he cannot even cause his pistols to fire!"

One result he did not reckon on was the further development of the

Jackson legend. Men had seen the fearlessness with which he faced what seemed certain death, and how he took charge of the situation calmly afterward. The image of the heroic old President grew still greater in the public mind.

But the General himself put the entire matter out of his mind.

A larger concern occupied him.

Sam Houston at last had been heard from. Down in Texas events were moving to a crashing climax.

8

When the letter, postmarked Natchitoches, Louisiana, was brought to him, Andrew Jackson instantly recognized Houston's handwriting. "I know who addressed that!" he exclaimed, and eagerly opened the envelope. With excitement, even anxiety, he read:

Gen. Jackson, Dear Sir: Having been so far as Bexar, in the province of Texas, I am in possession of some information that may be calculated to forward your views, if you should entertain any, touching the acquisition of Texas by the United States.

Ha! thought Jackson. *Views touching the acquisition* . . . a bold assumption, considering what he had told Houston. But then, *if you should entertain any* . . . that took the curse off it. The writer of the letter was discreet after all.

That such a measure is desireable by nineteen-twentieths of the population of the Province, I cannot doubt. They are now without laws to govern or protect them. Mexico is involved in civil war. The Government is essentially despotic and must be so for years to come. The rulers have not honesty and the people have not intelligence.

This was better. It reinforced the first paragraph by making it clear that the observations came from the writer himself, as occasioned by what he had observed and was reporting as an interested individual to the President. Jackson read on:

The people of Texas are determined to form a State Government and separate from Coahuila, and unless Mexico is soon restored to order and the Constitution revived and re-enacted, the Province of Texas will remain separate from the confederacy of Mexico.

The General pondered deeply for a moment. Reports had come from many sources of a contest for supremacy in Mexico between two military dictators, General Anastasio Bustamante, and General Antonio López de Santa Anna. Both, it appeared from information at hand, were overfree with the firing squad and the hangman's noose; and the Americans in Texas were caught in the middle between them.

There had been local outbursts. Americans, led by a man named James Bowie, ousted a Mexican garrison from Nacogdoches. Another group rescued a fire-eating Southerner named William Barrett Travis when he was arrested by the local military commandant at Anahuac. Evidently Sam Houston believed a revolution already was under way. Jackson turned again to the letter:

She [the writer apparently referred to Texas] has already beaten and expelled all the troops of Mexico from her soil, nor will she permit them to return. She can defend herself against the whole power of Mexico, for really Mexico is powerless and penniless. Her [now he assuredly must be referring to Mexico] want of money taken in connection with the course Texas must and will adopt, will render the transfer of Texas inevitable to *some power*.

The last two words riveted the General's attention. *Some power . . .* Britain! Exactly what he most feared. He wished fervently to prevent Britain, or any other European power, from gaining the benefits of such an uprising as Houston appeared to think inevitable. Yet what could he do? Certainly he could not intervene, even if Texas revolted, with political conditions as they were. The letter went on:

If Texas is desirable to the United States, it is now in the most favorable attitude perhaps that it can be to obtain it on fair terms—England is pressing her suit for it, but its citizens will resist, if any transfer should be made of them to any other power but the United States.

The President's white brows knit. Here was information of enormous value, which he could scarcely have obtained save from so close and interested an observer as Sam Houston. He turned again to the writer's great sprawling script:

I have travelled near five hundred miles across Texas, and am now enabled to judge pretty correctly of the soil, and the resources of the Country, and I have no hesitancy in pronouncing it the finest country to its extent upon the globe. For the greater portion of it is richer and more healthy, in my opinion, than West Tennessee.

Jackson's lips twitched in a slight grin. Astute fellow, that Houston! West Tennessee . . . Nashville and the Hermitage . . . he must have known how that paragraph would appeal to the man he was addressing. The letter continued:

There can be no doubt but the country east of the Rio Grand of the north [his rendition of Rio Grande del Norte] would sustain a population of ten millions of souls. My opinion is that Texas will by her members in convention by the 1st April declare all that country as Texas proper and form a State Constitution. I expect to be present at the convention and will apprise you of the course adopted, so soon as its members have taken final action. It is probable that I may make Texas my abiding place. In adopting this course, I will never forget the country of my birth.

An indication here of a larger purpose. The next step in Houston's campaign, it would appear, contemplated identifying himself with the activities of the colonists; a hope of having a directing hand in the future destinies of the province which Andrew Jackson himself once had said might be *a trigger to explode the nation across the continent.* A final paragraph, personal and warm:

I have with much pride and inexpressible satisfaction seen your messages and proclamations touching the Nullifiers of the South and their "peaceable remedies." God grant that you may save the Union! It does seem to me that it is reserved for you and you alone to render to millions so great a blessing. I hear all voices commend your course even in Texas where there is felt the liveliest interest for the preservation of the republic.

Your friend and obedient servant, Sam Houston.

For a time, after finishing the reading of the letter, Jackson sat plunged in profound thought. *Let not thy right hand know what thy left hand doeth:* right well was Houston obeying that injunction. His letter set forth conditions as if written purely on his own impulse; and yet it opened immense vistas for speculation merely by suggestion.

She has already beaten and expelled all the troops of Mexico . . . want of money . . . will render the transfer of Texas inevitable to some power . . . it is probable that I may make Texas my abiding place. . . .

The phrases and parts of other phrases added up to an important total in the mind of the President. Forces immense and explosive were gathering in Texas. They needed no more than a spark to set off the full fury of the blast. And his favorite subaltern, Houston, moving in that charged atmosphere, reckless, dynamic, might be the very spark of electric force to create the explosion.

He put the letter on the desk, and took up his pen. Should he answer it, counsel caution and circumspection?

He laid the pen down again.

If he knew his man—and he was sure he did—such a letter would be of little avail. Sam Houston was caught up in the midst of mighty events, and he would not withdraw from them now.

Andrew Jackson thought back on a time—it seemed centuries ago—when he himself got out of a bed of pain from which he should not have risen, because he felt he must plunge into action against the Creek Indians before timid orders from Washington stayed his hand.

He shook his silvery head almost wistfully. To be young again!

San Jacinto,
*** 1836

*I*n Texas affairs came to a troubled head. Civil war between power-hungry dictators ripped and tore all of Mexico, and hence Texas, which was a Mexican province.

American colonists had been welcomed by the Mexican government for two reasons: to develop the land, which the Mexicans would not colonize; and to act as a buffer against the wild and ferocious Indian tribes which had practically depopulated Texas.

The adventurous Americans accepted the role thus thrust upon them. In a few short years the savages learned that a raid on an American settlement was too costly; and not only that the American rifle was deadly, but American vengeance was often appalling. Even the Comanches found it expedient to ride wide of the newcomers.

Meantime, the Mexican government offered the colonists no aid or protection, but left them to shift for themselves, live or die. It was not strange that the people grew clannish and self-reliant, and regarded the central government as something outside, almost alien to them.

Among the Americans a relative newcomer was much discussed. In his three years of vicissitudes in Texas, Sam Houston had impressed everyone as gigantic: not only physically, but in his appetites, his ability to charm women and win either the admiration or enmity of men, and in the vastness of his ideas and visions.

He practiced law, but spent his time asking questions and acquainting himself with men and places, for an unspoken purpose. One personage, Juan de Veramendi, the Mexican vice-governor of Texas, suspected the nature of that purpose, and pronounced him a "very deep and subtile man." But Veramendi died in a cholera epidemic.

Then Texas, wearied of broken promises, injustices, and the repudiation of the national constitution, revolted against the government of the latest dictator, General Antonio López de Santa Anna. A hastily assembled "army" of individualistic Texas riflemen captured the fortified city, San Antonio de Bexar. Twenty thousand American colonists had defied a nation of seven million people, ruled by a vengeful and pitiless despot.

Desperately unprepared, they adopted a constitution and formed a provisional government, with David G. Burnet, a Bible-reading politician, as its president. The only man who seemed at all ready in this crisis, Sam Houston, was elected commander-in-chief of whatever military forces he could find or gather.

Very soon ominous news came. Santa Anna himself, with seven thousand veteran and well-equipped soldiers, marched north to wipe out the revolt in blood. Disasters multiplied. Scattered Texas detachments at the Alamo, at Goliad, at San Patricio, were successively overwhelmed and massacred.

Men drew a deep breath and looked at each other. Having sown the wind, Texas must prepare to reap the whirlwind.

Chapter Thirty-Three

There is the last hope of Texas.

SAM HOUSTON

1

The rains had begun almost as soon as the army left Gonzales. At first it looked like an average spring storm, cold and wet, but not necessarily persisting. Deaf Smith, however, shook his head as the downpour slanted chill out of the northwest from a leaden sky.

"This here ain't no ord'nary blue norther," he said. "She'll last. Afore she's done the hull country will be wet enough to bog down a blanket."

The scout's real name was Erastus Smith. He was no spring chicken, with fine lines crisscrossing his mahogany-colored face and his graying hair grown thin on top; but he had a whang-leather toughness that seemed to defy weariness, and though he was hard of hearing—hence his sobriquet—he had the keenest eyes in the force, and knew this wild empty land from hunting and Indian fighting over it.

He was right about the weather. For days on days the little column of men had marched in a driving rain almost continuously, sleeping in it, trying to cook their scanty rations in it. The rain obscured the distant scenery, made every step a soggy slop, soaked through any kind of garment to the wet and miserable skin.

On a little rise, looking down at the flooded Brazos River, Sam Houston brought his horse to a stop, watching the men as they passed below him. The horse was a stallion named Saracen, a fine specimen of blood, and normally white, but now so streaked by mud and wetness that his hide was a dirty gray. Deep creases in his thighs showed his gauntness; but he still had spirit and wanted to go, jerking impatiently with his head at the bridle.

The man on his back looked weather-beaten and grim. His vast head was leonine, with its light-colored, pin-pupiled eyes; and a tangle of reddish side whiskers—brindle-colored, rather, for he was past his forty-third birthday, and his whiskers were sprinkled with gray—sprouted from his hard jowls, to give him a maned look.

His attire was hardly military: an old black coat, very threadbare; a buckskin vest of Cherokee make; high-heeled Mexican boots with huge spurs; and a broad felt hat, pinned up from his face to keep the wet brim from flapping in his eyes. He did, however, wear a sword, and there were two pistols in his handbags, for he was now Major General Sam Houston, commander-in-chief of the Texas army.

Texas *army* . . . what army? As an army it hardly existed.

He had been given command of the Texas armed forces, and the people looked to him to save them from the almost certain fate of their temerity by some kind of an inconceivable miracle.

Miracle it would have to be, he considered, on the present prospects. From the outset he had encountered disobedience, jealousy, and disaster. Johnson and Grant and their filibustering expedition—lost, because they disobeyed Houston's orders. Fannin and his men—lost, because Fannin was jealous of Houston and did not obey a command to march from Goliad until too late. The Alamo—lost, after he ordered it blown up and abandoned.

The Alamo, to be sure, unlike the other losses, had produced an unexpected benefit. The bitter American fire of that hopeless defense cost Santa Anna so many men that he was forced to pause for a time and regroup his army, giving Houston a few precious days to raise some kind of a force to defend the country.

He thought of three men of more than ordinary fame who died in the Alamo: James Bowie, William Barrett Travis, and Davy Crockett.

Houston felt the loss of Bowie keenly. A loyal friend, Houston's first friend in Texas. It was Bowie who suggested to him the Texas adventure in the first place. Jim Bowie was mighty hard to replace.

For Travis—commonly called Buck Travis—Houston had less regard. A fighting man, granted, but a constant troublemaker. Nevertheless the Texas army could be using the likes of him now.

As to Crockett, Houston felt no sense of loss at all. He regarded the man as a big-talking lout, who deserted Jackson's army during the Creek War after helping in the massacre of an Indian village. Elected to Congress from a backwoods district, he divided his time in Washington between bragging about his own prowess, and making snide remarks about President Jackson, because he found this impudence brought attention and applause from Clay, Calhoun, and other anti-Jackson men. But the voters did not think much of that and retired him to private life; whereupon, unable to stand the humiliation, he migrated with a dozen Tennessee hunters to Texas, and to the Alamo. Houston regretted the loss of those twelve riflemen more than he did that of Crockett himself.

Harking back to the series of disasters: when Houston took command at Gonzales of what was left of the Texas armed force, he could count just three hundred and seventy-four men.

"There," he said, "is the last hope of Texas."

2

He was, this day, the seventeenth day of his retreat, weighted down by discouragement and disappointment; and yet there was a certain high pride in his situation.

Houston knew, every man in his army knew, that the Mexican forces were pursuing them in overwhelming numbers. But he confided to nobody how he hoped to meet this massive threat; his movements, to his men, seemed less a scheme than an adventure.

The word "adventure," in fact, appeared at this time to characterize the man better than any other. How much adventure meant to Houston, and also the freedom it implied and the spiritual preparation it required, he himself could not have expressed. But for the first time in his life he was his own sole commander; on his shoulders was the entire responsibility for success or failure involving vast consequences even beyond and above the fate of the thousands in Texas.

Until now he had lived under the tremendous shadow of Andrew Jackson: regarded with affection and pride by the old General, but still a subaltern. His achievements were bounded by the strength and fame of that mighty genius. Today, however, he stood alone, and in this lay his secret feeling of elation. Whatever he did now was Sam Houston's doing.

It would, he knew, require almost that miracle expected of him. Since leaving Gonzales he had picked up a few hundred more men—and also a great trailing mob of refugees. And he had lost some men by desertion. In this army he could command, he could lead, he could cajole, but he could not punish. There was no discipline for that. Thus far he had kept together his handful by beguiling them rather than by any real authority over them.

As example: this very morning when the army stood at the flooded Brazos and he ordered it to march upriver, two of his company commanders and their men rebelled outright. Captain Moseley Baker, a bull-built man with a foghorn voice, was a lawyer by profession—Houston had noticed how many lawyers, doctors, and others of the professional stamp had come to Texas, likely because they weren't much of a success at home. Captain Wily Martin was long-necked and long-legged, with a stoop and a dark-skinned face. Both were fighting men, but both of them thought they knew more about conducting this campaign than he did.

"You ordering the army north?" asked Martin.

"I am," said Houston.

"Upriver! It's *down*river where the settlements are that we ought to be defending!" bawled Baker.

"Where are you leading us?" Martin demanded.

"Let us hope," said Houston, "to a place where orders may be obeyed in a military manner without question."

"Military manner!" Now it was Baker. "You think running away day and night is military? We're not going that way!"

Houston looked them in the eyes. But he could not permit this insubordination to be erected into a mutiny. So he adopted an expedient.

"Gentlemen," he told them, "your orders are to proceed downriver and guard the crossings at San Felipe and Old Fort."

It was what they were going to do anyway, and they glared at him for the way he put it. But they could not repudiate the "order" since it chimed with their determination, and presently they marched off with their men—two hundred of them, leaving Houston only about nine hundred.

Somehow he got the rest of the army to follow him northward. But he needed, on this day, a special inner resolution.

He did have a definite plan, for he led unhesitatingly. But his march was in no straight direction. Rather it was a series of zigzags, sometimes even semicircles; and the army complained of the labor of this extra marching, and the lack of any purpose it could see in all that hard hiking.

But Houston knew things his men did not know. His scouts, such as Deaf Smith; and a free Negro named Hendrick Arnold, who was a great rider and watcher; and a little, round, red-haired man with a high-pitched voice, named Henry Karnes, who looked like anything but the tireless outrider and word-bringer he was, kept him informed.

The Mexican army was following him in at least four divisions, each stronger than his force. To the north was General Gaona. Directly west was Santa Anna himself with his second-in-command, General Filisola. Southwest was Urrea, the best of the Mexican generals, who had destroyed Johnson's and Fannin's forces. Still farther south was General Cos, Santa Anna's brother-in-law who had defected on his parole, given after he was captured at San Antonio de Bexar in the early stages of the war.

Thus far Houston had succeeded in throwing them off the trail. His march from Gonzales had been northeast to La Grange, thence southeast down the Colorado, branching northeast again to the Brazos, and now he was heading almost due north along that river, dodging like a desperate hare to escape the pursuing hounds.

3

The Texas army could hardly be said to be marching. Rather it straggled along, single file or in small groups, taking the higher ground to avoid the muddy waters of the Brazos, so swollen by the continuous rains that in some places it was miles wide.

Dirty, ragged, and wet, the men slopped along with the somber, stubborn step of weariness and gloom, their feet making squelching sounds. And they were grumbling.

Texans were horseback people who despised foot travel. But Houston believed the foot soldier was the eventual arbiter in battle; and so, except for a handful of scouts, mounted riflemen, and field officers, his men walked and carried their own guns and personal effects.

They grumbled about this. They grumbled also about the weather and about the short rations. They grumbled constantly and continuously about everything; but chiefly about this long and apparently aimless retreat. Houston could hear their voices, somewhat muted as they passed him, but sometimes not even then:

"Whar'n hell we headed now?"

"This here's the Brazos, ain't it? We're goin' nawth again."

"I'm hongry, an' I'm tired, an' I'm cold, an' damn it all, my feet hurts."

"I come to fight, not to peerade over the country."

Soldiers always grumbled; it was natural. But this grumbling lately had assumed a threatening tone. He could see them glance up at him on his little rise, disgust in some faces, malice on others. Still others walked past in groups, heads bent together, muttering, sometimes gesturing. The men were ripe for mutiny, and instigators played upon their discontent.

Houston knew that Andrew Jackson, assuredly, would have put the mutiny breeders under arrest; and probably stood them against a wall and had them shot. But maybe Old Hickory never had dealings with a stiff-necked, independent, cantankerous, go-to-hell outfit like these Texans. And when it came to shooting men for discipline, he had too few of them to waste. He counted each man in his army as a miser counts his coins; used every means he knew to keep it together, provision it, husband it.

Now he slithered Saracen down the wet side hill and trotted along the ragged column.

"Halt, men!" he cried. "Fall out. Take a rest."

They were glad to obey. The rain had temporarily let up, and they sat or half reclined on the wet sod. Some lit pipes or took chews of tobacco. Houston himself took a giant bite from a plug he carried in his saddlebags.

He reined in his horse and spat tobacco juice amicably.

"Friends," he said, "this march isn't entirely wasted. We're hungry and we're tired, but we've got acquainted with each other. And when we fight—and I promise that when the time's right we *will* fight—I think we'll at least understand the command 'Forward.' " He gave them his tigerish grin. "Now, I'm told that evilly disposed persons have been whispering that I'm marching you to the Nacogdoches Redlands. That's just plain not true. I'm only leading you up the Brazos as far as Groce's plantation. I know Jared Groce. He's got cattle, and he's got corn, and he's a Texas patriot. You'll get enough to eat there. Furthermore, it's a position where we can whip the enemy, even if he comes ten to one. Company commanders, get your men in motion in ten minutes."

He left them to think that over and pass it up and down the column, and spurred Saracen. The stallion, glad to be let loose at last, broke into a canter, blasting air in sheer abandon.

"Give that stud a bugle, an' he could play a tune," came a voice from the seated ranks.

Men began to laugh.

Houston grinned to himself. The harmless blasting of the stallion, ridiculous as it was, had relieved some of the tension.

4

The most pathetic sight was the families.

Santa Anna was reported to have a saying: "If you execute your enemies it saves you the trouble of having to forgive them." And terror gripped Texas with his invasion.

The story of the brutalities in Zacatecas, after the revolt there, where no able-bodied man escaped massacre, and no woman except those too old and those too young, and sometimes not even they, was spared violation in the three-day plunder of their beautiful city, had been told all over Texas.

Miserably hoping for protection, the refugees followed, or paralleled, or preceded the army's route. Most of them were women and children, but a few were men, old or crippled, who could do more good helping in this flight than by carrying a gun.

It concerned Houston, this haphazard scattering over the country of the helpless, and though he had scouts miles out to the west and far ahead of his main body to warn if enemy raiding cavalry appeared, he was obliged to devote far too great a proportion of his time to seeing after the welfare of the refugees. Some of them had wagons, but the boggy condition of the rain-swamped prairies had caused the breakdown or abandonment of scores of vehicles. Yet those who had no other means of travel continued to stumble along on foot.

Riding up toward the head of the army, he saw one small band consisting of two women with bundles on their heads, tagged along by five children. Some of the little ones carried burdens also, and the smallest of all, a wee boy no more than four years old, hung to his mother's skirts, crying.

He swung Saracen over toward them.

The two women halted and eased their burdens to the ground. One of them was middle-aged and slatternly in her ill-fitting dress, which was muddied to her knees. She was sallow and hollow-cheeked. Moreover, she was chewing snuff. The younger one could not have been more than twenty-five, her body still rounded. But her face also showed the marks of frontier hardship, and her hair hung down her back, tangled and uncombed.

"Don't you have any men to look after you?" he asked.

"No, mister," said the snuff-chewing woman. Then she added, "Our men were both at—Goliad."

Widowed in that massacre!

"How far have you come this way?" he inquired.

"Must be twenty mile. We had a cotton cart an' a mule, but the mule got away in the night, an' we couldn't ketch him."

"You've come twenty miles—*on foot*—with those children?"

"Every step, mister. But three nights on the way." The woman spat a slimy stream of snuff-juice.

One of the little girls began coughing, and the smallest boy begged the younger woman to take him up. She did so.

"It ain't Mayme an' me," said the older woman. "It's the kids we worry about. We been takin' turns carryin' Billy, the least one thar. But they're about tuckered out."

She was not complaining. It was a statement of hard fact.

A twist of pity went over the face of the man. "You stay here, ladies," he said.

The women sank on their bundles, as if exhausted, and the children hunkered down on the wet ground, staring after him as he galloped off.

The army was taking another of its ten-minute rests, a long scattering of seated men. Nearer to him an irregular procession of wagons began to pass.

Houston rode up to the first. Bony, sore-shouldered horses, ramshackle wagon with a felly sprung on a rear wheel. Driver, a thin-faced consumptive.

"What you got in there?" Houston asked.

"Family," said the driver. "What we could save from the place."

"Go ahead."

Each vehicle had its load, and its legitimate errand, until he came to the fifth in line. This driver was a lank man with scraggly whiskers, but he looked able-bodied.

"What you got in there?" Houston asked, as he had of the others.

"Trade goods. Calico. Terbaccy. Beads. Mirrors. Knives."

"Indian trader?"

"Yep. Headin' for the Caddo villages."

"We need this wagon."

"Cain't have her, mister. Private property."

Houston's glare bit into the man. "Get down off of there!"

Though he made no move for a weapon, the driver gave him one look, then clambered over the wheel to the ground.

A young officer, sandy-haired and wiry, rode up: Major George Hockley, a Nashville man and Houston's friend and personal aide.

"George," said Houston, "take a look into that wagon and see what it's got."

The major saluted and rode around to the rear.

"What's your name?" Houston asked the driver.

"Matt Toombs."

"Why aren't you in the army?"

"This ain't no fight of mine. I'm not a Texas citizen. Jest a trader, headin' north for the San Gabriel villages——"

Hockley interrupted him. "He's got mostly trade goods, like he said, General. And two kegs of rum back there."

"Liquor to the Indians?" Houston's eye bored into the man.

"Why not? Thar ain't no law ag'in it——"

"There is a law. The Eighth Commandment. Thou shalt not steal."

"Steal? Where's there any stealin' in——"

"You know damn well you sell the Indians liquor to steal from them. Toombs, the army's requisitioning this wagon."

"You cain't do that——"

"The hell I can't! Watch me do it!" Again the warning glare was in Houston's eyes, and Toombs stood silent, overawed.

"George," said Houston to Hockley, "stave in those rum kegs and have some of the boys come over and unload this wagon. You, Matt, you take your wagon over yonder, and carry those two women and their children to Groce's. This is war. So mind you treat them *good*. I know how to handle a man who doesn't obey orders!"

In his entire life Matt Toombs had never been confronted by anyone so overwhelming. He gulped, his Adam's apple bobbing under his thin beard. "Yes, sir," he said.

Houston rode on. When, a few minutes later, he glanced back, the commandeered wagon, already unloaded, was turning toward the refugee group.

5

Near the head of the column, a solid, grave-faced man in faded blue homespun stood beside a thick-legged gray horse—Colonel Edward Burleson, commander of the so-called First Regiment of the Texas army. He was an old Indian fighter, and was in nominal command of the Texans when they stormed San Antonio de Bexar, before the Alamo siege. But he was one officer who was not jealous of Houston, having had his fill of insubordination and indiscipline, so that he was glad to yield the responsibility to another.

"Ned," said Houston, "better get 'em going. We've got a far piece to march yet."

Burleson climbed on his horse and shouted a command. His men began to clamber to their feet. Houston continued to ride forward.

Up front were a few more refugee wagons and carts. He did not like it, their going ahead of the army that way, but he could hardly control the fleeing people.

A big freighter wagon was directly ahead, with three yoke of oxen hunching stolidly along. Beside them walked the bull-skinner—a woman by her shape and gait, but wearing men's pants of twilled blue cotton, and a man's coat, much too large. An almost shapeless old Mexican sombrero was crammed down on her head.

He rode alongside and glanced at her. Surprise here. The woman was young, strong, well-built—and pretty, in a determined, almost defiant sort of way.

He lifted his hat. "Madam, I am General Houston. Can the army be of any assistance?"

She gave him a level, appraising glance. "I reckon not," she said. "I've done pretty well so far."

"Where from?"

"My ranch on the Colorado."

"Married?"

"Widow. Connie Thoren. My husband died in the cholera epidemic two years ago."

"Nice outfit you've got."

"I aim to keep it nice. That wagon's got everything I own. Hyah, you Buck! Get along there, you double-blasted, yellow-backed, bastard-son-of-a-mangy-pothound-bitch!"

Her long whip sang out over the backs of the beasts and the tip bit accurately into the rump of the delinquent ox, causing a wholesome return to vigor of performance on its part. Houston observed that this young woman was a bull-skinner who knew the language, and knew the technique of her job. It was a relief to find a refugee so self-reliant and competent—and a woman at that.

"Anything we can do, Mrs. Thoren, just name it. Houston is thy servant always."

He gave her a rather special smile and rode on. Trudging beside her oxen she stared after him. But then she recovered herself and spoke even more severely to her animals.

The way the army was moving, with the intermittent rain and all, Houston judged it would make Groce's some time the next day. That meant he must find a camping place, and some sort of rations, and see to the routine of posting guards, and at the same time try to keep an eye on the refugees, meanwhile hoping the Mexican scouting cavalry would not catch up.

All at once he saw a woman, walking alone, carrying a child in her arms. It was not raining at the moment, but her face was wet. Tears.

"Madam—" he began. Then he stopped.

The child was dead.

How long she had been carrying it, knowing it was dead, in the despair of hopelessness and sorrow, there was no way of telling. She did not reply to him but continued to walk on, silently weeping.

He wheeled Saracen in front of her and dismounted.

"Madam," he said, "there are wagons coming. You can ride."

He saw the head of Burleson's column just topping the rise behind. "How long has the little one—been gone?" he asked gently.

"She died . . . this morning . . . I couldn't feed her. . . ." The woman broke into a storm of sobbing.

Burleson's column came up and halted. A good many of the men gathered about. But when Houston tried to take the child, the woman fought to keep it.

He ran his eyes around the circle of soldiers. "Is there a minister among you?"

A short, baldish man, in a long-tailed muddy coat, lifted his hand. "What's your name?" asked Houston.

"Turner, sir. Alexander Turner."

"*Reverend* Turner?"

"Once was, sir."

Houston looked at the woman. "This is a minister of the gospel, madam," he said. "He'll give your baby a Christian burial. Now, everyone here is your friend. Let us do the right thing by you, and—and yours."

At that she surrendered the child.

A three-yoke ox team pulling a freighter wagon came up and halted. Houston saw Connie Thoren go to the tail gate, and then come toward the group carrying a long-handled shovel: an act silent, capable, and understanding, for the men had nothing to dig a grave. In his heart he mightily approved of Connie Thoren.

The shallow hole was soon excavated in the wet sod.

"What is the child's name?" asked the little ex-preacher.

"Nancy—Nancy Hoag," said the mother.

It began to rain again, and the scene was strangely and solemnly picturesque: the rough, bearded soldiers standing hatless, some with tears in their eyes, the sobbing mother with Connie Thoren's arm about her, the bald "once was" minister saying the old, well-remembered words:

"Earth to earth, ashes to ashes, dust to dust; in sure and certain hope of resurrection unto eternal life . . ."

The tiny body, wrapped in a blanket, was covered, the mound of earth well patted down. Some of the men fetched stones from a nearby outcropping and heaped them on the grave to protect it from the wolves.

The mother gave her name as Mrs. Ellen Hoag, and seemed comforted somewhat by the proper burial. She said that the previous night when her baby grew so ill, her husband took the horse and buggy—that was all they had—and tried to find help. He must have got lost in the dark, for she did not know where he was.

Presently Connie Thoren's wagon pulled on, Mrs. Hoag now a passenger, Connie's whip singing as it got the oxen into motion, Connie's voice raised in the vivid metaphor of the trail.

Once more the army tramped ahead in the rain.

6

Major Hockley had come up, and with him Houston cantered on over the hill. As they reached the top, they looked down into a valley where a small creek ran toward the Brazos, fringed with cottonwood trees.

Far off to the left a rifle smacked its keen flat report.

"The enemy!" exclaimed Hockley.

Houston stood up in his stirrups and gazed.

"Some of the scouts, all right," he said. "But evidently no enemy alarm."

One man was driving a wagon with a team of horses down the valley, his own mount led behind.

"Looks like they've got some prisoners," said Hockley.

Four men were riding, their arms bound, their horses led by their mounted captors.

Houston spurred Saracen and the powerful stallion broke into a gallop, throwing up divots of damp sod with his iron-shod hoofs. Hockley followed.

As they rapidly closed the distance down toward the wagon in the bottom of the depression, one of the scouts swung toward them—Deaf Smith, riding like a Comanche to meet them.

The scout whirled his horse beside Houston.

"Them—them dirty, god-damned sons-a-bitches!" He spoke in a half-howling voice, as do many persons hard of hearing who appear to think others as deaf as themselves.

"What did they do?" asked Houston.

"They had two pore women, 'bout an hour's ride off to the west. Didn't figger nobody was near 'em——"

"Lone women? They were robbing them?"

"Robbin' 'em, yes—an' wuss!" Deaf Smith's voice lowered as if this was too awful to shout. "They had the hosses unhitched, ready to lead away, an' anything wuth a nickel tied up in a sack to carry off. But they was all inside the wagon. We wouldn't of got them buzzards but they was too busy with the women to keep watch. The boys could hear 'em cryin'——"

Deaf Smith described the shrieks from the wagon—shrieks of despair, shrill and penetrating like birth-cries. . . .

"Come on!" said Houston.

Hendrick Arnold was at the reins of the wagon, his black face gleaming with the wetness of the rain as Houston galloped up. He pulled up the team and Houston rode behind to look inside.

Under the old canvas tilt crouched a woman, holding in her lap the head of another. She turned toward Houston a haggard face . . . black *rebozo*, dark skin, Indian-set eyes. A Mexican.

When Houston gazed in she seemed frightened anew, holding her arms shelteringly over the head of the other. At a guess, she was in her middle thirties, though she looked older as women of her race often do; and she evidently had been abused, her clothing torn and rumpled, her hair disarrayed.

"I'm General Houston," he said. "Did those men harm you?"

No answer. But the one with her face in the other's lap lifted her head, then quickly lowered it again. She was young, very young, the older woman's daughter probably. Adolescent at perhaps twelve. She might have been pretty but her face was tear-streaked and swollen, and her body, in garments ripped to rags, heaved with her sobbing.

Obviously they did not understand his English. Houston turned to Deaf Smith, who had lived with the Mexicans—and had a Mexican wife, somewhere in this rout, though where she was the scout did not know.

"Ask her if the men harmed her," he said.

Deaf Smith turned to her with the question in Spanish.

The older woman's eyes filled with fury and hate. She began to speak, in broken sentences, which the scout slowly translated.

"She says her name's Margarita Salas—her husband, Francisco Salas, is with this army—a soldier."

"Must be in Seguin's company. They're a couple of miles back."

"She says those four men held her an' the other one down—that's her daughter, Luz—an' *took turns* on 'em. Nothin' they could do about it."

Another anguished spate of Spanish from the older woman.

"She's sayin' that she's been married a long time an' had childern, an' she could stand it. But the leetle one, Luz—she ain't thirteen yet, an' it never happened to her before."

Another break while the scout listened. Then he translated.

"She says she kep' tellin' the leetle one to give in—not fight 'em—it would only make it wuss. But Luz was scared out of her mind an' struggled. They beat her up to make her lay still. An' they hurt her somethin' awful—inside. She's bleedin' bad now." Deaf Smith turned a face bleak with bitterness on his commander. "*Four* of them devils! God, Gen'ral, it's hell to be a woman in Texas!"

Houston was pale with fury.

"Tell her," he said, "that we have doctors with the army. Hendrick will drive the wagon back until he finds Burleson's column. Dr. Ewing's with Burleson. Major Hockley will go along and explain that the doctor's to do everything he can. We'll try to find Mrs. Salas's husband. Sorry we can't do more for her. But *those* men—we'll attend to!"

He turned his horse and rode over to where the scouts had halted the prisoners.

Four degenerate criminals, such as too often hang about the outskirts of human disaster.

"What's your name?" he asked.

Long-nosed hound face answered: "Ed Jorrigy."

"Yours?"

Weak face, curled mustache, narrow between the eyes: "Sebastian Olmeda."

"You?"

Dirty beard on this one disguised a nearly absent chin: "Marvin Sorrells."

"And you there?"

Face with wide jaws like a rattlesnake, low forehead over reptile eyes: "Whut difference does it make?"

Under Houston's deadly scowl they did not look up. The long-nosed man was sweating on his upper lip . . . sweat of fear.

The general chose him for questioning. "You—Jorrigy. Where are you from?"

After hesitation: "Mississippi country."

"All of you?"

"Yes. Jest got down hyar."

"Mississippi, eh? River pirates? Cave-in-Rock? Running like rats since your boss robber, John Murrell, got taken?"

No response.

"Take 'em over to those cottonwoods!" Houston ordered.

The prisoners glanced over at the trees, suddenly understood.

"Ain't you even givin' us a trial?" bleated the bearded man with the weak chin.

"You've just had your trial." Houston's voice was iron.

All four culprits were sweating now, in spite of the cold wind that swept through the trees.

"You ain't a-gonna hang us?" The snake-faced man's composure was gone at last. "Them women? They ain't nothin' but Mexicans——"

"Mexicans?" said Houston. "They're *Texans!*"

The scouts knew their business and wasted no time.

By the time the army reached the place, four corpses, no longer kicking, twirled solemnly: hound face, chinless face, narrow-eyed face, snake face, each head twisted at a ghastly unnatural angle by nooses from which the bodies swung in the cottonwoods.

So Sam Houston drove his army, and the refugees accompanying it, through death and tragedy north along the flooded Brazos.

Chapter Thirty-Four

All new states are infested by a class of noisy, second-rate men.

SAM HOUSTON

1

At Groce's plantation there was food, and rest for a time, and for a time safety. Jared Groce was elderly, wealthy, and unafraid. Knowing he was ruined unless the Santa Anna army was beaten, he gave freely of his steers and his corn meal.

He also offered Houston his house as headquarters, but the general preferred a tent improvised of some tarpaulins, where he spent long hours studying a crude map of the country east of the Brazos.

On the second day Henry Karnes reported that he had found a great muddy trail where an army had passed across the country going eastward.

"Which way did it lead?" asked Houston.

"Southeast—near due southeast," said the scout in his piping voice.

Houston nodded. "Probably headed for San Felipe—way down the river. That must be Gaona's army. We fooled General Gaona by switching north so sudden. It means no Mexicans north of us—by that much we're a little safer."

Toward evening that day the people at Groce's heard a distant muttering as of thunder.

"Guns," said Houston. "For the first time I can thank that bull-headed Moseley Baker. The Mexicans have found him at San Felipe crossing and they must be bombarding him across the river. Luck seems to be playing with us. If they think Moseley Baker and Wily Martin are our whole army, they'll not be heading this way, perhaps for days."

Next morning a big, sandy-haired man was brought over the swollen river by Groce's ferry. As he dismounted from his horse, Houston greeted him with genuine joy.

"Tom Rusk! I do hope you've come to stay with us!"

Colonel Thomas Rusk, secretary of war for the provisional Texas government, was an old friend. He shook Houston's hand.

"I aim to," he said. "Too much arguing and too little doing in the cabinet of our eminent president, Mr. David Burnet. Do you know where that statesman and his retinue are now? Headed for Galveston as fast as they can travel."

"To find a ship and leave Texas entirely?"

"Perhaps. I couldn't stomach it. But when I told his nibs I was coming to you, he gave me a letter for you."

The letter was brief, bitter, insulting. It ended:

The enemy is laughing you to scorn. You must retreat no more. The country expects you to fight. The salvation of the country depends on your doing so.

Houston read it and looked up. "You know what's in this?"

Rusk nodded. "Burnet read it aloud to the cabinet."

"'Laughing to scorn—retreat no more—'" growled Houston. "What about Dave Burnet, our brave president? And his so-called cabinet? They're able-bodied men, every one of them, and could be carrying rifles with the army, which needs every soldier it can get. But they're retreating a damned sight faster than this army is."

Rusk nodded. "That's one reason I'm here. I'll serve under you, sir, in any capacity. Even as a private."

Houston looked at him. "You'll be my second in command from here on out." He led the way to his tarpaulin tent. "Tom, could you stand a drink after your ride?"

"Why, yes—don't mind if I do."

The general produced a bottle and Rusk drank thirstily. He wiped his lips with the back of his hand and grinned.

"Mighty good," he said. "Needed something to warm me."

But when he offered the bottle back, Houston shook his head.

"Big Drunk"—that epithet had followed him down from the Indian country. It had destroyed whatever hope he may have had of the one attractive girl in whom he took more than passing interest: Anna Raguet of Nacogdoches, who was too much woman quite to leave him alone, too wary of her security quite to accept him.

He had no success with Anna . . . but other women in Texas were sometimes not so difficult. . . .

He was no anchorite.

"I know I've got a reputation," he said at Rusk's look of surprise when he refused. "But Tom, it's the solemn truth that in this campaign I've not touched liquor in any form."

"Why?"

"Too much at stake. 'Inflaming wine, pernicious to mankind,' as the *Iliad* has it. Only substitute whiskey for the wine, and say that I've got to keep my wits about me and the respect of my men, at least in that regard. But do you know my abstaining from liquor has only been used against me?"

"How?"

"Deaf Smith, one of my scouts, apprehended a dispatch carrier traveling without authorization. He had a letter addressed to Mr. Robert Potter, who holds the high-sounding title of secretary of the navy, in Texas which has no navy, and is at present taking refuge with Mr. President Burnet. The letter was written by one of my own officers—Lieutenant Colonel James Perry, supposed to be an aide of mine but apparently a spy for Potter and Burnet, who hate me. Smith brought the letter to me. It said, 'Since Houston gave up liquor, he has taken to eating opium.'"

"The scoundrel!"

"I interviewed Perry. And admonished him—rather forcefully," went on Houston. "He knows he's now under my direct eye, and I don't believe he'll transgress in that particular way soon again. But how many other spies are in this camp? That opium canard is a cunning one, since it's known that Santa Anna is an opium addict. It would prejudice many against me. As God is my judge, I've never tasted opium in my life—don't know what it's like."

Rusk swore fluently.

"More than one of my officers worries me," said Houston.

"Which ones?"

"It's hard to pick them out. All new states are infested by a class of noisy, second-rate men, selfishly ambitious or greedy, and always in favor of rash or extreme measures. Texas is absolutely overrun by such. In this army are some—I mentioned Perry. I understand that Colonel Sidney Sherman has ambitions to replace me as commander-in-chief. Two of my company captains, Baker and Martin, took their men and left me. They're 'guarding crossings' over the Brazos now. There's another—Lieutenant Colonel Alexander Somervell—it's reported to me that he suggested 'beating for volunteers,' for the purpose of replacing Old Sam Houston." The general gave his tiger grin. "They found Old Sam hard to replace. I ordered two graves dug, and put up a sign calling attention to the fact that any who 'beat for volunteers' would occupy those graves. Nobody's beat for volunteers—the army saw four scoundrels Houston hung on the back trail, and they know damn well I'll do what I say."

"You have their very names," said Rusk. "Perry, Sherman, Somervell, Baker, Martin—the rest. Why not put them under arrest?"

"No." Houston shook his head. "I do not fear them."

"But *I* do—for your sake!"

"Now, Tom, just stop to think. Should I arrest those men because I'm afraid of them? It would only create sympathy for them and make this army distrustful. Men would begin saying I *was* afraid, and wonder who'd be next. That's no way to command an army, and by God I'm going to command this one. Furthermore, I need fighting men; and whatever their faults, those are all fighting men. So instead, I give them responsibility. For example, I've organized a new regiment, the Second, and put Colonel Sherman in command of it."

"Can you trust him?"

"He may have enough to keep him occupied—I gave him some of the toughest, most turbulent companies in the army to control and discipline. Similarly, I also heap the others with duties."

Rusk looked as if he hardly believed his ears.

"Command, under my circumstances, is a heartbreaking job," went on Houston. "I've picked up better than a thousand men. A mob. I'm trying to whip them into an army. Reveille before dawn, tattoo at nine o'clock at night. I handle the drum myself—learned the trick when I was a boy. All day long I keep 'em busy—drills, maneuvers, inspections, details, fatigue duty; and a third of them mount guard each night. Men who are working hard and are tired don't have so much time to worry over their problems. Another thing—Caesar or somebody said it—if you make life plain miserable for soldiers, when they face an enemy they'll fight him twice as hard, just to get even."

Rusk had listened intently. Now he said, "I know you're going to fight—sometime. But when?"

Houston hesitated. "I've not told a soul what my campaign strategy is, or where I'm going, or when I intend to fight. But to you, Tom, I'll say this much: A long time ago, when I was just a red-necked kid, I saw Andrew Jackson for the first time. Andrew Jackson is of no common clay, and that day he said something to me that I've never forgot: *When your enemy is superior to you in strength, extend him—lead him a chase until he exhausts himself—then close suddenly for the decisive blow.*"

He gave Rusk a look almost quizzical. "Whatever else Houston's critics may say, they must admit that I've led Santa Anna over more rain-drenched country, across more swollen rivers, through more canyons, mesquite, cactus, and mud, than he ever dreamed existed. He doesn't know which way I'll turn next. So he has to split his forces. He must leave garrisons to guard supply depots and lines of communication. If he could bring his four columns together he might even yet muster five thousand troops against my one thousand—if I have that many tomorrow, or the next day. I can only try to keep him from such concentration before I hit him."

Thomas Rusk, secretary of war for Texas, who was willing to fight in any capacity, even as a common soldier, knew he was listening to bravery, and greatheartedness, and wisdom. A theory of leadership and strategy subtile and keen had been expounded to him. The pain and loneliness of command were revealed to him, and the iron courage to carry it through to the end. He felt a devout belief in Sam Houston.

2

Connie Thoren was twenty-eight, competent, and used to hard work. She yoked and handled her oxen herself. She made her own camp, fed her own beasts. Her figure was almost boyishly lithe, and her face, with its short nose, square chin, and direct green eyes, had a boyish look also. But Connie was fully a woman.

Her hair, the color of new copper with highlights in it, and her short upper lip, told something about her; and so did her almost defiant manner.

Connie had been a widow for two years. The look of defiance was almost as much toward herself, as to keep at a distance men who perhaps might be inclined to presume on her loneliness: a presumption she was afraid of, because the loneliness, say what she would, was there; and she was a decent woman who did not fully trust herself.

Driving her ox wagon with the army, she had seen a lot of men, and she had refused even to answer them when they grinningly hailed her in passing. As far as those men were concerned, Connie had no fears of being tempted to forsake decorum.

But there was another: she had seen General Houston from a distance, and from close at hand. She had seen the pity in his face when they buried Mrs. Hoag's baby, and she had seen him superbly careering along on that white stallion, and she had seen another side of his nature in the four degenerate rapists he left hanging in the trees.

To Connie, Houston was as different from the other men as he was greater in stature and mental force. He seemed weary at times, or distraught, or gravely concerned. But in the days here in camp he had never passed her without speaking with courtesy. Sometimes it seemed to her more than mere courtesy . . . a warmth which left her wondering, speculating, perhaps inclining. . . .

This night she lay in her blankets in her wagon, and listened to a renewed brief pattering of rain on the canvas above, and she could not sleep. The oxen were quiet, lying outside, chewing their cuds with gentle rhythm. The momentary sprinkle of rain ceased, and water dripped from the trees in the dark. From down near the river—the soldier camp —came distant sounds: men moving about; a sentinel challenged and there were guffaws as he recognized the one he had challenged. Nearer her, in the refugee camp, a child wailed and its mother talked soothingly to quiet it.

From somewhere in the darkness stole a thin and remote sound, clear and frail as the note of a night bird. A flute, she thought, or perhaps a fife; and she recognized the tune, a simple thing. It was an air to which Tom Moore's poem "Come to the Bower" could be sung; and it was very popular just then. The faraway musician, to her ear, played it not badly, and she mentally supplied the words that went with the tune:

Will you come to the bow'r I have shaded for you?
Our bed shall be roses all spangled with dew.
There under the bow'r on roses you'll lie
With a blush on your cheek but a smile in your eye.

The distant love song came to an end. Then, softly, it began all over again.

. . . Under the bow'r on roses you'll lie
With a blush on your cheek but a smile in your eye.

And the words kept going over and over in her mind. Impertinent. Suggestive. She felt the hot blood in her face, and tried to turn her thoughts away, but they came back to the song. Indecent. Terribly, terribly suggestive. *Why* did he play that song?

A widow two years. Two interminable years alone . . . unholy torment . . . two unholy years. She almost sobbed.

She threw aside her blanket and rose on her knees to peer out through the rear of the canvas tilt.

Fifty yards away, apart from both camps, was the shapeless tarpaulin shelter they called the general's tent. From within it a light gave a faint luminosity to the thick canvas.

The man within the tent was awake.

What is he doing in there? she asked herself. Thinking? Alone . . . and perhaps lonely, too . . . ?

Her throat seemed to swell, and all at once a frantic impulse came over her. With hands that began to shake she opened a chest in the darkness and pulled something from it. A dress, a gray wool dress she had not had on for two years. At least she would be a woman again.

The dress was tight. She thought: if I only had a corset. But she had none. She slipped off her rough male clothing, and began to pull the dress over her head and down over her nude body. The clinging fabric clasped her about her breasts and body, but went loose and flowing from the waist down. Her limber arms and wrists worked with the buttons at the back.

Down toward the river the fifer began again his refrain in the night: "Come to the Bower."

He must hear it, too, she said to herself. He must know that song. . . .

And then: Decent and lonely these two years . . . oh, *what* is the matter with me?

She could not answer herself. But with deliberate caution she climbed down out of the wagon to the ground. One of the oxen gave a long sniff, but he knew her and placidly returned to his cud-chewing.

The night seemed pitch black, except for a few distant flickering spots of red where campfires still burned.

Her feet and legs were bare. The wet grass splashed her ankles and she held her skirt knee-high to avoid the moisture, so that the damp feathery stems made cold strokings on her limbs.

Suddenly, twenty feet from the tarpaulin tent, she halted. A voice seemed to cry out in her: Connie Thoren, what are you doing? What madness is this? Two years . . .

A sudden terrified thought: If he saw her what would he think? What *could* he think? A terrible blunder. She turned to flee back to her wagon.

The opening of the tent was thrust aside and a figure stepped out, towering black, the candle throwing a pale illumination behind it. She felt the light on her face, on her cowering body, already half-retreating to escape.

"Who is it?" he called sharply, and took two quick steps toward her. "Why . . . Mrs. Thoren——"

She had to say something.

"I—General Houston—I'm disturbing you—it isn't important——"

He looked at her keenly, his head thrust forward.

"You're not disturbing me. What is it?"

In the candle's light he saw her bare feet, and that she was shaking with cold or fear.

"It's damp out here, Mrs. Thoren," he said. "You'd better come inside."

She felt his hand close on her arm, and it seemed to her that she went like a cloud, as if without conscious effort, as if it were none of her doing.

They were in the tent: he closed the opening.

"Now," he said, "tell me what——"

"General, I must go. I must——"

"You wanted to say something."

"Oh, that." She thought desperately. "It was only—Mrs. Hoag——"

Oh, that . . . as if it were an afterthought! She was sure he could see through it all. He would know she was here . . . for exactly what she was here for. . . .

"Yes? Mrs. Hoag?" he prompted.

"Mrs. Hoag—her husband came—I thought you'd like to know." She was speaking rapidly, too rapidly, jumbling the words together. "He was all right—I saw them go away together——"

And a refrain seemed to beat in her mind: two years . . . decent these two years. . . .

He loomed suddenly nearer. Momentarily his eyes looked into hers, crude and piercing, seeing through her mask, hungering for her. Deliberately his two hands placed themselves at her waist, one on either side, and beneath the fabric of her dress was nothing but the smooth texture of her flesh. She felt him tremble.

"My dear," he breathed. "My dear . . ."

His hands seemed heated as by fire. She felt stupefied, eyes closed, conscious only of the tender roughness of his hands on her. Her mind was saying no to him, her body assenting.

His hands slipped about her, drawing her to him, pressing her whole body against him.

She was past all caprice, all coyness. She did not turn her face away, when he laid his lips upon hers in the kiss.

His kiss seemed to consume her, expressing the passion of the man, hot as the sun, lasting for an unmeasured aeon of time.

The lips were gone; so were the hands.

She opened her eyes. He had stepped backward a pace, and for an instant she saw in his face an expression fierce and startling, as of one suffering a harsh and powerful agony. Then he drew a gasping breath.

After a moment the emotion faded from his countenance and when he spoke again his voice was deep, almost subdued.

"You must forgive me," he said.

"There is nothing to forgive," she said weakly.

"Yes, but there is. You came to me with—with information. And I ——" He broke off, then said, "I hung four men back there on the trail. I have placed provost guards to keep my soldiers from transgressing with the women of the refugee camp. Yet I, their commander, was on the point—myself——"

He was rejecting her!

Humiliation flooded over her, and with it anger, and a need for defense.

"What makes you think—" she flared.

"I don't think." His voice was like a stone. "I *know*."

She gave him a look as if he had struck her. Tears filled her eyes. She turned to the tent entrance and burst out into the night.

3

Alone in the tent, Houston gave a little groan.

"Damn," he said.

He threw himself on his camp bed and bitterly berated himself for handling matters so crudely. Connie Thoren was no cheap wanton. He was certain that she was high-minded and self-respecting; just as he was certain that she had come to his tent to offer herself to him. And he had *wanted* her terribly. She would not understand why he did not accept her. In this would be a well of bitterness.

He understood her action as one of those things that happen not infrequently in times of war: the instinct old as the human race, woman sensing death, a diminution of the reservoir of her kind, driven by an urge transcending all logic to give herself, sometimes wildly, in order to maintain the strength of the nation or the people with a child begotten to replace, perhaps, the very man who fathered it.

He had greatly desired Connie Thoren: and self-denial was not his way, never had been. But a terrible responsibility now sat on his shoulders; it was that responsibility that forced him to take his hands from her body, so thrillingly soft and sleekly smooth under its single garment, when his whole being clamored for her.

But why did he do it the way he did? *I don't think . . . I know.* A flinging of her indiscretion into her very face. The insult—was that necessary?

He had not the least wish to insult Connie Thoren, and he knew he had hurt her terribly. He almost groaned aloud.

Then he realized precisely why it *was* necessary. It was because he understood himself. He had been stronger than himself—once. If the same temptation arose again he could not fully trust himself to resist it. Therefore, because of his damned sense of responsibility, he had to cut the affair off finally and completely, a clean and bitter lopping, by making Connie Thoren hate him.

He cursed the war that created such a necessity. All the things that made life pleasant—work and play, the building of a career or a fortune, the comfort of home, the warmth of friendship, the wonder of the love of women—from these things a man must turn to meet the summons that made a mockery of them all. He found himself hating war, this war, his part in this war. Yet he could not shirk that summons.

A thousand men, five thousand refugees, a newborn nation, the destiny of a people, depended on him and him alone. He must not allow his mind and will to be diverted from his grim and deadly duty by so much as a hair's breadth. And he knew that a night of love, an attachment to a woman, above everything else would create just such a diversion of his focus and will.

That night Sam Houston hardly slept. Not only had the episode with Connie powerfully stirred him, but he had reached a most important decision. No longer could he remain with his army at Groce's: it would invite the enemy to concentrate on him, surround him, destroy him. For a force like his, constant motion was the only safety. He must begin a new march on the morrow, and he knew he would have to twist his column across the country as one twisted the tails of draft oxen to make them pull harder.

He spent that night wakefully, and emerged from his tent next morning grimmer and more intent than ever before.

Yet, after the early formation, and when he had given instructions to his officers, he made it a point to walk past Mrs. Thoren's wagon. She was once more in her ill-fitting man's garb, the dress gone, packed away, a symbol now of her humiliation. He was very sure that she detested him, would despise him the rest of her life.

Yet he stopped where she crouched over a campfire at her breakfast. She turned up to him the old defiant face: short nose, square little chin, green eyes. But her skin seemed so fair and transparent that the movement of her blood colored it.

"We're going to start crossing the Brazos today," he told her.

She listened without a reply.

"I want to see all the people over before the army goes," he said.

"This outfit will be ready," she said curtly.

"I've come to ask a favor," he began; then, hastily: "Not for myself—for the army."

She looked at him coldly. "What?"

Just the single word. She was not wasting words on him.

"We've had an accession," he said. "Two pieces of artillery—six pounders—have arrived across the river from some friends of ours in Cincinnati. Getting them across the country in this heavy going will be hard. Do you need all six of your oxen for this wagon?"

"You're asking for a yoke to help with the guns?"

"That's what I'm asking."

"You can take that lead yoke. I'll make out with the rest."

Deliberately she turned her back on him. As a Texas woman, Connie Thoren would help; but her help was for Texas, not for Houston.

4

The crossing began, with the help of a little river steamboat and the ferry barge, and it required two days. A surprise during this period: Moseley Baker and Wily Martin, with their companies, rejoined the main army. They reported that Santa Anna had managed to get his forces across the Brazos and was somewhere to the south, direction of march unknown.

Houston considered: he had a notion where *El Presidente* might head, but he did not express it to anyone, not even Tom Rusk or George Hockley, the men closest to him in friendship.

For two days he fairly drove the army, and with it the column of refugees, along the road—if it could be called that—eastward from Groce's. Those two days proved the value of Connie's oxen.

Whenever the guns were stuck in the mud, which was often, the two powerful animals did better than any team of horses in hauling them out. Houston kept the oxen with the artillery train, which included two wagons loaded with ammunition—powder, and for missiles, since he had no cannon balls, hundreds of broken-up horseshoes, which he had caused to be cut to pieces during the wait at Groce's. He had organized an artillery company, thirty men commanded by Colonel Joseph Neill, a regular army officer, bluff and rough, with an untrimmed mustache that drooped heavily, hiding his mouth.

The army marched; and it grumbled as usual. Toward the end of the second day's journey, word went about that the road made a fork. One branch led straight east toward Liberty, on the Trinity River. The other turned south toward Harrisburg, on Buffalo Bayou, and thence to Galveston Bay.

Which fork Houston would take became a matter of heated discussion. Opinions were offered freely, sometimes bitterly.

"He's goin' to keep right on retreatin' east."

"Naw, mebbe not. They say the Texas gov'ment's moved to Galveston Island."

"Whut does he care? He might find a Mexican with a gun down thar —mebbe even two or three of 'em. That ol' Cherokee, he don't want nothin' that looks like a fight."

"I don't think he knows *whut* he wants to do."

"Sometimes I wonder if he ain't teched in the upper story."

As the fork was neared, half the army and all of the refugees believed the commander would continue his retreat eastward, to the Sabine River and the Louisiana border. Colonel Sidney Sherman, Captain Moseley Baker, and others shared this belief.

Sherman, his bearded New England face cold as stone, asked Tom Rusk the question:

"Which way will our high and mighty general decide to move?"

"Wait and see," said Rusk. He knew no more than anyone else.

"He's going to refuse again to face the enemy," said Sherman bitterly. "If he does, he's through. We'll *have* to elect a new commander—one who'll fight!"

"Will you be the one to notify him?" asked Rusk.

Sherman did not answer.

5

On the third day the fork in the road was reached.

Men saw Major Hockley galloping ahead to Colonel Burleson, in command of the advance regiment, and speculations grew into a fury of argument, inconclusive and unsatisfied.

Up front, Hockley said to Burleson, "General Houston's compliments, and you will take the route toward Harrisburg."

Burleson did not blink.

"You fellers, in the front company, thar!" he shouted, standing in his stirrups. "Turn down that trail to the right!"

The army had its answer. It was the first intimation of Houston's plan; and the movement of the advance guard brought a wail of fear from the refugees. Imploring faces surrounded him.

"You ain't desertin' us, is you, General?"

"My God, we cain't go thataway!"

"If we keep on, what protection we got ag'in the Injuns?"

Houston listened to them impassively. When they finished from sheer lack of breath, he said, "I'm sending a company to escort you—Captain Wily Martin's company. The rest of the army marches south."

Ugly pause. Wily Martin, ordered to march with the fugitives and thus possibly miss the fighting, looked like a man snake-bit.

But the general faced them without another word, and before his enormous certitude their eyes fell. The Martin company marched off obediently, and the refugee train took the fork of the road that led to the east and safety.

Houston followed his army, which already was turning an oblique to the right. Some of the men looked off toward the line of wagons where those women rode; but the habit of obedience they had acquired in the few days of drill at Groce's caused them to obey their leaders without too many questions.

Presently the general rode up to where one of the guns was half mired as usual. Men were hooking the oxen to the trail to pull it out.

All at once a woman in a man's coat and pants, with an old sombrero crammed down over her copper hair, confronted him.

"You've got my oxen. I want them."

"Mrs. Thoren!" said Houston. "You loaned them to us, didn't you? We need those animals for the cannon."

Her eyes blazed, but she did not hesitate. Drawing a sharp knife from a sheath at her belt, she slashed the rawhide thongs which fastened the chain from the ox yoke to the gun in the mudhole.

"Now get a-going!" she commanded. At the familiar voice the oxen swung away, their mistress behind them.

A bellow behind. "Whar's she goin' with them bulls?"

Houston turned. It was Pete Rohrer, the wagon master, whose voice could be audible at a mile's distance.

"Their owner seems to have repossessed them," said the general.

"We can't git along without them bulls!" exclaimed Rohrer. "The cannon is done bogged down!"

"We'll have to do the best we can," Houston said.

"General, I'm goin' to go an' bring them oxen back!"

As he rode away, Houston raised himself in his stirrups and shouted after him, "Captain Rohrer, that woman will fight!"

"Damn her fightin'!" the wagon master roared back.

Houston dismounted and tied his white stallion to a tree.

"Come on, boys," he said, "let's get her out."

He put his shoulder to a muddy wheel of the bogged cannon as a team of horses was hitched to the trail. Eight or ten of the men joined him, and together they brought the gun out of the wallow.

A few minutes later, as the march proceeded, Captain Rohrer appeared, riding back without the oxen.

"Hey, Captain," shouted one of the men, "whar's them bulls?"

"She wouldn't let me have them," said Rohrer sheepishly.

It was observed that his shirt was torn and beneath it was the mark of a bull whip. The men were gleeful; here was something new on which to vent their spirits.

"How come Rohrer's shirt is tore?" one would chant.

The rest would roar together: "A *woman tore it off'n him!*"

"Whut did she want it for?" the lone voice would inquire.

And the full chorus would crash in: "*She wanted it for baby rags!*"

Rohrer could only grin mirthlessly.

Connie Thoren was, at least in a measure, revenged. She had left her mark on the Texas army: on the back of its wagon master, perhaps on the heart of its general.

Chapter Thirty-Five

Remember the Alamo!

SAM HOUSTON

1

A stroke of unbelievable good fortune.

Scouting out ahead as usual, Deaf Smith and Henry Karnes saw two Mexican riders hurrying as if on an errand of urgency.

The mesquite was thick there, and the scouts found no difficulty in the ambush. The Mexicans might have been shot from their saddles, but when they saw the rifles looking their way, they hastily surrendered. A little later they stood shrinking before the giant Texas general.

One of them wore the uniform of a Mexican officer. The other was a mere *mozo* in uniform, not worthy of consideration.

In his hands Houston held a pair of saddlebags.

"Ask him where he got these," he said.

Beside him stood an aide, Major Lorenzo de Zavala, an educated Mexican, son of a former vice-president of that nation—who was now in exile with the Texas cabinet and certain to die if he was captured. The major, young, dark, and intelligent, interpreted for his commander.

"He says," said Zavala after questioning the Mexican officer, "that the saddlebags were given him by an officer of General Filisola's staff."

Houston held them up. On them, hand-tooled in the leather, was a name: *William Barrett Travis*.

"This man was at the Alamo massacre," he said.

At the name, and the look on his face, the Mexican officer needed no interpreter. He broke into a flood of protests in his own tongue, gesticulating in a terrified manner.

"He says," interpreted Zavala, "that he is Captain Miguel Bachillor, a *correo*—that is, a dispatch rider—from the City of Mexico, sent by General Filisola on this errand. And he swears by the soul of his mother that the saddlebags were given him as he has said."

Houston thrust a great paw into the bag and drew out some papers.

"He may be telling the truth," he growled. "Some of these dispatches do come all the way from the City of Mexico. Tell him it's lucky for him. If my men thought he was at the Alamo, they'd kill him."

At the renewed protests when Zavala rendered this, Houston said, "Take these men away and guard them well. Zavala, I'll need you."

Together, the major translating and he listening, they began to read the contents of the saddlebags. First was an adulatory letter from the Mexican secretary of state, congratulating Santa Anna on his "victories" at Goliad and the Alamo. One paragraph was fulsome:

Providence is propitious to us and has destined Your Excellency to be the savior and preserver of the Republic. Your Excellency has garnished your temples with laurels of everlasting fame.

Houston thrust it impatiently aside.

At the next dispatch his interest became suddenly intense. It was from Filisola, addressed to Santa Anna, acknowledging a requisition for five hundred more infantry, and stating that they were marching at once under General Cos. But what made Houston's eyes blaze was a sentence commenting on the fact that the Mexican dictator "with a thousand men," was at New Washington, where he had "dashed in hope of catching the rebel president, Burnet, and his suite, before they left the mainland."

Inspiration kindled Houston's face. New Washington, a village on Galveston Bay, was less than twenty-five miles, as the gaunt desert raven flew, from where he stood at that moment. It was, to be sure, on the other side of Buffalo Bayou, a sluggish tidal stream three hundred feet wide at this point, on the banks of which the army had halted in its southward march. And the road to it would be more crooked than straight. But Houston had not dreamed that he might catch Santa Anna without his entire army about him.

Beyond, on the opposite shore of the bayou, the men could see the blackened shells of houses: all that remained of Harrisburg, once a thriving little Texas town, burned at the orders of Santa Anna. It was almost evening, and Houston had driven his men savagely for three days, believing that sooner or later the Mexican forces would head for Galveston. The soldiers were dead beat, not only from marching every foot of the way with little to eat, but from manhandling the supply wagons, and especially the two awkward cannon, through the quagmires that beset the boggy trail. No use trying to cross the bayou this evening. The general gave an order:

"Tell the men to camp here. Be ready to move out at daybreak."

That night while his army slept in exhaustion, Houston crouched beside a candle in one of the supply wagons until two o'clock in the morning, poring over a crude map, made by some amateur cartographer, and purporting to show the country around Galveston Bay. His finger traced the contours of the crooked coastline. New Washington seemed to stand on a point extending into the bay. Behind it were some salt-water lagoons, if the map could be trusted. Buffalo Bayou ran into these lagoons from a direction generally west, and joined there a river from the north with the odd name of San Jacinto. Between all this and his army's present camp nobody in God's world knew what morasses, bayous, cutbank creeks, and pitfalls lay. But somewhere in that labyrinth was Santa Anna. . . .

At two o'clock he lay down for a nap, but was awake at four, in time to beat reveille as usual, on the army's only drum.

Breakfast, such as it was, was hastily eaten, and he ordered the men formed into a hollow square. Into the center of this he rode.

"Soldiers!" His great voice rose as he pointed off to the east, where in the early morning light a column of smoke smirched the horizon. "There is Santa Anna, burning New Washington as he burned Harrisburg!"

He reminded them grimly that this was the same Santa Anna who ordered the massacres of Texans.

"You've been asking for a battle—now you're going to have it!" he promised. And he concluded this brief peroration with a few stirring sentences:

"Victory is certain! Trust God and fear not! The victims of the Alamo and the names of those murdered at Goliad cry out for cool, deliberate vengeance! Remember the Alamo! Remember Goliad!"

From the massed ranks came a savage roar: "*Remember the Alamo!*"

All that day Houston, with infinite labor, supervised the crossing of his army over the bayou. Horses were swum over, their riders swimming with them. Other men and the vehicles, including the cannon, were transported on an old ferryboat, abandoned and leaking badly, and a crude raft of timbers on which puncheons from the floor of an old cabin were spiked.

Night was coming on when the operation at last was finished. Sick call was ordered, and the doctors examined the men who answered it. All who were pronounced ill or unfit were told to remain in camp beside the bayou. The rest, able to march and fight, numbered exactly seven hundred and eighty-three, officers and men together.

A small force, an insignificant force: but with it Houston set out at once in the gathering darkness.

No man who participated in that night march along the south bank of Buffalo Bayou ever forgot it. Minor bayous, creeks, and treacherous marshes cut across the execrable muddy route. Again and again the weary men halted, cursing, to help drag through the deep morasses wagons mired down, and especially the guns. In the beginning some romantic soul had christened those two cannon "the Twin Sisters," but by this time the army had devised other names for them, more and more descriptive and profane.

The men were wretched, and they were spent until it seemed that the very wind that blew coldly from the sea was a wall against which they could hardly make headway. But up and down the column stormed

Houston. In those hours he seemed possessed by some momentous force, a madness almost, demanding from them more than they could give, driving them on and still on when it seemed they could no longer drag one foot before the other.

In the darkness his eyes once more had the old, flat pin-pupiled glare of the great prowling jungle cat. Sam Houston, long the hunted, had at last become the hunter.

2

Two o'clock in the morning. The army groggily stumbled across a narrow bridge—Vince's bridge, somebody said—and heard the order to break ranks. Men dropped to the ground where they were, and instantly were asleep in the wet grass.

But only an hour was given them. Then their officers were among them, getting them into line once more. Complaints were sternly hushed.

"No noise, keep quiet," was the warning.

At that the men conceived they were nearing a hostile force. Talk became low, almost whispered, orders traveled muted down the lines, the Twin Sisters had their chains and rattling parts muffled by coats and leather straps.

Dawn. They reached a patch of live oaks, heavily hung with Spanish moss, on the boggy bank of the bayou, with an impassable morass on either side and a prairie covered with long grass sloping up from it.

"Fall out. Camp here."

A few cattle were found grazing in the woods. Butchering details cut their throats, and pieces of beef sizzled on ramrods over new-lit fires.

At sunup the men saw to the north a river—the San Jacinto—and beyond it a few houses, the hamlet of Lynchburg. Overlooking the village was a round hill, and upon it stood some people, watching the little army. They soon disappeared.

In after years that rise would be known as Tory Hill; for the persons on it, hoping to curry favor with Santa Anna, carried to him news of the arrival of the Texas force.

Silent as usual, Houston walked about, viewing the terrain and the position of his various units, occasionally talking briefly to one of his scouts, whom he at once dispatched on some errand, the nature of which he vouchsafed to nobody.

About their cooking fires the men, ragged and dirty—and in most cases itching with vermin—chewed their half-broiled meat, and talked as all soldiers do, about women, and next to that about rations, and after that about other things of less importance at the moment. But no enemy was in sight, and even the never-failing topic of women, and what the soldiers thought of them, and reminiscences of them sometimes lecherous, and hopes concerning them once this damned war was over, lagged presently from weariness. The men suffered from the exhaustion of forced marches, little sleep, precious short victuals—and now they at least had something in their bellies. Their numbed senses carried them off into snoring slumber.

Morning passed, and noon came. Scouts galloped into camp with an alarm. They had seen the main force of the enemy marching out of New Washington in the direction of the Texas position. Santa Anna had received his warning from the Lynchburg Tories.

Houston listened to the information as if he had been expecting it, looked forward to it. He rapped out orders:

"Have your men stand to arms, and inspect all rifles. Colonel Sherman, your regiment will occupy the left; Colonel Burleson the right. Colonel Neill, you will have your guns run out to the edge of the woods."

Within the shadow of the oaks, bearded with hanging moss, the riflemen mustered. Houston swung into his saddle and trotted the white stallion over to the two guns which stood in the open, just beyond the verge of the trees. Arms behind his back, legs wide apart, Colonel Neill was giving orders in a harsh voice.

"Load—powder! Prepare—charge!"

He looked up at Houston. "Hard to give proper commands. Powder, yes. But can you call broken horseshoes ammunition?"

"Depends," said Houston, "on their execution. Do you think your men can hit anything?"

"No," said Neill simply.

"Come, come." Houston grinned. "Be at least hopeful."

"I've drilled the boys in everything but target practice," said Neill. "Never had the powder for that. But, General, I'll train those pieces myself. My boys might not be able to hit anything, but with a little luck an old gunner like me might do some damage."

"Good, Joe."

From over the rise bugles suddenly sang out.

"Hyar they come!" cried voices in the trees.

A scattered line of figures appeared: skirmishers, advancing cautiously, looking toward the wood. They could see the two guns and a few men around them, but it was apparent that they feared what might be lurking among those moss-hung oaks.

Houston rode among the trees along the irregular line of his men. "Hold your fire, boys," he kept cautioning. "Don't shoot until you're sure. I don't have to tell you to pick out a target. Wait for 'em to come in closer, then make every bullet count."

Over the rise a sudden disturbance. Mules galloping forward through the center of the advancing Mexican skirmish line. They drew a piece of artillery: Santa Anna's twelve pounder, which the Mexicans called "the Golden Standard."

Houston watched the big gun—twice as large as either of his—wheeled into place, the gunners at work, the mules drawn off.

From a distance the enemy's bugles were heard again.

Zavala listened. "That's the 'Deguello'—the 'beheading song,'" he said. "It means no quarter—Santa Anna played it at the Alamo."

A cloud of smoke erupted with a great, authoritative thunder from the Mexican cannon. Overhead, ripping through the oak trees, howled a shell.

Houston spurred out to the Twin Sisters. "Try your hand on that gun, Joe!" he called to Neill.

Neill squatted behind one of the six pounders, sighting along its barrel, adjusting elevation and aim. The first shot boomed out. A splash of ripped-up sod—wide of the mark.

"Damn this kind of chicken feed!" growled Neill. "How can you gauge scrap iron? No trajectory basis!" His face was flushed with annoyance.

"Try the other gun."

Neill altered the elevation of the second muzzle, sighted it with great care.

"Fire!" he said.

With the echoing report of the cannon, Houston, sitting his horse to one side, to be clear of the smoke, saw Mexican mules down, and a mounted man, evidently an officer, on the ground.

A little cheer went up from the amateur gunners, but Neill was scowling. "I missed that damn gun——"

A second blast from the big Mexican cannon and a shell splintered with an ear-splitting crack near the Twin Sisters.

Neill was flat on the ground, his men bending over him.

"What is it?" asked Houston, dismounting beside him.

Neill looked up, his face gone white. "Hip," he said through clenched teeth. "Smashed, I'm afraid. And just when I was getting the range——"

He was actually more concerned by his failure to hit his target than he was over the wound which already splashed his trousers scarlet with hot blood.

"Take him to the rear," ordered Houston.

Now the Mexican skirmishers came bobbing forward at a clumsy run. He rode back to his riflemen.

"Three hundred yards," he said, his voice calm. "Two hundred."

From the oaks Texas rifles broke into a sudden clatter. Some of the running figures wilted down. The rest turned and ran away.

"Hold your fire!" shouted Houston.

The enemy was withdrawing, even hauling back its cannon.

"Don't waste powder," Houston told his men. "Haven't got enough for that. They were just feeling us out. Next time it will be the real article—root, hog, or die!"

3

Reveille, the morning of April 23, beaten as usual at four o'clock, but for the first time by another hand than the general's. The previous evening Houston had found in camp a free Negro named Dick, who once had played in a band and knew the drumbeats.

The long strain of incessant labor, worry, contentions, and sleepless nights, had told even on Houston's giant strength, and he slept through that morning formation. Not until the men had eaten their breakfasts did he at last turn over, yawn hugely, and sit up.

Colonel Burleson was standing beside him, looking down at him.

"How are you feeling, General?" he asked. A hint of concern in his voice. Houston sleeping after reveille? It was so unheard of that it might presage bodily illness. To Burleson the incapacity of his commander at such a time meant disaster.

But Houston grinned at him. "I feel better," he said. "Do you know that's the first time I've slept more than three hours at a stretch in six weeks?"

"There's some meat cooked for you. I had it brought over."

"Thanks. How are your men feeling?"

"Itching to get at the enemy," said Burleson stoutly.

"Probably itching from something else, too," said Houston, biting into a slab of roast meat, Indian fashion, then cutting off the piece close to his mouth with his knife. He chewed a moment. "Tell 'em to scratch their lice and wait. I've got to know what Santa Anna's intentions are."

He could see some of his officers at a distance, scowling at him as he squatted there, leisurely eating, when they believed he should be in action.

In his own good time he rose and looked off toward the enemy position. There was some excitement among the trees, for Mexican cavalry had appeared on top of the rise, six hundred yards away. He knew the enemy camp was beyond that rise, but it was invisible from where he stood.

"They're just observing us," he told Burleson. After a time the cavalry vedettes disappeared.

But around noon the camp was aroused by the arrival of Deaf Smith, his horse a-lather from a hard ride. His howling voice was heard by many of the men as he reported to Houston.

"More Mexicans!" he cried. "A hull bunch of 'em follered our track—

right over Vince's bridge! Lemme go cut down that thar bridge so's more of 'em won't cross over."

Houston saw the men listening. He gave the scout a quizzical look.

"I never thought anyone could fool you, old horse," he said. "Are you sure that wasn't Santa Anna marching his men around a hill, just to give you an idea there was more of him?"

The canny scout caught his half wink: a barely perceptible droop of an eyelid.

"Why, shore!" Deaf Smith burst into a laugh. "I declar', Gen'ral, now I think on it, that's jest whut it was—couldn't be nothin' else. I'm plumb shamed at myself."

The listeners turned away, chuckling. Not often, they said to each other, that Deaf Smith got taken in by a trick like that.

They did not hear the scout whisper:

"It's Cos, an' five hundred men, near as I can make it."

Houston nodded. "I've expected them. Filisola promised them in his dispatch."

Deaf Smith looked incredulous. "Ye *waited* for 'em?"

The general smiled. "Why take two bites of one cherry?" But then he added, "That's a good idea, cutting that bridge. Filisola himself might be on the heels of Cos. Take a squad of men and see to it."

4

In the camp the malcontents were busy as usual. He could see their smoldering eyes turned toward him, and was aware that some of his officers were going from mess-fire to mess-fire, dropping sneering remarks concerning him, trying to stir his men against him, in some cases finding willing ears to listen.

But he lay in the shade, his head resting on his saddle, thinking. Great responsibility is always heavy; but he bore a degree of responsibility such as few commanders ever carried in war. Under the grove of live oaks with him were all the fighting men left in Texas, less than eight hundred of them. And they were in angry dissension, blaming each other, blaming their officers, above all blaming him—for exactly what, they hardly knew.

He wished he could talk with Andrew Jackson, that unshakable and knowledgeable soldier. But the General was not here.

Only he, Sam Houston, was here: and it came over him with blinding clarity that, after all, he was not self-determining as he had once thought. What was he doing here? He was simply following instructions: pursuing a plan, a purpose never entirely put into words, but implicit in his understanding with his great chief.

Andrew Jackson's border captain!

He found that he did not resent the thought: where the General was concerned he knew no vanity. Instead he began hoping even more strongly that he could at the last make a report of success to his commander.

The crisis was imminent, not to be delayed, not to be avoided.

What if he blundered, and lost this last army of Texas? Disaster would be a weak word for what would ensue. Assuredly Santa Anna would purge Texas of everything American. The lands reclaimed by American industry from the harsh wilderness would be confiscated; the labor of years would be destroyed; hundreds, perhaps thousands, of colonists would dangle from gibbets or gush forth their lifeblood, riddled by firing squads, or massacred as they fled with lance or sword. Despotism would be ascendant, democracy stamped out.

Even worse, in the long view . . . *explode this nation across the continent* . . . he remembered those words and the old General's solitary enormous concern for his country. That—Andrew Jackson's epic dream— would be blasted, too.

He suddenly conceived that upon those ragged, half-starved men under the moss-hung oaks hung not only the fate of Texas, but the fate perhaps of a hemisphere.

How best to use this scanty resource? He bent his mind to that problem. Confronting him was a Mexican army better disciplined than his and double his numbers. With that army, commanding it, was the bloody despot, Antonio López de Santa Anna, himself.

Houston wanted that army. Above all he wanted Santa Anna. And for a purpose that suddenly seemed to flame like an inspiration in his mind. He desired above everything else to have Santa Anna alive, and in that moment of conception there was something greater than mere military strategy in the mind of Sam Houston. Farsighted statesmanship was in this secret thinking.

The question was how to destroy the enemy completely, and if rare luck played with him, capture the person of *El Presidente*.

To him it was obvious that Santa Anna was confident, perhaps overconfident, in his expectation of victory. Should the Texans await the Mexican attack where they were, Houston believed that one rifle in the hands of a Texan was worth two *escopetas* in the hands of as many foes. The attack might be beaten back, the enemy army perhaps driven from the field by hard fighting.

But what if, as seemed now probable, Santa Anna preferred to wait, secure in his fieldworks, for the arrival of still more troops, under Filisola perhaps, or Urrea? To face attack by such overwhelming numbers might be heroic, but it also might be a repetition of the tragedy of the Alamo.

No, he must bring on the battle before the odds became even more heavily weighted. And he must conduct it in such a way that the enemy would not merely be routed, but crushed.

Suppose Santa Anna attacked and was repelled—what would be the outcome? No more than an empty victory. The Mexicans might fly, but they would regroup, and it would all be to do over again. Moreover, Santa Anna would remain securely enough behind the battle line so that in event of a repulse he would at least be in position to escape and join his other, greater forces that now were marching toward this very point.

The thing became suddenly clear. The Texans must go after their enemies, not wait for their enemies to come to them.

Now, as to time: a surprise attack at night?

No, night-fighting was blind fighting. A phrase came to him, *Where the weakest link is, smite.*

And he considered that in war the Mexican's weakest link might be the national habit, almost a vice, the siesta. If he could catch them in the siesta hour . . .

The thought brought him to his feet. He began to walk through the trees, and as he passed one of the mess-fires the men looked up at him with the impertinence of indiscipline.

"When you goin' to let us fight?" one of them said.

Houston turned coldly on his heel.

"Fight and be damned!" he replied.

But he knew something must be done, and that quickly. He must quiet this incipient mutiny, and at once. His army, crude and untrained, would become worse—a mob without direction, because like all mobs it would ignore any authority. This was the work of his ill-wishers, the overambitious officers who were greedy to supplant him and too blind to see that by continuing to sow discord in the very face of the enemy they were risking not only the cause for which they protested they were fighting, but their very lives, for none would be spared should Santa Anna be the victor. He must shut those mouths, if only for the hour or two until he was ready to strike.

To Major Hockley he said, "George, since Colonel Neill is disabled, I'm placing you in command of the artillery."

Then he drew Major Zavala aside and told him, "Summon all the field officers for a council of war."

They gathered quickly. He knew his enemies: Sherman, Somervell, Lamar, Bennett, and Wharton. And also his friends: Rusk and Burleson. Also he knew that Millard and Wells would obey orders without question. But he gave no inkling of this in his expression or voice.

"Gentlemen," he said, "here is the proposition: Shall we attack the enemy or await his attack on us?"

The dissension in the army was immediately apparent. A heated argument ensued, and for more than an hour it continued. The upshot was that most were in favor of awaiting attack. Objections to attempting an assault were raised: the Texans must cross nearly a mile of prairie to reach the Mexican lines; veteran enemy troops were fortified; Texas soldiers were raw recruits, without even bayonets. At this grave moment the very men who lately had criticized most bitterly Houston's caution—men like Sherman, Wharton, and Lamar—suddenly themselves became cautious. Even Rusk and Burleson were for defense rather than bold offense. Of the nine only two, Millard and Wells, favored assault.

Houston listened, impassive as an Indian, to their long wrangling. At last he said, "Gentlemen, thank you. Return to your units."

They separated, were puzzled, resentful. Colonel Sherman grumbled:

"He asked us to vote, didn't he? But he gave us no indication of his own opinion. Wonder what the big Cherokee's going to do? I'll bet he *still* hasn't made up his mind."

5

But Houston had made up his mind. He glanced toward the top of the rise. No sign of Mexican cavalry now. Evidently Santa Anna was so sure of eating up the Texas handful that he was taking his time, ready to move when it suited him.

Having given no hint of his decision to the council of war, he mounted his big white stallion, and rode down through the trees along the lines where his army lay.

"Boys," he said to group after group, "get yourselves ready. We're going after them."

The men scrambled to their feet and gazed at him with a new look. Action at last! And they were lank and dirty and whiskered; but all of a sudden they were intent and dangerous.

These were men who knew their lives were forfeit. All they asked was to make the enemy pay as heavily as possible for those lives, and for the lives of their friends and relatives slaughtered in the bloody march northward.

Houston saw the gleam in their eyes, and felt new confidence.

"I heard someone playing a fife one night at Groce's," he said.

Voices responded:

"Yeah. Lemsky, that German feller."

"Thar he is—over yonder."

"Come hyar, Lemsky, the gen'ral wants to see ye."

Several thrust forward a sheepish-looking man with tousled blond hair and beard.

"Are you Lemsky?" asked Houston.

"Yah." He bobbed acknowledgment, awed by this attention.

"Can you play 'Yankee Doodle'?"

"*Nein.*"

"What in hell can you play?"

"Vell—I play 'Come to der Bower.'"

"Is that all?"

"Yah. I know dot vun tune."

Houston stared at him. He remembered the night he heard the fife tootling that tune in the darkness, and it evoked memories. . . . But then he grinned.

"Bring Dick, the Negro drummer," he said. And when this was done he spoke to the two of them: "You're to be this army's music. When we start for the enemy, you play 'Come to the Bower' for all you're worth!"

He looked down his awkward line of battle now forming. At the extreme right was his handful of cavalry, under a newly created colonel with the curious name of Mirabeau Buonaparte Lamar, flanked on a small bayou. Next in order were two companies of Texas "regular" infantry, under Lieutenant Colonel Henry Millard, who had voted for this attack.

A few yards ahead of these stood the Twin Sisters and their gunners, commanded now by Major George Hockley, upon whom Houston could depend.

There followed in order down the array: Burleson's First Regiment, the real backbone of the army; Moseley Baker's company; and then the Second Regiment under Sherman, its flank on a deep marsh. Behind this desperate line flowed Buffalo Bayou, deep and wide, cutting off any chance of retreat.

"Tom," said Houston to Rusk, "ride over to Sherman. You see that island of live oaks on the slope of the prairie in front of our left? It might help him to advance unnoticed for a little while. I want him to come around the enemy's flank on that side. You stay with him until you see he's headed right, then report to me."

"Yes, sir." Rusk saluted and galloped off.

Out in front of his line Houston rode, the white stallion champing his bit and whipping his tail with the excitement he sensed.

Houston's voice lifted:

"Texans! Remember the Alamo!"

"*Remember the Alamo!*" came back the fierce shout—the war cry of Texas, now.

"Remember Wash Cottle! I'm goin' to skin them Meskins for Wash Cottle!" rose a single high-pitched yell.

The men roared with laughter. It was Uncle Jimmy Curtis, the oldest man in the army, so toothless that his chin and nose almost met, but droll and well liked. Washington Cottle, his son-in-law, was one of the martyrs of the Alamo.

"We'll help you skin 'em, Uncle Jimmy!" several assured him.

Houston lifted his sword.

"Hold your fire until you can make it count! Forward! *Come on—Texas!*"

The German fifer and the Negro drummer struck up the one tune they knew:

Will you come to the bow'r I have shaded for you?
Our bed shall be roses all spangled with dew.
There under the bow'r on roses you'll lie
With a blush on your cheek but a smile in your eye.

The strangest music that ever took an army into battle. But to that love song the Last Hope of Texas, in a line nine hundred yards from end to end but thin as a sheet of paper, surged forward up the grassy slope toward Fate.

Chapter Thirty-Six

You killed Wash Cottle! Now I'm goin'
to kill you an' make a razor strop out'n
yore hide!

UNCLE JIMMY CURTIS

1

The voluptuous tastes of the Mexican dictator were a matter of whispered comment, even among his own men, though they knew that open criticism of *El Presidente* meant death.

General Antonio López de Santa Anna—who liked to refer to himself as the Hero of Tampico, or the Napoleon of the West—always campaigned luxuriously as far as his personal comforts were concerned.

His tent, a large marquee lined with silk, was floored with rugs. There was a fine bed, invariably made up with elegant coverings, and other rich furniture. Food served to him was prepared by a special chef, and his wines were notable. Conveniently near the bed in the imperial tent stood a medicine chest, beautifully hand-carved and ornamented. Its chief stock was a quantity of opium, to which *El Presidente* was a confirmed and notorious addict.

To these luxuries in Santa Anna's suite was added another: almost invariably he had with him a girl.

There had been many mistresses in his previous campaigns. During the present expedition he had for a time consoled his leisure hours with a pretty little thing named Melchora, seventeen years old, to whom he took a fancy in San Antonio de Bexar, and carried her away with him in spite of her mother's tearful protests. But Melchora had the bad judgment to become pregnant. So when he reached the Guadalupe River, and found it would be impossible for him to travel in his elegant coach any farther across the execrable Texas trails, he sent the girl back home in it. And he felt that he had done quite the handsome thing by her in dispatching with her an order that she be provided with a husband from among the soldiers he had left in garrison there—to give a name to his child by her.

After that, for a time, Santa Anna was without a woman in this Texas wilderness. But only four days previous to his arrival at the San Jacinto plain, he had chanced upon something in the feminine line, a little different and quite appealing to his rather jaded tastes as a libertine.

His army on that day arrived at a plantation owned by a certain Colonel James Morgan. Unfortunately, the proprietor had hastily departed —with most of his valuables. He was, it was reported, with the Texas president, Burnet, on Galveston Island.

But the plantation maintained some semblance of operation, and a gang of twenty slaves, of both sexes, was engaged under the eye of an overseer in loading a flatboat at the landing with sacks of flour.

One of the slaves caught *El Presidente's* eye: a woman—a girl, rather, for she was no more than twenty—light-skinned, evidently at least half white, with features quite comely, more Spanish than Negro. She had a fine, sinuous figure, her back exquisitely arched when she carried one of the fifty-pound sacks down to the flatboat; and she was opulent of bosom yet small of waist.

Her name was Emily. She did not know her father, but her mother told her he was a white man, "a Spaniard," and that was where she got her "looks." She possessed no surname.

Emily was a slave; but she also was a woman. She saw Santa Anna gazing at her from the bank. Though she did not know who he was, she observed his handsome uniform with its gold epaulets and medals, and his Napoleonic hat trimmed with gold lace; and she knew from these things that he was a "boss man."

As he continued to watch her, the woman in her could not help a smile at him. The flash of her white teeth and black eyes captivated Santa Anna.

A little later, when the Mexican army moved on from Morgan's plantation, Emily went with it, officially listed as a cook for *El Presidente*, but actually for purposes quite different from that. Santa Anna already had a chef, who was trained to prepare foods both tasty and bland, for the generalissimo's digestion was delicate.

Emily was wholly uneducated, but she did not require education to know what was ordained for her when she was told that she must go along, riding in one of the wagons of the Mexican headquarters entourage. At the first camp her new master sent for her, and she went to his marquee without any particular reluctance or false modesty.

She had known men before: no slave girl at twenty was a virgin, especially no pretty one was. If the black men did not get after her, there usually were white ones who did. Emily knew both kinds.

This particular white man, *El Presidente*, wore much perfume, to which she was unaccustomed, and insisted that she take frequent baths, which she considered a waste of time. But these were eccentricities that one could become used to, and Emily was far from unhappy in her new estate.

Being mistress to Santa Anna was better than carrying flour sacks from the warehouse to a flatboat. All that was required of her was that she be ready when she was wanted, and acquiesce in her purely instinctive manner, even to some of his practices that were novel and strange to her. Between times she had nothing to do but rest; and she had a new dress of fine dimity to replace her linsey, and a necklace and earrings, and a seat in a wagon to ride at ease when the army moved.

As for Santa Anna, he was delighted the first time he lay with her on his silk-covered bed. The girl knew tricks of the body, a matter of sheer instinct with her, and in their love-making she displayed a tropical fervor that was straight from the jungle.

El Presidente, a voluptuary who had experienced so many women that he was quite sated, found his appetites wonderfully restored by the sinuous writhings of the girl's tawny body. She was a new kind of enjoyment and he became fairly engrossed in her. Unsophisticated though she was, she seemed to anticipate and unite herself with his most sophisticated experiments, so that at times she left him quite emptied with sheer pleasure.

Houston had refused himself the digression of sex; his opponent allowed himself to be sensually entranced. But Santa Anna could not have foreseen, nor could Emily, the role she was to play in making history.

Having awakened from his siesta that afternoon of April 23, *El Presidente* ate a piece of opium from his medicine chest, and considered matters. His army was quiet, enjoying its siesta also. It lay behind a barricade of pack saddles and camp impedimenta in a line like a crescent moon, its right tip on a deep morass, its left on a wooded creek, its center curving back in an arc. Between the horns of that arc the rebel army was securely held. It could not escape.

Santa Anna was glad that his brother-in-law, General Cos, had arrived that morning after a forced march, bringing with him five hundred and forty *soldados*. This reinforcement raised his total force to something over fifteen hundred men; and he anticipated that Urrea or Filisola might join him next day, or the day after that.

For the present he could see no reason for hurrying. The rebels were bottled up; the fruit could be picked at leisure. Besides, Cos's men required rest. He had allowed them to camp in the rear of his lines, their arms stacked, while they scattered to sleep or cook rations.

All in all, *El Presidente*, what with the opium he had eaten, felt in a mood for relaxation. He yawned, lazily summoned an orderly by ringing a small silver bell at his bedside, and directed the man to send Emily to him.

The girl came promptly, entered the tent, and smiled at him. She had magnificent teeth and the dress she wore did not disguise her fine form.

He was in a playful mood this afternoon, and allowed himself the pleasure of disrobing her. She knew, and freely indulged him, in the preliminaries he required. Naked, on the silk-covered bed, she was especially satisfactory. Sex is, after all, a matter of team play, and they were becoming used to each other, thus deriving the added pleasure that comes from a knowledge of personal aptitudes and inclinations.

In the midst of his ecstasy Santa Anna heard a bugle; but his mind did not even accept it, so preoccupied was he with the delectation of the moment. Not until gunshots began to sound was he able to bring himself to awareness of the outside.

Men were shouting in warning or alarm. The racket of many muskets increased. Suddenly the "Golden Standard" thundered.

Santa Anna rose from his couch, attired only in an undershirt of linen studded with diamonds, and a pair of silk drawers.

He peered out of the marquee, and instantly bolted through the door, disappearing without.

Emily was still lying nude on the silken bed when the disaster struck. Whether by detaining the Mexican generalissimo with her seductions she unwittingly affected the decision of the battle, is a piquant question. But this is sure: she did detain him so long that he had no time to attire himself properly before he fled to escape the sudden onset of his enemies.

2

Up the slope toward the Mexican barricade toiled the thin single line of Texans, a strange, wild march of haggard men, knowing they were assailing an enemy of overwhelming numbers, knowing that only death awaited them if they did not win this day.

They did not keep formation, but each man sought, after a fashion, to remain in touch as close as possible with those on either side of him.

At first they did not fire their rifles; and at the beginning the curve of the hilltop allowed them to advance some little distance before they were observed from the Mexican camp.

But then came a high warning cry from in front; bugles sounded and Mexican muskets began to thud. Even then the Texas rifles did not reply.

Back and forth before the scattered line galloped Houston on his white stallion, encouraging his men. Now they greeted him with hoarse wild shouts, for at last they knew their leader and for what he had planned and labored all along.

The big Mexican cannon roared. But its charge went too high, and the Texas line still surged forward.

On the right the Twin Sisters toiled up the slope, hauled by rawhide ropes at the hands of their thirty swearing attendants. Houston rode over toward them and Hockley saw his sword jerk in the direction of the enemy barricades.

He shouted orders: his men leaped to the guns, swung them about, and the Twin Sisters blasted their eruption of horseshoe fragments. Too close to miss. Part of the barricade ceased to exist, and with it the men behind it.

Down the Texas line Deaf Smith rode like the wind, his great howling voice crying, "Fight for your lives! Vince's bridge is down! Fight for your lives!"

The Texans needed no reminder that all retreat was cut off. They were as men already dead.

Off to the left came a shout: "Remember the Alamo!"

In an instant it was taken up, a terrible roar for vengeance, by every throat in the Texas line:

"*Remember the Alamo!*"

In that line also, Captain Seguin's company of Texas Mexicans, fighting loyally, rendered it in their own tongue:

"*Recuerden el Alamo!*"

Here and there men stumbled and fell as the muskets from the barricade increased their volume of sound and powder smoke blurred the whole enemy position.

The Texans were no longer walking. They began to run forward, each man at such speed as he could maintain, but each furious to get at the enemy.

Never in any battle was there such a charge as this. Dirty, savage fighters had forgotten life and looked only for death. No mere bravery here; it was exaltation, an irresistible dedication to conclusion, for a payment in blood long delayed.

Houston, riding in front of the line, felt carried out of himself, believed with all his soul that nothing could stand against this charge.

Saracen gave a shuddering leap, sank to the ground. Houston loosed his feet from the stirrups and sprang aside as the stallion collapsed dead, riddled by musket balls.

A soldier caught a horse for him; and the men cheered when they saw him mount again, unharmed.

Now for the first time the Texas rifles began to crackle. Behind the barricade gray-clad figures went down.

Twenty yards to the enemy line. Moseley Baker, a fighter for all his insubordination, was down. Junius Mottley, Rusk's aide, was down. Others were down. Reeling, with their blood spattering from them, the wounded tried to keep their feet, stumbling, no longer cheering, until they fell behind, too weak to go on.

In the drifting clouds of smoke the barricade appeared just ahead, and the din of the battle rose to a crescendo. Through the blinding fog the Texans rushed, fierce as wolves at the kill.

"*Remember the Alamo!*"

It had become a view halloo, a death yell.

Burleson's regiment simply rolled over the barricade. Off to the left Sherman carried the flank position with a storming rush and fell upon Cos's disorganized brigade just behind.

Houston felt a shock in his right foot. Nevertheless he lashed his horse with the reins to jump the parapet.

In mid-leap a bullet caught the animal in the head. It seemed to check in midair, then came to a crashing fall on the other side of the barricade.

Thrown heavily, Houston struggled up. He had a bullet in his ankle, low down. At the moment the wounded foot seemed numb rather than painful, but he could not rest his weight on it. Nevertheless when another horse—the third of the day—was brought to him, he managed to heave himself into the saddle.

Behind the Mexican barricades now raged vast confusion. The soldiers of Santa Anna had broken, and were fleeing; the Texans were "remembering the Alamo" with a ferocity appalling.

In spite of his wound Houston rode back and forth, trying to get his men into some semblance of order.

"Parade! Parade, men!" he kept shouting. But nobody appeared to hear him; or if they heard, they ignored him.

Blood-lust had reached a stage almost of insanity. In every direction Mexicans scattered, flying in panic, the chin straps of their caps askew, weapons thrown away. And the Texans bounded after them, slaughtering them.

Some of the fugitives fell on their knees, with a piteous cry:

"Me no Alamo, me no Alamo!"

It availed them nothing. Death was the penalty Santa Anna had exacted: death was the penalty his men suffered now.

In the wild riot of bloodshed there were some appalling sights. Houston saw a lieutenant go by him on the run, shouting, "Boys, *you* know how to take prisoners! Remember how they took them at the Alamo!"

Deaf Smith rode past in the melee, howling, "Knock their goddamn brains out!"

His horse stumbled or was shot, and he fell prostrate. A Mexican officer, still fighting, cut at him with a sword, but the scout, whose pistol was empty, threw the weapon in the man's face, dazing him, then killed him with his own saber.

A Texan slashed with his fifteen-inch bowie knife, catching a Mexican across the throat. The jugular was severed and a stream of blood jetted ten feet out as the man sank dying to the ground.

Here and there hand-to-hand combats took place, but the Texans, with their knives or clubbed rifles, were everywhere in the ascendancy. Brains were spattered out by great swinging blows of the guns. Wounded in many cases were stabbed to death where they fell.

Most of the Mexicans made no effort to resist, but simply fled for their lives, doubling, and dodging like rabbits in helpless terror.

Scores plunged into a morass, fifteen feet deep in soft mud, and there perished. Others attempted to swim a bayou, and were shot down by Texans standing on the bank, who made bets as to who would sink such and such a head.

Off toward the east Lamar's horsemen were ruthlessly cutting down fugitives.

One Mexican ran with a woman clinging to his arm. She was a camp follower, dressed in the loose trousers and jacket of a man, but her shape, and her way of running, and her long hair flying behind her, should have identified her as a woman to any but a blood-mad killer.

The Mexican was cut down by a Texan, and the woman halted beside his body, which was still kicking in the death throes. Apparently she was too bewildered to turn in any direction. Perhaps she thought that her sex might save her. But a crude-faced man in a leather hunting coat swung a great knife at her. Hilt-deep into the soft round of her belly the long blade plunged. She fell forward, with a little stricken whimper, and he finished her with a stab in the back.

But even the Texans were revolted by a crime so unnatural. To them the murder of a woman was a horror. The man who had done the deed disappeared and never was fully identified.

Uncle Jimmy Curtis knocked down a Mexican colonel with his clubbed gun.

"You killed Wash Cottle!" the oldster yelled. "Now I'm goin' to kill you an' make a razor strop out'n yore hide!"

Colonel Wharton intervened and helped the Mexican to his feet.

"Mount my horse behind me!" he said.

The officer understood the gesture better than the words. He obeyed, but an instant later Uncle Jimmy furiously shot him off the horse.

Everywhere men, begging for mercy, were unpityingly slain by the vengeful victors. Sickened by the blood and violence, Houston felt a new grave concern. If one of Santa Anna's other columns chanced to arrive while his army was in this state of desperate confusion, disaster could be the only result.

But the men were utterly out of hand. Long weeks of built-up hatred were having a merciless outlet.

To one blood-spattered crowd rushing by he called out half-humorously:

"Gentlemen! I applaud your bravery, but damn your manners!"

A sensation of faintness came over him. He looked down at his wounded foot. Blood there. A ragged hole in the boot, and from it a scarlet stream was oozing.

For the first time he was conscious of intense pain.

One of the surgeons saw he was wounded and offered to dress his hurt.

Houston shook his head. "No. I'll have it attended to when I get back to our camp. I can last till then." And he inquired politely, "Did you suffer any damage in the assault, Doctor?"

The surgeon shook his head.

Beside his horse stood Major Hockley, looking up at him anxiously.

The last contingent of Mexican troops with any kind of cohesion was being surrendered by its commander, Colonel Almonte.

The sun was setting, red in the west.

The Battle of San Jacinto was over: won.

A sudden blackness seemed to close about Houston. When he recovered consciousness he was lying on the ground. He had fainted from loss of blood into George Hockley's arms.

Chapter Thirty-Seven

That man may consider himself born to no common destiny who has conquered the Napoleon of the West.

GENERAL ANTONIO LÓPEZ DE SANTA ANNA

1

The sheer splendor of one man's leadership had wrought a miracle in the history of warfare.

With an undisciplined, half-starved, half-mutinous army, Sam Houston not only had defeated but virtually annihilated a disciplined, well-armed, well-arrayed force of twice his numbers.

The magnitude of the victory was not fully realized until the dead were counted. So perfectly had Houston's inspiration timed his attack, and so complete had been the surprise of the overconfident enemy, that in that sudden incredible charge only six Texans were killed or mortally hurt, and twenty-four others wounded. Amazingly, when compared to this, six hundred and thirty Mexican dead were counted, and seven hundred and thirty, of whom two hundred and eight were wounded, were prisoners, herded together in a cattle corral under guard.

That added up to thirteen hundred and sixty out of perhaps fifteen hundred men Santa Anna had commanded. Some were drowned in the morass and could not be counted. A few escaped. The dictator's army had ceased to exist.

But where was Santa Anna himself?

They found Emily, cowering in his silken love bower, wildly protesting, "Ah b'longs to Cunnel Morgan." As to where her quondam lover had gone she could give no information.

Neither, for that matter, could any of *El Presidente's* officers or men. The self-styled Hero of Tampico and Napoleon of the West had departed so rapidly at the first sight of the Texans that few remembered having seen him at all.

Emily might have supplied the interesting information that he left his couch with her so hastily that he had no time properly to attire himself, and had on only white silk drawers, a linen undershirt with diamond studs, and red morocco slippers. But the slave girl was too terrified to think of describing this singular costume.

In the Texas camp Houston lay on a blanket while Dr. Alexander Ewing, the chief surgeon, attended his wound. His boot, when removed, was full of blood. The wound itself was serious: a copper ball from a Mexican *escopeta* had smashed his lower leg.

"I'm afraid I'm going to have to hurt you," said the surgeon.

"Then give me a good swig of whiskey," responded Houston.

A bottle was offered him. He took a swallow, and his face contorted in a grimace. "Is this whiskey?" he said. "It tastes like a tincture of the common carpet tack of commerce!"

"Texas whiskey, General," someone told him.

"Oh, in that case——" Houston took a long pull, without making a face. "Ah! That's the first taste of liquor that's passed my lips since this campaign began. Go ahead, Doctor, with your butchering."

He grew white-lipped with the pain, but did not groan as Dr. Ewing removed the ball, along with some splinters of bone, washed the mangled limb, and bound it up. The surgeon found time to wonder at such stoicism until he reminded himself that this man probably learned fortitude in his Indian days.

"You through now?" Houston asked.

"Yes, General. We'll hope for the best," said Dr. Ewing.

But secretly he expected the worst; for among other things, such as infection and blood-poison, lockjaw was a frequent and fatal complication of severe battle wounds.

"Then thank you, sir," said the patient.

Already, in spite of the pain of the surgery, and the large drink, Houston's mind was racing. He knew he had won a great victory, but while his men celebrated by gulping the Mexican supplies of liquors and wines, dancing and whooping like wild Comanches, he refused a second drink when the doctor finished with him, and pondered his next steps.

Of one thing he was certain: unless Santa Anna was found and taken, the Texas travail was by no means ended. He had plans for Santa Anna and he dreaded the thought of trying to continue the campaign, with his men even more disorganized than before, and himself almost incapacitated.

In the darkness his scouts scoured the country, looking for some sign of the Mexican generalissimo. But when they returned at dawn—and even Deaf Smith was exhausted by his continuous riding—though they had a handful of frightened prisoners, they had seen nothing of *El Presidente.*

What with his deep concerns and the pain of his wound, Houston slept not at all that long night. For that matter most of the camp was wakeful. Wolves had found the bodies of Mexican dead, scattered for ten miles, and their horrible howling and snarling as they gathered and fought each other at times in their macabre feasting, was enough to make men's flesh cringe and banish slumber.

At dawn Houston sent for Colonel Burleson.

"Ned," he said, "you've got to be eyes and legs for me. I'd like you to pick thirty men on good horses. Go out and try to get Santa Anna— *alive,* mark you—*alive!*"

"Yes, sir," said Burleson.

Houston added, grimly, "You'll likely find the 'Hero of Tampico'— if you find him at all—retreating on all fours in high grass. And he'll be dressed badly: at least like a common soldier. So I want you to examine every Mexican you find very closely. And—I can't emphasize strongly enough the importance of this—if you find him, *bring him in alive!*"

Houston watched Burleson quietly choose thirty men and ride away, with profound anxiety. Heavy, heavy were the tides of fortune the stocky colonel carried with him.

2

All the next day Houston lay under the trees, fighting off flies, questioning prisoners, deciding the myriad problems that arose concerning the feeding of his army and its prisoners, the caring for the wounded both Mexican and Texan, the burial of the Texas dead, the direction of camp duties.

Santa Anna's war chest was found. It contained about twelve thousand dollars, United States valuation.

"Spoils of war," ruled Houston. "Divide it among the men."

Though the sum for each was small when divided among so many, the soldiers felt better with a few coins to jingle in their pockets. It was a matter of comment that the commander kept none of the money for himself.

Houston's wounded foot was swelling and throbbing painfully, and he fretted because the surgeon insisted that he lie quiet on the blanket under the tree. Continually he asked if any word concerning the whereabouts of Santa Anna had been brought in. None had.

In the afternoon an indignant woman presented herself in the Texas camp. Blue-black hair, bright blue eyes, typical South Irish, and with an Irish temper.

"I'm Mrs. Peggy McCormick," she said. "This is my land, and I'll thank you to take your stinking Mexicans off of it!"

Houston attempted to soothe her. "Madam, your land will be famed in history."

"To the devil with your history!" she stormed. "They'll haunt me the longest day I live."

"I assure you that we'll do everything that can be done. And I beg you to have patience with us. Ah, here is Dr. Ewing. Will you pardon me, Mrs. McCormick? I've been wounded and the surgeon is here to attend to my hurt."

She withdrew, and he was glad for the providential arrival of Dr. Ewing, because a thoroughly upset woman was in some degrees more difficult to manage than an army. Yet he could hardly blame her for being upset. Several hundred dead men, bloating and festering and already beginning to give off the evil stench of putrefaction, were enough to bother anyone.

As soon as the surgeon finished with his foot, he asked to have Colonel Rusk report to him.

"Tom," he said, "we've got to do something about cleaning up this battlefield. It's owned by a lady, and she's understandably mighty vigorous in protesting the way it's now festooned."

"How can we dig graves for all those dead?" asked Rusk, somewhat dismayed by the task given him.

"We have a few hundred prisoners," Houston pointed out. "They're doing nothing now but eat. Take 'em out by squads—under close guard, of course. Get shovels. Impress 'em that they've got to work, or no rations. Long, deep trenches is the best plan. I want all those cadavers on Mrs. McCormick's place underground not later than tomorrow night."

"The prisoners! Never thought about them. Of course. Good idea, and I'll have a man from Seguin's company with every squad, as one of the guards and as an interpreter."

Rusk saluted and departed. Within half an hour Mexican soldiers were laboring at carrying out the general's commands.

And still no word of Santa Anna.

3

Houston grew increasingly worried. Had the dictator made good his escape across the bayous? It was more than likely; and if so he was probably well on his way now to call together his armies for a vengeful counterblow. If only Santa Anna could have been captured . . . the disappointment created almost a sense of nausea.

Nothing, however, to do but wait, lying under the tree, feeling the constant throb in his swollen ankle, wondering if he ever would walk again, wondering how he could longer keep his men together, wondering . . . until every hope was extinguished.

One after another, squads of Burleson's men returned, some with prisoners, but none with the prisoner Houston wanted most of all, on whom the next stage of his daring plan hung.

Toward evening five men rode into camp. One of them had on his horse behind him a little, filthy captive, attired in the blue linsey shirt and pants of a slave, with a slave's dirty leather cap on his head.

The patrol had found this man crouching in the tall sedge near Vince's ruined bridge. He would have been killed had not one of them, Private Joel Robison, who could speak Spanish, intervened by asking him if he had seen *El Presidente*. As soon as the little man found that his captor could speak what he called "the Christian language," he was all eagerness to talk, even kissed Robison's hand.

No, he had not seen Santa Anna. He did not know where *El Presidente* had gone, but believed he had escaped toward the west—to Filisola's army, perhaps. He, himself, he said anxiously, was only a cavalryman, a poor devil of a soldier who but followed orders.

Out of pity Robison took him up on his horse. On the way to camp the prisoner rode meekly, but gathered courage to ask questions.

"Did General Houston command in person at the action yesterday?" was the first.

"Yes," said Robison.

"How many men did he have?"

"Less than eight hundred."

"Oh, but Señor Soldado, you must be mistaken! This is impossible! He had many more—four thousand, perhaps?"

Robison laughed.

They approached the corral in which the Mexican prisoners, those who for lack of tools were not working on the grave-digging details, were held under guard. The captives crowded to the fence, and as the squad passed, they caught sight of the dirty little figure on the horse behind Robison.

Immediately many of them removed their caps, and some bowed their heads humbly.

"*El Presidente!*" they exclaimed to each other, in voices soft and muted with awe and wonder. "*El Presidente!*"

"*Ini la boca!*" shouted one of their officers.

But his command to shut their mouths came too late. In that moment Joel Robison, private in the Texas army, received the greatest surprise in his life. It was the generalissimo himself who was riding behind him, his prisoner! He had won a niche in history.

With this amazing disclosure the squad with the captive did not halt at the corral, but rode straight to the Texas camp.

Houston was lying on his side upon the blanket under the tree, his eyes closed, feverish and half-stupefied with pain, when Major Hockley laid a hand on his shoulder.

"General," he said, "they've just brought in Santa Anna."

Houston turned over. It seemed that it required a few seconds for his mind, in its sick condition, to grasp the full force of the news.

But then he raised himself on his elbow, and his face returned to the old alert lines. "Alive?" he asked.

"Yes, sir. He's here."

An expression of joy almost demoniac flashed across the wounded giant's countenance.

Around him voices were raised vengefully by the gathering Texans: "Shoot the son-of-a-bitch!"

"String him up!"

"Naw—cut out his guts with a bowie knife!"

Houston's face stiffened with anger. "Shut down that clamor!" he shouted furiously.

His officers flung themselves among the men, commanding silence.

The dirty, dejected prisoner slid down from the horse. "I am General Antonio López de Santa Anna," he said weakly. "I place myself at the disposal of the brave General Houston."

Most of this speech, which was in Spanish, was unintelligible to Houston, but the name was sufficient. He hated this man; but he had use for him. And he could be polite in the manner that a cat is gentle with a mouse helpless between its paws.

"Ah, General Santa Anna, take a seat." He gestured toward an ammunition box.

The little man sank down. For a moment there was almost complete silence as the Texans, as usual ignoring all military rules, crowded about to stare at him. Pallid face, unshaved, with a twitching cheek. Narrow shoulders, bent now in weariness and fear. Soft, weak hands, continuously wringing each other. Slave's garments. How could they at any time have been afraid of such a creature?

But some of them remembered that they *had* been afraid, that only the wounded giant on the blanket at all times seemed without fear, appeared really to know what he was doing. A few men began to leave the circle, to go off to think matters over. They remembered their own complaints and insubordinations: and *he* was right all the time, patient with them, moving among them, humoring them, leading them in spite of themselves. Some of these men, in sincere shame, avoided for a time the eyes of others.

But now Major Zavala—the man whose father the dictator had sworn to hang—came hurrying to act as interpreter.

Santa Anna recognized him and rose from the ammunition box with a fawning smile.

"Ah, my old friend—son of my old, my very dear friend!" he exclaimed. And he would have embraced Zavala, but the young major coldly pushed him away.

Once more the dictator sank down on the ammunition box. He gathered enough strength to explain through Zavala that he had bogged down the horse on which he escaped, in the morass when he found the bridge burned down, and culled his curious costume from an abandoned cabin while he was hiding.

Vince's bridge! Thank God for Deaf Smith's enterprise in destroying it!

"General," interrupted Burleson's voice, "you must have the gift of second sight, sir. That man's dressed like you said he'd be, and he was crawling through tall grass, like you said he would!"

In the circle wiseacre heads nodded: Houston's words were well remembered. With steadily heightening respect they gazed at their prostrate leader.

By this time Santa Anna had bethought himself of a flamboyant speech which might mollify his captor.

"That man may consider himself born to no common destiny who has conquered the Napoleon of the West," he said. "It now remains for him to be generous to the vanquished."

When this was rendered to him, Houston looked at him, pitiless as a hawk. "You should have remembered that at the Alamo," he said.

Visibly, it shook the prisoner.

At the moment a high, cracked voice rose. Old Uncle Jimmy Curtis had just joined the circle.

"Is that Santy Anny?" he shrilled. "I'm goin' to kill him an' skin him for Wash Cottle!"

"Who is that man!" snapped Houston. "If he makes another sound around here, place him under immediate arrest!"

But then he said to Zavala, "Translate what Uncle Jimmy said for the general. And tell him that Washington Cottle was at the Alamo."

Zavala obeyed. As the meaning dawned on Santa Anna his eyes went to Houston again, and in them was fear—crawling, shaking fear.

"What does the general want of me?" he asked Zavala.

His eyes fell: he passed a hand over his brow, and it trembled.

"Did you—discover my medicine chest?" he asked in a weak voice.

"Yes," Zavala told him.

"Could I—could I have it?"

"Bring it to him," ordered Houston.

When the carved case was placed on the ground beside him, the prisoner's face became sickly with avidity as he drew open one of the drawers. From it he took a sticky brownish lump.

Opium. He thrust it into his mouth.

The crude drug seemed somewhat to restore him, but still he could not meet Houston's eyes. He gazed down at the ground.

"Tell General Houston that I am at his disposal, to do what he requires," he said almost pleadingly to Zavala.

Abject surrender.

Houston experienced a mighty sensation of relief. Had Santa Anna been enough of a man to refuse to do his bidding, his entire plan and hope for the future might have collapsed.

But Santa Anna was cowed: victory was complete.

Through Zavala, Houston began to dictate to his prisoner: and *El Presidente*, cravenly glad that his life was spared, humbly wrote the orders and letters to his subordinates in the field, and to his government in Mexico, whereby an armistice was declared, his invading armies to be withdrawn from Texas.

A thousand-to-one chance had come off. Texas had her independence.

Late that night, by the light of a dim lantern, Sam Houston began a letter of his own. It was a report which would go to its destination as fast as relays of horses could carry it. The message began:

General Andrew Jackson, President of the United States, Dear Sir:

The Hermitage,
*** 1845

*O*n March 4, 1837, a deeply moving event took place.

Martin Van Buren—elected successor to Andrew Jackson—was inaugurated as the eighth President of the United States.

But the enormous throng that gathered before the steps of the Capitol building in Washington was there, not to see the new President take the oath of office, but for a last glimpse of the man more loved by the people than any other before him.

Chief Justice Roger Taney administered the oath, and Van Buren gave his inaugural address, to which few paid any attention. All eyes were on the tall, wasted figure in black, with the inevitable crape on the sleeve, standing beside the new President.

When the last words of the speech were said, Andrew Jackson, a private citizen once more, began to descend the marble steps alone.

A strange, almost awesome thing happened then. In all that vast multitude every man removed his hat in a spontaneous, heartfelt gesture of reverence.

And when the old figure was halfway down the steps to the carriage which waited below, there burst from the crowd a single, tremendous shout. Thomas Hart Benton best described that salute to the departing hero:

"It was a cry such as power never commanded, nor a man in power received. It was affection, gratitude, and admiration; the acclaim of posterity breaking from the bosoms of contemporaries. I felt an emotion which had never passed through me before."

434   Magnificent Destiny

Others felt it too. Hundreds of faces, of men and women alike, were wet with tears.

The old General paused for a moment on the steps, removed his hat, and gave his last obeisance to his people, a simple bow which was his farewell.

In that instant, as his silvery hair was stirred by a light breeze, stillness fell.

As he descended, entered his carriage, and was driven away, not a voice, not a whisper, was heard in all that vast gathering. The hats remained doffed, nobody stirred.

It was the silence of awe, of sadness, and of overpowering affection: an even mightier tribute to the departing chieftain than had been the tumult.

Chapter Thirty-Eight

If Texas—as by right—claimed the Pacific as her western border, she might bind together the Union.

ANDREW JACKSON

1

There were days when the old man felt such weariness that, contrary to his lifetime habit, he could not bring himself to rise early in the morning.

The first time this occurred it created alarm in the Hermitage household.

Andrew Jackson lying a-bed? Impossible! Something must be very wrong!

But to anxious inquiries he returned the ghost of a dry smile.

"Don't you think old bones have a right to rest?" he asked.

That morning they brought him his breakfast in bed. But he disliked trying to eat propped up by pillows, with a tray in his lap; and thereafter he managed to get up and sit at a table for his meals.

It was now the spring of 1844; seven years since, nearly worn out, he laid down his duties at the White House to spend his last days at the Hermitage.

Seven years. Sometimes he smiled when he remembered the old Roman senator Similis, who after a stormy public life under the Emperors Trajan and Hadrian, retired to his country estate, where he spent seven years in calm and quiet, far from the tumults and excitements of the court, and ordered an epitaph carved on his tomb:

> *Here lies Similis,*
> *Who was in this world many years,*
> *But only lived seven.*

His own seven years had now brought him to the age of seventy-seven, a great age for his time, when a man was considered old at fifty. And he had lived far more strenuously in his life than most men.

He thought back on the day when in his deep depression he considered himself too old, at forty-six, to accomplish anything of importance in the time left to him. And yet it was precisely *afterward* that everything of importance in his life had occurred: the Creek War, the New Orleans campaign, the Florida adventure, his defeat and later election as President, the great political battles, his acts of statesmanship—all were the fruit of his later years, after he had almost given up hope of rising above mere mediocrity.

But now his old body, which had been ailing from wounds or sickness almost all his life, and which he had always called upon to do more than its frail strength should have permitted, at last had reached the stage where it could no longer recover its resilience as it once had done.

He had a chair in his study: a large chair with a cushion in it, and a comfortable back on which to lean. Nobody else ever ventured to sit in that chair, even when he was not there. It was near enough to the fireplace for comfort on cold days, but also convenient to a window from which he could gaze out. And he could lean his cane against the wall where he could reach it easily.

The Hermitage these days was filled with the life and turmoil of children, and he loved children. But now in his age he watched, rather than participated, in the incomings and outgoings, the fevered excitements of the young. He accepted everything and refused nothing: or perhaps it would be better said that he refused everything and accepted nothing.

Sometimes he dozed with the sleep of weakness and age; and there were those who wondered if he was not, perhaps, beginning to lose some of his mental faculties. One who could have told them different was Sarah, the young wife of Andrew Jackson, Junior.

The old General's adopted son was handsome and attractive like all the Donelsons—which he truly was by blood—but not highly responsible, and with little head for business, so that the Hermitage under his management had gone ever more deeply into debt. He gambled and drank somewhat, though not to great excess; and not to the disapproval of the General, who considered such indulgences natural in any young gentleman of spirit.

"Games a little?" Jackson chuckled, when it was brought to his attention. "Well, so do I—or did, when I wasn't bound down to my chair by the failure of my legs to do their work."

But one thing young Andrew did was of lasting benefit, when he brought Sarah Yorke to the Hermitage as his wife. She was hardly beautiful, at least to a cold stranger, but she possessed indefinable warmth and pleasantness that made her beautiful to her intimates; a sort of divine charm that grew on all who knew her.

Andrew Jackson, who at first received her with due regard as his daughter-in-law, found her so full of exquisite affection that before long she became far more to him that a mere daughter-in-law. In his heart and his thoughts she was a real daughter in truth, as if she had been born to him.

Sarah had given him grandchildren: four of them now, including not only the new little Rachel but a new little Andrew Jackson, the third of the name. Perhaps she understood better than anyone the worries he suffered, for when he left the White House he was heavily in debt, and his son's inefficiency as manager had done nothing to alleviate this load, which at times caused him to wonder if he should sell his home.

She also, in a measure, became his eyes, for he had almost lost the sight of one, and the other was dim; and she read for him his mail, and the newspapers. Sarah could have told doubters that the mind in that old white-thatched head was as keen as ever, although Jackson revealed its workings rarely, and chiefly to her.

Thus, at a newspaper article saying that Martin Van Buren would again try for the Presidency, the old man exclaimed:

"I made Van Buren President, for I had high hopes of him. But he was a heavy disappointment—I see in him a vacillating politician, no statesman." He paused. "It was for that reason—his temporizing—that he lost to William Henry Harrison four years ago."

He smoked a moment, ruminatively, then: "I regret the death of any man; although death is inevitable. Yet on the scroll of history death sometimes creates great changes. Harrison was against the annexation of Texas. He was dead within thirty days of assuming office. John Tyler, who succeeded him, was no friend of mine. He fought me in the Senate when I smashed Calhoun and the Nullification conspiracy. But Tyler is a Virginian and favors annexation. In this regard Providence may have taken a hand."

"President Tyler says he'll not run again," said Sarah.

The white head nodded. "He's at outs with the Whigs who elected him. That means Clay again, I foresee. Sarah, I have few regrets, but two I will carry with me to the grave."

"What are they, Father?"

"That I did not hang John Calhoun and shoot Henry Clay!"

His eyes blazed so wrathfully that she was struck silent. But then he smiled at her.

"The way things are going, I sometimes long for the days when I had a keen eye, a straight back, a close-clinging knee in the saddle, and the power that makes a man. Ten years ago—aye, *five* years ago—I might——" He broke off with a sigh. "But that time is past. No need for old bones any longer. Younger men shoulder the burden."

She left him smoking his pipe, once more withdrawn into his half-dreaming contemplation of matters no longer a part of his existence.

Another time she read to him an article stating that any action toward annexation of Texas was unlikely "at the present," because of "fear of foreign intervention."

"Bah!" Jackson fairly spat the word. "Lily livers! Incompetents! I gave them an example—showed the way. Britain—I faced her boldly. She not only settled with us the Maine boundary dispute justly, but removed her West Indies embargo against American shipping. France—delayed paying her reparations until I notified her I'd take reprisals. A flurry of martial bombast in Paris, the French demanded an apology from me, and I dared them to turn loose their dogs! They thought it over—and paid. Foreign powers think twice about 'intervention' if they know this nation is ready to face them, if necessary, with the sword!"

He learned of the death of Nicholas Biddle, whose Bank failed after repeated futile efforts by Clay to recharter it.

"Nicholas Biddle—I never actively disliked him," Jackson commented. "A good man, perhaps, by his own lights: even, I think he conscientiously believed, a benefactor of the people. But blinded by lust for power. I sometimes smile at his characterization of me: 'Andrew Jackson is about as amenable to reason as a bolt of lightning.' He was like unto John Marshall, now gone, with his unyielding heresy of Federalism. Now that I'm old and the heat of battle is past, I'm ready to concede that both those men were sincere, however wrong, in their beliefs."

Of all his acts he looked back with deepest pride to the payment of the national debt; and he remembered the banquet given in honor of himself and the event, and especially Thomas Hart Benton's toast:

"The national debt is paid! This month of January, 1835, in the fifty-eighth year of the republic, Andrew Jackson being President, the national debt is paid! And the apparition, so long unseen on earth—a great nation without a national debt—stands revealed to the astonished vision of a wondering world! Gentlemen, my heart is in this double celebration, and I offer you a sentiment which, coming direct from my own bosom, will find a response in yours: President Jackson! May the evening of his days be as tranquil and happy for himself as their meridian has been resplendent, glorious, and beneficent for his country!"

There was pleasure and comfort for the old heart in such approbation from his friends.

But that was in the past. Everything, indeed, was in the past, save for one thing: his single supreme failure. Texas! He never spoke of this, even to Sarah, for it was too sore a matter. But he considered that his inability to gain admission for Texas, in a Senate divided by jealousies, politics, and sectional bickering, blunted his farthest-reaching dream for his nation.

Well he remembered those days, eight years before, in his last year as President, when he took time from his duties of state to watch with deepest anxiety the movements of Sam Houston, his friend. Disaster at first, in the Texas revolt, and sickening massacres. All depended on Houston and his desperate handful of Texas soldiers.

In those tense days, as the old General traced on a map in his office the strange zigzag course of the retreat from Gonzales, a memory came to him: a long-legged, gray-eyed boy, more than twenty years before, who overthrew a town bully at Maryville . . . could that boy be remembering an injunction given him on that far day?

Exhaust . . . then close . . . for the decisive blow. . . .

Question became conviction as he studied the wild reports from Texas. And when others hoped that Houston might escape to American soil, Jackson shook his head.

"No! I know Sam Houston. In his good time he'll turn and fight—about *there!*"

Was it accident that the tip of his bony finger indicated on the map a point where two strangely named streams—San Jacinto River and Buffalo Bayou—joined together to run into Galveston Bay?

Never would the old man forget his supreme thrill when on a morning in May a dispatch arrived, written in a familiar sprawling script and dated *San Jacinto, April 24, 1836.* It contained news almost incredible: the scanty Texas force had defeated—annihilated—Santa Anna's army; and Santa Anna himself was a prisoner, signing the terms of peace dictated to him.

"Yes, that's his writing!" exclaimed Jackson with blazing eyes. "It's Sam Houston's writing—and his signature! There can be no doubt of what he says!"

He exulted as greatly over Sam Houston's victory as if he had won it himself . . . in a way it *was* his victory, the first step in his vast, secret, continental plan for his nation.

But elation gradually faded. The first step was complete, true: but there remained the next step—the addition of Texas to the Union.

If *that* victory were won, it might be greater even than the battle. But that victory had not been won. And Andrew Jackson felt that somehow he was at fault. The Senate was divided, seeking small ends and petty triumphs, true. But in some manner he should have been able to unite the country. He had been unable to do so. The burden of failure had lived with him all these years. He could not ease it from his thin shoulders.

2

The old man knew he was near his end. His cough was now nearly constant, racking his gaunt chest, and he often spat blood. The swellings of his feet and ankles made it impossible for him to wear anything but loose carpet slippers. So feeble had he become that he could scarcely walk the one hundred and fifty paces out to Rachel's grave without someone to support his arm.

Yet he sometimes liked, on a pleasant day, to have a chair placed for him in the shade of a large weeping willow tree he had planted almost twenty years before beside her tomb, and make his way there, with assistance, to sit.

At such times they forbore going near him or speaking to him. Yet it was whispered among the house servants that the General at times talked to himself. Or, perhaps—white eyeballs rolled in superstitious black faces—to "somebody down dar in dat grave."

If he did seek communication of this kind with his dead, he never spoke of it. Indeed, he spent those hours as if in an invisible company of influences seeking to meet him and draw him back into their old friendship.

None but the aged can know how keenly dependent we are upon our contemporaries. Andrew Jackson knew it. Old names, old faces, were gone; and it was as if each was a prop of his old world taken away. Much of that world now seemed misty, a little out of focus.

How many of his friends, whom he had loved, had departed!

Rachel, of course. He took comfort merely from sitting near her sleeping place. It eased his loneliness to be near her, and he thought, almost with longing, of the time when he would lie, also in complete rest, beside her.

Others, many others. Young John Reid, dead in his splendid youth. General John Coffee and General John Overton, stanch friends, gone now these many years. Old Judge Trimble and Rachel's minister, Dr. Hume, departed with the rest. Emily Donelson, his sweet Emily, wife of his favorite nephew, who gave to the White House her grace and charm, taken suddenly, leaving her husband Jack Donelson desolate. Flamboyant old General Humbert, who lustily seconded him at New Orleans, gone to the shades. Even that engaging rascal Jean Laffite, buried somewhere in Yucatan. With especial tender affection he remembered Aaron, black Aaron, his personal servant and faithful friend, laid to rest not far from Rachel's tomb. There were others, the list was long, and he could meditate on each with thankfulness that he had known them and felt their understanding and sympathy.

Not even the Hermitage was the same. The house in which Rachel died was gone, destroyed by fire. Wistfully the old man had yearned to spend his last days in that house, with memories of her present all around him. But that wish was denied.

Before he could leave the White House and return to his home, a frantic letter from young Andrew told of the loss. It was like a blow to his heart, for a home is the center of dreams and recollections, a place tender and intimate beyond expression. Yet at that time he wrote a letter of comfort:

The Lord's will be done. It was he who gave me the means to build my dwelling house and he has the right to destroy it. Tell Sarah to cease to mourn its loss. If a benevolent Providence will spare me long enough I will have it rebuilt.

Under his orders the work began and a new Hermitage rose on the ruins of the old, though at the cost of his going more deeply into debt. It was finer and larger than the old Hermitage, two stories high, with six tall Grecian columns supporting a portico and balcony across its front, white-painted, all its rooms ample and fine.

Yet to the old General it still seemed almost strange, as if it hardly belonged to him, was not really his home. The white marble dome of Rachel's tomb alone remained familiar, something for his heart to cling to.

3

One there was, close to him by the strongest ties of the heart, whom the Dark Angel had not taken.

Sam Houston. Often and often the white-haired General turned his thoughts to him, knowing his great concerns and disappointments.

Houston at last was divorced from Eliza Allen, who had remarried. Tiana, the Cherokee wife was dead, so at least he had for the present no domestic problems.

After winning Texas independence, Houston as by right had been elected president of the new republic. He wished, all Texas wished, recognition by the United States and after that annexation.

But at the very outset the curse of John Calhoun was placed upon the project, when the hollow-jawed South Carolinian rose in the Senate, a few days after the news of San Jacinto, and proposed both recognition and annexation of Texas by the Union.

But Calhoun was the acknowledged spokesman for the slave states!

Coming from such a source the proposal was ill-timed and ill-considered. Jackson was aware that a new crop of hotheads was arising, both North and South, and the nation might yet see a blood bath. In the North immediate opposition grew to Calhoun's project.

In this manner the Texas question became what Jackson hoped it would not: a sectional issue. Abolition leaders raged that it was a plot to increase the power of the slave states. So suddenly inflamed was part of the public mind, that when Santa Anna, that treacherous and cruel despot and murderer, was sent to Washington under guard by Houston —to save his scoundrelly neck from Texas lynch mobs—he was actually lionized in some places and by some persons. Northern newspapers took a strangely unrealistic view of him, like that comment in a Rhode Island journal:

How can we style him tyrant who opposed the efforts of rebels and used them with deserved severity, and fought and bled to contravene the efforts of those who wished to substantiate the horrible system of slavery?

"Deserved severity" . . . did the writer of that screed consider the heartless massacre of four hundred helpless men at Goliad in that light?

"Fought and bled" . . . when Santa Anna had fled like a craven cur and left his army to its fate!

"Those who wished to substantiate . . . slavery" . . . the Texans were fighting for their lives and their freedom, and the whole shibboleth of slavery did not enter their thinking.

Jackson snorted anew as he remembered articles and statements such as these, the interjection of the emotional question of slave bondage into every issue. He recognized the whole dire problem of slavery as a deadly peril to the nation, and he sometimes believed that the unluckiest day America had ever known was when the first boatload of Africans was landed in Virginia two centuries before. He did not at the present see how the matter could be settled without a holocaust of war. In any case there were mighty few slaves and slaveholders in Texas. There it was, however, the issue; and the devil himself could not have invented one so baffling to Jackson's far-reaching vision for his country.

El Presidente had proved as shifty and venal in Washington as he was in Mexico City, and Jackson returned him to his own country in an American warship. But he knew he could not summon, during his own Administration, the two-thirds majority in the Senate to ratify a treaty of annexation.

Nevertheless he contributed one subtle suggestion, leaving it for the Texans, and particularly for Houston, to think over, since it was an indirect approach to that great dream of a continental power he had held for so long a time. To William H. Wharton, a Texas envoy, he spoke confidentially as follows:

"Texas is in a state of change, of transmutation. What are its present borders? No man can say."

"True, sir," nodded Wharton.

"Therefore," resumed Jackson, "Texas has the right to claim them anywhere, if she has the power to uphold them. Am I correct in this thinking?"

"Yes, sir," said Wharton wondering to what this was leading.

"Now, suppose—I do not suggest, I only say *suppose*—Texas should claim the Californias." Jackson paused. "I have tried to purchase the Californias, as I tried peacefully to purchase Texas, without success. The Mexican dictator, unable to retain them—for California has thrown off Mexican authority also—yet will not yield title to them, without heavy bribery to him personally, and to bribery I will not be a party."

Jackson leaned forward and tapped Wharton on the knee to emphasize his next words. "But if *Texas*—as by right—claimed the Pacific Coast as her western border, she might bind together the Union instead of creating dissension in it. Only think of this one factor: the fishing industries of the North want and need harbors on the Pacific Coast. If you offered that to them, might not the senators from that section forget their outcry against Texas?"

This, he knew, went direct to Houston, and it might have some effect—eventually.

But meantime, before and after he left the White House, efforts to annex were rejected again and again by partisan and jealous factions in the Senate. It failed in Van Buren's Administration, and it had failed thus far under Tyler.

And Sam Houston, down in Texas, stood as if at a breaking dike, trying to hold back the flood of disaster from his people.

4

The old General felt far out of the stream of events, like a weathered bit of driftwood, cast up on the bank by a surging river and left to rot. He did not particularly resent this. He was old, and he was tired.

Nevertheless, he listened eagerly to tidings of friends, especially if the tidings were pleasant. In this respect he one day heard news of Houston: Sam Houston was married!

The letter, from a friend in Texas, was brief:

The new Mrs. Houston is the former Margaret Lea, of a good family in Mobile. She is beautiful and accomplished and Houston seems to be deeply in love with her—takes her with him everywhere. She has made him quit drinking, gambling, and chewing tobacco. Everything, in fact, except swearing.

At the last a grin creased Jackson's face. "It would require something like a miracle for that, I venture." The letter went on:

She even got him to join the church. She was brought up in the Baptist persuasion, and he was baptized in a creek. When the minister told him the water had washed all his sins away, Houston said, "God help the fish!"

That brought a laugh of real merriment from the old man.

"It sounds like Sam Houston!" he exclaimed. "A wife—so Sam Houston has a wife at last, and one that pleases him. This may give him the one thing his nature has lacked—balance. I'm happier over this news than over anything I've heard in months."

Chapter Thirty-Nine

In the event annexation should fail . . .
Houston here says to you that the glory
of the United States already has cul-
minated.

SAM HOUSTON

1

Major Jack Donelson, slowly recovering from the grief of the loss of his wife, had been appointed Chargé d'Affaires for the United States in Texas by President Tyler at Jackson's suggestion. He paid a visit to the Hermitage, to see his children, whom the old General had added to the household at Emily's tragic death from what the doctors called galloping consumption; and to confer with the General himself.

Within a week he was riding south toward Texas; a journey by no means to be undertaken lightly. It was the season of cold rains; and the rivers and creeks were running full, with few ferries and even fewer bridges. He forded streams that he could not cross otherwise and once or twice had to swim his horse and himself, arriving at the other bank soaked to the skin and violently shivering with cold.

But he found the people uncommonly hospitable, and the greeting was "'Light down, Stranger. 'Light down. Shore, we're glad to give yo' a shakedown an' bite, an' yo' look cold, would yo' mebby enjoy a bit of toddy—hot with lemon an' sugar in it?"

He learned to accept this hospitality with thanks, and not to offer the people money next morning, because they were sensitive in unexpected spots, and considered such offers in the nature of affronts, or at least the vagaries of a pilgrim unused to proper dealings with folks well brought up.

The houses were few and far between. At times he slept in verminous taverns; at times in lofts of log cabins, like as not with a half-dozen children sharing the same corn shucks and blankets; once even in a barn on hay in front of the mangers with the horses stamping and chewing in their stalls on the other side and the night dripping wet outside.

But he traveled with what speed he could make, for he carried greetings from Andrew Jackson to the president of Texas—and instructions from Andrew Jackson for himself.

At last one day, with the clouds driving overhead and under them a thin, cold rain, he came to the Brazos River, running muddy and full and carrying along brush and dead trees which showed it was still on the rise. A ferry there took him over to a scattering of mean log cabins and shacks of unpainted clapboard style, beside the river on the raw and unfinished Texas prairie.

Stores—also unpainted, and with false fronts—straggled down what might be called—but only in derision—the main street. At hitch racks gaunt horses stood, humped against the rain, their heads bowed as if in silent shame at their surroundings. In this hamlet, he was to learn, vehicles in wet weather customarily carried fence rails to help pry them out of mudholes; while in dry weather dust arose in clouds and flung itself in the hot wind, or in the frequent "sand devils," those miniature tornadoes that afflicted the Texas landscape.

Yet this crude and unsightly collection of wretched habitations had some importance in distant and magnificent chancelleries of the world. It was called Washington-on-the-Brazos, and it was the capital of the young Texas republic.

Jack Donelson found a tavern, and stabled his horse, and looked about in spite of the dismal day. He discovered that the members of the Texas house of representatives met in a room formerly devoted to gambling, located above a saloon, to the offerings of which the members had frequent recourse during sessions. And the Texas senate sat in a loft over a grocery shop, the principal staple of which was liquor, and the senators, like their brethren of the lower house, were seldom lacking a rich, pervading aroma of whiskey on their breaths, while deliberating the legislative problems of the republic.

But the true center of the government—toward which the eyes of other nations turned—was a log house, of two sections, with a roofed passage between called in the vernacular of the country a "turkey walk." This was known as the Executive Mansion, and there dwelt the president of Texas. There he conferred with officers of his nation, and with envoys of foreign powers, and there he penned a voluminous correspondence relating to the affairs of his sprawling, disorganized, threatened country.

On the open roofed passage the president of Texas made a practice of shaving each morning, using no mirror—a trick from his campaigning and Indian days—making the event a kind of a levee, for the citizens formed the habit of gathering sometimes in considerable groups to watch the interesting operation of the razor gliding about the presidential side whiskers; and at the same time making requests, offering advice, and giving criticism of the executive policies and acts in a manner most free and outspoken, to which the president replied in a manner equally outspoken and free.

It being late in the day when Donelson arrived at Washington-on-the-Brazos, he did not announce himself immediately. But the next morning—and it was still raining—he made his way across the muddy street from his tavern, and down a row of houses, to the "Mansion," which he considered egregiously misnamed.

A servant, Esau, greeted him, and summoned his master.

Houston appeared, tall as a tree, and his face lit up at the sight of an old friend.

"By Almighty God—Jack Donelson!" he exclaimed and gave his visitor's hand a grip that numbed his arm to the elbow. Then, "Have you had breakfast?"

"Yes, sir. I've eaten," said Donelson.

"Well, come back and see Margaret and the baby!"

Warmed by the hearty greeting, Donelson followed his host back along the breezeway from the eaves of which the drizzling rain dripped, to the rear section of the log house which was the living quarters of the presidential family. At the back of the yard he noticed two small cabins.

"Servants' quarters," said Houston. "The one on the left is occupied by Esau, my body servant, and Tom Blue, my coachman and handy man. The other one is where Tabitha, Margaret's young maid and nurse to the baby, lives, along with old Aunt Lucy, the family cook. Aunt Lucy," he added, "also serves as a duenna for Tabitha, who has saucy eyes for gentlemen of color, even one as old as Esau, who's old enough to be her father."

They entered the rear section of the so-called "Executive Mansion," and Donelson observed that it was divided into two rooms—the parlor-dining room, and a second room, evidently the bedroom of the presidential pair. The front room was quite tastefully furnished with soft chairs, lace curtains, rugs, a silver candelabrum, the appurtenances of a nice woman with pretty tastes; and a piano, which Houston told him with some pride was the only one west of the Brazos, and Margaret's solace.

Then Margaret herself came into the room. Donelson had been looking forward to seeing her and her first smile captivated him. A clear-cut girl—she could not be half Houston's age—slender, and sweet was his first impression. She wore a blue gown, which set off her magnificent violet-blue eyes, and her hair, light brown, was upswept from her smooth forehead, with little ringlets curling naturally and almost golden about her temples.

He said to himself that this was no ordinary young woman. She had grace and delicacy, and beauty, certainly. But there was something besides prettiness there. He read character, courage, and perhaps determination in her straight little nose, strong round chin, and steady gaze; and sweetness and perhaps humor in the curve of her lips—and God knows, he thought, she may need humor in dealing with a man like

Houston. Margaret, he decided, would be her husband's ablest and most loyal supporter.

"Your most humble servant, ma'am," he said as Houston introduced them, "and seeing you for the first time, I can only rejoice at the great good fortune of my old friend, who won a lady so completely charming."

Her cheeks grew delicately pink at the compliment, and she smiled; but Houston interrupted.

"My dear—show Jack the baby."

"Oh, we shouldn't inflict—" she began, but Donelson could see her sidewise glance at him, as if wondering whether he consented.

"I would most sincerely appreciate it," he said, and she was gone.

A moment later she was back, carrying a burbling, blond infant, and followed by a bright-looking young colored nursemaid whom he supposed was the Tabitha of the "saucy eyes." The infant, he knew, was Sam, Junior, the first fruit of Margaret's union with the Texas giant, and she held the child up, glancing at the visitor in a way timid, yet somehow appealing and confident, like any young mother exhibiting her first-born for approval.

"Let me take him," said Donelson. He loved children and knew how to do with them, and for a few moments he held the baby on his knee, making ridiculous faces that brought a crow of laughter from the little one, and a smile to the faces of his parents, both quite normally proud of this small bit of themselves.

But Margaret was too much of a born hostess to let this continue, and presently she returned the child to the nursemaid, who retired to the rear of the house, while Margaret herself devoted her charm to Donelson, and Houston looked on with an indescribable blending of fondness and delight.

Donelson found himself wondering, as he had wondered more than once, at the power of woman. This girl was perhaps a shade over five feet tall and weighed not much more than a hundred pounds—the kind of a diminutive woman a huge man like Houston so often finds entrancing. Her husband, six feet six, and two hundred and sixty muscular pounds, would make two of her and more. Yet it was evident that when she wished she could "wrap him around her little finger," as the old, apt saying went.

He remembered that it was she, as Andrew Jackson had informed him, who caused Houston to give up liquor, gambling—"everything but swearing." And even induced him to join her church. In itself this proved her power over that great barbarian, her husband. But it proved something else, also. Power like that does not come to a woman unless she has something to offer for it. In his mind Donelson compared her with Eliza Allen, whom he knew. Eliza he considered shallow, vain, and selfish; and Margaret, he sensed, was the opposite, with depth of understanding, warmth of passion, and loyalty without reserve.

2

When Houston took Donelson off to talk business, Margaret sat by the fireplace, where the flames danced and warded off the wet cold outside, and she knew in her intuitive heart that the visitor liked her, and that he was wondering how she came here. Others had wondered, too, but only Margaret knew the full story of her becoming the wife of that turbulent giant, Sam Houston.

A fireplace leads the mind to turn back the scroll of days and months, and looking into the flames, Margaret saw a different time and place, and also herself as a different person.

It was—she remembered—in 1836, and the news of the Battle of San Jacinto had just created a storm of excitement in New Orleans. She was going to school there, a sixteen-year-old girl, shy and subdued, and wearing the unbecoming uniform that girl scholars in the convent school had to wear, for the Catholic academies were the best in the country, and she was sent to one of them, although she herself was a Baptist, and fully convinced of the efficacy for salvation of total immersion.

Word came that General Houston, a man already of legendary proportions, was being brought to New Orleans to be treated for his wound received in the battle; and Margaret Lea stole away from school, and was down at the dock when the dirty little coasting schooner came in.

There were a few cheers, but all she could remember was looking down on the filthy deck, and seeing a man lying there, almost in a coma because of his pain, and hardly conscious of the mass of avid faces staring down at him.

But when someone tried to raise him, he seemed to rouse himself and refused help, struggling to his feet without aid, a great, disheveled figure, supported by two improvised crutches—forked branches from trees cut on the San Jacinto field, she was later told. He was haggard and almost savage with pain, and, on top of that, incredibly foul, his garments rags, his face unshaved. Yet when he hobbled up the gangplank to the wharf, he fairly awed the people there.

Margaret felt her eyes fill with tears, and unnoticed in the crowd, she tried to dry them but could not, from sheer pity. Disreputable as he looked, Houston was to her no mere object of curiosity. She knew she was gazing upon greatness; and though he did not even see her, for he was at once taken to a hospital, no other man ever after seemed remotely to approach him in her young heart.

In later years she heard about him now and then. His wounded foot apparently healed; he was in Texas; president of Texas; doing great and heroic things, or so she believed; and she listened to every word about him intently, so that her younger sister, Emily Antoinette, teased her about "that wild Texas man" who was "old enough to be her father." They had quite a spat about it, but got over it, for they were fond of each other; and Emily Antoinette did not tease her any more about what was, after all, the most impossible of impossibilities. As for that, Margaret herself did not take the matter seriously, or tried not to do so; but she was so indifferent to young men, of whom not a few paid attentions to her, that she let her sister, who was two years younger than she, get married first.

She was maid of honor at Emily Antoinette's wedding to William Bledsoe, when Emily was seventeen; and she was glad that her sister married so well, for Mr. Bledsoe owned Spring Hill, one of the finest plantations around Mobile. He was older, past thirty, but he was good to his bride, and Margaret and her mother frequently visited at Spring Hill, which was not far from their home in Mobile.

Then there came a new word about Houston. He was in New Orleans, having finished his first term as president of Texas, and he was being feasted and wined and flirted with; and it also was said he was looking for some blooded horses for his stable, which gave him an excuse for this vacation.

From Spring Hill went forward to General Houston a letter signed by William Bledsoe, inviting him to Spring Hill to look over the stables there, which had some thoroughbred stock widely known. A return note bore Houston's acceptance, naming the date of his arrival.

Margaret smiled a little to herself as she gazed into the fire. Sam Houston did not know it, but he was then being led into a series of events which he, being a mere man, did not dream were being concocted for him, but in which he was guided by the most invisible of all gossamer webs, the artful wiles of women.

It would be impolite to accuse a lady of conniving; and the Lea girls were ladies by the most exacting standards. But the sisters laid their heads together, and Margaret had to admit (to herself only) that there was a little connivance in what followed.

William Bledsoe's letter of invitation was written at the instance of his bride, Emily Antoinette, after she and Margaret had whispered and laughed secretly over the plan. Mere curiosity was what prompted Emily Antoinette, and Margaret did not tell her of a deeper, hardly acknowledged, interest beyond any curiosity she felt.

The sequence of events, which seemed so casual that it could only have been the result of carefully sly stage management, went as follows.

When Sam Houston arrived at the Spring Hill mansion on a lovely May afternoon, he beheld a charming sight. On the front lawn was a perfect flowering of pretty young ladies in bright spring dresses. Emily Antoinette had invited a score of friends of her own age to a strawberry festival at that precise time.

The girls crowded about, thrilled to be introduced to the hero, and Houston, always delighted with pretty young women, charmed them with his impressively graceful compliments and courtesies.

But Emily Antoinette had further plans for him: and among the girls on the lawn Margaret was somehow absent when Houston arrived.

She took him into the house, to show him his room, and then invited him to look at her rose garden, which was behind the residence. He agreed with pleasure, and they walked along the sanded paths, he de-lighted with her pretty ways, she prattling about this or that blooming bush.

All at once he saw, coming down the sanded path along which he and his young hostess were slowly advancing, another lovely vision, a girl carrying a basket of strawberries. It was Margaret herself. She was wear-ing, she remembered, her most charming white dress, sprigged with tiny embroidered rosebuds, and the strawberries she was carrying were the exact color of those rosebuds.

Perhaps a man would not notice such details; but to a girl they were perfect for the time and setting.

She remembered that she stopped, as if surprised, but really with a beating heart. He looked so different from the way she had once seen him before: a handsome, finely attired giant, his face clean-shaved and pleasant, and there were those strangely hypnotic eyes. . . .

Emily Antoinette took her cue, and as if surprised also, said, "Oh, General Houston—I don't believe you've met my sister, Miss Margaret Lea."

It had all worked out exactly as the sisters had slyly planned: the invitation from Mr. Bledsoe; the strawberry festival, so coincidental; and the walk through the rose garden with the appearance of the girl carrying strawberries—a girl, incidentally, who had not been presented before when there was a galaxy of beauties about. And Margaret smiled once more at this feminine scheming, and said to herself: Poor dear—but it was for his own good, after all.

From that moment on, events took care of themselves. Houston advanced and stood towering over her, with a single word which thrilled her, "Charmed!"

Emily Antoinette excused herself with smooth tact, taking the basket of berries and pleading her duties as a hostess to the ladies in front; and Houston and Margaret strolled along the paths. She was twenty, and he was in his middle forties. She was a mere unknown, and he was one of the most famous men of his day. She was slim and small, and he was a burly giant. But the mystical leveler of sex made light of all these things. Sam Houston was entranced; and Margaret knew it, and was half fright-ened, yet inexpressibly fascinated by him.

At one point she said half shyly, "I'm glad you have quite recovered from your wound, General Houston."

"My wound?" He seemed at a loss.

"The wound you received at San Jacinto," she reminded him.

"Oh, that. Yes, I'm quite recovered. But how did you know of it? You could have been no more than a child at the time——"

"I was at school in New Orleans, and I saw you when your ship tied up at the dock. You came hobbling up the gangplank, and I could see how you suffered. I . . . cried." The last in a small voice as if of half-shamed confession.

He stopped and looked down at her, as if he had never seen anyone like her before. Then he took her hand and raised it to his lips.

"Dear lady, I'm not worthy of such sympathy. But it is a treasure beyond words to me." Her heart swelled at the ring of sincerity in his voice.

So Margaret met Houston. The rest, as she remembered it, followed by a sort of inevitability, in which, now that she was launched, she was swept along so that she could not have stopped if she had wished.

Houston spent the rest of the afternoon and evening becoming acquainted with her, instead of the horses in the Bledsoe stables. That night when she played the piano, he stood beside her and turned the pages. His interest in her was so intense and open that now there was alarm in her family.

Her mother, her brother-in-law William Bledsoe, even her sister Emily Antoinette—who until now had been her accomplice—took separate occasions to caution her. Houston was a drunkard they had been told; he was a man whose past with women was the subject of whispers that could hardly be repeated to a young girl; in spite of his fine appearance he was a savage; he was not the kind of a man who would make a happy marriage for a wife; he was violent and unpredictable; he was too old for her; he lived in Texas, a country of wild Indians and wilder frontiersmen.

She listened to these things. And promised to be sensible.

But when, a little later, Houston asked her to be his wife, she forgot all her resolutions, and said, "Yes! Yes, darling!" and accepted his kiss.

Then she wept again.

Why? From fear of the future after all the warnings? From sorrow that she must leave her family and friends?

Perhaps from happiness. She was very much in love with him.

And she could, sitting before the fire, tell herself that even the prophets of misfortune must admit now that her marriage was successful, her husband devoted, herself proud and happy.

That was the story of Margaret Lea, and nobody but herself, not even Houston or Emily Antoinette, knew all the woven threads of it. She could smile over it now, the best proof that the means had been justified by the end she had achieved.

3

The front part of the house, reached through the turkey walk, was a single room, with a stone hearth in which a fire was burning; bare puncheon floors; a table covered with papers and writing materials; stools, chairs, and several spittoons placed in handy locations but showing inexactitude of marksmanship by the stains on the floor; a couple of trunks and some boxes about the walls; and a whiskey barrel complete with spigot and dipper—for though the president did not "participate in the ardent," as he put it, since his promise to Margaret, he observed the amenities toward his visitors who did.

It was in this room that the business of the republic was conducted, and on that morning, with the rain drizzling outside and a leak dripping from the roof into a tin pan placed to catch it, Houston seated himself at the desk and faced Donelson, who sat across from him. The United States Chargé d'Affaires once more was struck by the fact that though the room was barren, Houston needed no surroundings. His face, with its lines of force and intelligence, and his herculean figure, were enough to impress anyone who viewed him. He had grown older, no doubt of that, his side whiskers gray; his hair, too, and growing thin on top. But the lion look in his eyes was now permanent; and so was the steel-trap set of his mouth, and the picturesque scowl, imbedded now so that even when he smiled his brows appeared to be knit. A man who had dared and done much; and who would dare and do more when necessity called upon him.

The topic of conversation was a touchy one: the relations of the Republic of Texas with the United States of America. But as Chargé d'Affaires Donelson felt bound to bring it up, for among his instructions was that he discover if possible exactly what Houston's personal attitudes were after the rather shabby manner in which his young nation had been treated.

"It has ever been Houston's hope and plan to bring Texas into the Union of States," the president was saying, and Donelson remarked to himself how Houston still loved to refer to himself in the third person. "But evidently the matter is of small moment to the American people. I am," he paused and frowned, "in no mood to continue this futile game longer. I must act: and that without great delay, for this nation is in gravest danger. Santa Anna is feeling his oats again, and very recently had his troops again in Texas—as far as San Antonio de Bexar. We chased them out; but a Texas party of three hundred men, after a very heroic defense at the town of Mier against twenty-seven hundred of the enemy, was captured. Do you know what happened to them?"

Donelson shook his head.

"One of Santa Anna's cruelest inventions—a death lottery. Every tenth man was to die, and he arranged it so that the doomed ones must *condemn themselves*. The Mexicans put into a clay *olla* a number of beans equal to the number of the prisoners. Of those beans one in ten was black, the rest white. My men in turn reached down into the *olla* to draw forth a bean. Imagine the sensations of a prisoner, knowing he might be pronouncing his own death sentence if he drew a black bean! Those who lost in this lottery were seated on a log, blindfolded, and there and then shot to death before the eyes of their helpless comrades. Of the survivors most are still in Mexican dungeons."

Houston rubbed his craggy chin.

"Confronted by such a foe, you can understand that our situation is critical. Nor am I responsible for it. When I concluded my first term as president of Texas, I left the country strong, solvent, and hopeful. In the two years in office of that afflorescent ass Mirabeau Buonaparte Lamar"—his lip curled at the flamboyant name—"he wrecked everything I'd done. He bankrupted the nation, strained our relations with Mexico to the breaking point, by his treachery brought the wild Comanches like hornets about our heads, in short, made so many other blunders that when I took office for my second term Texas was in a worse situation, actually, than she was April 22, 1836—the day before San Jacinto!"

Donelson did not interrupt this outburst, wondering if it was for effect —on himself. Then he tried tactfully to bring the conversation back to its original line.

"I suggest, sir, that there is still hope that Texas may become one of the states of the Union," he said.

Houston reared his huge form from behind the desk, and paced back and forth, his scowl darkening his features.

"That hope is dim and distant," he said. "If Andrew Jackson were at the helm, I can conceive how it would be possible. But Andrew Jackson no longer—by the way, just how was the General, last time you saw him?"

"Old—old and feeble," said Donelson. "He sits by a fire, or on nice days sometimes by Rachel's grave. He is worried by debts, but speaks little, and much of the time seems lost in contemplation of the past."

"His mind? What of his mind?"

"There's nothing wrong with it. When he exercises it his acuteness in thinking and breadth of vision are astonishing."

"The greatest man of our time, in his or any other nation. If only Jackson would arouse himself." Houston broke off his tramping, and stood tugging at a side whisker. "But Jackson is, as you say, old, content to rest——"

"He deserves to rest."

"Granted. Yet I wonder if Jackson has any conception of the gravity of the present situation." Houston threw a look indescribably keen at

Donelson. "With annexation blocked by the United States Senate, Texas has reached a pass where she can go only in one of two ways."

"And those?"

"One is alliance with a foreign power. And that's well within possibility. I've had conversations"—another sharp glance—"with Captain Charles Elliot, the British Chargé d'Affaires. More than once, he's taken tea with Margaret and me." He smiled briefly. "The captain praises my wife's tea as the best he's had in Texas, and good tea is an important way to an Englishman's heart. But to return: England, as you quite well know, wishes to keep Texas out of the United States. I am informed that she is willing to guarantee Texas her safety—at a price."

"The price?"

"That Texas renounce forever any desire or willingness to be annexed by the United States. By thus bringing Texas within her own orbit, Britain could at one stroke isolate the United States through sponsoring a rival which might eventually outshine her."

Donelson experienced an acute alarm, for this was very close to his own apprehension. "You said there were *two* alternatives," he said. "One you've described. What is the other?"

"Did you know," said Houston cunningly, "that—following a suggestion said to have come from a highly honored personage in the United States—the Texas congress has passed a resolution annexing the two Californias and all the intervening territory? Under international law, since the borders of Texas have never been defined, she is free to claim whatever she can defend."

He paused, with that shrewd look, and seated himself again.

"Houston vetoed that resolution," he continued, "as a matter of policy, knowing it would be repassed over his veto, which it was. The resolution is there today—a valid Texas claim to all the country west to the Pacific Ocean, a territory greater than the expanse of the United States."

Donelson, in spite of himself, was impressed. And he knew the "highly honored personage." The suggestion had come from none other than Andrew Jackson.

"In the United States," continued Houston, "the American Anti-Slavery Society has made a personal issue out of Texas, as if Texas were the beginning, the middle, and the end of all the slavery difficulties. That rabble-rouser, William Lloyd Garrison, has stated, 'All who would sympathize with that pseudo-republic'—and he means Texas—'hate liberty and would dethrone God.' Now I hold no brief for slavery, and believe with most intelligent men—including Andrew Jackson—that it must and will be abolished whenever a way is found to do so, without injustice or bloodshed. But in Texas the slaveholders are few in comparison with the population. So you can imagine how such a statement as Garrison's sets with Texans who know what it is to fight, and also to die, for liberty, and I might add, how to fear their God. The arrogance of the Abolitionists in the North has created ill-feeling in the South, out of all proportion to its importance. On the other hand, we must face the fact that it is the Slave Expansionists in the South who have made the biggest noise for annexation, and Texas does not desire that kind of an aegis, either. Jackson halted Calhoun's disunion move, but the seed is still there."

The gigantic president took up from his desk a paper knife, whittled out of wood—and he was a great whittler—and began to play with it between his fingers, his almost hypnotic opalescent eyes fixed on Donelson.

"The times are big with events of coming circumstance—to Texas, and to the world. In the event annexation should fail, which can only result from selfishness and political expediency on the part of the government or of Congress, Houston here says to you that the glory of the United States already has culminated."

Donelson was startled. "Sir, what do you mean?"

"I mean," said Houston with deep solemnity, "that you will see a rival power built and flourishing on this continent. The Pacific, as well as the Atlantic, will be component parts of Texas. Virginia, and all the states south of the Mason-Dixon line, will be invited to join us—and will accept, for the logic is inevitable. Westward the new nation will sweep to California, as far north as the Columbia River. Nothing can prevent the Anglo-Saxon race from mastering that illimitable and empty domain."

That was it; but that was enough. The interview was ended.

Captain Elliot, the British agent, had described Houston in one of his confidential reports to Lord Palmerston in London, as having "two sides to his nature, one very clear indeed, the other impenetrably dark."

The dark side—Houston's Indian instinct for concealment of his innermost thoughts and schemes—had puzzled more than one man before Captain Elliot. Houston knew Jack Donelson well, and liked him. But that morning he had played with him a devious game.

He knew the full report of the conversation would go at once to Andrew Jackson; and he knew also that Andrew Jackson would take it at its full weight, because Andrew Jackson knew Sam Houston.

As Don Juan de Veramendi had once said, "This is a very deep and subtile man."

4

But that night Sam Houston sat glooming at his table.

For Margaret, whom he loved for herself, and treasured for her courage to live in these squalid surroundings when she had been used all her life to elegance and pleasantness, he had hardly a word. Even when she brought to the table her child, and fed him, Houston derived no pleasure from a sight which always had amused and delighted him: the little face so knowing, the little eyes so bright, the little mouth opening so expectantly to receive the food.

Margaret Houston had seen her husband in periods of great stress: when he wrote to Santa Anna a letter that was tantamount to a declaration of war if the Mexican dictator dared to accept the challenge, which he did not; when, in the face of rumors of assassination, he walked calmly back and forth before his lighted windows at night, as if to give those lurking outside every chance to shoot him, while she valorously played her piano; when he rallied his Texas Rangers to repel Comanche assaults; when he looked a furious man in the eye and coldly refused to meet him on the dueling field, saying, "Houston never fights downhill."

But she had never seen him in a mood so black and silent as on this night.

At last she ventured a timid question. "What has gone wrong, Sam?"

He turned toward her a face she had never seen before, a face with a cold shadow in the eyes, an expression as harsh and dreary as that of a criminal bracing himself for inevitable detection. She was startled, almost terrified by that face.

At first he said nothing. But a man in travail seeks comfort; and this was a woman who loved him; if he could confide in anyone in the world, he could confide in her.

After a time Houston answered her. "Have you ever cruelly hurt—wounded to the heart—*deliberately and purposely*—someone you greatly loved?"

She shook her head, not daring to speak, awed by the deep-drawn lines of his countenance.

"I have—this day—committed such a cruelty," he said. "To a man who has been more than a father to me—to whom I owe everything. And I did it, God help me, knowing I was doing it—with malice aforethought——"

He broke off as if he could no longer control his voice. She sat silent, bewildered by his emotion, wondering whom he meant, and how.

Presently he resumed, in a low, tense voice. "Margaret, you have the right to despise me—every decent person has the right." A pause, and he turned his tortured face away. "Yet *he* it was who taught me—that in the affairs of nations, individuals, no matter how dear, do not count in comparison with the greater objective. *He* would throw himself into a fiery furnace to do his duty."

"My dear—what are you trying to tell me?" she asked.

"Margaret, I have this day stabbed Andrew Jackson, my friend, to his vitals, forfeited all his love for me, convinced him that I am a traitor and an ungrateful cur."

"You are neither!" she cried in protest. And then, doubtfully, in the face of his terrible earnestness, "If you did all this—why?"

He said, very slowly, "I lacerated the heart of that great man whom I revere—but did I not do it as much for himself as for any other reason? *More* for himself! After all, it is *his* dream, isn't it? His dream that is in gravest peril. And no man in all the world can save that dream, except Andrew Jackson. He is old, sick, perhaps dying. But I *had* to do what I did, didn't I? I had to do it in the cold hope that somehow it might rouse him in spite of his age and weakness for one last effort. . . ."

She did not understand what he was trying to say to her, for she knew nothing of the dream. But she saw the tears start in her husband's eyes and she went to him. And when he put his arms about her, she felt his great shoulders shaking.

Chapter Forty

There's still some use for old bones after all.

ANDREW JACKSON

1

In the white-pillared house on the Lebanon road out of Nashville, the old General received a letter from Jack Donelson, Chargé d'Affaires in Texas.

Sarah read the letter to him as he sat in his chair by the window. When she looked up, she was startled. He had gripped the arm of the chair until the knuckles of his hand were white, and he had reared himself into a straight position, no longer lying back, and his face looked stunned.

"Read that again—over slowly," he said.

When she did so, he spoke as if to himself.

"I can't understand Sam Houston. I would swear he is as true as steel. But if what Jack Donelson reports——"

"Please don't excite yourself, General," said the girl.

"Excite! It's time someone was excited!" he exclaimed. But then he leaned back in his chair. "Leave me, child. I must do some thinking."

That long afternoon he spent slowly turning over in his mind the various questions presented in Donelson's lengthy letter to him. The failure of the Texas project had grieved him before, but until now he had considered himself out of the stream of events. Nevertheless . . .

The old man at once recognized in the scheme revealed by Houston to Donelson the offspring of his own great plan. Yet it was an offspring somehow perverted; not only contrary to the very basic premise of his dream, but presenting an ugly danger to the Union for which he had fought and labored without stint all his life.

Could Sam Houston really intend such a thing? Jackson, with the hope of age clinging to a belief preconceived, told himself at first that he did not intend it; if Sam Houston said such a thing it must have been with tongue in cheek.

But, no: Donelson emphasized that he was deadly serious.

The peril in the scheme of Texas expansion, when one examined it closely, was that it was so plausible that it might easily become a reality. The North, which had again and again defeated the proposition to admit Texas to the Union, was ignored in the plan. But to the South a strong appeal was made. Notable Southern leaders were certain to be highly interested . . . he thought of Calhoun, and Hayne, and their like.

The other part of Donelson's report, in Jackson's eyes, was almost worse. Both England and France had diplomatic representatives in Texas; and England actually had on foot negotiations to take under her "protection"—no doubt as a colony, or even a dominion—the orphan little Republic of Texas.

The General had no love for the British. Twice he had fought them. But it was the conception that *any* crowned power from the Old World might gain control of a nation in the New World that made his white hair bristle. He conceived of Europe as corrupt, cynical, decadent, rotten to the core, an everlasting breeder of wars and troubles, its people bred and reared in subservience to those "above" them by accident of birth rather than merit, its chancelleries greedy and dishonest, everything about it evil.

The fact that he had never seen Europe, and might perhaps be less than entirely just in his estimate of the Old World, did not enter Andrew Jackson's considerations. Britain—or France—with a foothold in Texas, he passionately believed, would be a sword poised and pointed at the heart of his country.

His was the mind that first conceived the vast plan of western expansion by the United States; and it was the very danger he apprehended of European occupation, with the perils involved in such an eventuality, that had caused him to probe the possibilities and lay his secret schemes looking toward that bold advance.

He still hoped to see his nation spreading across and making fruitful that vast empty region. But should the West be won by a Texas obligated to Europe—perhaps with the aid of British or French guns, money, even men—the whole great conception of a continental United States would be shattered, his beloved country already doomed to be a secondary power among the nations of the world.

That evening the old man sat in bodily and mental anguish, and wrote a letter to Sam Houston:

My dear Genl I tell you in all sincerity and friendship, if you will receive this annexation your name & fame will become enrolled amongst the greatest chieftains. Now is the time to act & that with promptness & secrecy & have a treaty of annexation laid before the United States Senate where I am assured it will be ratified. It will be an unfailing laurel to your ploom. I am scarcely able to write—the Theme alone inspires me with strength. Let me hear from you if only three lines. Your friend,

Andrew Jackson.

In all his life he had pleaded to no man before. But now at last he was pleading; pleading with his former subordinate. Had Houston forgotten all he had taught him? Was his border captain in the end to prove disloyal to him?

He fretted with impatience while he waited for a reply. In due time it came, and the salutation of Sam Houston's letter was *Venerated Friend*.

But it gave no unequivocal assurance. Instead the writer recounted the difficulties and perils surrounding his young republic, and the necessity of looking for some guarantee of her safety—by a foreign nation or nations, since the United States seemed uninterested in helping her. He described himself as still full of affection for the land of his birth, but expressed doubts that the Senate ever would sufficiently compose its differences to ratify a treaty of annexation such as Jackson proposed. He dropped in a hint that Texas might exist without the United States, but the United States could not exist without Texas, except at great hazard. And this to the man who first saw and recognized that hazard!

At the end were lines of ominous import:

Now, my venerated friend, you will perceive that Texas is presented to the United States, as a bride adorned for her espousal. But if, so confident of the union, she should be rejected, her mortification would be indescribable. She has been sought by the United States, and this is the third time she has consented. Were she now to be spurned, it would forever terminate any expectation on her part; and she would seek some other friend among the nations of the world.

Andrew Jackson laid down the letter, shocked to his very soul.

2

That stinging letter: Andrew Jackson did not know it was written by a grieving Sam Houston. And had he known, it might not have achieved the purpose for which it was designed.

But it did achieve that purpose. For the last time, the old warrior gathered himself for one more great battle. Texas must be saved: his cherished hope for his nation must come true.

He was old, feeble, and when he looked about him he wiped his ailing eyes for the room seemed misty, he was almost blind. And he was stiff and weak with illness. On some days when he tried to get up from his bed he could hardly lift his head from the pillow.

Nevertheless he only, *he* must do what must be done. His invincible mind, the only part of him spared by his nearly four-score years of constant risks and labors, seized upon the problems. From somewhere the will that had always driven him found resources—frail enough, but resources just the same—which not even his physicians had suspected he could summon.

He knew his gigantic task. In some manner, and very quickly, the nation must be aroused and united. To accomplish such an end an incredible number of things must be done, and done exactly and surely. Enormous difficulties lay ahead: delays and hindrances; opposition from enemies on every hand; above all, and the most baffling of his problems, the effort to overcome the inertia and stagnation of the people, into which they had sunk since he led them. It was a task young, strong men would consider impossible, and with every good reason. But to Andrew Jackson, neither young nor strong, no such thing as an impossibility existed.

In those next weeks the nation saw a marvelous thing; almost a miraculous thing. He could plan, and he could write, and when he could not write he could dictate messages, for his mind flamed incessantly, even beneath closed eyes. Sometimes Sarah took down letters for him, and sometimes young Andrew, and sometimes one of his old friends like Major Lewis, who had been White House major-domo, or even Jimmie Polk, home during Congressional recess.

In distant parts of the land, old comrades, old supporters, old followers of Andrew Jackson received those letters. Newspapers printed communications from the same hand.

It was as if the aged, sick man stretched out his gaunt arm across the nation and pointing his finger at those who in the past had believed in him and rallied to him, said to them, "Once more, come march with me for our country!"

Men looked at each other, and a new light flamed in their eyes. That letter! That article in the paper! They had the ring of Old Hickory sure enough! It was Andy-by-God-Jackson speaking again, and when Andy-by-God-Jackson spoke, men grew alert, waiting for the orders to come, the leash to be thrown off.

As in the old days, riders once more came galloping across the country to the Hermitage with messages, reports, assurances of loyalty. And as in the old days the General conferred for long hours with men who came to offer their fealty to him and ask what must be done. Sometimes he thus busied himself all day long even when he was anchored to his bed by weakness; the long frame too gaunt, it almost seemed, for life; the voice a scarcely audible whisper. On those days, when his friends left his room, they shook their heads silently at one another.

But on other days he was up: a new access of strength from some mysterious well. And always, in bed or sitting in his chair, he still was the incredible leader, inspirer, doer, darer.

Sarah, terrified as she saw him so prodigally expending the little strength he possessed, begged him to desist.

"I can't stop, child," he replied.

"But—if you don't—it may kill you—" she protested.

"All I want of this old body is to keep me going until this battle's won. It will be my last. After that they may throw what is left of me on the rubbish heap."

"Oh—no——" Tears sprang into Sarah's eyes.

"Daughter," he said tenderly, "there's still some use for old bones after all. I want to live to see the day when all is safe—for my country. After that . . . rest, perhaps?"

With that she had to be content, though she watched him and cared for him with fear growing greater each succeeding day.

His letter-writing continued at an ever-growing pace. Sometimes it seemed impossible to her that a being so thin and frail could accomplish the work he daily accomplished. But he had stimulated the country to causes before, and he knew the immense groundwork that must be done before it slowly stirred at first, then moved with growing momentum in the needful direction.

To this—providing the nation once more with leadership it had lacked for years as Whigs and Democrats checked and counterchecked each other with fatuous futility—he bent his waning energies.

With his sure political instinct he saw in the coming Presidential campaign the one great chance to crystallize public opinion and win—or forever lose. For opportunity would never again return.

He surveyed the field. As he had predicted, Henry Clay was the candidate once more—for his third race—of the Whig Party. The Democrats were divided more hopelessly than they had ever been, the chief figures to be considered in the coming convention in Baltimore being General Lewis Cass, once Jackson's Secretary of War, and Martin Van Buren, defeated once but still hoping for re-election.

Neither of these suited the General. To his friends and aides who had gathered at the Hermitage, Major Lewis, young Andrew, Willoughby Williams, and now Jack Donelson, back again from Texas, the patriarch spoke:

"Cass could never muster enough support to carry the country. Van Buren is not to be depended on. I hear he's lately had a tête-à-tête with

Clay himself. That means conniving, and I can tell you what they con-
nived. Unless I misjudge the gentlemen, neither of whom likes to meet
a thorny issue squarely, they'll agree between themselves to *keep Texas
out of the campaign*. Mark my words. They'll have an understanding to
conduct their campaigns on gentlemanly, pussyfooting lines, sticking to
the time-honored worn-out issues, and refraining from throwing the
Texas wildcat into the middle of the hen house. Clay is against annexation. Van Buren fears it. A man who's too timid to fight for his principles is too weak for the White House. Nothing that Van Buren touches
will prosper."

"But who?" asked Lewis.

The General was silent for a time, brooding, in his mind's eye seeking
a man upon whom dependence could be placed to fight for what he
believed, and who believed rightly.

"What about Jimmie Polk?" he said suddenly.

Their faces showed astonishment.

"Jimmie Polk?" said Lewis. "I'd never thought about Jimmie
Polk. . . ."

But on consideration there were things to be said for Jimmie Polk.
His home was in Columbia, Tennessee, no more than forty miles from
Nashville. Jimmie Polk was a friend of Sam Houston; he had succeeded
Houston in Congress; he had led the fight in behalf of Houston during
the Stanbery hearings. Jimmie Polk was Jackson's Administration leader
in Congress. Jimmie Polk had proved a good parliamentary strategist
in fighting Jackson's legislative battles. Jimmie Polk had never once been
false to the General's precepts. The more Jackson thought about Jimmie
Polk, the more he was drawn to him.

But Jimmie Polk was reserved, almost shy, with his wide, childlike
eyes, and his round, unlined boyish face. The question was not Jimmie
Polk's loyalty, but whether he could be elected. Opposed by an orator
and personality like Henry Clay, he must appear unimpressive, almost
inarticulate. And yet Andrew Jackson, conning the field, knew that
Jimmie Polk was his only hope.

The next day after this conference, the General took to his bed again,
suffering from a recurrence of his cough, with an alarming hemorrhage
that persisted for hours. Nevertheless an invitation from the Hermitage
was dispatched to James Knox Polk, and as swiftly as he could ride, he
was at Jackson's bedside.

Their talk was necessarily brief, for the old man was very weak and
panting for breath. But when Polk left the Hermitage, he carried with
him the backing—and the instructions—of the old chief. The instructions were simple and definite:

"Throw the Texas issue headfirst into the campaign. Never pussyfoot
on it. The people will *always* rally behind a good cause, and I'll give

you a slogan: *Texas and Oregon.* We might as well bag two 'possums from that tree."

He fought for breath and Polk waited, his eyes on the drawn white face. Presently Jackson resumed, in a voice noticeably weaker, though the words still rang like steel.

"I'm concerned about Oregon, as I'm concerned about Texas. We're entitled to the Oregon Territory, not only by right of discovery, but more importantly by right of occupation. If Britain moves into Oregon, and gains ascendancy in Texas, she will, with her West Indies and Canadian possessions, form an iron hoop around the United States. So go after Oregon. Do not fear. I've never loved the English, but I'll say this for them: in the end they're usually willing to listen to the justice of a question when they might not accede to a show of force."

Another long pause. Then:

"Now listen: Mexico has already notified our government that if we annex Texas, a state of war will exist."

"Yes." Polk nodded.

"It is a threat only, I think. But dictators are vainglorious, and maintain themselves by building mass hysteria. Therefore, it might come to war. If so, fight your war. But try in every way to avoid the wastage of lives by seeking a peaceful agreement with Mexico on what is an accomplished fact. Do not strike the first blow: but once that blow is struck against you, make the enemy repent—and *protect Texas.*"

White as a ghost, his deep-sunk eyes closed, their brows already yawning with the hollow shadow of death, the old man sank back on his pillows. James Knox Polk stole out of the room wondering if the General had enough of life and power in him, after all, to bring about what he demanded and desired of the American people.

Andrew Jackson was well aware he was fighting his last great campaign. He waged it like a wary leader, husbanding himself as he would have husbanded the men in a small and weak army beset by overwhelming foes. Time was what he fought for. In those days he seemed to hold off death by sheer refusal to surrender to it. After each sinking spell, and they became more frequent, he aroused himself, from somewhere summoned a little more pathetic weak vitality, and struggled on.

To the nation, however, it was as if once more the Jackson trumpet rang across the land. Jack Donelson traveled to the Democratic convention at Baltimore, where the delegates were divided between Van Buren and Cass. The divisions were forgotten when he gave them the message he carried from the old chief. After an all-night adjournment, the convention by acclamation nominated the man Andrew Jackson asked it to name. James Knox Polk, now hailed as "Young Hickory," was the standard bearer, his running mate George M. Dallas, a lawyer of Pennsylvania.

3

With growing alarm, and sick at heart over the sacrifice, Sarah watched her old General, propped up at his desk, writing letter after letter in his feeble hand. But those letters, though the handwriting seemed at times to falter, were composed by an unfaltering mind, and they were signed with a signature better known than any in the nation: *Andrew Jackson.*

"I flicker like a taper at times," he said to her one day with his brief smile. "But like a taper I burn brightly again . . . for a time . . . for a time."

He had been assured after a private count by Francis Preston Blair that thirty-nine votes for annexation could be mustered in the Senate—more than the two-thirds required. One of his letters, therefore, was to President Tyler, urging that the treaty be placed before that body at once for ratification.

It was done. But twelve days after Polk was nominated, with Henry Clay still ascendant, and Daniel Webster and other giants supporting him, the treaty was once again rejected.

A death blow?

Sam Houston, who had obeyed his old commander in drawing up that treaty, was bitter. It seemed the last possible chance, and now word came that the Texas giant had begun serious negotiations with Captain Elliot, and through him with Lord Aberdeen, British Secretary for Foreign Affairs; also that a new invasion from Mexico was brewing.

"I do not blame Houston!" the old General exclaimed. "He has been most cruelly treated. I feel nothing but scorn for those cravenhearted Senators, traitors to our country and our glorious Union. Must we now go to war with England and France to gain Texas, which was offered us on honorable terms and rejected for political effect?"

But he was by no means through. In those days the old warrior's face grew thinner and grimmer, and still his letters went forth, suggesting, directing, commanding, although at times he had to fight to keep from fainting from weakness.

In this extremity Jackson's continental conception, which seemed mere audacity to the conservatives, took an even more daring and inclusive form. He turned his attention to the Oregon Territory, which was in serious dispute with Great Britain. By right of discovery and occupation he felt that the United States was entitled to the lands north of the Columbia River—which Britain denied—as far as the Forty-ninth parallel, which coincided with the general northern border of the nation. But because he was the shrewdest of international bargainers, he used the old horse-trading technique—at which he was a master also—of demanding more than he expected to get.

He therefore, for the time being at least, espoused the cause of some of the extremist Oregon settlers who believed their territory should extend as far north as the lower tip of Russian Alaska—at fifty-four degrees, forty minutes, north latitude—and coined a tongue-catching campaign phrase:

"Fifty-Four Forty or Fight!"

The cry swept the country. Henry Clay, desperate as he saw the new trend building up, and making his last bid for the supreme honor he had sought all his life, stumped the North and West with his soaring eloquence and the magnetism of his personality.

"James K. Polk and George M. Dallas—one for the devil and the other for the gallows," chanted Clay supporters.

To this Jackson continually urged Polk, "Lash Clay on Texas."

The Democratic candidate knew full well that he was colorless, and made few speeches. But the newspapers of the land continually carried statements from the old soldier at the Hermitage, who, as all knew, was the real head of the campaign.

With the inevitability of a tide, public feeling rose as it always did when the General took charge. Even in the North, newspapers began to editorialize that annexation was a subject on which the whole nation, regardless of section, should unite.

The campaign drew to a smashing climax.

"It will be close," predicted Jackson, the shrewdest political analyst of his time.

Close it was. But as the reports came in it was apparent that Jimmie Polk had won. His count in the Electoral College was one hundred and seventy to Clay's one hundred and five. An unparalleled victory, considering all the odds, fashioned by the hand of the dying man in the Hermitage.

Henry Clay made a rueful statement when he saw his long-schemed Presidential hopes ended:

"My greatest mistake was February 8, 1825."

By that he meant his manipulation of Congress to defeat Jackson and elect Adams. But his real tragic error was when he permitted the name of Rachel Jackson to be drawn into the campaign.

Meantime Andrew Jackson fought for life and looked with painful anxiety toward Texas. Down there Sam Houston had completed his second term as president, and was succeeded by the man he named, Dr. Anson Jones.

"I believe the reins of power still remain in Houston's hands," said Jackson when Polk visited him after the election. "But how long will a man in retirement hold such power? We must strike again, and strike at once. Tyler must present the Texas treaty for reconsideration."

James Knox Polk hurried to Washington to aid President Tyler in that crucial historical moment.

4

The precarious nature of the historic action by the Senate, and the small things upon which the destinies of nations sometimes hang, are illustrated by one of many episodes connected with it, of which neither Andrew Jackson nor any of the other major figures on the political scene ever knew. But as a brief digression it is worth recounting.

In the extreme southeast corner of Indiana lay the backwoods area of Switzerland County. On election day that fall of 1844, old Freeman Clark, a farmer, lay seriously ill in bed. But he begged his sons to carry him over a mountain road to the county seat, so that he could vote.

The candidate for whom the old man wished to vote was David Kelso, who once had defended him on a murder charge and obtained his acquittal. Thus, gratitude was a motive to Freeman Clark. But even more impelling was the fact that he was a long-time Jackson man, and Kelso, running for the state senate, was a Jackson man also.

His wish was obeyed. The old farmer voted, was carried home by his sons, and the exertions of his journey caused his death. David Kelso was elected to the Indiana state senate by a single vote: Freeman Clark's.

Sitting at Indianapolis, the state senate had a task of high importance: the election of a United States senator. Counting Kelso, the Democrats in the state senate had a majority of just one. A caucus was held and it developed that a majority of the party delegation favored a man who, it was known, would vote against the Texas annexation, if elected.

But Kelso refused to vote for the party choice. A deadlock resulted between the Democratic and Whig candidates which continued for days.

Finally, Kelso made his move. He proposed a new candidate: Edward A. Hannigan. And in the party caucus he notified his Democratic associates that he would bolt and vote with the Whigs—thus electing a Whig to the Senate—unless they supported Hannigan.

The Democrats felt constrained to accept Hannigan. He was elected by a single vote: Kelso's.

The first great issue before the United States Senate when Hannigan took his seat was the reconsideration of the Texas treaty of annexation, placed before it again by President Tyler. Texas sentiment had grown, but in spite of that, the treaty was ratified with the necessary two-thirds majority by only one vote: that of the new Indiana senator, Edward A. Hannigan.

Can it not thus be said that the vote of a dying man in the hills of a backwoods county in Indiana made Texas a state, and Andrew Jackson's mighty plan a reality?

5

Now, on March 15, 1845, Andrew Jackson entered upon the seventy-eighth year of his life.

For four months he had made no attempt to eat with his family. When he felt strong enough, he sat in an easy chair, with a table beside him on which were Rachel's Bible and hymnbook, for toward his latter days he had embraced Rachel's religion.

Yet with eagerness he continued to look forward to the mail, particularly the letters postmarked at the capital and the Washington newspapers. President Tyler had signed the treaty March 1, three days before he turned the reins of his office over to James Knox Polk.

Remaining now was the question of whether Texas would accept this tardy offer to become one of the states rather than continue as a separate nation; and Texas was still the old man's all-absorbing interest.

In May he took to his bed, and he knew, like all the others, that it now was his deathbed. But still he held back the Dark Angel, awaiting the tidings on which everything depended.

No longer could he even lie down. They propped him in a half-sitting position to enable him to catch his faltering breath. Sarah took turns with Hannah, the old woman in whose arms Rachel died, and George, the General's body servant, in keeping a round-the-clock watch.

At times the dying man's pain was severe, and under the doctor's instructions opiates were administered. One eye was now entirely blind, the other almost too dim to see. But still he fought to live.

"What will Houston do?" was his constant inquiry. "I must not leave my mortal body until I know."

He had received a copy of Houston's farewell speech when he gave over his presidency in Texas: the speech delivered after the third rejection of the treaty by the Senate, and before the final passage of that resolution. The wounded spirit of the man sounded in his words to the Texas congress:

"The attitude of Texas is one of peculiar interest. The United States have spurned her. Let her, therefore, work out her own political salvation. If Texas goes begging again for admission to the United States she will only degrade herself."

Yes: but Texas had not been asked to "go begging." By the peculiar talents of Andrew Jackson himself, the treaty once rejected—but the *same* treaty—had been ratified. No question now of saving face.

The old man summoned strength to write a halting letter to Houston, assuming that his old subaltern would throw his power on the side of joining the Union, even though another was now president of Texas.

With all his old heart Jackson believed Houston would be true. And yet . . . the question still remained.

On May 26 a lathered horse brought a hard-riding messenger who had used relays of mounts all the way from Texas to the Hermitage. He carried a letter. It was from Houston, and revealed that the old subaltern had done as his chief hoped: set in motion the necessary machinery for acceptance of the treaty by Texas. A question now only of a little time, a formal sitting of the Texas congress, a formal signature by the new Texas president, and the ensign of the United States would be raised over the Lone Star State. The letter, full of affection and devotion, concluded:

I hasten to bring the full report in person and ask your blessing on my son. Your devoted friend,

Sam Houston.

The old man knew the exaltation of great joy.

"I knew Sam Houston would prove true," he whispered. And then, fighting for breath, "My life is nearly burned out and the last glimmer has come."

Yet he still clung to the thread of life spun now incredibly fine, hoping against hope that his "old friend and comrade in arms" would be able to reach him before he passed the portals to another world.

Chapter Forty-One

Always try to remember, my son, that you have looked upon the face of Andrew Jackson.

SAM HOUSTON

1

The race was against death, and the red coach bounded over the rough road at speed. Texas folks living in the vicinity of Huntsville knew that coach well. It was General Sam Houston's coach; and the general himself was in it, along with his wife, and his small son.

Texas folks also knew that the general was in a powerful hurry. Word was out that General Andrew Jackson, up in Tennessee, couldn't be expected to live long, and the great man of Texas and the great man of the United States were close and devoted friends.

In the box of the coach sat Esau and Tom Blue, to spell each other at the reins of the four horses that drew the vehicle, and the whip was not to be spared. Sam Houston was in a hurry—a big hurry. And he counted on Texas to help expedite him.

"I *must* see him—I must find if he's forgiven me," he had said to his wife Margaret.

"Forgive you? For what?" she asked, almost impatiently.

"For forcing him to use his last strength in bringing Texas into the Union," he responded. "I made him do that. I feel as if I shortened his life. If I could just see him—and assure him of my devotion—and hear him say, 'Well done'——"

"He's forgiven you—if he ever felt you needed forgiveness," she said reasonably. "I think he would thank you—it was his greatest desire, didn't you say?"

But she agreed to make the wild ride that it was certain to be, to try to reach the Hermitage in time for her husband to assuage a feeling of remorse, even guilt, which seemed to her almost unnecessary, when the great matters at stake were taken into consideration. Sam Houston was Sam Houston. Long ago she had ceased trying fully to understand that strange, tidal personality she had married. She would loyally second her husband in what he so mightily desired.

Now, within the coach, Margaret Houston clung desperately to her seat and grasped at her hat, as she was tossed about. Houston, holding their small boy in his arms, looked at her anxiously.

"Shall I order Tom Blue to slow down?" he asked.

"No—oh, no!" she replied. "I'm doing f-fine. Just see that little Sam —doesn't bump his head."

She was all spunk, was Margaret Houston; but it was a thousand miles to Nashville, and they had only just started. An old man was dying up there. Hurry! Oh, hurry!

Miles of being thrown back and forth in the coach, and the Trinity River just ahead. No bridge here. A ferry scow, operated on the power of the current pushing it on a pulley along a cable stretched across the river, shoved slowly over.

Out, everybody. Houston stood with his boy in his arms and his wife beside him while the ferry pushed its flat nose against the bank.

"Giddap!" from Tom Blue.

The horses half-snorted as they drew the rumbling coach on the unstable scow deck. Houston followed with his little family, standing at the flimsy rail, the child's eyes round with wonder at the rushing of the muddy water beneath them.

"How are the horses?" Houston asked.

"Good, Gen'ral," replied Tom Blue. "That Felix hoss on the lead team's a little ga'nted, but he'll do till we git a change."

A jar as the ferry reached the far bank.

"Stand back," said Houston to Margaret. "Tom, let them take a run at it. That bank's steep."

Tom Blue prided himself on his driving. At the crack of his whip and his whoop, the horses surged into their collars, and up the grade went the empty coach with a rush, safely to the level ground above. Houston paid the ferryman and followed his wife, who climbed on foot up to the waiting vehicle.

Now the road became a narrow lane through a jungle of trees, vines, and undergrowth.

"We've entered the Big Thicket," said Houston.

Brilliant blossoms in the tangle brought from Margaret exclamations of delight. But her husband felt for a pistol in his pocket. No use to alarm her, but outlaws, wild men, sometimes infested such areas, and he had a precious cargo to protect.

The lead horses reared back, snorting, as a streak of golden yellow, spotted with black, bounded across the road.

"Whoa up there, Felix! Git goin', Jerry!" Tom Blue had them straightened out and on a half gallop again.

"What—was that?" gasped Margaret.

"Jaguar," said Houston. "Scouting for game. There are a few still up here. He won't bother us unless we bother him."

Later they saw deer, and ducks came springing up from occasional creeks and potholes, and once a small herd of javelinas—wild little pigs, grizzled and white-collared, but dangerously tusked—scrambled to get out from under the hoofs of the horses.

Luck held. The coach arrived at a clearing and a roadside inn after twenty miles through the jungle, without encountering a human being.

"General Houston!" exclaimed the rubicund landlord.

"Yes, sir. In a hurry. A change of horses——"

The landlord glanced at the four that had drawn the coach. "I reckon so. They're about done. I'll have the stable boys put on a fresh tandem. You can leave 'em at Daggett's, up the road. Privilege, sir. No, a fair trade, General. I'll keep your horses until mine are returned, an' no favors asked. Now, if your charming lady and the little boy will come in, there's supper——"

A single large public room, with an immense open fireplace at one side, and a bar at the other. At the rear the dining room, the sleeping rooms above.

"A glass, sir—compliments of the house?" asked the landlord.

Houston shook his head. "No, I thank you. But a bite, and a bed?"

"Our best, sir."

Houston glanced at Margaret. "How long . . . ?"

"Three hours," she said.

"The boy?"

"He'll sleep in the coach."

A wife in a thousand, Margaret Houston.

2

The Camino Real—the King's Road—on the second day about noon. For all its name, only a wagon road through the brush, but a little smoother than the trace through the Big Thicket.

Heading northeast now, and Esau at the reins, giving Tom Blue a rest. As night fell, they crossed the Neches by a shaky bridge, and just beyond something snapped.

Esau pulled up the horses and he and Tom Blue and Houston got out to examine the damage.

"Hell's fire! The thoroughbrace is broken!" exclaimed Houston, and swore like the old soldier he was. Nor did Margaret remonstrate with him in this instance, as she usually did.

What to do?

The thoroughbrace, a cradle of straps which eased the jolting of the coach, must be mended before they could proceed.

From somewhere in the darkness, a winking light: a lantern seemed to blink as a pair of lanky legs scissored the beam. The owner of the legs came to the road and held up the lantern.

"General Houston, by all that's holy!"

Everyone seemed to know him.

Consideration of the thoroughbrace.

"I got some rawhide," said the man with the lantern. "Ye kin cut it in strips, an' tie that thing up. Might git ye as far as Henderson."

A rawhide improvisation.

Henderson by morning, a raw new town, with a sawmill. At the inn Mrs. Houston and the little boy had breakfast and a nap, while Houston stood over the harness maker who was mending the thoroughbrace.

Two hours of delay here while the vehicle was repaired, and a change of horses arranged: the animals had to be fetched from a distance away, and when they arrived they were half-broken and fractious.

Houston alternately paced and cursed; and he almost, in his desperation, broke over and had a "sip of the ardent." But he gave the matter a second thought, and constrained himself to remain in the path of rectitude and right into which Margaret had guided his errant feet.

Margaret showed the strain and weariness, and little Sam was fretful and tired, and small wonder. But when the red coach—now gray with dust—resumed its way, the giant figure of Houston himself was in the box.

The four new horses were not used to harness, and tried to take it off. But they had a master at the reins, and the surety of his whip at malfeasance shortly brought their plunging and rearing to a halt, and before two miles they became models of discretion.

Thereafter Houston took his regular turn in the box, allowing one of the weary servants to ride in the coach and snatch a brief period of jolting sleep opposite Margaret and the child.

3

The great ride continued: and it was a ride men talked about for years after.

Across East Texas sped the coach, fording or ferrying such streams as the Angelina, Sabine, and Red. Over the Arkansas line, at Washington, another delay. A rear wheel with a broken spoke. The roads, as Houston remarked, were hell on a vehicle, and they had come four hundred miles in four days.

"How are you standing it?" he asked Margaret.

She was weary, but she was game. "I'll stand it," she said. "You see about the horses. I'll see about the boy and me."

While a wheelwright repaired the damage, she managed to bathe her child and freshen herself. The rest was all too short, for presently her husband appeared.

"Ready again," he said.

At that Margaret jumped up as if she had never known weariness, and entered the coach with little Sam, to resume the journey without complaint.

They angled toward the northeast, and crossed rivers like the Ouiachita, Saline, and Arkansas. On the far side of the Arkansas it began to rain, and mired roads were the great enemy of travel.

Houston took the driver's seat. Rain increased, and so did the mud. For hours he kept the lines in his hands. More than most men he knew how to navigate roadbeds which were sometimes for a mile at a time under water, and a foot deep in muck.

Higher stretches were all ugly ruts, and rain dappled the ponds and lagoons on either side.

Worse yet. A stretch of gumbo road. Four times he was forced to halt while Esau and Tom Blue, with stakes, cleared the spokes of the wheels of the thick waxy mud that clung to them.

But luck, after all. The rain area was local. It took most of a whole day to do twenty miles, but before they reached the White River at nightfall, Houston could surrender the reins to one of his drivers.

He crawled into the coach, and Margaret fed him fried chicken and buttered bread from a hamper; and he seemed to revive. She wondered where lay the hidden springs of his vast energy.

Bridges across the White and St. Francis Rivers, and at last they stood on the bank of the Mississippi itself. Over yonder was Memphis, and a good shuttle ferry plied back and forth.

They crossed. Tennessee. One hundred and fifty miles yet from Memphis to Nashville. Should they stop?

They had been on the road nine continuous days. Margaret was hollow-eyed and wan, the servants nearly dead.

But when Houston asked her, his wife promptly vetoed any long halt. "There isn't time," she said. "You've *got* to get there."

In his soul he silently thanked the Almighty for her.

Rolling again. Now the country seemed to smooth the way.

Trot, trot, gallop, gallop. Coach rattled, cloud of dust sucked up after the whirling wheels. And Nashville swung into view late in the afternoon of Sunday, June 8.

The Nashville Inn.

"Pull up here, Tom," said Houston.

As he got out he saw on the porch an old friend, Willoughby Williams.

"Why—General——" The former sheriff made as if to come down the steps.

But Houston interrupted. "Any news of the General?"

Williams halted. "Bad. Mighty nigh the end. May be gone by now——"

Houston swung back into the coach and shouted to his driver.

"Nine miles, now! Gallop them all the way!"

Ah, if only they could come in time . . .

4

The forenoon of that Sunday, Andrew Jackson lost consciousness.

They thought it was over, and the wailing of the servants rose through the house. But the keening was premature.

Bending over his bed, Sarah saw the eyelids flutter.

"Andrew, come!" she called to her husband. "Brandy——"

A spoonful of the spirit. She gave it to the dying man with the skill of her long attendance on him. The General opened his eyes.

But he *knew.*

"I want . . . to say good-by . . ." he whispered.

To each of the house servants and his son and grandchildren he gave a faint smile and a whispered farewell. Sarah kissed him, sobbing.

His hand, almost transparent, went up to touch her hair. "Dear Sarah . . . you have been . . . more than a daughter to me."

He seemed to gather his strength for one more utterance.

"My dear children, and friends . . . I hope and trust to meet you all in heaven . . . both black and white—both black and white."

His eyes closed. But after a time he whispered again.

"If only . . . I could have waited . . . for Sam Houston."

Another long silence in which only the muffled sounds of weeping women could be heard. Then the white lips moved again.

"Tell my beloved friends . . . Tom Benton . . . Frank Blair . . . Sam Houston . . . that I ask God to bless them."

The voice trailed away, while Sarah and her husband leaned over to catch any word. Houston's name seemed to set the old mind working for almost the last time; and his final thought was of his country and the future.

"Houston . . . was true to his trust." A brief panting pause.

And then in his last moments it seemed that he received a vision from a light within, when the light from without no longer entered his eyes. From that inner world they heard his voice coming as from a great distance.

"All is safe at last!"

The evening shadows were creeping into the room. The white head fell to one side.

Andrew Jackson passed into Time.

5

Early darkness, and a coach, its horses laboring at a gallop, came whirling around the drive.

From it stepped a weary, haggard giant, and helped out a woman thin and stained from travel, and a small child.

Too late, Sam Houston.

He saw the windows of the Hermitage alight, for many persons had gathered there in sorrow. Through the gloom the sad, weird chanting of the Negroes came eerily.

At the door he was admitted by an old acquaintance . . . Margaret Eaton . . . there with her husband and others mourning.

One glance told Houston the story.

And then Sarah came to him, her eyes red from weeping.

"Oh, Sam—" she said. "Almost his last word was of you. . . ."

His own eyes were filled with tears. "What . . . did he say?"

"He said, 'Houston was true to his trust.' "

Ah, so the old friend had not blamed him! The General had spoken with affection of him!

They took him to the death chamber.

On his bed lay the old warrior, white as marble, and his glory was like a cloak about him.

A flood of indescribable emotion went over Sam Houston; a sense of irretrievable loss, of reverent love, of awed thankfulness that it had been his lot to know such a man, so well.

Down on his knees went Houston, and laid his head on the breast of his greatest friend. And he began to weep as if inconsolable, and unashamed of the tears he shed.

In the room those who saw were struck with sad wonder by the depth of his grief, the spectacle of a man so great and renowned, crying almost uncontrollably, his sobs seeming to tear him apart.

It continued for minutes. But at last Houston mastered himself and rose. He wiped his eyes with a handkerchief, and after a time turned to his wife, who stood weeping as if her heart would break, with her little boy.

He took his son by his chubby hand and led him toward the bed.

They stood together, the father and the son, gazing. Houston's long, intent, searching look at the great dead was as if to stamp every lineament forever on his mind.

On the white, still face of Andrew Jackson there seemed to be a smile; a little, intimate smile, as at some bright personal happiness.

Houston bent over the child, his voice shaking with his feeling.

"Always try to remember, my son," he said, "that you have looked upon the face of Andrew Jackson."

Aftermath

When, with his dying breath, Andrew Jackson whispered, "All is safe at last," those in the room who heard him perhaps thought he spoke only of the reception of the new state of Texas into the Union.

Sam Houston, who arrived too late to hear these words, might have told them differently. He alone was in the full inner confidence of the old General. It was more probable that Jackson, with the prescience sometimes granted to men in their last moments on this earth, saw the magnificent destiny he had dreamed for his beloved nation.

Texas was the initial step: but once that step was taken, the rest must follow inevitably as the night the day. The dying warrior envisaged the resistless sweep of the United States across the empty lands of the West, to the far Pacific. His plan and leadership at last had set in motion that great surge of a people, and once in motion it would be as irresistible as an avalanche.

It befell as he dreamed. The toplofty vanity of one man—Santa Anna—and the necessity he knew, as all dictators know it, that by continued adventure only can they keep their power, led Mexico into war with the United States. Concerning this war, Lynn Montross, the celebrated military historian and analyst, has the following to say in his monumental *War through the Ages*:

Of all American conflicts the one with Mexico has been most often condemned as dishonorable. This tradition may be traced back to the rabid politics of the day, for the Whigs and Abolitionists came dangerously near to treason in their opposition. Such leaders as Clay and Webster denounced the struggle as a conspiracy to bring more slave-holding states into the Union; and a Whig newspaper declared that it would be "A joy to hear that the hordes under Scott and Taylor were every man of them swept into the next world."

That such strictures are not to be taken too seriously is shown by the fact that both the victorious generals became Whig candidates for the Presidency. Nor is there any more reason for accepting at face value the denunciations of American motives by Whig orators. The fact is that slavery had been the "burning issue" of the republic ever since its foundation, and the actual causes of the Mexican strife were obscured by the causes which would soon lead to Secession.

An understanding of this background is necessary to dispel a commonly held belief that the United States crushed a weak and unprepared neighbor by overwhelming bulk. On the contrary, the actual odds in the field weighed heavily against the Americans. The northern army faced four times its own numbers in the principal battle; and as a triumph of skill over obstacles, Scott's campaign has no equal in the world during the half century after Waterloo. . . .

Nor could it be said that the Mexicans were unworthy opponents. A generation of civil war had trained a hardy native soldiery which defended a formidable terrain with ability as well as courage. In the critical campaign the Americans found the enemy particularly strong in engineering and artillery—two arms which are not the resources of a military rabble.

The Mexican War was begun by Mexico, when its troops crossed the Rio Grande and struck a small American force in Texas. The invaders were repelled after three battles on American soil.

Thereafter Santa Anna, who after a brief exile was again dictator of Mexico, rejected one peace offer after another, until his unhappy country, in great measure through his own lack of generalship, was prostrate and conquered. By the terms of the peace the United States gained the present states of New Mexico, Arizona, Utah, and Nevada (considered almost worthless deserts), and California (where nobody dreamed great gold deposits lay), paying for them, even after the victorious war, more than was originally offered for them by President Polk.

Even before the conclusion of the Mexican War, President Polk was able to obtain Great Britain's treaty agreement to the forty-ninth parallel as the northern border of the Oregon Territory, thus completing Jackson's great plan of continental expansion.

The world pre-eminence of the United States may be said to be the final fruition of Andrew Jackson's dream for his country.

It is pleasant to record that Jackson's trusted lieutenants all remained faithful to his precepts. Sam Houston, greatest of them all, after dominating Texas politics for twenty years, sacrificed his friendships, his wealth, and his political power in a desperate effort to save Texas from what he called "the heresy of Secession." He died in 1863, in the middle of the Civil War, shortly after he learned of the Union victories at Vicksburg and Gettysburg which sealed the fate of the Confederacy;

and though his policies were unyielding, he watched with infinite sorrow the fate of his people, for he loved them.

Thomas Hart Benton also sacrificed himself for his Union principles, and died rejected in Missouri; yet he is now remembered as its first great statesman.

James Knox Polk labored so hard in his single term as President that he died shortly after it expired. During his incumbency, the United States acquired more territory than during the term of any other President including Thomas Jefferson.

Of Jackson's chief enemies, Henry Clay may be said to have achieved true greatness when he ceased to be ambitious for the Presidency. He labored to his death to keep together the states. John Calhoun, whose writings formed the philosophical basis for the theory of Secession, is now generally conceded to have been sincere in his constitutional theories, though overly ambitious personally.

These men lived at a time when the whole theory of the government of the United States was in a state of flux, but whether we now regard them as right or wrong, they were giants in those days.

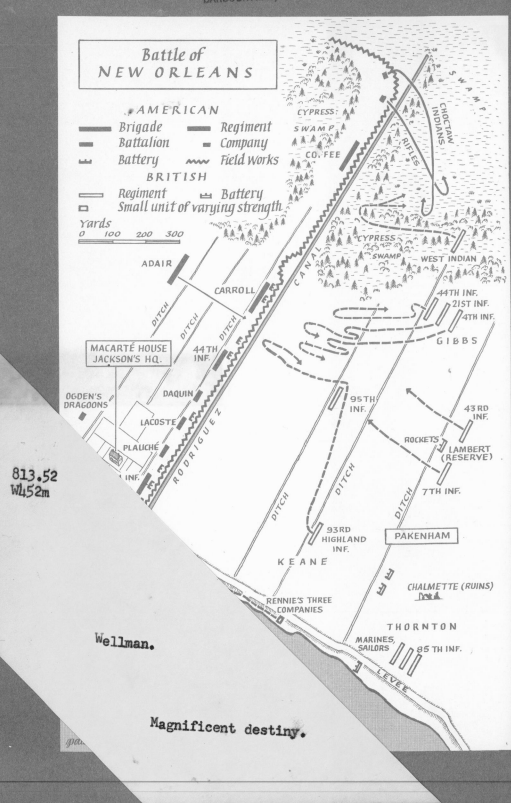

Battle of
NEW ORLEANS

AMERICAN

━━━ Brigade   ━━ Regiment
▬▬ Battalion   ▬ Company
▬ Battery   ∿∿ Field Works

BRITISH

▭ Regiment   ▭ Battery
▫ Small unit of varying strength

Yards
0   100   200   300

CYPRESS
SWAMP

COFFEE

RIFLES

CHOCTAW INDIANS

CYPRESS SWAMP

WEST INDIAN

ADAIR

CARROLL

DITCH   DITCH   DITCH

CANAL

MACARTÉ HOUSE
JACKSON'S HQ.

44TH INF.

44TH INF.
21ST INF.
4TH INF.

GIBBS

OGDEN'S DRAGOONS

DAQUIN

LACOSTE

PLAUCHÉ

INF.

RODRIGUEZ

95TH INF.

43RD INF.

ROCKETS

LAMBERT (RESERVE)

7TH INF.

DITCH   DITCH   DITCH

93RD HIGHLAND INF.

KEANE

PAKENHAM

RENNIE'S THREE COMPANIES

CHALMETTE (RUINS)

THORNTON

MARINES, SAILORS

85TH INF.

LEVEE

Wellman.

Magnificent destiny.